14th Edition

WRECKS & RELICS

Compiled by Ken Ellis

**MIDLAND PUBLISHING
LIMITED**

Contents

Cover Photographs:

Front : This edition covers the retirement of a depressing number of types from RAF service. The magnificent Victor ended its career with a couple of delivery flights to good homes. XM715 *Teasin' Tina* was delivered to Bruntingthorpe, Leics, on November 19, 1994. [Robert Rudhall]

Back : The Phantom gave up the ghost as well... Most of the breed were destined to be very openly scrapped as part of arms limitations treaties. The stunningly-painted FGR.2 XV404 was taken from Wattisham, Suffolk, by Hanningfield Metals of Stock, Essex. The firm hoped to display it at their premises but to comply with treaty obligations, it was scrapped in front of MoD observers during mid-April 1994. [Alan Allen]
    Former PanAm Boeing 707-321 HZ-TAS lingers on at the 'mini-Mojave' at Manston, Kent. With a fabulous executive interior, the fuselage is being kept in the hope that someone will want the fittings. [Colin Strachan]

This fourteenth edition published by Midland Publishing Limited
24 The Hollow, Earl Shilton, Leicester, LE9 7NA

Printed and bound by
WBC Bookbinders Ltd, Bridgend, Wales.

In Memory of Ken Whitehurst 1927 - 1994

Introduction

T HIS EDITION marks 33 years of continuous publication of **Wrecks & Relics**. On a personal note, the 14th edition also clocks up 20 years at the helm for the current compiler. There are great temptations to dwell in comparisons, but I will only make one — and a very obvious one at that. When it was published in August 1974, **W&R4** weighed in at 88 pages. I can assure readers that in those far off days I thought that a nice round 100 pages was a possibility one day, but could never have foreseen the 336 page monster you have before you. That **W&R14** has reached this size is a tribute to the researches of many people who never cease to amaze me with their dedication and depth when it comes to the subject of the UK's aviation heritage.

Things being as they are, this edition could well be the zenith in terms of the number of pages. It will not take long while thumbing through **W&R14** to realise that the UK's armed forces have disposed of a serious amount of aircraft in the last couple of years and that this level of activity will never be seen again. The commercial sector has also helped to swell the pages. The recession has seen the laying up of a large number of airliners — some straight off the production line — with many staying inert long enough to merit mention within these pages. The *Preface* (page 7) takes a deeper look at trends and major events since the publications of **W&R13**.

Other than the increase in size there has only been one major change to the contents and that has been to increase the number of pages of photographs — going by my mailbag this will be a welcome development. There have been a few more 'tweaks' to layout and readability with items such as code-letters or code-numbers being added to the tabled text — again at the request of readers.

Deep Fraught IIIa, the ever-loyal word processor, tells me that 884,852 characters make up the pages that follow. Those typeset characters appear courtesy of the human characters listed below and on the following pages. Their contributions, large or small, are the vital spark to this work.

Tackling a varying flow of draft pages and helping to refine and polish the contents were **John Coghill**, **Paul Crellin**, **Alan Curry**, **Trevor Green** and **Robert Rudhall** with additional input from **Roy Bonser** and **Dave Peel**. Not content to just wade through a sea of paperwork and cross-check it, **Tom Poole** also undertook the monitoring of the *LOST!* section. **Roger Richards** supplied a vast amount of photographic material, not just for potential publication, but helping considerably in checking references — you'd be amazed how many answers can come from the *backgrounds* of photos! Talking of answers, **Alan Allen** undertook a huge amount of work in sorting out many 'chestnuts', often answering questions before they were even thought of! As ever, **Dave Allport** spent many, many hours checking references and their histories. The depth and size of **W&R** owes much to Dave's industriousness. (Both Dave and Robert Rudhall are gluttons for punishment, as they work alongside me on the aviation titles at Key Publishing and yet are still — apparently! — happy to undertake a *Busman's Holiday* for **W&R**!)

My many thanks go to all the staff at Midland Publishing, the publishers of **W&R**, especially to **Neil Lewis** and **Chris Salter**.

And to **Pam** — who seems to think it perfectly normal behaviour for me to spend all day thrashing a word processor for a living, only to want to do the same for 'relaxation' in my 'spare' time! (Not forgetting *Fleas* the cat, who tends not to dwell on such philosophical blockbusters!)

Deadline for **Wrecks & Relics 15** (when the title sees its 35th birthday) is **December 1, 1995** for illustrations and **January 31, 1996** for information and comments.

Ken Ellis
April 1994

Myddle Cottage, Welland Terrace, off Mill Lane, Barrowden, Oakham,
People's Republic of Rutland, LE15 8EH

Acknowledgements

A S WITH EVERY edition of **Wrecks & Relics,** the 14th example has been produced with the help of a wide number of people. The Compiler would like to thank the following specialists for their help : —

Peter R Arnold, Spitfire restorer and historian; **Rod Brown,** DHC-1 Chipmunk historian; **Barry Cooper** and the Thames Valley Aviation Society for detailed notes on the demise of Abingdon; **Brian Dillon** for comprehensive jottings on Ireland; **John G Chree** for his superb digest of things Scottish; **Malcolm Fillmore** of Air-Britain, compiler of their superb *UK and Ireland Civil Aircraft Registers,* for much 'feedback' on that front; **Alan Johnson** of Air-Britain for his regular updates of the UK civil register; **Chris Michell** for many notes on 'warbird' comings and goings; **Paddy Porter** for a 'grapevine' like no other!; **Lloyd P Robinson** of Aviation Data Research (and **The Herald Society**); **Peter Spooner** for his extensive notes, particularly from the south; **Graham Taylor,** for his extensive researches into the UK Phantom *phleet*; **Gavin Troon** for his detailed knowledge of the Scottish scene.

P REPARATION for **Wrecks & Relics** includes a mail-shot to all British Aviation Preservation Council (BAPC) members and to other organisations within the UK and Eire. The Compiler is indebted to the following for their help and, in many cases, constant up-dating. If the name of a Museum or Group does not appear below then the entry within the main text is as accurate as can be made and the organisation concerned owes the Compiler an SAE!

Val & Tony Agar, Night Fighter Preservation Team; **Cliff Aldred,** Blyth Valley Aviation Collection; **Diana Andrews,** Airborne Forces Museum; **John Bagley,** formerly of the Science Museum; **Philip Baldock,** Robertsbridge Aviation Society; **Bill Baker,** Brenzett Aeronautical Collection; **Colin Baker,** Derby World War Two Avionics Museum; **John Bigger,** East Midlands Airport Volunteers Association; **Ray Burrows,** Ulster Aviation Society; **Steve Challis,** British Classic Aircraft Restorations; **Dave Charles,** North East Aircraft Museum; **Chris Chippington,** Imperial War Museum, Duxford; **Bob Cole,** Second World War Aircraft Preservation Society; **Major John R Cross,** Museum of Army Flying; **John Davidson,** The Aeroplane Collection; **Lewis Deal,** Medway Aircraft Preservation Society; **Paul Doyle,** Mosquito Aircraft Museum; **David Dunstall,** Shoreham Airport Heritage Centre; **Colin Durrant,** 390th BG Memorial Air Museum; **Tony Dyer,** The Air Defence Collection and the Wiltshire Historic Aviation Group; **Phil Earthey,** Classic Warbirds; **Dave Edwards,** Flambards Village Theme Park; **Steve Edwards,** Phantom Restoration Group; **Mark Evans,** Midland Warplane Museum; **Huby Fairhead,** Norfolk & Suffolk Aviation Museum; **Ken Fern,** Vintage & Rotary Wing Collection; **Keith Fordyce,** Torbay Aircraft Museum; **John Francis,** Aerospace Museum, Cosford; **Gordon Fraser,** Kennet Aircraft; **W Gadd,** East Essex Aviation Museum; **Bruce Gordon,** Mosquito Aircraft Museum; **Steve Hague,** Night Fighter Preservation Team; **Bill Harkness MBE,** Aircraft Preservation society of Scotland; **Eric Haywood,** Jet Heritage; **Dennis Headley-Green,** Museum of Army Transport; **Howard Heeley,** Newark Air Museum; **Mike Hodgson,** Thorpe Camp Preservation Group; **Stewart Holder,** Jet Aviation Preservation Group; **Harry Holmes** on behalf of the Avro Aircraft Restoration Society; **James Howley,** Restorations Unlimited; **Dianne James,** Midland Air Museum; **Roger Jones,** Gloucestershire Aviation Collection; **Ian Kingsnorth,** South Yorkshire Aviation Museum; **Air Cdre David Lawrence CBE,** RAF Museum; **David Lee,** Imperial War Museum, Duxford; **Phil Maloney,** Military Aircraft Preservation Group; **Richard Mason,** Fenland Aircraft Preservation Society; **Trevor Matthews,** Lashenden Air Warfare Museum; **Bob Major,** Museum of Flight; **Paul May,** Bomber County Aviation Museum; **A J Moor,** Brenzett Aeronautical Museum Trust; **John Moore,** Ulster Folk & Transport Museum; **Bill Morton-Hall,** Brimpex Metal Treatments; **Graham Mottram,** Fleet Air Arm Museum; **Brian Nicholls,** Lincolnshire Aviation Heritage Centre / Lincolnshire Aviation Preservation Society; **John Nixon,** RAF Millom Museum; **Dick Nutt,** Douglas Boston-Havoc UK Preservation Trust; **Dell Paddock,** Wellesbourne Aviation Group; **Andrew Parkin,** North East Aircraft Museum; **Jeremy Parkin** of Computair Consultants; **Alan Partington,** Catford Independent Air Force; **Mike Phipp,** Wessex Aviation Society; **Nigel Ponsford & Anne Lindsay,** 'Ponsford Air Force' and Real Aeroplane Company; **Elfan ap Rees,** International Helcipter Museum; **David Reid,** Dumfries & Galloway Aviation Museum; **Ken Rimell,** Museum of *D-Day* Aviation; **Mike Russell,** Russavia Collection; **Andy Saunders,** Tangmere Military Aviation Museum; **Trevor Scarr,** Duxford Aviation Society; **Geoff Simmons,** Museum of Army Transport; **Richard Simpson,** RAF Museum; **D R Sims,** Wales Aircraft Museum; **Kelvin Sloper,** City of Norwich Aviation Museum; **Peter Smith,** Friends of Biggin Hill; **Peter Stoddart,** Leicestershire Museums, Arts & Records Service; **Tom Stoddart,** Carlisle; **Dave Stubley,** Lincolnshire Aircraft Recovery Group; **Peter Symes,** Shuttleworth Collection; **Dave Tappin,** Yorkshire Air Museum; **Bill Taylor** of the Aerial Application Collection (and for all things agricultural and Auster); **Julian Temple,** Brooklands Museum; **Steve Thompson,** Cotswold Aircraft Restoration Group; **S/L Andy Tomalin,** Battle of Britain Memorial Flight; **R Tuck,** Lightning Preservation Group; **Robert Turner,** Fleet Air Arm Museum; **Alison Vincent,** Manchester Museum of Science & Industry; **Lawrence Wait,** 39 Restoration Group; **Graham Warner,** Aircraft Restoration Company & British Aerial Museum; **Kevin Whittaker,** Macclesfield Historical Aviation Society; **Paul Wiggins,** Solway Aviation Society; **Nick Wilson,** 39 Restoration Group, **Colin Wingrave,** Thameside Aviation Museum; **John & Maureen Woods,** Friends of the DC-3.

FROM FAR AND WIDE come snippets and reports — large and small — from the book's myriad 'eyes and ears' all over the UK. My thanks to all readers who take the time to jot down their comments, corrections, additions and suggestions. Without them this edition would be far less comprehensive. It is encouraging to see the number of contributors who are now making sure that their notes carry 'last seen' dates — a great boon to keeping track of **W&R** airframes. I look forward to hearing from them all again in the coming two years and encourage readers new and old to join their ranks.

Gerry Allen, Kevin Anderton, Roy Ashby, Keith Attfield, M D Back, Nigel Bailey-Underwood, P R Baker, Brian Barnes, Martin Barsley, Len J Batchelor, Alan J Beale, David Bennett, Peter Birchinall, Peter Bodle, George A Brown, Hugh John Budgen, David Burke, B J Burt, Peter Burton, Kate Bush, David Byrne, Russell Carter, Richard Cawsey, John Cockerton, John D Coleman, Martin Paul Condon, Peter Cook, Martin Coombes, Andrew Denholm, Michael Drake, Frank Drebin, Keith Duckett, Paul Dunn, Neil Dunridge, Bryn Elliott, Simon Ellwood, Helen Fairchild, Bill Fisher, Jodie Foster, Chris Frantz, Tom Gibbons, Ken Gillham, Ian Grierson, Ian Grove, Melvyn Halsey, Ian Hancock, John Hancock, Mark Harris, Steve Harris, Jerry Harrison, Jeremy Hassell, Paul Hewins, Nigel Hitchman, Richard Hodgkinson, Gawayne Hodgkiss, A L Hone, Ian F Howell, Kevin Isaac, Paul A Jackson, David W James, Martyn Janes, Alf Jenks, Sue & Roy Jerman, Derek Johnson, D A Jones, Derek Jones, Geoff Jones, Keith Jones, M A Jones, Martyn Jones, Bob Kent, Stewart Lanham, Morley Lester, Geoff Lewis, Lintilla, John Lloyd-Martin, A Lock, J Lowe, Malcolm Lowe, Charles E MacKay, Tony McCarthy, Fraser McKay, David McNally, Roger Marley, Tony Marsh, Ian Martin, Pete Mears, Paul Merriman, Paul Middleton, Simon Murdoch, Dave Murray, Tim Murray, Sid Nanson, Alistair Ness, Ian Oliver, Alan Paine, Bob Parnell, Andy Patsalides, Geoffrey Pennycook, Martin Perkins, Col Pope, James Porter, Andrew Powell, K Preen, Nigel Price, Gerry Raggett, Ken Reid, John Rennison, Mark Roberts, E Robinson, Brian Roffee, Phil Rogers, Colin Rooke, Neill G Rush, Robert M Rushton, Chris Sayer, Bernard B Scott, Paul Shaw, Dave Smith, Mike Smith, Paul Snelling, Colin Strachan, Harry Stripe, Mike Stroud, John Sutherland, Barry Swann, Barry Taylor, G K Thomas, Alan Tomlin, Lily Tomlin, David E Thompson, Dave Lee Travis, D Underwood, Steve Vessey, John Wegg of *Airliners*, Paul Webb, Michael Westwood, Tina Weymouth, Dave Whitaker, Chris Wiltshire, Andy Wood, Steve Wright.

Notes

Scope

Wrecks & Relics serves to outline, in as much detail as possible, the status and whereabouts of all known PRESERVED (ie in museum or other collections, under restoration etc); INSTRUCTIONAL (ie static airframes in use for training); and DERELICT (ie out of use for a long period of time, fire dump aircraft, scrapped or damaged etc) aircraft in the United Kingdom and Eire and Forces aircraft based on Crown Territory. Where information permits, all aircraft that fall into these categories are included, with the following exceptions : —

■ Airworthy aircraft not part of a specific collection.
■ Aircraft that fall into any of the above categories for only a short period of time.
■ Aircraft without provision for a human pilot , below the size of the GAF Jindivik (unless registered in the BAPC system).
■ In general, aircraft will only be considered if they are at least a cockpit/nose section.

Entries

Generally, entries are all dealt with in a standard manner. As **W&R** covers a two year period, in this case 1992 to 1994, beyond the location header there is a narrative explaining the current status of the entry and outlining any airframes that have moved since the last edition. Airframes moving on are given underlined forwarding references, including the county that reference can be found in. Thus, if the reader wishes, it is possible to follow the more energetic examples around the book! Any aircraft which fall out of any of the four categories above, or are exported, will not have forwarding references and their entry should be considered closed. The *LOST!* section acts as a 'safety net' for aircraft that have no determined fate. Entries new to a heading in this edition are marked * after the registration/serial. From this edition, aircraft that are generally considered to be airworthy are marked with a **Δ** after the aircraft type.

Where possible, brief historical details of the aircraft listed are given, in a necessarily abbreviated form. This information varies slightly in presentation, but can mostly be found in column three in the tabulated entries or, rarely, in brackets behind an entry in the narrative. In each case, units etc are listed in *reverse* order, ie first use of an aircraft is listed *last*. Readers should have little trouble with these potted histories, especially with continued reference to the Abbreviations section.

'Last noted' dates are given wherever possible. These appear in column five. The listing of these dates, it is hoped, will persuade some readers and plenty of enthusiast magazines to actually note the dates of sightings in future jottings — the *date* of an observation can be a crucial form of evidence in many cases.

Locations

Directions to the location in question are given after each place name. Readers should note that these directions are to the town or village mentioned and not necessarily to the actual site of the aircraft in question. Directions are *not* given in the following instances : —

■ Where specific directions to the site are not fully known. (At the request of several aircraft owners, who have every right to preserve their peace and quiet as well as their aircraft, some locations have been 'generalised'.)

■ Where the location is a large city or town.

From this edition a form of notation relating to the status of an 'aerodrome' is given. Bearing in mind that in the Air Navigation Order *all* places where flying is conducted are known as aerodromes, a wider interpretation has been employed. Here the word 'aerodrome' signifies a civilian flying ground used by aircraft up to King Air, 'biz-jet' etc size. 'Airfield' is used to signify a flying ground used by the forces, test establishments or manufacturers. 'Airport' is used to denote a flying ground that takes 'serious' sized airliners on a regular basis. For privacy and security purposes, private strips etc are not denoted as such.

Access

Unless otherwise stated, all locations in this work are PRIVATE and access to them is strictly by prior permission, *if at all*. Museum opening times etc are given as a *guide only* and readers are advised to contact the museum in question *before* setting out on a journey. A diamond (♦) is used to define locations that are happy with public access, details beyond this explain times of admission or who to apply to if prior permission is needed.

Serial and Registration Presentation

Aircraft are listed alpha-numerically, using the following rubric. British civil first (except in Ireland where EI- comes first), followed by BGA and 'B Condition' markings, then overseas civil registrations in alpha-numeric order. British military serials follow (with reversal again in Ireland) followed by overseas military serials listed by country — ie France before Netherlands before USA. Finally, come BAPC identities as these can take in both civil or military airframes. Anonymous airframes are inserted where it is thought most logical! Incorrect or fictitious registrations and serials are marked in single quotes, eg 'VZ999' or 'G-BKEN'. From this edition codes worn by aircraft are given wherever possible, eg 'AF-V' or '825-CU'.

Registrations/serials, where applicable, are given a two-column treatment. The first column gives the primary identifier (if applicable). The primary identifier for the airframe is most often the one worn on the airframe. A secondary identifier may be a registration not yet painted on the airframe or, with military airframes, most likely an 'M' number or similar, or with an aircraft wearing a military serial, but also having a current civil identity, that is given. The secondary identifier, where applicable, is given in column two. Readers should have little difficulty with this presentation.

Preface

Armed Forces

British and US forces have continued their scale down with a large amount of airframes being released for sale or scrap. A whole series of **retirements** were chalked up. March 1994 saw the bowing out of the might **Buccaneer** from RAF service (and quietly alongside them, the Hunter). The RAF flew its last-ever **Canberra** B.2 sortie out of Wyton, Cambs, in July 1993, with the end in sight for all but a handful of PR.9s with 39 (PRU) Squadron. The loyal **Jet Provost** was phased out during 1993 and hit the headlines when Global Aviation of Binbrook, Lincs, announced that they had come to a deal with the MoD to acquire no less than 65 examples for onward sale. The Lightning Preservation Group at Bruntingthorpe, Leics, received **Lightning** F.6 XS904 during January 1993 — the last flight of a Lightning under UK military aegis. During 1992 there was a wholesale slaughter of **Phantoms**, with the graveyards at Wattisham, Suffolk, and Leuchars, Fife, being greedily depleted by a bevy of scrapmen. No 55 Squadron stood down at Marham, Norfolk, on October 15, 1993, bringing the **Victor K.2** to its close, a handful went to museums. **Vulcan** B.2 XH558 was offered for disposal during early 1993 and made an emotional last flight to Bruntingthorpe, Leics, in March.

Bases closing or going into care and maintenance included : — Abingdon, Oxon; Bentwaters, Suffolk; Church Fenton, N Yorks; Elvington, N Yorks; Kemble, Glos; Swinderby, Lincs; Upper Heyford, Oxon; West Drayton, Gtr Lon; Woodbridge, Suffolk; Wroughton, Wilts. Passing by almost unnoticed was a major element in RAF training, Course 155 was the last to come through **1 School of Technical Training** at Halton, Bucks, in June 1993. The large number of airframes held there underwent a rapid dispersal. No 2 SoTT at Cosford, Shrop, took up the famous 1 SoTT 'numberplate'.

Battle of Britain Memorial Flight took delivery of Dakota III ZA947 at Coningsby, Lincs, during July 1993, partly as a *Lanc* continuation trainer and partly as a para-platform for the Parachute regiment during their many commitments in *D-Day* anniversary year. No movement on the rebuild of Hurricane II LF363. **Royal Navy Historic Flight** accepted the BAe Brough, Humb, restored Swordfish W5856 during May 1993.

On the gate guardian front, **Phantoms** provided a sprinkling of newness although unlikely places like Woodvale, Merseyside, even received one. RAF base closures took several names (and aircraft) off the gate guardian 'map'. In the 'private sector' BAe Brough, Humb, took delivery of a **Buccaneer S.2B** during October 1993 for display within its place of birth. While they have been largely on the retreat, the USAF succeeded in placing an **A-10A Thunderbolt** on display within the camp at Alconbury, Cambs, although the base is due to go into a form of care and maintenance. USAF Croughton, Northants, took on the two former Upper Heyford guardians.

With the test establishments, it was also a case of contraction. Flying at **DRA Bedford**, Beds, and **DRA Farnborough**, Hants, stopped in March 1994.

British Aviation Preservation Council

Mike Hodgson stood down from the post of **Chairman** after some ten years in office — years that have seen great maturity in the status and scope of the Council. David Lee, of the Imperial War Museum, Duxford, took up the reins from February 1994. Following the careful researches of John Bagley, the Council published its first definitive **listing of significant airframes** during the early part of 1994. Not an easy task, John grasped the thorny subject of trying to define airframes within museums that should receive governmental protection in terms of preventing potential export. As can be imagined, arguments relating to who's on who's list abounded, but the difficult subject has been initiated and this listing will provide a springboard for future policies. The series of successful *Stopping the Rot* seminars continued with more planned.

Classics

Ben Cooper's Newbury Aeroplane Company succeeded in putting a shape into UK skies unseen for decades when **BA Eagle** G-AFAX made its first flight in 1992. At Breighton, Humb, Tony Smith's Real Aeroplane Company flew **Miles Magister** G-AKAT during early 1993. They have taken on a much more ambitious Miles project — see below. Tim Moore of Skysport at Hatch, Beds, produced the wonderful **Sopwith Dove** reproduction G-EAGA for Roger Reeves. It made its first flight from Henlow during mid-1993 and resides with the Shuttleworth Collection at Old Warden, Beds. See below for details of Tim's Westland Wallace rebuild.

Commercial

The recession has meant a large number of airliner types have been laid up in the UK, some coming straight off the production line. Filton, Avon, became the centre for **BAC 1-11** storage, with the acquisition of the former British Airways Series 500s from Bournemouth Airport, Dorset, by European Aviation. Some went straight into service, others will take longer to find new homes. Filton was also the venue for stored **BAe 146**s, as was East Midlands, Leics. 'EMA' will see the retirement of the last active **Merchantmen** (née Vanguards) during 1994. Cambridge, Cambs, also taken some 1-11s, but from late 1992 was also home to a pair of former BA **TriStars**.

At Exeter, Devon, the store of **Shorts 330**s very much diminished, although some of the breed, and **HS.748**s continue to spend long periods in store. Bournemouth Airport, Dorset, also acted as a *Shed* store for a while. The skyline changed at Southend, Essex, during February 1994 when two **Belfasts** were scrapped, with a third reported to be following.

Groups

The **Bristol Aero Collection** took another step towards its plans of establishing a museum when it took up the kind offer of Meggitt Aerospace of Banwell, Avon, of storage space at its factory. Working in co-operation with BAC is the **Britannia Aircraft Preservation Trust**, who moved their G-ANCF into the new facility on March 27, 1993.

At the ever-expanding Duxford, Cambs, the **Duxford Aviation Society** added to their airliner collection with the arrival of a BAC 1-11 from Bournemouth, Dorset, during October 1992.

At Wisbech, Cambs, the **Fenland Aircraft Preservation Society** acquired a hangar and are busy setting to in erecting it. They also took on two Lightning T.5s, greatly expanding their acquisitions. The **Gloucestershire Aviation Collection** acquired a Javelin FAW.9 during 1993 and work was underway with a Gamecock replica.

Medway Aircraft Preservation Society again exhibited their considerable prowess during December 1992 when the Tangmere Flight Spitfire PR.XI PL965 made its first post restoration test flight at Rochester, Kent. They have taken on the Short SHERPA previous stored at Duxford, Cambs. **Meteor Flight** established themselves at Yatesbury, Wilts, having sorted their vast spares-holding and started work on their four examples.

Night Fighter Preservation Team at Elvington, N Yorks, made excellent progress with the Mosquito NF.II. During 1992 they moved into 'their' own workshop, allowing much more workspace. An Anson T.21 has been acquired as a future project.

At Bacup, Lancs, the **Pennine Aviation Museum** was forced to vacate its premises during late 1992 and a severe clear out of airframes and artefacts took place thereafter. **South Copeland Aviation Group**, having established a small museum on the former RAF Millom, Cumbria, took on a *Flying Flea* for restoration and display during March 1994.

The Aeroplane Collection had to leave its base at Warmingham, Cheshire, but found its feet again with the up-and-coming transport museum being established by the **Griffin Trust** at Hooton Park, Merseyside. Settled in at Langford Lodge, Antrim, the **Ulster Aviation Society** are at work on the control tower and are making good progress with their Wildcat V restoration.

Museums

Tony Bianchi and friends opened the **Blue Max Movie Aircraft Museum** at Wycombe Air Park, Bucks, on June 20, 1992. Their largely active fleet of aircraft coming open to public gaze — a most welcome move. The museum may face a change of venue during 1994. At Helston, Corn, the **Flambards Village Theme Park** continued to reduce the number of airframes on show, with nine going, in one form or another.

Carrier, the huge new exhibition at the **Fleet Air Arm Museum**, Yeovilton, Som, meant great upheaval at the museum, but the results should prove worth it. A number of exhibits were repainted and refurbished for this and the Korean War exhibition.

Imperial War Museum, Duxford, Cambs, continued to refine and expand its staggering collection of airframes and artefacts. (Warbird operators and other parties at Duxford are mentioned elsewhere.) Acquisitions included some impressive hardware :— F-111E, MiG-15, Phantom FGR.2 and U-2C. The SARO SR.A.1 jet flying-boat fighter was transferred to the far more relevant home of the **Hall of Aviation** at **Southampton**, Hants, during late 1993.

At Weston-super-Mare, Avon, the **International Helicopter Museum** continued to expand both in terms of exhibits and facilities, with the opening of the Raoul Hafner restoration workshop being great achievement. It terms of airframes, the list includes : Sud Frelon, Mil Mi-4

Hound, WSK SM-1 and the Cierva Rotorcraft Grasshopper series from the moribund Helicopter Museum of Great Britain at Blackpool airport, Lancs. Other exotic types are in the pipeline...

A whole Trident 3B was donated to the **Mosquito Aircraft Museum** of London Colney, Herts, by BAe at Hatfield, Herts, where it will firmly remain. Now that Hatfield has closed, MAM have hopes for some form of development on the site. A Dragon Rapide has been acquired in an exchange that should see their former BE.2 take to the air again. **Museum of Army Flying** at Middle Wallop, Hants, continued to expand its collection, with the most significant additions being an Avro 504K and an Alouette AH.2.

At Woodley, the **Museum of Berkshire Aviation** opened its doors to the public on a permanent basis on March 27, 1993. The day also saw the launch of the associated **Miles Aircraft Collection**, who in early 1994 came to an arrangement with the **Real Aeroplane Company** at Breighton, Humb, to undertake an ambitious reconstruction of a Miles Master I from the components they have collection. The aim is for the Master to fly. Also based at Woodley, the **Herald Society** saw their G-APWA arrive on site in August 1992 with restoration well underway.

Midland Air Museum at Coventry Airport experienced a busy period, with a lot of heavy metal coming inbound :— HS.125, Sea Vixen FAW.2 and a nose section; a second Phantom and a second T-33A.

Newark Air Museum continued their reputation for the exotic when a Saab Draken of the Royal Danish Air Force dropped into Scampton in February 1994, ready for roading to their Winthorpe, Notts, site. Major building work starts during 1994 on their new reception/shop/display hall. Member Ian Hancock provided a boost to the **Norfolk & Suffolk Aviation Museum** with the loan of a Canberra T.4 from the moribund Staffordshire group and an early Lightning from display at Swinderby.

North East Aircraft Museum at Sunderland, T&W, joined the 'cover-up club' during 1993 with the completion of the ere large aircraft display hall. This has freed up the 'workshop' to do just that and a refurbishing programme is underway on exhibits. A series of new airframes have also come along :— Austin Whippet replica; FMA Pucara; Short SD.330; Westland Widgeon and Whirlwind HAR.9.

Handley Page Hampden P1344 was exchanged for a Spitfire out of St Athan, S Glam, by the **RAF Museum** as it filled yet another major 'hole' in its collection. The airframe is at Cardington, Beds, and will be next in line for restoration when the immaculate Supermarine Southampton is delivered to public exhibition at Hendon, Gtr Lon, in September 1994. There were several additions at Hendon itself :— Westland Wallace II fuselage, lovingly restored by Skysport of Hatch, Beds; a Kittyhawk IV; a Sabre F.4 from The Fighter Collection at Duxford, Cambs; a Phantom FGR.2 and a Jet Provost T.5A. At Cosford, Shrop, the **Aerospace Museum** took on a BAC 1-11, Buccaneer S.2B, Canberra PR.9 and a Victor K.2. Additionally, many changes to displays etc were completed as part of a comprehensive upgrade.

In London, the **Science Museum** opened its rejigged aviation hall under the simple banner of *Flight* during October 1992. With the addition of a HS.125, the new displays are stunning, bringing this collection very much back into focus.

Mixed blessings at the **Shuttleworth Collection**, Old Warden, Beds. Reaching the 50th anniversary of the setting up of the Trust, 1994 will see many celebrations for this great institution. The closure of the BAe airfield at Hatfield, Beds, put a question mark over the operation of the DH.88 Comet reconstruction *Grosvenor House* — in the craft's 60th anniversary year. The decision was reached to road the aircraft to Old Warden and to ground run it only. A sad turn of events.

South Yorkshire Air Museum had a busy time, with a series of acquisitions. Most dramatic was a Lightning saved literally from the axe. The wings were damaged before the scrapman was persuaded to desist, but a new set have been tracked down.

Tangmere Military Aviation Museum's wonderful aircraft display hall brought benefits in the form of the Meteor IV Special and the Hawker P.1067 on loan from the RAF Museum. Other acquisitions are in the pipeline. **Yorkshire Air Museum** at Elvington, N Yorks, unveiled their Halifax reconstruction project during August 1993 and have acquired a hangar to put it into. Among other acquisitions, they took delivery of Victor K.2 XL231 in November 1993 — perhaps their last airborne arrival with the closure of RAF Elvington next door.

Dumfries & Galloway Aviation Museum, Tinwald Downs, D&G, salvaged presentation *Spitfire V* Blue Peter with the help of an 819 Squadron Sea King in May 1993 and 'starred' in the TV programme of the same name for their sins! At East Fortune, Lothian, the **Museum of Flight** acquired a MiG-15, plus a cockpit section.

Warbirds

Duxford-based **Aircraft Restoration Company** flew their magnificent second 'Blenheim' on May 18, 1993 and countless people have gloried in seeing her in the air since. With respect, the engineering achievement paled into insignificance against the team's conquering of horrendous prospect of picking up the pieces and doing it all over again. Well done! (They also flew their T-6 *Thumper* and completed several static restorations for the IWM.)

Historic Flying at Audley End, Essex, had a productive time : — Spitfire XVI TD248 first flew in November 1992; Mk IX TE566 in July 1992; Mk XVIII TP280 in July 1992 and Mk XIV NH799 in January 1994.

The **Old Flying Machine Company**, another Duxford operation, acquired a Spitfire V from Canada for restoration and took on the operation of the Tangmere Flight Spitfire PR.XI PL965 and the Golden Apple Trust's F-86A Sabre. Their Avenger was exported to New Zealand during October 1992. They have some 'aces' up their sleeve, planned for unveiling during 1994...

Also at Duxford, **The Fighter Collection**, continued to extend the horizons for the world warbird 'fleet' : the P-38 Lightning arrived from the USA in June 1992; Spitfire XIV MV293 first flew in August 1992; FM-2 Wildcat from the USA in April 1993; Spitfire XIV NH799 was transferred to Historic Flying at Audley End, Essex, in November 1993 to make its first flight from there. The first Russian treasures began to arrive, a P-40B, a Spitfire IX and then a Lavochkin La-11.

On the jet front, the **fatal accident** to Hunter T.7 G-BTYL on June 11, 1993 looked set to send shockwaves through the movement. Potentially serious implications may arise from the **ejector seat problem** encountered by *JP* T.3 G-BVEG near to North Weald, Essex on April 3, 1994. Miraculously, the passenger survived. Two operators acquired **Canberras** with the intention to operate them on a Permit to Fly, one at Duxford, Cambs, and the other at Bruntingthorpe, Leics.

At Bournemouth Airport, Dorset, **Jet Heritage Ltd** succeeded in acquiring charitable status and made moves towards opening the collection regular public viewing. Several aircraft within the fleet were offered for sale and some have moved on, on the plus side they flew their Hunter F.4 during January 1994. As **W&R** closed for press, the **Lightning Flying Club** had received the 'green light' to operate a **Lightning** F.6 with their T.5 hard on its heels. Two **Hunters** have also been acquired to act as continuation trainers and chase planes.

During November 1992, Doug Arnold of **Warbirds of Great Britain** died. What followed was apparently a wholesale exodus of the collection, from both Bournemouth, Dorset, and Biggin Hill, Gtr Lon, with the most likely destination being Florida, USA.

Other notables included : — the Dutch Spitfire Group's **Spitfire IX** MK732 first flew at Lydd, Kent, during June 1993; **Spitfire Tr IX** G-BMSB first flew from Coventry, Warks, during November 1993; Robs Lamplough's **Spitfire VIII** 'MT928'/G-BKMI was nearing flight test at Filton, Avon, as these words were processed; Lea Aviation Inc's **Tigercat** was returned to the USA from Duxford, Cambs, during May 1993.

Part 1

ENGLAND

Avon 12 - 16	Hereford & Worcester 94 - 96	Nottinghamshire 154 - 158
Bedfordshire 17 - 23	Hertfordshire 96 - 100	Oxfordshire 158 - 162
Berkshire 24 - 28	Humberside 101 - 103	Shropshire 162 - 171
Buckinghamshire 28 - 33	Isle of Man 103 - 104	Somerset 171 -178
Cambridgeshire 34 - 46	Isle of Wight 104	Staffordshire 175 - 178
Cheshire 46 - 50	Kent 105 - 110	Suffolk 178 - 183
Cleveland 50	Lancashire 110 - 113	Surrey 183 - 188
Cornwall 50 - 54	Leicestershire 113 - 120	East Sussex 188 - 190
Cumbria 54 - 57	Lincolnshire 120 - 130	West Sussex 190 - 195
Derbyshire 57 - 58	Greater London 130 - 140	Tyne & Wear 195 - 197
Devon 58 - 60	Greater Manchester 140 - 143	Warwickshire 197 - 203
Dorset 60 - 65	Merseyside 144	Wiltshire 203 - 209
Durham 65 - 66	West Midlands 145 - 146	North Yorkshire 209 - 212
Essex 66 - 77	Norfolk 146 - 151	South Yorkshire 212 - 215
Gloucestershire 77 - 80	Northamptonshire 151 - 153	West Yorkshire 215 - 216
Hampshire 80 - 94	Northumberland 153 - 154	

BADMINTON (east of the A46, east of Chipping Sodbury)
The para-trainer Cessna 172M G-BBJD moved to <u>Oaksey Park</u>, Wilts, by August 1992.

BANWELL (on the A371 east of Weston-super-Mare)
■ **Bristol Aero Collection** (BAC) / **Britannia Aircraft Preservation Trust** (BAPT) :
Meggitt Aerospace have very kindly agreed to undertake the short term storage of the Bristol Aero
Collection and Britannia Aircraft Preservation Trust's Britannia 308F G-ANCF. The fuselage of the
latter was moved to the site from Brooklands, Surrey, on March 27, 1993. (The wings can be found at
Quedgeley, Glos.) While the B.206 may at first seem out of place, Bristol did much of the early design
work on the type, on behalf of Beagle. BAC is working towards a major artefact collection with a view
to establishing a museum, hopefully at Filton, Avon. The Meggitt site is very apt, being a shadow
factory for Bristol, Beauforts, Beaufighters and Tempests having been built on the site.
◆ Visits to the site are not possible, but general enquiries can be made to : ✉ Bristol Aero Collection,
PO Box 48, Patchway, Bristol BS12 5AA. ✉ Britannia Aircraft Preservation Trust, Roger
Hargreaves, 8 Mill Park, Park Road, Burgess Hill, Sussex, RH15 8ET.

☐ G-ANCF*	Britannia 308F	ex Brooklands, Manston, 5Y-AZP, G-ANCF, LV-GJB, LV-PPJ, G-ANCF ntu, G-14-1, G-18-4, N6597C ntu, G-ANCF. CoA expired 12-1-81. Fuselage, arrived 27-3-93. BAPT. See notes.	12-93
☐ G-ARRM*	Beagle 206-1X	ex Brooklands, Shoreham, Duxford, Shoreham. CoA exp 28-12-64. Arr 29-1-94. Stored.	01-94
☐ 'N5419"* N5419	Bristol Scout D	ex Cardington, USA. US civil regn = 'serial'. Arrived 30-10-93.	12-93
☐ XJ917*	Sycamore HR.14	ex Helston, Wroughton, CFS, 275. 'S-H'. Arrived 30-4-93. Loan, from Sycamore Gp.	12-93

BRISTOL
■ **Bristol Industrial Museum** : As well as the Sycamore, there are many aero engines on show.
◆ Tuesday to Sunday 10am to 1pm and 2pm to 5pm. ✉ Prince's Wharf, Bristol BS1 4RN.
☎ 0272 299771.

☐ XL829	Sycamore HR.14	ex 32, MCS, Khormaksar SAR Flight.	10-93

■ **Bristol Plane Preservation Unit** (BPPU) : Now sponsored by Air Total, Jim Buckingham
and friends operate the well-known *Miles Duo* that can be seen around and about at airshows and fly-
ins. Visits to the strip are not possible, but both aircraft can be seen in the air regularly.

☐ G-AKKB	Gemini 1A ∆	-	01-94
☐ 'RG333' G-AIEK	Messenger 2A ∆	ex Miles 'B' condition U-9.	01-94

■ **Brunel Technical College** : Located on Ashley Down, off the A38 north of the city centre.
Cessna F.150H G-AWUK is thought to have left the College — most likely scrapped. The Beagle 206
is owned by the Midland Air Museum of Coventry Airport, Warks, and is on temporary loan. The
College maintains other airframes at Bristol Airport — which see.

☐ G-AIZY	J/1 Autocrat	ex Caldicot. Damaged 8-89. Restoration.	06-91
☐ G-ASWJ* 8449M	Beagle 206-1	ex Halton, Rolls-Royce. Arrived 5-93. See notes above.	05-93
☐ G-ATHA	Apache 235	ex Aviation West, Bristol Airport, N4326Y. CoA exp 7-6-86.	06-91
☐ G-AVDR	Queen Air B80	ex Bournemouth, Shobdon, Exeter, A40-CR, G-AVDR. CoA expired 30-6-86.	06-91
☐ G-AVDS	Queen Air B80	ex Bournemouth, Exeter, A40-CS, G-AVDS. CoA expired 26-8-77.	06-91
☐ G-AVVW	Cessna F.150H	ex Bristol Airport. CoA expired 31-5-82.	06-91
☐ G-AWBW	Cessna F.172H	ex Bristol Airport, Compton Abbas. Damaged 20-5-73.	06-91

■ **City Museum and Art Gallery** : The Bristol Boxkite replica remains the main aeronautical
attraction at the Museum, although there are other aviation artefacts on show.

◆ Every day including Sundays, 10am to 5pm. ✉ Queen's Road, Clifton, Bristol, BS8 1RL.
☎ 0272 299771.
☐   BAPC.40   Boxkite replica   ex Old Warden. (c/no BM.7281).   10-93
■ **Winbolt Collection** : Contrary to the speculation in **W&R13**, the Sea Vixen nose is still with the
private collection of avionics and radio gear here.
◆ Strictly by prior permission. ✉ Dr G E Winbolt, The Cottage, Castle Road, Pucklechurch, near
Bristol, Avon.
☐ XN651   A2616   Sea Vixen FAW.2   ex Culdrose, SAH, 766, FAW.1, 893. Nose.   10-93
■ **Others** : Tim Cox is *thought* to be still hard at work on his Auster composite. Spitfire VIII
MV154/G-BKMI moved to Filton, Avon, as it neared completion.
☐ G-AJEI   J /1N Alpha   ex Fiskerton, Boston, Bodmin, fuselage frame,
                                         with wings of J/1N F-BFUT. Restoration.   12-88
                                         [Original fuselage, G-AJEI still flies.]

BRISTOL AIRPORT (or Lulsgate, on the A38 south west of Bristol)
Written out of **W&R12**, Varsity T.1 WF376 has tenaciously remained on the dump and so this edition
will bow to this fact and re-insert it! Apache 160 G-ARJW, mentioned in **W&R13**, had moved on to
Hullavington, Wilts, by September 1992. Accordingly, other than WF376, all the **W&R** candidates
here are presently Brunel (ß) airframes — see also under Bristol, Avon.
☐ G-ANAP   Dove 6   ex CAFU Stansted. CoA expired 6-9-73. ß   01-94
☐ G-AVFM   Trident 2E   ex BA and BEA. CoA expired 2-6-84. ß   01-94
☐ G-AVHN   Cessna F.150G   Damaged 28-1-85. Fuselage only. ß   06-89
☐ WF376   Varsity T.1   ex CFS, CAW, 5 FTS, 151, 201 AFS. Dump.
                                        See notes above.   01-94
☐ WF410   Varsity T.1   ex 6 FTS, 2 ANS, 5 FTS, 2 ANS, RAFC, CNCS,
                                        201 AFS. 'F'. ß   01-94

FILTON AIRFIELD (south of the M5 at Patchway, north of Bristol)
■ **Airfield** : The skyline here is crowded with unsold BAe 146s (or, if you will, Avro International
Avroliners — Roe, Chadwick *et al* spinning in their graves). Most of these are too transitory for the
W&R 'treatment', although some do qualify. Largest input here has been the purchase by European
Aviation of many of the former British Airways BAC 111-510EDs. Some are for operation, G-AVMX
arriving on May 13, 1993 and noted crew training at Jersey in August, wearing 'European' titling. G-
AVMH, flew in June 25, 1993; G-AVMI, flew in July 1, 1993, G-AVMK flew in on June 3, 1993, G-
AVMT, flew in July 1, 1993 and G-AVMW, flew in June 3, 1993, are all for Air Bristol. All were
stored at Bournemouth Airport, Dorset, and reference should be made there for the full story. The
market being what it is, these aircraft could be here for a long time. The identity of the MB.339 here is
at long last confirmed. One VC-10 from Abingdon arrived here by road, acting as a spares source for
the K.4 conversion programme. Robs Lamplough's Spitfire VIII was engine running by April 1993
— first flight should have occurred by the time these words are read.
☐ G-AVMJ*   BAC 111-510ED   ex B'mouth, BA, BEA. Flew in 25-5-93.   07-93
☐ G-AVML*   BAC 111-510ED   ex B'mouth, BA, BEA. Flew in 13-5-93.   07-93
☐ G-AVMM*   BAC 111-510ED   ex B'mouth, BA, BEA. Flew in 25-5-93.   07-93
☐ G-AVMR*   BAC 111-510ED   ex B'mouth, BA, BEA. Flew in 25-5-93.   07-93
☐ G-AVMY*   BAC 111-510ED   ex B'mouth, BA, BEA. Flew in 13-5-93.   07-93
☐ G-AVMZ*   BAC 111-510ED   ex B'mouth, BA, BEA. Flew in 13-5-93.   08-93
☐ G-BBDG   Concorde 100   CoA expired 1-3-82. BA spares, stored.   06-90
☐ G-BKXN*   ICA IS-28M2A   CoA expired 26-5-90. Stored.   06-93
☐ G-BMYE*   BAe 146-200   ex Hatfield, G-WAUS, G-5-146, G-WISC. CoA
                                        exp 2-3-88. Stored.   01-94
☐ G-BTUY*   BAe 146-300   ex G-6-202. Stored. Arrived 21-10-92.   08-93
☐ G-BUHW*   BAe 146-300   ex G-6-217. Stored. Arrived 28-7-92.   08-93
☐ G-CHSR*   BAe 146-200   ex G-5-088. Stored. Arrived 4-9-92.   08-93
☐ G-6-210*   BAe 146-200   Arrived 24-6-92. Stored.   08-93
☐ G-6-213*   BAe 146-200   ex N889DV ntu. Stored. Arrived 21-7-92.   08-93
☐ 'MT928'* G-BKMI   Spitfire VIII   ex 'Bristol', Huntingdon, Duxford, Australia, RAAF
                                        A58-671, MV154, 82 MU, 6MU. Robs Lamplough.
                                        'ZX-M', 145 Sqn c/s. Engine running 4-93.   08-93

□ WH665	8736M	Canberra T.17	ex Samlesbury, Cosford, 360, RNZAF, 45, 10. 'J'. Dump.	09-93
□ ZD243*		Super VC-10	ex Abingdon, G-ASGR, Prestwick, BA, BOAC. Arrived 6-92. Sectioned. Spares.	09-93
□ 0767		MB.339AA	ex Yeovilton, Stanley, Argentine Navy. Composite airframe. Engine change test-bed for JPATS *T-Bird II* programme. See notes.	07-93

■ **Bristol Aero Collection** (BAC) : The main store for this nascent collection has been established at Banwell, Avon — *qv*.

■ **Rolls-Royce Heritage Trust - Bristol Branch** (RRHT) : The Branch had established an astounding collection of aero engines, centred on a former test shell building within the R-R plant.
◆ Visits by prior permission only, and well worth it. ✉ Peter Pavey, AITD (GP2/1), Rolls-Royce plc, PO Box 3, Filton, Bristol BS12 7QE.

■ **Rolls-Royce Technical School** : Also within the R-R complex is the Tech with its Provost.

| □ XF603 | | Provost T.1 | ex Bristol, 27 MU, CAW, RAFC. 'H'. | |

KEYNSHAM (on the A4 south east of Bristol).

■ **K Baker** : Construction/restoration of the Pup is assumed to continue.

| □ G-EAVX | B1807 | Sopwith Pup | ex Dorset. Crashed 21-7-21. | |

■ **Others** : A farm in this area holds the wreckage of a Robin HR.100-200B. Likely identities include the erstwhile G-BLAY (ex F-BSJY and last heard of at Eversden, Cambs) or -210 G-BFWW which crashed at Moreton-in-the-Marsh on May 3, 1990. How say you?

| □ | | HR.100-200B | wreck. See notes above. | 11-93 |

LOCKING (on the A371 east of Weston-super-Mare)

■ **RAF Locking** : Is still looked over by a Gnat.

| □ XM708 | 8573M | Gnat T.1 | ex Halton, 4 FTS, CFS, HS. *Reds* c/s. | 10-93 |

WESTON-SUPER-MARE

Appearing in a field near here during mid 1992 was the unlikely vista of a Nord Noratlas fuselage. Acquired from France, where it had been used as a para-trainer, the owner has turned it into a travelling theatre — it has already been seen in Dorset!

| □ 108* | | Noratlas | ex French AF. Fuselage only, first noted 7-92. See notes above. | 12-93 |

WESTON-SUPER-MARE AERODROME (on the A371 east of Weston)

■ **International Helicopter Museum** (IHM) : Prospects get brighter and brighter for IHM as the site continues to improve and further airframe acquisitions underline the truly international flavour of this world-class collection. The land occupied by the aerodrome has been allocated by the local Council for open space/recreational flying and aerial activity and the possibility of this usage resuming is getting stronger. Meanwhile, the eight acres for IHM expansion — which include the original 1936 control tower — are still reserved but await completion of planning and legal detail before they can be handed over. Since **W&R13**, IHM has witnessed the arrival of an Mi-1 from Poland and a Frelon from France. The former is the first Soviet-designed helicopter to go on show in the UK and the latter the largest helicopter to be displayed. Whirlwind Srs 3 G-AYNP (see under Redhill, Surrey) is destined for the *Hubschrauber* Museum in Germany in exchange for a Mil Mi-2. Two helicopters long-planned to arrive have yet to happen for a variety of reasons and have been removed from the listing so as not to confuse readers. Sikorsky CH-37C Mojave N7393/BuNo 145872 awaits the complex logistics of bringing such a sized beast from the USA. Kaman HH-43F Huskie 62-4552 patiently awaits collection in Pakistan, having been lovingly restored by the Pakistan Air Force. The problem here is paperwork as the helicopter was supplied to Pakistan under MDAP. A re-export certificate has so far been refused by the Pentagon, as they are worried that the Huskie may fly with a belligerent air arm somewhere. Yet the US government, however, was quite happy to give the IHM a UH-1 *Huey* — a far more 'liquid' commodity in the international arms trade! Thanks to the Raoul Hafner hangar, the IHM is steadily working on the restoration and conservation of its exhibits. Latest to emerge is the WSK SM-2. Westlands at Yeovil continue to be very supportive and took on the restoration of Whirlwind HAS.7 XG596 at their plant from October 1993. Two of the Wessex 60s have been disposed of G-AWOX was reduced to spares and G-AZBY has moved on. A Lynx rig and the three CR.LTH-1 Grasshoppers were bagged during the auction of the former Helicopter Museum of Great Britain at Blackpool airport, Lancs, in January 1993. The Lynx's identity is proven, but it leaves question marks hanging over both Blackpool Airport and Lancaster, Lancs — qv. RG-05 has 'WG.0012' and 'WA.262' on a plate inside it, does this make it the 12th down the production line, ie in between XX911 (00-11) and XZ166? Clearing up **W&R13**, SARO P.531 XN332/A2579 was never here, see under Wroughton, Wilts, and Yeovilton, Somerset, for its pedigree. Efforts have been made to make the airframes in store available to inspection by visitors, but readers should note that not all airframes held by IHM at Weston can be viewed. Wessex Srs 60 G-AZBZ left during January 1994 bound for Hi-Lift Helicopters of Kissimmee, Florida. Airframes marked ® are on loan to IHM from Elfan ap Rees.

◆ On the A371 east of Weston. Open daily 10am to 6pm and 10.30am to 4pm November to March. *Open Cockpit* days are held every second Sunday in the month, March to October and the annual *HeliDays* fly-in is held on the Weston Sea Front each July — 23/24 in 1994. ✉ Weston Airport, Locking Moor Road, Weston-super-Mare, Avon BS22 8PP. ☎ 0934 635227, **Fax** 0934 822400.

☐ G-ACWM	Cierva C.30A	ex Staverton, AP506, 529, 1448 Flt, 74 Wing, 5 RSS, G-ACWM. Frame. ®	12-93
☐ G-ANFH	Whirlwind Srs 1	ex Redhill, Great Yarmouth, Bristow, BEAH. CoA expired 17-7-71. Stored. ®	12-93
☐ G-ANJV	Whirlwind Srs 3	ex Redhill, Bristow and VR-BET. ®	12-93
☐ G-AODA*	Whirlwind Srs 3	ex Redhill, 9Y-TDA, EP-HAC, G-AODA. *Dorado*. CoA exp 23-8-91. Arr 7-8-93.	12-93
☐ G-AOUJ	Fairey ULH	ex 'Essex', White Waltham, XJ928. CoA expired 29-3-59. ®	12-93
☐ G-ARVN	Grasshopper 1	ex Shoreham, Redhill. CoA exp 18-5-63. Stored. ®	12-93
☐ G-ASCT*	Bensen B.8M	ex Hungerford. CoA expired 11-11-66.	12-93
☐ G-ASHD	Brantly B.2A	ex Oxford and area. Cr 19-2-67. Spares.	12-93
☐ G-ASTP	Hiller UH-12C	ex Biggin Hill, Thornicombe, 'Wales', Thornicombe, Redhill, N9750C. CoA expired 3-7-82.	12-93
☐ G-ATBZ G-17-4	Wessex 60 Srs 1	ex Bournemouth, Sykes, Weston. CoA expired 15-12-81.	12-93
☐ G-AVKE	Gadfly HDW-1	ex Southend, Thruxton. Stored. ®	12-93
☐ G-AVNE G-17-3	Wessex 60 Srs 1	ex Bournemouth, W-s-M, 5N-AJL, G-AVNE, 9M-ASS, VH-BHC, PK-HBQ, G-AVNE. CoA expired 7-2-83.	12-93
☐ G-AWRP*	Grasshopper III	ex Blackpool, Heysham, Shoreham, Redhill. CoA expired12-5-72. Arrived by 3-93.	12-93
☐ G-AXFM*	Grasshopper III	ex Blackpool, Heysham, Shoreham, Redhill. Ground running rig. Arrived by 3-93.	12-93
☐ G-AZAU*	Grasshopper III	ex Blackpool, Heysham, Shoreham, Redhill. Power and lift grouping. Arrived by 3-93.	12-93
☐ G-AZYB	Bell 47H-1	ex Thruxton, LN-OQG, SE-HBE, OO-SHW. Crashed 21-4-84. ®	12-93
☐ G-BAPS	Cougar	ex Weston-super-Mare. CoA exp 20-5-74.	12-93
☐ G-BGHF	WG.30-100	ex Yeovil, Westlands. CoA expired 1-8-86.	12-93
☐ G-HAUL G-17-22	WG.30-300	ex Yeovil. CoA expired 27-10-86.	12-93
☐ G-OAPR	Brantly B.2B ∆	ex G-BPST ntu, N2280U. ®	12-93
☐ G-48-1 G-ALSX	Sycamore 3	ex Duxford, Staverton, G-ALSX, VR-TBS ntu, G-ALSX. CoA expired 24-9-65. ®	12-93
☐ D-HMQV (c/n 6216)	Bo 102 Helitrainer	ground trainer, but capable of flight. ®	12-93
☐ F-BTRP*	SA.321F Frelon	ex Aerospatiale, Olympic, F-WKQC, F-OCZV, F-RAFR, F-OCMF, F-BMHC, F-WMHC and SA.321 c/n 116. Arrived 28-4-93.	12-93
☐ VR-BEU G-ATKV	Whirlwind Srs 3	ex Redhill, VR-BEU, G-ATKV, EP-HAN, G-ATKV. Spares use.	12-93

☐	5N-ABW		Widgeon 2	ex Cuckfield, Shoreham, Bristow, G-AOZE. ® 12-93
☐	VZ962		Dragonfly HR.1	ex Helston, BRNC Dartmouth. FAAM loan. Spares. 12-93
☐	WG719	G-BRMA	Dragonfly HR.5	ex 'WG718', Shawbury, Weston, Yeovilton, Yeovilton SF, 705. ® 12-93
☐	XA862	A2542	Whirlwind HAS.1	ex Coventry, Wroughton, Lee-on-Solent, Seafield Park, Haslar, Lee-on-Solent, Fleetlands, 781, 771, 700, *Protector* Flt, 700, *Protector* Flt, 705, G-AMJT ntu. 12-93
☐	XD163	8654M	W'wind HAR.10	ex Wroughton, CFS, Akrotiri SAR Flt, MoA, 228, 275, 155, MoA. 'X'. ® 12-93
☐	XE521		Rotodyne Y	ex Cranfield, W Waltham. Large sections. ® 12-93
☐	XG452	G-BRMB	Belvedere HC.1	ex Ternhill, 2 SoTT 7997M, Westlands. ® 12-93
☐	XG462		Belvedere HC.1	ex Henlow, W-super-M, 72, 66. Crashed 5-10-63. Nose. 12-93
☐	XG547	G-HAPR	Sycamore HR.14	ex CCAS St Athan 8010M, Kemble, CFS. 'S-T'. ® 12-93
☐	XG596	A2651	Whirlwind HAS.7	ex Wroughton, 705, 829, 771, 705, 737. '66'. ® 12-93
☐	XL811*		Skeeter AOP.12	ex Stoke-on-Trent, Warmingham, Southend, 9/12 Lancers, 17F, 652, 651. Arr mid-1993. ® 12-93
☐	XM556	G-HELI	Skeeter AOP.12	ex Connah's Quay, Middle Wallop 7870M. Boom of XM529/7979M. 12-93
☐	XP165		Scout AH.1	ex Yeovilton, Weston, HAM Southend, RAE. 12-93
☐	XP404	8732M	W'wind HAR.10	ex Finningley, Benson, 22, SAR Wing, 202, 228. Stored. 12-93
☐	XS149		Wessex HAS.3	ex Templecombe, Wroughton, 737. '661-GL'. 12-93
☐	'XS463'	XT431	Wasp HAS.1	ex Fleetlands, Lee-on-Solent. Parts from XS463/A2647 ex G-17-1. 12-93
☐	XT472		Wessex HU.5	ex Hullavington, Netheravon, Wroughton, 845. 'XC'. 12-93
☐	XW837		Lynx 1-06	ex Lee-on-Solent, Foulness, Boscombe Down, Yeovil. Stored. 12-93
☐	ZE477		Lynx 3	ex G-17-24, Yeovil, Westlands. 12-93
☐	622	N6699D	HUP-3	ex RCN, 51-16622. 12-93
				[Data panel reads 53-16622 and therefore an UH-25 Mule?]
☐	9147*		Mil Mi-4 *Hound*	ex Poland, Czech AF. Arrived 1-94. 01-94
☐	S-881		S-55C	ex Panshanger, Elstree, Dan AF Esk.722. ® 12-93
☐	S-882		S-55C	ex Panshanger, Elstree, Dan AF Esk.722. ® 12-93
☐	S-886		S-55C	ex Panshanger, Elstree, Dan AF Esk.722. ® 12-93
☐	S-887		S-55C	ex Panshanger, Elstree, Dan AF Esk.722. ® 12-93
☐	FR-108	CDL	Djinn	ex France, ALAT. 12-93
☐		1005	WSK SM-2	ex Poland. '05'. 12-93
☐	2007*		Mil Mi-1 (SM-1)	ex Poland. Arrived 2-9-93. 12-93
☐	66-16579*		UH-1H-BF	ex US Army. Arrived 29-8-92. 12-93
☐	*	RG-05	Lynx static rig	ex Blackpool, Coventry Airport, Yeovil. Arrived by 3-93. see notes above. 12-93
☐	*		Lynx HAS.3	ex Yeovil. Mock-up, built 1984 using Lynx and WG.30 parts.
☐		BAPC.128	Watkinson CG-4	ex Bexhill. Man powered rotorcraft. 12-93
☐		BAPC.153	WG-33	ex Yeovil. Mock-up ultra-light *helo*. Stored. 12-93
☐		BAPC.212	Bensen B.6	Stored. 12-93
☐		BAPC.213	Vertigo	ex Cranfield, Yeovil. Man powered helicopter. 12-93

BEDFORD
■ **Manders Technical College** : It is thought that the Cessna still serves here.
☐ G-AVCC   Cessna F.172H   damaged 31-12-87. Inst airframe.   04-88

BEDFORD AIRFIELD (or Thurleigh, east of the A6 north of Bedford)
■ **Defence Research Establishment** (DRA) : The DRA vacated the airfield — letting a 10,500ft runway go to waste, during March 1994 and the story here is of exodus. (The wind tunnel site will be staying, apparently.) The Apprentice School closed by the end of August 1992. Disposals have been as follows :— Blanik CVB/BGA.1831 is airworthy, delete; Hunter F.6 XG210 appeared at Beck Row, Suffolk, by February 1992; Gnat T.1 XM694 to Portsmouth, Hants, early 1993; Puma XW241 to Farnborough, Hants. Five DRA Bedford airframes were entered into the MoD auction held in London on July 8, 1993:— Canberra T.4 WJ992, Canberra B.6(mod) XH568, Viscounts XT575 and XT661, Buccaneer S.2B XX897 (see Appendix D). Only the former RRE Viscounts, Srs 837 XT575 and Srs 838 XT661 really fall into the **W&R** bracket and they were bought for their Darts only. Both travelled to Stock, Essex, during August 1993. The nose section of Canberra PR.9 XH174 arrived from St Athan, by December 1991 for fitment trials, but had returned to St Athan, S Glam, by September 1992. Accordingly, the items listed below are awaiting a change in their prospects, or it's already happened.

☐ G-BBSO	Cherokee 140F	crashed 28-5-82. Fuselage. Spares.	03-90
☐ G-BCSY	Taylor Titch	unflown, but completed. Stored.	03-90
☐ G-BFZA	Alpavia RF-3	ex Twinwood Farm, F-BLEL. Fuse, off-site.	03-90
☐ XK530	Buccaneer S.2	ex RAE catapult trials and S.1. Dump, poor.	08-92
☐ XV748*	Harrier GR.3	ex 233 OCU, 1, 233 OCU, 1. '3D'. First noted 4-90.	12-93
☐ XW626	Comet 4 AEW	ex A&AEE, MinTech, G-APDS, BOAC. Open store.	12-93

CARDINGTON AIRFIELD (south of the A603, south east of Bedford)
■ **Friends of Cardington Airship Station** (FOCAS) : The job of fund raising to open the FOCAS **Airship and Balloon Museum** goes on. Planning permission has been obtained for the site and museum building and there are possibilities of accommodation in the former headquarters building now abandoned by the RAF. Thanks to the RAF Museum, a display room has been established within the Restoration and Storage Centre and this includes a superb range of models, a balloon basket and many other items. Over at the Shuttleworth Collection (Old Warden, Beds), FOCAS have established an excellent airship and balloon display — this is open whenever the collection is open. The gondola of the Skyship 500 is stored within the site, another '500 is in store for FOCAS at Kirkbymoorside, N Yorks (*qv*) and work on the K88 gondola continues at St Athan, S Glam (*qv*).
◆ Access to the FOCAS display room is by prior permission only, apply to the address below.
✉ G/C P A Garth, 5 Orchard Lane, Brampton, Huntingdon, Cambs, PE1 8TF.
☐ G-BIHN   Skyship 500   wrecked in gale 27-4-87. Stored.   11-93
■ **Royal Air Force Museum Restoration & Storage Centre** (RAFM) : The work being carried out here for the RAF Museum, be it readying a uniform, preparing a model, or continuing to bring the stunning Supermarine Southampton to life, carries on with vigour. The latter is breathtaking and when the fuselage is installed at Hendon (scheduled for late 1994) it will raise eyebrows forever more. The fabulous fuselage is like no other — bedecked in deep varnish and brass screws and nail heads — a thing of rich beauty. When the craftsmen have finished on this milestone restoration they will take on the Hampden — a very different construction technique and a whole new set of challenges. The Hampden will be restored as a 'half-and-half' exhibit, one side will show how it looked after the forced-landing, the other side will show a pristine 144 Squadron example. Work on the Tempest makes good progress. Arriving in the stores area during the summer of 1993 were the remains of the former Shuttleworth Trust Bristol Bulldog IIA 'K2227'/G-ABBB which crashed at Farnborough, Hants, on September 13, 1964. The remains have been gathered to assess if a rebuild to static condition is possible. At present, the collection of somewhat gruesome bits does not constitute a 'tabular' reference within **W&R**, but we will watch the project with great interest. The nose of a Victor K.2 has arrived for preparation for display at Hendon as a 'walk-through' exhibit.

In quick succession during 1992, Cardington was custodian to two V-1 *Doodlebugs*. One has been held here probably since the days of the clear-out at Henlow, Beds. During 1992 it was exported to the *Museum für Verkehr und Technik* in Berlin in exchange for the precious lozenge printed fabric and other items to bring the RAFM's Fokker D.VII to fruition. No sooner had the dust settled from this move, than *another* arrived from St Athan, having been 'found' in their sort-out there! For a brief moment, RAFM had *five* V-1s (Cosford, Duxford — on loan, Hendon, the one now in Berlin and the 'new' one from St Athan).

Receiving much attention at Cardington was the fuselage of the Mitsubishi *Dinah* from the Aerospace Museum, Cosford, Salop — more details under that heading. Departures from the facility have been as follows :— by November 1992 work was complete on the Sopwith Tabloid '168'/G-BFDE and it had returned to Hendon, Gtr Lon; Hart Trainer K4972/1764M moved to Cosford, Salop, by June 1992; Bristol Scout D replica 'N5419' moved to Banwell, Avon, by June 1993; Hawk Major DG590/8379M was noted still in store here during September 1992, but was not present in June 1993 and is unaccounted for.

☐ G-AHED		Dragon Rapide	ex Henlow, RL962, DH Witney. CoA expired 17-4-68. Stored. 11-93
☐ F-HMFI		Farman F.141	ex Henlow and Nash Collection. Stored. Wings recovered & restored. (Note change of type.) 11-93
☐ N9899		Southampton I	ex Henlow and Felixstowe. Fuselage and 'tail feathers'. Restoration. 11-93
☐ P1344*	9175M	Hampden I	ex Hatch, Petsamo, USSR, forced down 6-9-42, 144, 14 OTU. 'PL-K'. Arrived late 1992, pending restoration. See notes above. 03-94
☐ NV778	8386M	Tempest TT.5	ex Hendon, Foulness, Middleton St George, 233 OCU, Napiers. Composite. Restn. 11-93
☐ VX275	8884M	Sedbergh TX.1	ex St Athan, BGA.572. On charge here. 05-93
☐ XE946	7473M	Vampire T.11	ex Henlow, Habbaniya SF, Nicosia SF. Pod. Stored. 11-93
☐ XM717*		Victor K.2	ex Marham, 55, 57, 55, 543, Witt Wing, 100. Nose, arrived 2-3-94. See notes above. 03-94
☐ XS695*	A2619	Kestrel FGA.1	ex Yeovilton, Culdrose, SAH, Manadon, Tri-Partite Evaluation Sqn, A&AEE, RAE. Arrived by 2-94. Stored. 02-94
☐		FE.2b	cockpit nacelle. Stored. 11-93
☐ 8417/18		Fokker D.VII	ex Hendon, Cardington, Hendon, Cardington. Restoration. See notes above. 11-93
☐ 01120*		MiG-15*bis*	ex South Lambeth, Hendon, Middlesborough, Polish AF. Arrived 1991. Restoration. 11-93
☐ 15195		PT-19A Cornell	ex Henlow, Canada. Stored. 09-92
☐ 13064		P-47D-40-RA	ex Bittesswell, Yugoslavia, USAAF 45-49295. Restoration. 11-93
☐		BAPC.180 AEA Silver Dart	ex Farnborough, Canada. Replica. Stored. 11-93
☐		BAPC.237* Fi 103 (V-1)	ex St Athan.. Stored. First noted 9-92. See notes above. 11-93

■ **Others** : Within one of the huge airship hangars, the fuselage of a '707 — suitably dwarfed by its surroundings — is use for smokehood trials.

☐ G-APFG		Boeing 707-436	ex Stansted, British Airtours, BOAC. Fuse. 07-93

CRANFIELD AERODROME (east of Newport Pagnell)

■ **Cranfield Institute of Technology** (CIT) : Additions here have included a Harrier T.4 and a Jindivik. Of the airframes used by CIT, Cherokee 180D G-AZZT is assumed to have expired. Another expiry is the building which held G-BGGY and XT439. The Wasp is confirmed as having relocated, but what of the JetRanger?

☐ G-AWZN		Trident 3B-101	ex BA, BEA. CoA exp 16-1-86. Inst. 09-93
☐ G-BBOJ		Aztec 250E	ex 5Y-AOK, N14130. Crashed 3-12-80. Fire dump. 12-90
☐ G-BGGY		AB JetRanger III	crashed 13-9-84. Inst. 03-90

☐ XT439	Wasp HAS.1	ex Wroughton, 829 HQ Flight. Crashed 25-3-86. '605'. Inst. 10-93
☐ XW270*	Harrier T.4	ex Wittering, 4, 1, 233 OCU, 1, 233 OCU. Spares use? First noted 9-93. 09-93
☐ A92-805*	Jindivik	ex Llanbedr (?). First noted 12-92. 12-92

■ **Kennet Aviation** : Tim Manna's collection of aircraft, previously based at Thatcham, Berks, has gravitated here and occupied the hangar previously used by VAT (see below). Major event has been the arrival of the restored Jet Provost T.1 G-AOBU which was undertaking taxying trials as **W&R14** was compiled. A former Halton Gnat T.1 has also arrived for restoration to flying condition. Kennet are looking after the Cranfield-based aircraft of Butane Buzzard Aviation (BBA), who also have a base at North Weald, Essex.

☐ G-AOBU*	Jet Provost 1	ex Winchester, Thatcham, Old Warden, Loughborough, Luton, XM129, G-42-1. CoA expired 24-5-56. See notes above. 11-93
☐ G-FRCE*	Gnat T.1 ▲	ex North Weald, 8604M, Halton, XS104, 4 FTS, CFS, 4 FTS. BBA. 09-93
☐ G-HUEY*	UH-1H-BF ▲	ex Argentine AE-413, 73-22077. BBA. Arrived 15-1-94. 01-94
☐ WK511* G-BVBT	Chipmunk T.10 ▲	ex Shawbury, Kemble, BRNC, Wittering SF, Lon UAS, 61 GCF, Bri UAS, 22 RFS, 5 BFTS. '901' Arrived by 11-93. 11-93
☐ WW453* G-TMKI	Provost T.1	ex Thatcham, Strathallan, Perth, Huntings, 1 FTS, 2 FTS. 'W-S'. Arr 25-11-93. 11-93
☐ XF690* G-MOOS	Provost T.1 ▲	ex Thatcham, G-BGKA, 8041M, XF690, CATCS, CNCS, 64 GCF, Queens UAS. Flew in 17-3-94. 03-94
☐ XM405* G-TORE	Jet Provost T.3A ▲	ex 1 FTS, RAFC, 1 FTS, 2 FTS. BBA. Flying by 1992. 09-93
☐ 'XM693'* G-TIMM	Gnat T.1 ▲	XP504, ex Leavesden, Halton 8618M, 4 FTS, CFS, 4 FTS. Arrived 12-93. 12-93
☐ XP534* 8620M	Gnat T.1	ex Halton, 4 FTS, CFS, 4 FTS, CFS, 4 FTS. '64'. Arrived 23-11-93. 11-93
☐ XR538* G-RORI	Gnat T.1	ex Halton 8621M, 4 FTS. '69'. F/n 10-93. 10-93

■ **Vintage Aircraft Team** (VAT) : During 1992/1993 VAT thinned down their airframes quite considerably, while the move (in part) to Bruntingthorpe, Leics, was undertaken. It will be some time — if ever — that the full story of airframes held with VAT comes to light and the list of disposals/removals given here should be regarded as somewhat tentative. During their tenure at Cranfield, VAT have worked upon and maintained several of the Butane Buzzard Aviation (BBA) fleet — see also under North Weald, Essex. BBA aircraft based at Cranfield will be looked after by Kennet Aviation (see above) from the 1994 season. Chipmunk T.10 WD386 arrived here in an exchange for Tiger Moth bits for WHAG of Salisbury, Wilts. See under Binbrook, Lincs, for comings and goings of *JP*s. (Note that the Militair operation was dissolved several years ago.)

Moving on have been the following :— Venom FB.50 'WE402'/G-VENI flew on to its new base at Southampton, Hants, on October 24, 1992. Venom FB.50 J-1601/G-VIDI left by road on January 22, 1993 initially for temporary storage at Dunsfold, Surrey, before moving on to Bournemouth, Dorset, early in 1993. CM-170-2 MT-11/G-BRFU moved by road to North Weald, Essex, during June 1993. Provost T.1 WV495/7697M (last noted in July 1991) exported to the USA. Provost T.1 WV686/G-BLFT exported, this time to Keith Clarke in Australia. The two anonymous Tiger Moth frames have gone. Correcting **W&R13**, Vampire T.55s G-DHVV, G-DHWW, G-DHZZ; and FB.6 G-DHXX did not fly in here from Switzerland, going instead to Southampton, Hants.

Plus the following, confirmed as having made the trek to Bruntingthorpe, Leics :— Vampire T.11 WZ507/G-VTII; Hunter T.7 XL578 arrived from St Athan on April 3,1992 later making the move on February 1, 1993; Jet Provost T.3 XN637/G-BKOU; '91007'/G-NASA T-33A-1-LO. Chipmunk T.10 WP845 (ex Stroud, Glos) transited through here, arriving on May 28, 1992, moving on to Bruntingthorpe, Leics.

☐ G-APLK	Student 2	ex G-MIOO, Duxford, G-APLK, Glasgow, Shoreham, XS941, G-35-4. Crashed 24-8-85. Stored. 12-93

☐	G-AYUA	XK416	Auster AOP.9	ex Bushey, Luton area, Sibson, Middle Wallop, 7855M, 651, 19 MU.	12-93
☐	G-BKRN		Beech D.18S	ex Perth, Prestwick, CF-DTN, Capitol Air Surveys, RCAF inst A675, RCAF 1500. CoA expired 26-6-83. Dismantled.	12-93
☐	G-SHOW		MS.733 Alcyon	ex Wycombe Air Park, F-BMQJ, FAF 125. CoA expired 24-5-83. Restoration.	12-93
☐	G27-239	G-BNCA	Lightning F.2A	ex Warton, 8346M, Saudi Support Unit, XN734, R-R, A&AEE, BAC. Stored, sectioned.	12-93
☐	'VZ304'	G-MKVI	Vampire FB.6 ∆	ex Swiss AF J-1167. 'A-T'. 112 Sqn c/s. First flown 20-7-93.	12-93
☐	WD386*		Chipmunk T.10	ex Tenby, St Athan, 1 FTS, Ox UAS, 22 RFS, 2 BFTS. SOC 29-7-70. Arrived by late 1992. See notes above.	07-93
☐	WL505	G-FBIX	Vampire FR.9	ex St Athan, Ely, 19, RAFC, 73. Restn.	12-93
☐	'WR410'	G-BLKA	Venom FB.54 ∆	ex G-VENM ntu, Swiss AF J-1790.	12-93
☐	WZ553		Vampire T.11	ex Lichfield, Winthorpe, South Wigston, Bruntingthorpe, Loughborough, East Midlands Airport, Liverpool Airport, Woodford, Chester, St Athan, 4 FTS, 7 FTS, 202 AFS. Dism.	12-93
☐	J-1632	G-VNOM	Venom FB.50	ex Swiss AF. Dismantled.	12-93

■ **Others** : Ka 6E CHZ/BGA.1568 was flying again by 1992. All of the stored Lightnings held here by Arnold Glass were put up for auction by Sotheby's at their Billingshurst sale on November 27, 1993 (see Appendix D). At least two sold, high bids were as follows :— XS452 £5,800; XS458, £6,000; XS898 £2,500; XS899 £2,200; XS923 £2,200 and XV328 £3,200. XS452 is due to move to Bruntingthorpe, Leics, and XS458 has joined the migration to Cyprus. Lansen G-BMSG is also reported due to move to Bruntingthorpe, but only as a transit stop, bound eventually for Sweden.

☐	G-AJIW		J/1N Alpha	ex Panshanger. CoA exp 16-10-82. Restn	03-90
☐	G-BDUX		Motor Cadet	CoA expired 23-2-84. Stored dismantled in trailer.	07-90
☐	G-BMSG		SAAB Lansen	ex VAT area, Swedish AF, Malmslatt, Fv32028. Stored.	12-93
☐	XS101	G-GNAT	Gnat T.1 ∆	ex Cranwell 8638M, Red Arrows, CFS. †	12-93
☐	XS452	G-BPFE	Lightning T.5	ex Binbrook, 11, 5, 11, LTF, 11, 5, 11, LTF, 5, LTF, 11, 56, 111, 29, 111, 226 OCU. 'BT'. See notes above.	11-93
☐	XS458		Lightning T.5	ex Binbrook, LTF, 11, LTF, 5-11 pool, LTF, 5, 226 OCU. 'DY'. See notes above.	11-93
☐	XS898		Lightning F.6	ex Binbrook, 11, 5. 'BD'. See notes.	11-93
☐	XS899		Lightning F.6	ex Binbrook, 11, 5-11 pool, 23, 5. 'BL'. See notes above.	11-93
☐	XS923		Lightning F.6	ex Binbrook, 11, LTF, 5-11 pool. 'BE'. See notes above.	11-93
☐	XV328		Lightning F.6	ex Binbrook, 11, LTF, 5, LTF, 5, 29. 'BZ'. See notes above.	11-93

DUNSTABLE AERODROME (on the B489 south east of Dunstable)
Both the anonymous Pawnee frame and Weihe AKC had gone by July 1993. However, the site remains a haven for historic gliders, several in the **W&R** category. Also of great note is the continued existence of a famous glider trailer, made from the upper fuselage of the former Rolls-Royce Tyne test-bed, Avro Lincoln RF533/G-37-1.

☐	AAF*	BGA 236	T.6 Kite I	ex G-ALUD, BGA.236, BGA.222. Stored.	07-92
☐	BBG*	BGA 833	T.8 Tutor	ex Eaton Bray, Lytham St Annes, VW535. Arrived by 7-92, for restoration.	07-93
☐	CLY*	BGA 1639	Minimoa	ex PH-390. CoA expired 1-79. Restoration.	07-93
☐	CYJ*	BGA 1910	Grunau Baby IIB	ex D-6021. CoA expired 1-90. Stored.	08-93

EATON BRAY (west of Dunstable)

■ **Peter Underwood** : The glider workshop has seen some changes. Kite 1 AHC moved to Brooklands, Surrey, by May 1993. T.8 Tutor BBG had moved to Dunstable, Beds, by July 1993.

☐ ALZ	BGA 493	Dagling	ex BAPC.81, Dunstable, Duxford, Warton. Restoration. 07-93
☐ BDB*	BGA 2238	Grunau Baby IIb	ex Bicester, RAFGSA.380, D-5766. First noted 7-93. For restoration in *Luftwaffe* markings. 07-93
☐ CRU	BGA 1754	Grunau Baby III	ex RAFGSA. Last flown 1986. Stored. 07-93

HATCH (off the B658, south west of Sandy)

■ **Skysport Engineering** : Tim Moore's workshop maintains its name as a centre for excellence. Roger Reeves' magnificent Sopwith Dove G-EAGA moved to Henlow, Beds, for flight testing during 1993 and then took up residency at Old Warden, Beds. Completed other than the engine installation (a Falcon is still awaited), The Fighter Collection's Bristol F.2b Fighter 'D8084'/G-ACAA moved to Duxford, Cambs. Falcon Major G-AEEG was flying again by 1993 and Stampe SV-4C G-SVIV was in the air again by August 1992. Bleriot XI G-AVXV was cancelled as sold in France during July 1992. The RAF Museum's incredible Westland Wallace rebuild, K6035, moved to Hendon, Gtr Lon, by March 1993 for official hand-over — an incredible achievement, 'plugging' a large 'hole' in the Museum's collection. **W&R13** could not give a 'forwarding address' for Messenger 3 G-AGOY, it moved to West Chiltington, W Sussex. The BE.2 for the Historic Aircraft Collection of Jersey will be a restoration to flying condition. The Hunter nose is an unusual commission, being worked on for 1940 Squadron, ATC, at Levenshulme, Gtr Man — they currently have a Tiger Moth. (See also under Sandy, Beds.)

☐ G-ANZT		Jackaroo	ex Reading, Thruxton, T7798, Wunstorf SF, 19 RFS, 5 RFS, 28 EFTS. CoA expired 15-3-68. Restoration. 02-93
☐ G-BLOL		SNCAN SV-4A	ex G-AXRP, F-BDCZ. Frame in rafters. 01-91
☐ G-BTVE		Demon I	ex Cardington, 2292M, K8203, 9 BGS, 9 AOS, 64. For Aero Vintage.
☐ G-DINT	X7688	Beaufighter I	ex Halton, 3858M, 29, 153. Restoration. 01-91
☐ N5595T		C-47A-85-DL	ex Benington, Thruxton, Blackbushe, G-BGCG, Spanish AF T3-27, N49V, N50322, 43-15536. Stored. 02-87
☐ A1325*	G-BVGR	RAF BE.2e	ex London Colney, Norway, Norwegian AF '37' and '133'. Arrived by 10-93. Restoration for Historic Aircraft Collection. 11-93
☐		Wallace	flying replica, under construction. 11-91
☐ WN890*		Hunter F.5	ex Hedge End, Boscombe Down, A&AEE, AWA. Nose. Arrived by 3-93. Restn. See notes. 03-93

HENLOW AIRFIELD (on the A6007 south west of Biggleswade)

■ **RAF Henlow** : Here it is a case of departures or uncertainties. Departing in a terminal manner has been the Exhibition Production Flight, which provided material for the RAF Exhibition Flight (which was based at Abingdon, Oxon) and held Gazelle HT.3 XX396/8718M on 'detachment' from that unit. It was 'subsumed' into the newly-established, and SERCO-operated, Exhibition, Production & Transportation Unit at St Athan, S Glam. Vampire T.11 XH278/8595M was put up for tender during July 1992 and moved to Felton, Northumberland. That leaves : —

☐ AQQ	BGA 580	EoN Primary	ex Twinwood Farm, G-ALPS. Stored with VGS. ATC unit (2482 Squadron?).
☐ WT612	7496M	Hunter F.1	ex Halton, Credenhill, Hawkers, A&AEE. Gate. 12-93

■ **Locally** : The fuselage of Pup 150 HB-NAV has moved on, reportedly to an ATC unit at Woodley, Berks, but this is unconfirmed.

LUTON AIRPORT (off the A505 east of Luton)

The dump is much as before, although the Navajo may have left this mortal coil. The status of the Skeeter and Djinn could do with confirmation.

☐ G-AOVS		Britannia 312	ex Redcoat, 'G-BRAC', Lloyd, BOAC. CoA exp	
			31-7-79. Fuselage. Fire.	03-93
☐ G-TAXY		Turbo Navajo	ex LN-PAD, LN-NPB, SE-EZK. *Memphis Belle*.	
			CoA expired 17-3-83. Nose.	
☐ 5N-AWD		HS.125-1	ex G-ASSI. Fire dump.	03-93
☐ XN341	8002M	Skeeter AOP.12	ex St Athan, 4 SoTT, 3 RTR, 651. Stored.	08-91
☐ FR-145		Djinn	ex Duxford auction 28-4-90, Bouilly, Dax,	
			ALAT F-MCDL. Stored.	08-91

OLD WARDEN AERODROME (west of Biggleswade, signposted from the A1)

■ **Shuttleworth Collection** : In April 1944 Mrs Dorothy Shuttleworth founded The Richard Ormonde Shuttleworth Remembrance Trust to mark the achievements of her son who had been killed piloting a Fairey Battle in a night flying training accident in August 1940. Richard was born in 1909, 85 years ago and within days of the Channel crossing. It is ironic that Richard's first aircraft acquisition was a Bleriot, which still flies with the Collection that bears his name. It is arguably the very earliest original aeroplane flying and powered by the very earliest aero engine still going aloft — a 24hp Anzani. The Bleriot will feature notably in the three purpose-staged Sunset Flying Displays during the Golden Anniversary programme of flying events planned for the 1994 season. Marking its Diamond Anniversary will be DH.88 Comet G-ACSS *Grosvenor House*, which won the MacRobertson Air Race of October 1934. The runways at Old Warden are too restrictive for the Comet and it operated from Hatfield, Herts, courtesy of London Business Aviation. The closure of Hatfield has brought the decision to ground *Grosvenor House* sometime in 1994 and base her, in taxiable condition, at 'Warden. Refer under Hatfield, Herts, for now. Acknowledgement is also due to Birmingham International Airport, for their continued sponsorship of the DH.53 Humming Bird G-EBHX (Birmingham's airfield identifier being 'BHX') that really got flying during 1993. 1993 also saw the English Electric Wren take to the air, albeit with the impetus of lots of bungee and brawn. The propeller problems of the Tomtit are cured and it too is back in the air. The Golden Anniversary year should also see the Sea Hurricane make is first flight from Duxford, Cambs (*qv*) and the Desoutter make its first flight from Old Warden. Nieuport 28 G-BSKS, owned by the Historic Aircraft Collection, was exported to the USA during September 1992, but its loss has been more than compensated for by the arrival of the AJD Engineering Camel and Roger Reeves' Dove. Percival Mew Gull G-AEXF moved to AJD at Sudbury, Suffolk, for assessment of rebuild possibilities after its crash on July 17, 1991. The collection of bits that constitutes the Dixon Ornithopter is really too small for consideration by **W&R** and has been deleted from this edition.

Shuttleworth Collection aircraft can also be found listed under the following headings : —
❑ Dewsbury, West Yorks (Bristol M.1C); ❑ Duxford, Cambs (Sea Hurricane); ❑ Hatfield, Herts (DH.88 Comet); ❑ Yeovilton, Somerset (Sea Gladiator).
◆ Open daily throughout the year, but is closed for up to 14 days covering Xmas Eve, and up to and including New Year's Day. Open 10am to 4pm (3pm November to March), the hangar displays are closed one hour after the last admission time. ⌗ Old Warden Aerodrome, Biggleswade, Beds SG18 9ER. ☎ 0767 727 288. **Fax** 0767 627745.
■ **Shuttleworth Veteran Aeroplane Society** (SVAS) : Supporting the Collection in many ways (including the restoration of the Desoutter and the Blake Bluetit), SVAS welcomes new members.
⌗ SVAS, c/o The Shuttleworth Collection, Old Warden Aerodrome, Biggleswade, Beds SG18 9ER. ☎ 0767 627 398.

☐ G-EAGA*		Sopwith Dove ▲	ex Hatch, Australia, G-EAGA, K-157.	12-93
☐ G-EBHX		Humming Bird ▲	ex Lympne No 8. *L'Oiseau Mouche*. First	
			flight 27-6-92.	12-93
☐ G-EBIR		DH.51 ▲	ex VP-KAA, G-KAA, G-EBIR. *Miss Kenya*.	12-93
☐ G-EBJO		ANEC II	ex Lympne No 7. CoA exp 30-11-35. Restn.	12-93
☐ G-EBLV*		DH.60 Moth ▲	ex Hatfield. On loan from BAe.	12-93
☐ G-EBNV	BAPC.11	EE Wren ▲	No 4. (Parts G-EBNV.) CoA exp 23-6-87.	12-93
☐ G-EBWD		DH.60X Moth ▲	Bought by Richard Shuttleworth in 1932.	·12-93
☐ G-AAIN		Parnall Elf II ▲	ex Southend, Fairoaks, Badminton.	·12-93
☐ G-AANG	No 14	Bleriot XI ▲	ex Ampthill, Hendon. BAPC.3.	12-93
☐ G-AANH	No 43	Deperdussin ▲	ex Ampthill. CoA expired 14-5-83. BAPC.4.	12-93
☐ G-AANI	No 9	Blackburn Mono ▲	ex Wittering. BAPC.5.	12-93

☐	G-AAPZ		Desoutter I	ex Higher Blagdon, Old Warden. CoA expired 3-3-39. Restoration.	12-93
☐	G-AAYX		Southern Martlet	ex Woodford. CoA exp 12-4-49. Restn.	12-93
☐	G-ABAG		DH.60 Moth ▲	ex Perth.	12-93
☐	G-ABVE		Active II ▲	loan from Desmond Penrose.	12-93
☐	G-ABXL		Archaeopteryx	ex Chillwell. CoA expired 22-9-82. Taxies.	12-93
☐	G-ADGP		Hawk Speed Six ▲	ex Hamble, Florida, Old Warden. On loan.	12-93
☐	G-ADPR		Gull Six ▲	ex Auckland, Old Warden, Ampthill, Old Warden, AX866, FTC CF,20 (P)AFU, 4 GTS, Ringway SF, 110 Wing, G-ADPR. *Jean.*	12-93
☐	G-AEBB		HM.14 *Flea*	ex Southampton. CoA exp 31-5-39. Taxies.	12-93
☐	G-AEOA		Puss Moth ▲	ex ES921, 5 GCF, 1660 CU, 5 GCF, ATA, G-AEOA, YU-PAX, UN-PAX. On loan.	12-93
☐	G-AFCL		Swallow II ▲	Loan from A Dowson.	12-93
☐	G-ARSG	BAPC.1	Triplane replica ▲	ex *Those Magnificent Men...* Hants A/C built.	12-93
☐	G-ASPP	BAPC.2	Boxkite replica ▲	ex *Those Magnificent Men...* Miles built.	12-93
☐	F904	G-EBIA	SE.5A ▲	ex 'D7000', Farnborough.	12-93
☐	B6291	G-ASOP	Camel ▲	ex Sudbury, Middle Wallop, 10 Sqn RNAS. ff 27-7-93. On loan from AJD Engineering.	12-93
☐	D8096	G-AEPH	Bristol F.2b ▲	ex Filton, Watford, D8096, 208.	12-93
☐	H5199	G-ADEV	Avro 504K ▲	ex G-ACNB, 'E3404' and Avro 504N.	12-93
☐	K1786	G-AFTA	Tomtit ▲	ex 5 GCF, 23 GCF, 3 FTS. Ff 25-6-92.	12-93
☐	K3215	G-AHSA	Tutor ▲	ex HSA, RAFC.	12-93
☐	K4235	G-AHMJ	Cierva C.30A	ex Hayes, Fairey, Middle Wallop, 529, 1448 Flt, SAC, Richard Shuttleworth. CoA expired 10-7-47. Taxiable.	12-93
☐	'K5414'	G-AENP	Hind (Afghan) ▲	ex 'K5457', Kabul. BAPC.78.	12-93
☐	L8032	G-AMRK	Gladiator I ▲	ex 'N2308', L8032, 'K8032', Gloster, Hamble, 8 MU, 61 OTU, 1624F, 2 AACU. 247 Sqn c/s, 'HP-B'.	12-93
☐	'N6181'	G-EBKY	Sopwith Pup ▲	ex N5180, Sopwith Dove. *Happy.* 3 (Naval) Sqn c/s.	12-93
☐	'N6290'	G-BOCK	Sopwith Triplane ▲	ex Dewsbury. 8 Sqn RNAS c/s, *Dixie II.*	12-93
☐	P6382	G-AJRS	Magister I ▲	ex 'G-AJDR', P6382, 3 EFTS, 16 EFTS. Complex composite.	12-93
☐	T6818	G-ANKT	Tiger Moth II ▲	ex Aston Down, 21 EFTS.	12-93
☐	W9385	G-ADND	Hornet Moth ▲	ex Chester, W9385, St Athan SF, 3 CPF, G-ADND. Impressed c/s for 1994.	12-93
☐	AR501	G-AWII	Spitfire V ▲	ex Duxford, Henlow, Loughborough, CGS, 61 OTU, 1 TEU, 58 OTU, 422, 312, 504, 310. 310 Sqn colours 'NN-A'.	12-93
☐	WB588	G-AOTD	Chipmunk T.10 ▲	ex Chessington, 22 RFS.	12-93
☐	7198/18	G-AANJ	LVG C.VI ▲	ex Stanmore, Colerne, Fulbeck.	12-93
☐		BAPC.37	Blake Bluetit	ex Winchester. Under restoration by SVAS.	12-93

SANDY

Hampden I P1344 was actually held at Hatch, Beds, but required a 'holding address' for the currency of **W&R13**. The RAF Museum accepted it during August 1992 and it moved to <u>Cardington</u>, Beds.

STANBRIDGE (south of Leighton Buzzard)

■ **RAF Logistics Establishment** : The Hunter still guards the base. The local ATC's Buccaneer nose has not been recorded since its arrival.

☐	WP190	8473M	Hunter F.5	ex Upwood, Finningley, Bircham Newton 7582M, Nicosia, 1, 41. 'K'.	09-93
☐	XN979		Buccaneer S.2	ex Cranfield, 801. Ditched 9-6-66. Nose.	04-89

ARBORFIELD (on the A327 south of Reading)

■ **Princess Marina College** : The exodus from RNAY Wroughton, Wilts, has increased the number of instructional airframes here, but note that many of the inmates here could do with the luxury of 'last noted' dates and/or fates. There are plans to expand the College further, yet to be confirmed.

☐ XM379		Jet Provost T.3	ex Shawbury, 3 FTS, 6 FTS, 2 FTS. Fuselage.
☐ XM413		Jet Provost T.3	ex Shawbury, 2 FTS, 7 FTS, CFS. Fuselage.
☐ XP244	'M7922'	Auster AOP.9	ex St Athan. 7864M. Fuselage, engine test bed.
☐ XP855*		Scout AH.1	ex Wroughton, 652, 651, 655. Arr 29-6-92. 06-92
☐ XP886		Scout AH.1	ex Wroughton.
☐ XP899		Scout AH.1	ex Middle Wallop. Crashed 1-11-79.
☐ XR601		Scout AH.1	ex 657.
☐ XT623*		Scout AH.1	ex Wroughton, 655, 659, 655. Arr 30-6-92. 06-92
☐ XT633*		Scout AH.1	ex Wroughton, 659, 653, 661, 660, Wroughton. Arrived 1-7-92. 07-92
☐ XV139		Scout AH.1	ex Wroughton.
☐		Gazelle TAD	possibly TAU.3/WA.67.

BINFIELD (north of the B3034, north west of Bracknell)

Unless there are some *real* sightings, instead of presumptions, of the two choppers reported as being here, they are heading for *LOST!*

☐ G-ASXF	Brantly 305	ex Thruxton, Biggin Hill. CoA exp 16-2-79.	03-91
☐ G-AYNS	Airmaster H2/B1	ex Blackbushe, Redhill. CoA exp 13-2-73.	02-89

BRACKNELL

■ **RAF Bracknell** : Is still guarded by its Hunter.

☐ XG196	8702M	Hunter F.6A	ex Kemble, 1 TWU, TWU, 229 OCU, 19. '31'. Gate guard.

■ **John & Maureen Woods / Friends of the DC-3** : John & Maureen's Harvard EZ259/G-BMJW moved to Ottershaw, Surrey, on March 4, 1992. They also run Friends of the DC-3 :— ✉ Friends of the DC-3, 3 *Dalcross*, Crown Wood, Bracknell, Berks, RG12 3UJ.

FINCHAMPSTEAD RIDGES (on the B3016 south of Wokingham)

■ **Staravia** : Vampire T.11 XH362 had been done to death at the yard here by June 1992.

HAMSTEAD MARSHALL

Tiger Moth EI-AGN moved to Hungerford, Berks, by November 1992.

HUNGERFORD

■ **Newbury Aeroplane Company** : Ben Cooper's skills were shown off for all to see when BA Eagle G-AFAX flew again in 1992. Since then the workshop has received some more candidates for 'the works'. Tiger Moth G-ANTS was exported to Sweden during November 1992. Tiger Moth G-APMX arrived by November 1990 for repair following a crushing from a snow laden hangar on January 14, 1987, it was flying again by July 1993. SNCAN SV-4C G-AZGC is thought to have gone to the Reading, Berks, area by the same time.

☐ G-AAUP		Klemm L.25	*Clementine*. CoA expired 21-11-84. Stored.
☐ G-ACEJ		Fox Moth	ex Old Warden. Collision 17-7-82. Restn. 08-90
☐ G-ACOJ*		Leopard Moth	ex Congleton, F-AMXP. For restoration. Arrived by 11-91. 11-91
☐ G-AFGH		Chilton DW.1	ex Billingshurst. CoA exp 7-7-83. Restn. 02-89
☐ G-AMNN		Tiger Moth	ex Huntingdon, Redhill, NM137, Brize Norton SF, Tarrant Rushton SF, 312. Cr 27-5-64. 03-90 [See also Shoreham, W Sussex.]
☐ G-ANEM* R5042		Tiger Moth	ex Hamstead Marshall, Bristol, Weston, EI-AGN G-ANEM, R5042, 14 RFS, 3 RFS, 6 EFTS. UK CoA expired 13-11-54. 11-92

| ☐ G-BIIZ * | Great Lakes 2T | ex Wycombe AP, N603K, NC603K. Wreck. First noted 11-92. | 11-92 |
| ☐ G-BSZN* | Bü 133D-1 | ex N8103, D-ECAY. Wreck, f/n 11-92. | 11-92 |

■ **Others** : A former Spanish Bf 109E arrived here during December 1993 for storage on behalf of Robs Lamplough.

| ☐ C4E-88* | Bf 109E | ex Tangmere, Stubbington, Spain. Poor state. Arrived for storage 12-93. | 12-93 |

MEMBURY (close to the Membury services, east of Swindon on the M4)

■ **Southern Sailplanes** : Tiger Moth G-AJHU fled the coop in fine style during 1991, by taking to the air again. Otherwise the cache here is thought unchanged.

☐ G-AHAG	Dragon Rapide	ex Blandford Forum, Ford, Whitney, RL944. CoA expired 15-7-73.	09-89
☐ G-AHVV	Tiger Moth	ex Lympne, EM929, 25 EFTS. Cr 12-12-71.	01-94
☐ G-AMIU	Tiger Moth	ex Wycombe Air Park, T5495, 16 EFTS, 54 OTU, Church Fenton SF. Crashed 15-10-69.	07-89
☐ G-APZJ	Super Cub 150	crashed 12-6-83.	
		[*Original* fuselage — G-APZJ still flying with a replacement fuselage frame!]	
☐ G-BAMT	DR.400 Knight	crashed 8-1-78. Wreck.	09-89
☐ G-BAVA	Super Cub 150	ex D-EFKC, ALAT 18-5391. Crashed 20-11-77. Frame. Stored.	09-89
☐ 'Z7258' G-AHGD	Dragon Rapide	ex Old Warden, NR786. *Women of the Empire.* Crashed 30-6-91. Wreck.	12-91

NEWBURY

■ **British Balloon Museum and Library** (BBML) : Two new inmates with the Museum, otherwise nothing to report. BBML envelopes are occasionally inflated during events such as the Icicle Meet and the occasional BBML inflation day. BBML maintains strong links with FOCAS at Cardington, Beds, and looks after the display in the local Museum and Library, see below.

✉ Norman Pritchard MBCS, Secretary, 75 Albany Road, Old Windsor, Berkshire, SL4 2QD.

■ **Newbury District Museum and Library** : Current BBML artefacts on show here are marked ¶ in the listing below.

◆ At The Wharf in Newbury and is open April 1 to September 30 10am to 6pm Monday to Saturday and 2pm to 6pm Sundays and Bank Holidays. October 1 to March 31 from 10am to 4pm Mondays to Saturdays and closed Sundays and Bank Holidays. The Museum is closed every Wednesday. ✉ The Wharf, Newbury, Berks RG14 5AS. ☎ 0635 30511.

☞ For this entry only, Column 3 of the table is used to define just how much of each balloon the Museum has : **B** Basket; **C** Car, **E** Envelope; **G** Gondola and combinations thereof. Column 4 gives the balloon's name and Column 5, notes. All are hot air balloons/airships, unless noted.

☐ G-ATGN	Thorn Coal Gas	E	*Eccles*	See below for basket.	
☐ G-AVTL	HAG Free	E	*Bristol Belle*		
☐ G-AWOK	Sussex Free Gas	E	*Sardine*	Never flew.	
☐ G-AXVU	Omega 84	E	*Henry VIII*		
☐ G-AXXP	Bradshaw Free	E / B	*Ignis Volens*		
☐ G-AZSP	Cameron O-84	E	*Esso*		
☐ G-AZUV	Cameron O-65	E / B	*Icarus*		
☐ G-BAMK	Cameron D-96	C / B	*Isibidbi*		11-90
☐ G-BBGZ	Cambridge	B	*Phlogiston*	¶	
☐ G-BBLL	Cameron O-84	E	*Boadicea*		
☐ G-BBOD*	Cameron O.5	E / B	*Little Titch*	Off-site.	12-93
☐ G-BCAR	Thunder Ax7-77	E	*Marie Antoinette*		
☐ G-BCFD	West	E	*Hellfire*		
☐ G-BETF	Cameron SS	E *Champion*		Spark-plug shape.	
☐ G-BETH	Thunder Ax6-56	E	*Debenhams I*		
☐ G-BHKN	Colt 14A	E	*Green Ice 2*	Includes harness/ burner.	

☐ G-BHKR	Colt 14A	E	*Green Ice 5*	Includes harness/ burner. ¶	
☐ G-BIAZ	Cameron AT-165	E	*Zanussi*	Inner gas cell, Atlantic attempt.	
☐ G-BIGT	Colt 77A	E	*Big T*	Fire damaged.	
☐ G-BKES	Cameron SS 57	E	*Robinson's Barley Water*	Bottle shape	
☐ G-ERMS*	Thunder AS-33	E / C	*Microbe*	Off site.	12-93
☐ G-PERR	Cameron SS 60	E	*Perrier*	Bottle shape.	
☐ G-PNUT	Cameron SS	E	*Mr Peanut*	Peanut-man shaped.	
☐ EI-BAY	Cameron Ax8	E	*Godolphin*	Original envelope. ex G-AYJZ.	
☐ HB-BOU	Brighton Gas	B	*Verdi*		
☐ 5Y-SIL	Cameron A-140	E	*Cumulonimbus*	Ex F-BTVO, F-WTVO, G-AZUW.	
☐	Gas balloon	B		*circa* 1949.	
☐	Cam' DG28 Gas	G		airship gondola	
☐	Military Gas	B		*circa* 1941	
☐	Military Gas	B		*circa* 1941. Was used on G-ATGN — see above. ¶	

READING

■ **Ben Borsberry** : Both Tigers are thought still to be in the area. Dragon Rapide G-AGTM arrived on March 1, 1994 for restoration on behalf of its new owner.

☐ G-AGNJ	Tiger Moth	ex VP-YOJ, ZS-BGF, SAAF 2366. Restn.
☐ G-AGTM*	Dragon Rapide	ex Rush Green, Audley End, Duxford, Biggin Hill, Duxford, JY-ACL, OD-ADP, G-AGTM, NF875. Dam 21-6-87. Arr 1-3-94. Restn. 03-94
☐ G-BRHW	Tiger Moth	ex 7Q-YMY, VP-YMY, ZS-DLB, SAAF 4606, DE671.

■ **John Bradshaw** : Keeps his 'spares-ship' for G-AWPH here. John's Fury ISS N36SF can be found at Benson, Oxon.

☐ WW447	Provost T.1	ex Exeter, CATCS, CNCS, RAFC. Stored.

■ **Others** : A damaged Stampe is stored in the area and a Tiger Moth has moved in for restoration.

☐ G-AHLT*	Tiger Moth	ex Ludlow, Heathfield, Manston, Rochester, N9128, 19 FTS, 11 EFTS, 5 CPF. Crashed 28-6-57. Restoration. Arrived by 8-90. 08-90
☐ G-AZGC*	SNCAN SV-4C	ex Hungerford, Booker, F-BCGE, French military. Accident 1988. Stored. First noted 11-92. 11-92

SHAWDENE (to the north of Newbury, on the old A34)

Stored Jodel G-ATIC, as threatened, has been confined to *LOST!*

THATCHAM (north of the A4, west of Newbury)

■ **Alan House / Provost Team** : Alan House and his dedicated team continue to work on Provost T.1 XF836 as well as several other projects. Alan's airworthy Provost T.1 XF597/G-BKFW is based at a strip nearby. The former Linton-on-Ouse Provost arrived here by November 1993, but is thought to be ultimately bound for the USA. Tim Manna established his operation as Kennet Aircraft and during 1993 set up a base at Cranfield, Beds. His Provost T.1 will appear with Alan's team whenever required. His aircraft not listed here, have moved on as follows : — Jet Provost 1 G-AOBU moved to Winchester, Hants, for the restorative attentions of Dick Melton, during 1992; Provost T.1 WW453/G-TMKI moving to Cranfield, Beds, during 1993 (having arrived here from Strathallan, Tayside, on March 13, 1992).

☐ WV486	7694M	Provost T.1	ex Reading, Halton, 6 FTS. 'N-D'. Spares.
☐ XF545*	7957M	Provost T.1	ex Linton-on-Ouse, Swinderby, Finningley, Shawbury, 6 FTS, 2 FTS. 'O-K'. Arrived by 11-93. See notes above. 11-93

| ☐ XF836 | G-AWRY | Provost T.1 | ex Popham, Old Warden, 8043M, 27 MU, CATCS, CNCS, RAFC, Man UAS. Force-landed 28-7-87. | 08-91 |
| ☐ 181 | | Provost T.51 | ex Casement, IAAC. Spares use. | |

WHITE WALTHAM AERODROME (north of the B3024 south of Maidenhead)
A case of a clean sweep here, all of the inmates listed in **W&R13** departing by air. Chilton DW.1 G-AFGI was flying again by November 1992. Apache 160G G-ASMN finally became N772MM and had departed by November 1992. Finally, Pembroke C.1 N4234C/XL954 flew to <u>Tatenhill</u>, Staffs, on October 21, 1992.

WINDSOR
■ **Gordon King** : Harvard IIB B-163 moved to <u>East Tilbury</u>, Essex, by July 1992.

WOODLEY
■ **Museum of Berkshire Aviation** (MBA) : Much work and determination came to fruition on March 27, 1993 when the MBA was opened formally to the public. With superb support from the local authority, MBA have established an excellent display within a repositioned and reclad Robin hangar, that once served as part of the famous Miles Aircraft Aeronautical Technical School on the adjacent former airfield site. While most of the displays and artefacts relate to the legendary Miles era, the history of all aspects of aviation in the county is taken into account. An appeal is underway for another display building and an extension of the site. Co-operating within the site are several other bodies. The founding body of the MBA is the **Royal Berkshire Aviation Society** (RBAS - formerly the Berkshire Aviation Group) and they are the technical custodians of the Magister. Alongside RBAS can be found The Herald Society (see below) who are undertaking the restoration of *Whisky Alpha*. Formed two days after MBA opened, the Miles Aircraft Collection, serve to support the Miles theme of the MBA and wider efforts at keeping the immortal name of Miles to the fore (see below). No 1116 Sqn ATC have a building on the same site and co-operate closely — see below.
◆ Saturdays, Sundays and Bank Holidays March to October, 10.30am to 5pm. During May, June and July also open Wednesdays to Fridays 11.30am to 4pm. ✉ Museum of Berkshire Aviation, Mohawk Way (off Bader Way), Woodley, near Reading, Berkshire RG5 4UF.
■ **The Herald Society** (THS) : *Whisky Alpha*'s fuselage arrived by road from Southend Airport, Essex, on August 29, 1992 and the wings dutifully followed in October. The aircraft was assembled in its own compound ready for the official opening of the MBA the following March — a very creditable effort to all involved. Restoration will be a long process, but several airlines and other industry sources are being superb in finding parts to help complete this, the first production Herald, which first flew from the adjacent airfield on October 30, 1959. THS serves to unite all interested in supporting *Whisky Alpha.*, and all those with an interest in the type.
✉ Lloyd Robinson, 12 Tiger Close, Woodley, Berks, RG5 4UY.
■ **Miles Aircraft Collection** (MAC) : Formed on the 60th anniversary of the first flight of the Miles Hawk (March 29, 1993), MAC serves to enhance and research the name of Miles Aircraft. Specific objectives are support of the MBA/RBAS, to produce a complete Miles Master from the many components held and to finish the restoration of Gemini G-AKHZ. (By January 1994, the Master bits and pieces, including three wings etc had moved to Breighton, Humbs, for long term attention.) A newsletter is planned to link Miles lovers everywhere.
✉ Peter Amos, 4 Castle Bungalows, Storrington, near Pulborough, West Sussex, RH20 4LB.

☐ G-AHUI	Messenger 2A	ex Henley, Cranfield, Bushey, Caistor, Elsham Hall, Goxhill, Handforth, Wolverhampton. CoA expired 4-9-60. Fuselage. Stored, off-site.	11-93
☐ G-AJFF	Messenger 2A	ex Henley, Cranfield, Bushey, Caistor, Elsham Hall, Egham, Elstree, Swanton Morley. CoA expired 16-3-68. Stored, off-site.	11-93
☐ G-AKER	Gemini 1A	ex Henley, Cranfield, Bushey, Elsham Hall, Tattershall. CoA exp 18-9-65. Off-site.	11-93
☐ G-AKGD	Gemini 1A	ex Henley, Cranfield, Bushey, 'Sussex', Southend. CoA exp 14-11-66. Sections. Stored, off-site.	11-93

☐ G-AKHZ   Gemini 1A   ex Henley, Cranfield, Bushey, Elsham Hall,
                                   Handforth. Complex composite, including parts
                                   from G-ALMU, G-ALUG, G-AMME. G-AKHZ
                                   CoA expired 6-1-64. Stored, off-site.   11-93
☐ G-APWA*   Herald 100   ex Southend, BAF, PP-SDM, PP-ASV, G-APWA.
                                   CoA expired 6-4-82. THS. Arrived 29-8-92.   11-93
☐ 6W-SAF* F-GEFU C-47A-65-DL   ex Kew, Cranfield, Le Bourget, Senegalese AF,
                                   USAF MAAG Brussels, USAAF 42-100611. Nose.
                                   Arr 19-2-94. Loan from Barry Parkhouse.   03-94
☐ 'L6905' BAPC.44 Magister I   ex Brooklands, Woodley, Wroughton, Frenchay,
                                   G-AKKY, T9841, 11 EFTS, 16 EFTS.   11-93
☐ *   BAPC.233 Wanderlust   ex Farnborough. Arrived 28-11-92   11-93
☐ *   Hang glider   first noted 3-93.   11-93
■ **1116 Squadron ATC** : Located on the same site as the MBA, the unit have a travelling *JP* nose.
☐ XS218*   8508M   Jet Provost T.4 ex Halton, Shawbury hack, 3 FTS. Nose.
                                   First noted 6-92.   06-92
■ **Bob Ogden** : Continues to work on his Moth Major and to store Barry Welford's Minor Coupe.
☐ G-ABZB   Moth Major   ex Sweden, SE-AIA, G-ABZB. Restoration.
☐ G-AFNI   Moth Minor   ex W7972, 100 GCF, Foulsham SF, 241, G-AFNI.
                                   CoA expired 26-5-67. Coupe. Stored.

Buckinghamshire

AYLESBURY
■ **1365 Squadron ATC** : Should still keep their Hunter nose at the TAVR Centre.
☐ XF522   Hunter F.6   ex Bucks Ambulance Service, Aylesbury, Aylesbury
                                   Fire Service, Halton, 92, 66, 92. Nose.

CHEDDINGTON (west of the B488 south of Linslade)
Auster Alpha G-APBW is completing its restoration here.
☐ G-APBW   Auster 5   ex Southend, Audley End. Crashed 25-7-82.
                                   Restoration.   04-90

FINMERE AERODROME (on the A421 west of Buckingham)
Shield Xyla G-AWPN has not been noted here for a long time and is thought to have moved on, possibly to Sussex.

HALTON AIRFIELD (north of Wendover)
■ **RAF Halton, 1 School of Technical Training** (SoTT) : Apprentice Course No 155 graduated here on June 24, 1993 and a major piece of RAF history came to an end. Cosford became the venue for RAF apprentice training after this date and indeed, from September 1993, took on the 'numberplate' of 1 SoTT. Despite this writing on the wall, deliveries of new airframes continued inbound almost up to the day of the last graduation. The move will take a couple of years to truly complete and it will be **W&R15** that charts the final chapter. The move looks set to produce a 'cull' of *JPs* and the end of the Gnat. There will continue to be some RAF presence at Halton, but the days of massed airframes are soon to be a thing of the past.
　　　　Disposals, by type, have been as follows : —
Beagle 206-1 G-ASWJ/8449M was long ago promised to the Midland Air Museum and left, initially for a period at Brunel Technical College, Bristol, Avon, 4-93.
Gnat T.1 XP511/8619M put up for tender 3-92 and sold in the USA 7-92 as N6145X along with XS109/8626M, as N61457; XP534/8620M was put up for tender 10-93 and moved to Cranfield, Beds, 23-11-93; XR538/8621M was entered in the Philips' auction of July 8, 1993 and moved to Cranfield, Beds by 9-93, becoming G-RORI.
Hunter F.6 XE656/8678M and XG274/8710M were offered for tender during June 193 and moved to Ipswich, Suffolk.

Jaguar GR.1A XX746/8895M left by road on 21-10-93 — destination?; GR.1 XX747/8903M moved to <u>Cranwell</u>, Lincs, by 10-93; T.2 XX837/8978M left by road 19-10-93 — destination?; GR.1 XZ382/8908M moved to <u>Coltishall</u>, Norfolk, 13-10-92.

Jet Provost T.3/A T.3As XM358/8987M, XM412/9011M and XM414/8996M all moved to <u>Colsterworth</u>, Lincs, by 8-93; T.3A XM371/8962M was put up for tender 3-92 and was sold in the USA (*possibly* as N4427Q); T.3 XM386/8076M to <u>St Athan</u>, S Glam, by 9-93; T.3 XM409/8082M was up for disposal during 6-89 — as noted in **W&R13** — its rear fuselage was to be found at St Athan, S Glam, during 9-93; T.3 XM410/8054AM to <u>North Luffenham</u>, Leics, by 4-92 along with T.3 XN554/8436M; XM404/8055BM to <u>Moreton-in-the-Marsh, Glos</u>, by 4-93; T.3A XM473/8974M was put up for tender 3-92 and acquired by Air UK, moving to <u>Norwich Airport</u>, Norfolk, on 13-6-92; T.3 XM480/8080M moved to <u>Finningley</u>, S Yorks, 9-2-94; T.3A XN494/9012M to <u>Middle Wallop</u>, Hants, by 7-93; T.3 XN512/8435M to <u>Wroughton</u>, Wilts, by 7-93; T.3A XN548/8971M was up for tender 3-92 and went to the USA by 12-92, becoming N4421B; T.3A XN584/9014M was noted on a lorry 31-10-93 — destination unknown. See under Binbrook, Lincs, for details of the Global Aviation mass *JP* purchase.

Jet Provost T.4 XP567/8510M to <u>Ipswich</u>, Suffolk, by 4-93 along with XR701/9025M and XR704/8506M; XP585/8407M to <u>Wrexham</u>, Clwyd 27-10-93; XP629/9026M and XP686/8502M to <u>North Luffenham</u>, Leics, by 4-92; XP640/8501M to YAM at <u>Elvington</u>, N Yorks 10-93; XP672/8458M was up for tender 3-92 and registered as G-RAFI to R MacGregor Muir of Ramsey, Isle of Man 12-92, see under <u>Jurby</u>, IoM; XP688/9031M noted on the back of a lorry 31-10-93 — destination?; XR643/8516M and XR653/9035M both sold to International Air Parts (IAP) of Sydney, Australia; XR669/8062M not noted since 1982 — assumed scrapped; XR650/8459M to <u>Boscombe Down</u>, Wilts, by May 1993; XR651/8431M had gone by 10-92, details?; XR662/8410M moved to <u>Finningley</u>, S Yorks, 9-2-94; XR674/9030M moved to <u>North Weald</u>, Essex, 27-10-93; XS176/8514M and XS179/'8237M' moved to <u>Salford</u>, Gtr Man, 3-11-93; XS180/8338M to <u>St Athan</u>, S Glam, by 4-93; XS186/8408M also made the trek to <u>North Luffenham</u>, Leics; XS210/'8239M' sold to IAP, Australia; XS218/8508M was reduced to a nose section by 6-92 and moved to <u>Woodley</u>, Berks. See under Binbrook, Lincs, for the Global Aviation mass *JP* purchase.

Jet Provost T.5 See under Binbrook, Lincs, for the Global Aviation mass *JP* purchase.

Wessex HU.5s XT755/9053M left by 10-93 and XT766/9054M left 25-11-92, both travelling to <u>Bruntingthorpe</u>, Leics, the latter staying there only fleetingly.

Whirlwind HAR.10 XD165/8673M to <u>Netheravon</u>, Wilts, by 1-92 along with XJ435/8671M and XR458/8662M; XJ727/8661M moving to <u>Dishforth</u>, N Yorks, by 4-93; XP354/8721M moved to <u>Colsterworth</u>, Lincs, by 8-93.

☐ WZ559	7736M	Vampire T.11	ex Oakington, 5 FTS, 94, 145. Pod. Dump. 10-93
☐ XE597	8874M	Hunter FGA.9	ex Bentley Priory, Brawdy, 1 TWU, 2 TWU, TWU, 229 OCU, West Raynham SF, 1, 54, MoA, 208, 56, 63, 66. Nose section. 06-93
☐ XF527	8680M	Hunter F.6	ex 1 SoTT, Laarbruch SF, 4 FTS, CFE, 19, Church Fenton SF, Linton SF. Gate. 10-93
☐ XG164	8681M	Hunter F.6	ex Kemble, West Raynham SF, 74, 111. Up for tender 6-93. 10-93
☐ XM362	8230M	Jet Provost T.3	ex Kemble, Shawbury, 3 FTS, 2 FTS. Sectioned and camouflaged. 10-93
☐ XM369	8084M	Jet Provost T.3	ex Shawbury, 2 FTS. Wings of XM409. 'C'. 10-93
☐ XM411	8434M	Jet Provost T.3	ex St Athan, Shawbury, Kemble, CFS. 'L'. Dismantled by 4-93. 10-93
☐ XM417	8054BM	Jet Provost T.3	ex Shawbury, 6 FTS, 7 FTS, 2 FTS. 'D'. 03-<u>88</u>
☐ XM425	8995M	Jet Provost T.3A	ex 7 FTS, 1 FTS, RAFC, 3 FTS, CFS. '88'. 10-93
☐ XM478	8983M	Jet Provost T.3A	ex 1 FTS, 7 FTS, 1 FTS. '33'. 06-93
☐ XN467	8559M	Jet Provost T.<u>4</u>	ex Kemble, Shawbury, CFS, A&AEE, Hunting. 'F'. Withdrawn on the field by 4-93. 10-93
			[Note change of mark, XN467 was the T.4 prototype.]
☐ XP530	8606M	Gnat T.1	ex 4 FTS, CFS. '60'. For tender 10-93. 10-93
☐ XP556	9027M	Jet Provost T.4	ex Shawbury, CATCS, SoRF, 6 FTS, RAFC. 'B'. 10-93
☐ XP563	9028M	Jet Provost T.4	ex Shawbury, CATCS, SoRF, 6 FTS, CATCS, RAFC. 'C'. Withdrawn on the field by 4-93. 10-93

☐	XP573	'8236M'	Jet Provost T.4	ex Kemble, Shawbury, Rolls-Royce, 1 FTS, CFS. Really 8336M. '19'. Up for tender 6-93.	10-93
☐	XP638	9034M	Jet Provost T.4	ex Shawbury, CATCS, CAW, 6 FTS. 'A'.	10-93
☐	XR574	8631M	Gnat T.1	ex Cosford, Kemble, 4 FTS. '72'.	10-93
☐	XR672	8495M	Jet Provost T.4	ex SoRF, 6 FTS, CAW, CATCS, 3 FTS, 1 FTS. '73' and 'C'. Fuselage in use as horse jump by 7-92!	10-93
☐	XR673	9032M	Jet Provost T.4	ex Shawbury, CATCS, SoRF, 6 FTS, RAFC, 2 FTS. 'L'.	10-93
☐	XR953	8609M	Gnat T.1	ex 4 FTS. '63'. Up for tender 9-93.	10-93
☐	XR954	8570M	Gnat T.1	ex 4 FTS, CFS, 4 FTS. '30'. Corrosion Control Shop.	10-92
☐	XR980	8622M	Gnat T.1	ex 4 FTS, CFS, 4 FTS, CFS, 4 FTS. '70'. For tender 2-94.	02-94
☐	XR998	8623M	Gnat T.1	ex 4 FTS. '71'. For tender 9-93.	10-93
☐	XS100	8561M	Gnat T.1	ex 4 FTS. '57'. Corrosion Control Shop.	10-93
☐	XS181	9033M	Jet Provost T.4	ex Shawbury, CATCS, RAFC, 3 FTS. 'F'.	10-93
☐	XS209	8409M	Jet Provost T.4	ex St Athan, Kemble, Shawbury, CAW. '29'. Up for tender 6-93.	10-93
☐	XS215	8507M	Jet Provost T.4	ex CAW. '17'. Dismantled by 4-93.	10-93
☐	XS217	9029M	Jet Provost T.4	ex Shawbury, CATCS, CFS, RAFC. 'O'.	10-93
☐	XS488	9056M	Wessex HU.5	ex Wroughton, 846. 'XK'.	07-92
☐	XT257	8719M	Wessex HAS.3	ex A&AEE.	04-93
☐	XT770	9055M	Wessex HU.5	ex Wroughton, 845. 'P'.	04-93
☐	XV738	9074M	Harrier GR.3	ex 4, 3, 233 OCU, HCT. 'B'.	10-93
☐	XV753	9075M	Harrier GR.3	ex Abingdon, St Athan, 233 OCU, 1, 3, 233 OCU. '3F'.	06-93
☐	XV808	9076M	Harrier GR.3	ex 233 OCU, 3, 20. '3J'.	06-93
☐	XW292*	9128M	Jet Provost T.5A	ex Shawbury, 3 FTS, RAFC, CFS. '63'. First noted 6-92.	10-93
☐	XW294*	9129M	Jet Provost T.5A	ex Shawbury, 3 FTS, RAFC, Leeming SF, 1 FTS, CFS. '45'. First noted 6-92.	10-93
☐	XW299*	9146M	Jet Provost T.5A	ex 1 FTS, RAFC, 1 FTS. '60'. F/n 6-92.	10-93
☐	XW301*	9147M	Jet Provost T.5A	ex 1 FTS. '61'. First noted 6-92.	10-93
☐	XW303*	9119M	Jet Provost T.5A	ex 7 FTS, 1 FTS. '127'. First noted 6-92.	06-93
☐	XW312*	9109M	Jet Provost T.5A	ex 1 FTS. '64'. First noted 6-93.	10-93
☐	XW320	'9018MA'	Jet Provost T.5A	ex 9015M, 1 FTS, Leeming hack, 3 FTS, RAFC. '71'. Really 9016M.	06-93
☐	XW327*	9130M	Jet Provost T.5A	ex CFS, 7 FTS, 6 FTS, 7 FTS, 1 FTS, CFS, RAFC. '62'. First noted 6-92.	06-93
☐	XW335	9061M	Jet Provost T.5A	ex Kemble, 3 FTS, RAFC, CFS, RAFC. '27'.	06-93
☐	XW351	9062M	Jet Provost T.5A	ex Kemble, 3 FTS, RAFC, 1 FTS, RAFC. '31'.	06-93
☐	XW365	'9015M'	Jet Provost T.5A	ex 1 FTS, RAFC. '73'. Really 9018M.	06-93
☐	XW366*	9097M	Jet Provost T.5A	ex 1 FTS, 3 FTS, RAFC. '75'. Arr by 6-90.	06-93
☐	XW375*	9149M	Jet Provost T.5A	ex CFS, 6 FTS, RAFC. '52'. F/n 6-92.	06-93
☐	XW413*	9126M	Jet Provost T.5A	ex 1 FTS, RAFC. '69'. First noted 6-92.	10-93
☐	XW419*	9120M	Jet Provost T.5A	ex 7 FTS, 1 FTS, RAFC. '125'.	06-93
☐	XW421*	9111M	Jet Provost T.5A	ex Shawbury, CFS, 3 FTS, Leeming SF, 3 FTS. '60'. First noted 2-92.	10-93
☐	XW427*	9124M	Jet Provost T.5A	ex 1 FTS, CFS, 3 FTS, CFS, 3 FTS. '67'. First noted 6-92.	10-93
☐	XW434	9091M	Jet Provost T.5A	ex 1 FTS, 7 FTS, 3 FTS, CFS. '78'.	10-93
☐	XW436*	9148M	Jet Provost T.5A	ex 1 FTS, CFS, 3 FTS, Leeming SF, 3 FTS, RAFC. '68'. First noted 6-92.	10-93
☐	XW768	9072M	Harrier GR.3	ex 4, 1, 4, 20. 'N'.	06-93
☐	XW924	9073M	Harrier GR.3	ex 4, 1, 4, 233 OCU, 4. 'G'.	06-93

☐	'XX110'	BAPC.169	Jaguar GR.1 rig	engine systems rig, made of GRP.	07-93
☐	XX118	'8821M'	Jaguar GR.1	ex Shawbury, 6, Indian AF JI018, G-27-318, XX118, 226 OCU, JOCU. Centre section. Really 8815M.	02-91
☐	XX726	8947M	Jaguar GR.1	ex Shawbury, 6, 54, 14, 54, 6, JOCU. 'EB'.	06-93
☐	XX739	8902M	Jaguar GR.1	ex Shawbury, Gibraltar Det, 6. 'I'. Less wings.	06-93
☐	XX743	8949M	Jaguar GR.1	ex Shawbury, 6. 'EG'.	06-93
☐	XX757	8948M	Jaguar GR.1	ex Shawbury, 20, 226 OCU, 14. 'CU'.	06-93
☐	XX818	8945M	Jaguar GR.1	ex Shawbury, 31, 20, 17. 'DE'.	06-93
☐	XX824	9019M	Jaguar GR.1	ex Shawbury, 14, 17, 14. 'AD'.	06-93
☐	XX825	9020M	Jaguar GR.1	ex Shawbury, 17, 31, 14. 'BN'.	06-93
☐	XX956	8950M	Jaguar GR.1	ex Shawbury, 17, 31, 14, 17. 'BE'.	06-93
☐	XX966	8904M	Jaguar GR.1A	ex Shawbury, 6, 54, 20, A&AEE, 20, 17. 'EL'. Less wings.	06-93
☐	XX975	8905M	Jaguar GR.1	ex 226 OCU, 31, 17, 226 OCU. '07'.	06-93
☐	XX976	8906M	Jaguar GR.1	ex Shawbury, 17, 31. 'BD'.	06-93
☐	XZ389	8946M	Jaguar GR.1	ex Shawbury, 17, 31, 20. 'BL'.	06-93
☐	XZ967	9077M	Harrier GR.3	ex 4, 3, 4, 233 OCU, 1417F, 233 OCU. 'F'.	10-93

HIGH WYCOMBE
■ **RAF High Wycombe** : Wasp HAS.1 XV638/8826M was disposed of during 1991.
■ **Chris Warrilow** : The Spitfire recovered from Papua New Guinea is stored in the area.

☐	EF545		Spitfire V	ex Trobriand, RAAF A58-149. Forward, fuselage. Stored.	03-94

MARLOW
■ **Staravia** : With no news to the contrary, it is thought the two Hunters are still stored here.

☐	PH-NLH		Hunter T.7	ex Exeter Airport, NLR Amsterdam, Neth AF N-320, XM126 ntu.	
☐	E-420	G-9-442	Hunter F.51	ex Ascot, Dunsfold, Aalborg, Danish AF *Esk*.724. Fuselage.	

NEWPORT PAGNELL
■ **Peter R Arnold** : Peter continues to work on his Seafire and Spitfire projects.

☐	EN224	G-FXII	Spitfire XII	ex Cranfield, 595, 41. Restoration.	04-94
☐	LA564		Seafire F.46	ex Redbourn, Newark, Southend, Charnock Richard, Carlisle, Anthorn, 738, 767, A&AEE and cancelled Spitfire F.22 PV585. Restn.	04-94

TURWESTON AERODROME (east of Brackley)
■ **Brackley Gliding Club** : The glider store has increased.

☐	AQH*	BGA.573	T.21B	ex G-ALJU, BGA.573. Stored.	05-93
☐	BFF	BGA.928	Skylark 3F	stored. '161'. I/d amended from **W&R13**.	05-93
☐	BGB*	BGA.948	T.21B	ex RAFGSA.282, BGA.948. Stored.	05-93
☐			Grasshopper TX.1	stored. SSK/FF/2120.	05-93

TWYFORD
■ **Peter Woods** : The Seafire restoration project continues in the area.

☐	SX336	G-BRMG	Seafire XVII	ex Newark, Warrington, Stretton A2055, Bramcote. Restoration.	03-94

WOBURN SANDS
On the A5130 to the north of the town there may still be a former Panshanger S-55.

☐	ZS-HDG		Sikorsky S-55B	ex Panshanger, Elstree, Luton, Court-Line.	12-91

WYCOMBE AIR PARK (WAP — or Booker, on the B482 south west of High Wycombe)

■ **Booker Aircraft Museum** (BAM) : The Museum and its contents have been acquired by Barry Parkhouse (see under Camberley and Ottershaw, Surrey). It is due to change its name and some of its exhibits. Known changes have been as follows :— DH Dove G-ARHX was acquired by NEAM and moved north to <u>Sunderland</u>, T&W, by January 1993. By April 1993 the composite Harvard KF435 had moved to <u>Ottershaw</u>, Surrey. The nose of Javelin FAW.1 XA571/7722M moved to <u>Catford</u>, Gtr Lon, by 1993. The nose section of C-47A 6W-SAF moved to <u>Woodley</u>, Berks, during March 1994.

◆ Pending re-organisation, visiting times etc unknown.

☐	WG789		Canberra B.2/6	ex Kew, Burgess Hill, Bedford Airfield, RAE, 231 OCU. Nose. 12-93
☐	WZ550	7902M	Vampire T.11	ex Slough, Ewyas Harold, CATCS, CFS, 8 FTS, 7 FTS, 202 AFS. 'R'. 12-93
☐	XM665		Whirlwind HAS.7	ex Chelsfield, Chertsey, Wroughton, Fleetlands, 829, 847, 848, 846, 737, 700H. On loan. 12-93
☐	417657	N99218	B-26K Invader	ex Canterbury, Southend, Chino, USAF 64-17657. Nose. 12-93

■ **Lindsay Collection** (LC) : MS.230 G-AVEB (see under PPS below) has been sold off and SNCAN SV-4C G-BHFG was airworthy again by January 1990 and now flies from Goodwood. Great Lakes 2T G-BIIZ moved to <u>Hungerford</u>, Berks, by November 1992, thus bringing to an end this long-standing entry.

■ **The Blue Max Movie Aircraft Museum / Personal Plane Services** (PPS) : Opened on June 20, 1992, the Museum capitalises on the years and years of film flying experience accumulated by Personal Plane Services and includes many of their famous airframes and many artefacts that have not seen the light of day since the particular film or TV feature was filmed. With the establishment of Museum status here, the airworthy PPS machines immediately become eligible for listing. Please note that the contents will vary from time to time as some of the aircraft are very much 'fliers' and that other PPS aircraft may not be on public show. All aircraft are listed together for ease of entry. The dramatically-posed Pilatus P.2 fuselage at the entrance is a film mock-up from *Harrison Ford Misplaces the Holy Grail*, or similar. As will be noted above, MS.230 G-AVEB of the Lindsay Collection has been placed under this heading. Two aircraft have moved on, one in a physical sense, the other as a 'book-keeping' exercise. EKW C-3605 C-558 had moved to <u>Little Gransden</u>, Cambs, by January 1991. Not reported for a very long time, SNCAN SV-4C G-AZIO has been confined to *LOST!*

◆ Open daily. The Blue Max Pilot's Shop is also available. ✉ Wycombe Air Park, Marlow, Bucks, SL7 3DP. ☎ 0494 29432 or 0494 449810 or **Fax** 0494 461236.

☐	G-AWBU* 'MS821'	MS 'N' replica ▲	PPS.	04-93
☐	G-AWXZ*	SNCAN SV-4C ▲	ex F-BHMZ, French mil No 360, F-BCOI. PPS.	04-93
☐	G-AYFO* N40BJ	Bü 133C	ex Tamiami, G-AYFO, HB-MIO. F/n 4-92. For restoration for Kermit Weeks.	04-93
☐	G-AZTR*	SNCAN SV-4C ▲	ex F-BDEQ. Airworthy.	04-93
☐	G-BAAF	MF.1 replica	CoA expired 26-5-88.	04-93
☐	G-BLKZ*	Pilatus P.2-05 ▲	ex Swiss AF U-125, A-125. Autokraft Ltd [See under Brooklands, Surrey.]	04-93
☐	G-BPVE*	Bleriot XI replica ▲	ex N1197.	04-93
☐	G-BTBJ*	Cessna 190B ▲	ex N4461C.	04-93
☐	G-BTZE	Yak C-11	ex Egypt (?), OK-JIK Dismantled.	04-93
☐	EC-ACB*	Miles Falcon	ex EC-CAO, EC-BDD. Fuselage. Arrived by 9-93.	09-93
☐	N6268*	Travel Air 2000	ex USA, Fokker D.VII look-alike '626/18', NC6268. Restoration.	04-93
☐	LV-ZAU (?)*	Fw 44 Stieglitz	ex Tamiami, Argentina. Restoration for Kermit Weeks. First noted 6-92.	06-92
☐	'B2458'* G-BPOB	Camel replica ▲	ex N8997, Tallmantz Av. PPS. 'R'.	04-93
☐	AR213* G-AIST	Spitfire Ia ▲	ex Patrick Lindsay, Old Warden, *Battle of Britain*, Allen Wheeler, 8 MU, 53 OTU, 57 OTU. Victor Gauntlett - Proteus Petroleum. Lodges with PPS. 'PR-D' 609 Sqn c/s.	04-93

☐	MV262*	G-CCVV	Spitfire XIV	ex Winchester, Bitteswell, Blackbushe, Calcutta, Ind AF, ACSEA, 9 MU. Weeks. First noted -92. Stored. Dismantled.	03-94
☐	PL344*	G-IXCC	Spitfire IX ∆	ex Winchester, Netherlands, Anthony Fokker School, 129, 130, 401, 442, 602. Weeks. Flew in -92. Restoration.	03-94
☐	TE476*	N476TE	Spitfire XVI	ex Tamiami, USA, G-XVIB, Wycombe, Northolt 8071M, Kemble, Henlow 7451M, 11 GCF, Martlesham SF, North Weald SF, Biggin Hill SF, St Athan, Kemble, 1 CAACU. Returned -92. Restn for Kermit Weeks.	03-94
☐	TE517*	G-CCIX	Spitfire IX	ex Winchester, Nailsworth, G-BIXP ntu, Duxford, Israel, Israel DF/AF 2046, Czech AF, RAF TE517, 313. Weeks. Arrived -92. Stored.	03-94
☐	'157'*	G-AVEB	MS.230 Et2 ∆	ex F-BGJT, French mil No 1076. 'M-373'. See notes above.	04-93
☐	'422/15'*	G-AVJO	Fokker E.III rep ∆	built by PPS.	04-93
☐			Yak C-11	ex La Ferte Alais (?), Egyptian AF. c/n 172623. Stripped frame. Stored off-site.	03-90
☐	*		Pilatus P.2	fuselage. Film mock-up. *Luftwaffe* colours.	
☐		BAPC.103	Hulton hang-glider	erroneously given as Pilcher type in **W&R13**. Built 1969.	04-93
☐	*	BAPC.238	Ornithopter	built by PPS for *Young Sherlock Holmes*, Professor Waxflatter's ornithopter.	04-93

■ **Others** : The multi-identity Heron was acquired for spares during the summer of 1993 and is due to be scrapped. Also in store in the open is a French Alcyon.

| ☐ | 'G-ORSJ' | G-ODLG | Sea Heron C.1 | ex XR443, Shawbury, Yeovilton SF, Culdrose SF, 781, G-ARKV, VR-NCE. Open storage. Mispaint — see G-ORSJ at Gloucestershire Airport. See notes above. | 12-93 |
| ☐ | 'No 143'* | F-BLXV | Alcyon | ex French military. *Aéronavale* c/s. Stored. | 04-93 |

Cambridgeshire

ALCONBURY AIRFIELD (north west of Huntingdon at the A1/A604 junction)

■ **USAF Alconbury** : Another base facing imminent changes. The *Warthogs* have gone, leaving only a GA-10 to guard the 'inner' gate of the base. The special operations *Herks* and choppers are to go to Mildenhall, leaving the airfield open as a communications site for nearby Molesworth. As noted in **W&R13**, U-2CT 66692 made the move to <u>Duxford</u>, Cambs, by June 1992.

☐	'01532'		F-5E Tiger II	mock up on 'outer' gate, 527 TFTAS c/s.	03-94
☐	63-7419		F-4C-15-MC	ex Texas ANG. 'SA'. BDR.	08-93
☐	80-0219*		GA-10A T'bolt II	ex 509th TFS, Bentwaters. 'Inner' gate guard. 10th TFW, 509th TFS-511th TFS c/s. Accident 4-4-89. *Phoenix*. First noted 5-92.	08-93
☐	153008		F-4N-MC	ex VF-154 - USS *Coral Sea*. BDR.	08-93

BASSINGBOURN (north of Royston)

■ **Allenbrooke Barracks** : The Canberra is still preserved within the camp.

| ☐ | WJ821 | 8668M | Canberra PR.7 | ex RAE Bedford, 13, 58, 82. | 02-93 |

■ **2484 Squadron, ATC** : During 1992 acquired the nose of a former Wyton Canberra TT.18, which remains 'parented' by that base. It is assumed to based within the Army base, but clarification of this would be appreciated.

| ☐ | WK127* | 8985M | Canberra TT.18 | ex Wyton, 100, 7, 10. Accident 13-12-88. 'FO'. Nose section. See notes above. | |

■ **East Anglian Aviation Society** (EAAS) : The tower here is the basis for a superb museum dedicated to the history of the once resident 91 BG, 11 OTU and 231 OCU.
◆ Visits by prior arrangement only. ✉ M Reynolds, EAAS, 8 Pringle Lane, Northborough, Peterborough, PE6 9BW.

BOURN AERODROME (on the A45 west of Cambridge)
The dominant theme here is the MBB Bo 105 workhorse. It should also be explained that '105s are capable of much in the way of metamorphosis and it could be that G-AZTI listed below is not the only one with a 'split personality'. This comes about from the 'DBS conversion which involves effectively a fatter fuselage 'pod' almost slipping over where the previous 'pod'/undercarriage etc were. The original pod of G-AZTI (the rest of *Tango India* being rebuilt and is flying as G-BUTN!) was noted dumped out by August 1993 but had gone by the end of the year, reported to the Netherlands. G-BGKJ has not been seen for a long time and is reported to have gone into 'G-BOND' at Land's End, Cornwall, but that is supposed to be mostly G-BCXO — help! Still another Bo 105 pod is reported to have gone to a technical college in Cambridge. The anonymous Bell 47G noted in **W&R13** had gone by 1992, without revealing either its identity or its destination. Long-termer Sea Prince T.1 WP321/G-BRFC made a ferry flight to <u>North Weald</u>, Essex, on November 20, 1993. Finally, C.337 PH-RPD mentioned in **W&R13** became G-BTVV.

☐ G-AZLO	Cessna F.337F	ex Lands End. CoA exp 22-4-82. Poor state.	03-94
☐ G-BBXB*	Cessna FRA.150L	CoA expired 28-7-89. Stored. F/n 6-93.	03-94
☐ G-BCUB	J-3C-65 Cub	ex F-BCPC, 45-4446. CoA exp 18-9-86. Frame. Restoration.	03-94
☐ G-BEZS*	Cessna FR.172J	ex Cranfield, Stapleford, I-CCAJ ntu. Crashed 15-6-79. Stored.	03-94
☐ G-BGKP	MBB Bo 105D	ex D-HDGC. Cr 16-2-81. EMS demonstrator.	
☐ G-BTBD*	MBB Bo 105D	ex VH-LCS, VH-HRM, G-BCDH, EC-DUO, G-BCDH, D-HDBK. Damaged 30-6-91. Pod and boom. Arrived 28-11-91. Stored.	05-93
		[G-BTBD rebuilt with DBS-4 pod as G-BUDP, then G-DNLB.]	
☐ G-PASA*	MBB Bo 105D	ex G-BGWP,F-ODMZ, G-BGWP, HB-XFD, N1533BB, D-HDAS. Stored. F/n 08-93.	08-93
		[G-PASA rebuilt with DBS-4 pod as G-BUXS.]	
☐ G-PASB*	MBB Bo 105D	ex VH-LSA, G-BDMC, D-HDEC. Stored.	08-93

CAMBRIDGE

■ **Arbury College** : Their Cessna 310 instructional airframe has been joined by an obligatory *JP*.

☐ G-XITD	Cessna 310G	ex Tattershall Thorpe, Leavesden, Denham, G-ASYV, HB-LBY, N8948Z. Accident 14-7-88. Instructional airframe.	
☐ XM355* 8229M	Jet Provost T.3	ex Bruntingthorpe, Halton, Shawbury, 1 FTS, 7 FTS, CFS. 'D'. Arrived by 6-93.	06-93

CAMBRIDGE AIRPORT (or Teversham, on the A1303 east of Cambridge)
On the heavy metal front, two former British Airways TriStars are in long term store, for some reason shunning the delights of the Mojave Desert, where the rest of the fleet are to be found. During August 1993, two other BA machines, this time of different proportions, also arrived for storage.

☐ G-AVMN*	BAC 111-510ED	ex Bournemouth, BA, BEA. Flew in 11-8-93, for storage.	12-93
☐ G-AVMV*	BAC 111-510ED	ex Bournemouth, BA, BEA. Flew in 11-8-93, for storage.	12-93
☐ G-BHBM*	TriStar 200	ex BA. CoA expired 27-11-92. Stored. First noted 11-92.	12-93
☐ G-BHBR*	TriStar 200	ex BA. CoA expired 28-5-93. Stored. First noted 11-92.	12-93
☐ WJ863	Canberra T.4	ex 231 OCU, 360, Akrotiri SF, 231 OCU, Honington SF, C'more SF. Nose, dump.	12-93

CHATTERIS (On the A141 south of March)

The one-off Fixter Pixie G-AXNY has not been noted for some time and has been moved into the limbo of *LOST!* It is thought the Colt and Proctor are still to be found in the area.

☐ G-ARNH		Colt 108	ex Elstree. Damaged 1-9-72. Dismantled.	05-91
☐ NP184	G-ANYP	Proctor IV	ex Higher Blagdon, Brooklands, G-ANYP, Thruxton, Andover, Yatesbury. CoA exp 18-4-64. Restn.	07-90

COMBERTON (on the B1046 west of J12 of the M11)

A Moth has arrived in the area for restoration to flying condition.

☐ G-AANO*	DH.60GMW	ex Southampton, N590N, NC590N. Arrived by 11-91. Restoration.	11-91

DUXFORD AERODROME (south of Cambridge, Junction 10 M11)

■ **Imperial War Museum** (IWM) : By far and away the single largest reference in **W&R**, there is little that can be said about the shrine that Duxford has become. The last two years have shown that even this Mecca is not immune to the recession, but it has to be said it has weathered it well. Fundraising for the huge American Air Museum continues to gain ground, but construction is still a fair way off. The IWM itself continues to gain exhibits with the following arriving since **W&R13** : General Dynamics F-111E; McDonnell Douglas Phantom FGR.2; MiG-15, Lockheed U-2C; and Westland Wasp HAS.1. For one addition, we take you back to **W&R5** (page 30) and Hatfield, Herts (do you remember Hatfield?). Here it was noted that *JP* T.4 XS183 had been reduced to a rear fuselage by February 1976 and posed the question, who has the nose? Well, the answer was not to remain rhetorical, it could be found in store with the IWM here by November 1992!

SB.4 Sherpa G-36-1, always a bit hard to justify within the IWM collecting policy — and a legacy of course from the Skyfame rescue — moved to Rochester, Kent, on March 10, 1993 for restoration. With similar logic, SARO SR.A.1 TG263 moved to Southampton, Hants, in late 1993. With two examples in the collection, it has long been on the cards that IWM would dispose of one of its Varsities. WF425 was accordingly scrapped on site during October 1993 and its remains were trucked to the yard at Stock, Essex. In a similar manner, the much-corroded Comet C.2R XK695 was returned to the MoD during late 1992 — with DAS possessing a very fine Mk 4 there was a strong duplication case — and the fuselage was moved to Newton, Notts, during October 1992. The wings joining the fire dump here. Sea Vampire T.22 XG743 moved to Wymondham, Norfolk, for restoration during June 1993. On April 5, 1993 Duxford said goodbye to one of the pioneering warbirds, Lindsay Walton sold F4U-7 Corsair 133722/NX1337A to Jack Erickson in the USA and it left by container that day. Elster B 97+04/G-APVF moved to Tadlow, Herts, to be based during 1992.

◆ Open daily 10am to 6pm from mid-March to the end of October and 10am to 4pm the remainder of the year. It is closed New Year's Day and December 24-26. On days other than special events two of the civil airliner collection are open to inspection free of charge, one of which is normally Concorde. A large SAE will bring a leaflet on special events and opening times.

✉ IWM, Duxford Airfield, Duxford, Cambs, CB2 4QR. ☎ 0223 835000 or 0223 835155 for direct dialling by touchtone 'phones. **Fax** 0223 837267.

☞ The Duxford site is base for a wide series of organisations, all working under the umbrella of the IWM. All aircraft are treated as one listing, but briefer details of happenings within all components on the site are given in narrative form below. Abbreviations are used to denote ownership of aircraft within the main list. Aircraft noted as being 'IWM-L' are on loan to the IWM and not part of any of the operations listed below.

■ **Duxford Aviation Society** (DAS) : Continues to support the operation of this complex site in many ways. The principal 'high visibility' operation of DAS is the airliner collection which gained a BAC 111-510ED from British Airways, adding to its very impressive line-up. Ambassador G-ALZO moved from the *Weather Beater* hangar into the restoration hangar (No 5), next to the York, on October 25, 1993. Viscount G-ALWF is now in the *Superhangar* (No 1) being prepared for painting in BEA colours during 1994.

✉ DAS, Duxford Airfield, Duxford, Cambridge, CB2 4QR. ☎ 0223 835594.

■ **Aircraft Restoration Company / British Aerial Museum** (ARCO - BAM) : Without a doubt, one event over-shadowed all others with the team here: the second Blenheim made its first flight — in the hands of *Hoof* Proudfoot — on May 18, 1993. An engineering triumph and shining example of restoration skills, the Blenheim more than anything else is a tribute to human endeavour and determination. The year before, ARCO flew their pristine T-6 Texan restoration *Thumper*. Other activity was centred around the liaison aircraft world, with the completion of the Lysander for the IWM and the start of work on the Fi 156 *Storch* for Aero Vintage. During 1993 there was a 'Beaver-shuffle' with the Museum of Army Flying, XP822 (anonymous in **W&R13**) travelled back to Middle Wallop, Hants, on May 11, 1993 with another example coming the other way. Also making the same journey — this time airborne — was the all-yellow Auster AOP.9 during June 1993. The former Lympne Fiat G.46 was acquired during May 1993, but in the words of Graham Warner was found to be "beyond help" after inspection. It will probably be reduced to spares. This is an example of ARCO's policy of leaving no stone unturned, which also produced the long-lost Bristol Scout replica 'A1742'/BAPC.38 in "the proverbial barn" — it will doubtless be put to good use. By July 1992 Tiger Moth 'G-ADNZ' arrived from Hampton, Gtr Lon, and is in store awaiting a 'slot' for restoration. John Fairey's lovely Flycatcher replica 'S1287'/G-BEYB returned to storage at Middle Wallop, Hants, in 1993. Chipmunk 22 '671'/G-BNZC moved to Tattershall Thorpe, Lincs, during October 1993.

✉ ARCO, Building 66, Duxford Airfield, Cambs, CB2 4QR. ☎ 0223 835313.

■ **B-17 Preservation Ltd / *Sally B* Supporters Club** : *Sally B* continues to be coddled by Elly Sallingboe and her team and is a regular attender at displays across the country. The second Great Warbirds Air Display was held at Wroughton, Wilts, during August 1993 and the venue looks set to remain the host for this famous show.

✉ B-17 Preservation Ltd, PO Box 132, Crawley, Sussex, RH10 3YD. ☎ 0293 883213.

■ **Essex Aviation Group** (EAG) : Viewable on Sundays is the Group's excellent display of aviation archaeology and other artefacts.

✉ Mick Skeels, 142 Leigham Court Drive, Leigh-on-Sea, Essex, SS9 1PU.

■ **The Fighter Collection / Friends of The Fighter Collection** (TFC) : A whole host of arrivals and 'firsts' to record : — the long-awaited P-38 arrived by road on June 11, 1992 and was soon flying. (It suffered a wheels-up landing at Lydd, Kent, September 6, 1992 but again was soon flying.); Spitfire XIV MV293 made its first flight on August 15, 1992; the Bristol F.2b replica arrived on site during February 1993, it still requires a Falcon engine to complete it; 1993; Spitfire V EP120 from St Athan during January 1993 in exchange for F-86 XB812; an airworthy FM-2 Wildcat arrived from the USA during April 1993. The first of the rumoured Russians arrived in June 1992 in the form of a P-40B, then followed by a Spitfire IX in January 1993 and, above all else, a Lavochkin La-11 from Monino in May 1993. Sabre F.4 MM1966 arrived on June 18, 1993 from Rome, and preparation to turn it back into the colours it wore with 92 Squadron as XB812 started almost immediately. Completed, it moved by road to Hendon, Gtr Lon, on January 30, 1994. Former Thai F8F-1B Bearcat 122095/G-BUCF was crated for the USA during November 1992, having been traded for the airworthy FM-2 Wildcat. A MiG-15 was noted in dismantled state within the TFC hangar by February 1993, it stayed but a brief time and then moved on — more details appreciated. (It is *not* the one taken on by the IWM during 1993.) Spitfire XIV NH799/G-BUZU was despatched to Audley End, Essex, by November 1993.

■ **Old Flying Machine Company** (OFMC) : Ray, Mark, Sarah and team have had a busy time, both of the Hunters mentioned in **W&R13** arrived on site late 1993. A second *Buchon* arrived during May 1993 and this will give OFMC even greater film and TV scope. By late 1992 the SE.5E once with the Lindsey Collection began to be operated by OFMC. On October 13, 1992 Phantom FGR.2 XV474 — once flown in service by Mark Hanna — flew in and it is intriguing to think of such a beast being flown under Permit to Fly conditions!! During 1993 Harvard IV/*Zeke* N15798 was exported to New Zealand. Tangmere Flight's Spitfire PR.XI PL965 was ferried to Duxford during February 1993 and is operated in a 'shared' arrangement with OFMC. Spitfire XIV MV370/G-FXIV arrived from North Weald, Essex, by December 1991 and was prepared for export to a museum in Germany, leaving during 1992. Spitfire V AR614 arrived from Canada during October 1992 and is in store off-site. TBM-3E Avenger N6827C was freighted out to New Zealand via Ipswich and Felixstowe on October 2, 1992. OFMC have taken over the operation of F-86A G-SABR on behalf of the Golden Apple Trust. OFMC have an Fw 190 reconstruction underway for them in the USA, it will arrive in the UK at the earliest in 1995. One, perhaps two, gems will arrive on the circuit for the 1994 season — stay tuned!

■ **Plane Sailing** (PS) **/Lea Aviation Inc/The Catalina Society** (PS/LAI) : F7F-2 Tigercat 80483/N6178C was sold to Dick Bertea of the USA and left on its trans-Atlantic ferry flight during May 1993. LAI's Pilatus P.2-05 G-BJAX was dismantled and moved to <u>Tattershall Thorpe</u>, Lincs, during September 1993. The Catalina took up Bermudan registry during March 1994 for a charter to Peter Stuyvesant Travel, taking on their striking colour scheme at the same time.

✉ 24, Batts Hill, Reigate, Surrey, RH2 OLT.

☐	'G-ADNZ'*	Tiger Moth	ex Hampton, Hayter, Christchurch, Tunbridge Wells, 6948M, DE673, 9 RFS, 22 RFS, 22 EFTS, 19. Arrived by 7-92. Stored. ARCO.	11-93
			[Not the original G-ADNZ.]	
☐	G-AFBS	Magister I	ex Staverton, G-AKKU ntu, BB661, G-AFBS. CoA expired 25-2-63. IWM.	03-94
☐	G-AGJG	Dragon Rapide	ex X7344, 1 Cam Flt. CoA expired 15-5-74. Restoration. IWM-L.	03-94
☐	G-AGTO	J/1 Autocrat ▲	DAS.	03-94
☐	G-AKAZ	L-4A-PI ▲	ex F-BFYL, French military, 42-36375. USAAF colours, coded 'HL-6'₋ₓ '(!) TFC.	03-94
☐	G-ALDG	Hermes 4	ex Gatwick, cabin trainer, Silver City-Britavia, Falcon, Airwork, BOAC. Fuselage. CoA expired 9-1-63. DAS.	03-94
☐	G-ALFU	Dove 6	ex CAFU Stansted. CoA exp 4-6-71. DAS.	03-94
☐	G-ALWF	Viscount 701	ex Liverpool Airport, Cambrian, British Eagle, BEA. CoA exp 16-4-72. DAS. See notes.	03-94
☐	G-ALZO	Ambassador	ex Lasham, Dan-Air, Handley Page, Jordan AF 108, BEA. CoA exp 14-5-72. Restn. DAS.	03-94
☐	G-ANTK	York	ex Lasham, Dan-Air, MW232, Fairey Aviation, 511, 242. CoA exp 29-10-64. Restn. DAS.	03-94
☐	G-AOVT	Britannia 312	ex Monarch, BEIA, BOAC. CoA expired 11-3-75. Monarch colours. DAS.	03-94
☐	G-APDB	Comet 4	ex Dan-Air, MSA 9M-AOB, BOAC G-APDB. CoA expired 7-10-74. Dan-Air c/s. DAS.	03-94
☐	G-APWJ	Herald 201	ex Norwich, Air UK, BIA, BUIA. CoA expired 21-12-85. Air UK colours. DAS.	03-94
☐	G-ASGC	Super VC-10	ex BA, BOAC. CoA expired 20-4-80. BA c/s. DAS.	03-94
☐	G-ASTG	Nord 1002	ex Sutton Bridge, F-BGKI, French AF. CoA exp 26-10-73. Lindsay Walton. Restn by ARCO.	03-94
☐	G-AVFB	Trident 2E	ex BA, Cyprus 5B-DAC, BEA. CoA expired 30-9-82. BEA colours. DAS.	03-94
☐	G-AVMU*	BAC 111-510ED	ex Bournemouth, BA, BEA. Flew in 29-10-92. *County of Dorset.* DAS.	03-94
☐	G-AWAH	Baron D55 ▲	TFC *hack.*	03-94
☐	G-AXDN	Concorde 101	ex BAC/SNIAS. CoA exp 30-9-77. DAS.	03-94
☐	G-AZSC	Harvard IIB ▲	ex North Weald, PH-SKK, Dutch AF B-19, FT323, 43-13064. Gary Numan - Radial Pair. IWM-L	03-94
☐	G-BOML	HA-1112-MIL ▲	ex Nick Grace, N170BG, Spanish AF C4K-107. OFMC.	05-93
☐	G-BTTA	Fury ISS ▲	ex '115', VH-HFX, N28SF, Iraqi AF 243. *Luftwaffe* c/s for film 2-94. Will take on Iraqi colours for the 1994 season. OFMC.	03-94
☐	G-BTWR	P-63A	ex N52113, OFMC, Biggin Hill, USA, 42-69097. TFC. Under restoration.	03-94
☐	G-FIST*	Fi 156C-3	ex Paddock Wood, Seaton Ross, Ludham, Watton-at-Stone, Amsterdam, D-EDEC, I-FAGG, MM12822. Aero Vintage. Arr 5-93 for restn by ARCO.	03-94
☐	G-USUK	Colt 2500A	gondola. *Virgin Atlantic Flyer.* IWM-L.	03-94

☐ CF-EQS		PT-17-BW	ex Canada, USAAF 41-8169. Restn. IWM.	05-93
☐ CF-KCG		TBM-3E	ex Canada, RCN 326, USN 69327. IWM.	03-94
☐ EI-AUY		MS.502	ex USA, F-BCDG, ALAT. Restn. IWM.	03-94
☐ LN-AMY*		AT-6D Harvard Δ	ex Norway. 'TA-849'. Arr 4-93. OFMC.	03-94
☐ N47DD		P-47D-30-RA	ex Chino, USA, Peru AF FAP 119, USAAF 45-49192. Major project, including parts from other airframes. IWM.	03-94
☐ NX700HL		F8F-2P Bearcat Δ	ex N1YY, N4995V, BuNo 121714. TFC.	03-94
☐ NX5224R*		Yak-50 Δ	ex USA, USSR. Arrived 6-5-93.	03-94
☐ N4845V*		FM-2 Wildcat Δ	ex USA, 86711. Arrived 15-4-93. TFC. FAA colours as 'F' from 3-94.	03-94
☐ N7614C		B-25J-30-NC	ex Shoreham, Dublin, Prestwick, Luton, USAF 44-31171. Restoration. IWM.	03-94
☐ N9938*		HA-1112-M1L	ex USA, *Battle of Britain*, G-AWHK, Spanish AF C4K-102. Arrived 25-5-93. OFMC.	03-94
☐ VR-BPS		PBY-5A Δ	ex G-BLSC, 'JV928' Barkston Heath, South Africa, C-FMIR, N608FF, CF-MIR, N10023, USN 46633. PS. See notes above.	03-94
☐ 'A1742'*	BAPC.38	Bristol Scout rep	ex Avon area, St Mawgan, St Athan, Colerne, Weeton. Arrived mid-1993. ARCO. Stored.	08-93
☐ 'B4863'*	G-BLXT	SE.5E Δ	ex Rendcombe, Middle Wallop, Wycombe AP, Orlando, N4488, USAAC 22-296. OFMC. First noted late -92.	03-94
☐ 'D8084'*	G-ACAA	Bristol F.2b	ex Hatch, Weston-o-t-Green. F/n 2-93. TFC.	03-94
☐ E2581		Bristol F.2b	ex South Lambeth, 2 GCF, 30 TS, HQ Flt SE Area, 1 Com Sqn. IWM.	05-93
☐ F3556		RAF RE.8	ex Lambeth. *Paddy Bird from Ceylon*. IWM.	03-94
☐ N4877	G-AMDA	Anson I	ex Staverton, Derby Airways, Watchfield SF, 3 FP, ATA, 3 FPP. CoA expired 14-12-62. 'VX-F', 206 Sqn c/s. IWM.	03-94
☐ V3388	G-AHTW	Oxford I	ex Staverton, Boulton Paul, V3388. CoA exp 15-12-60. IWM.	03-94
☐ 'V6028'	G-MKIV	Bolingbroke IVT	ex G-BLHM ntu, RCAF 10038. Crashed 21-6-87. Spares. ARCO.	11-93
☐ V9300	G-LIZY	Lysander III	ex Canada, RCAF 1558, V9300. 'MA-J', 161 Sqn. Restored by ARCO for IWM.	03-94
☐ Z2033	G-ASTL	Firefly I	ex Staverton, G-ASTL, SE-BRD, Z2033. '275', 1771 Sqn, colours *Evelyn Tentions*. IWM.	03-94
☐ 'Z5722'	G-BPIV	Bolingbroke IVT Δ	ex Strathallan, Canada, RCAF 10201. 'WM-Z', 68 Sqn c/s. *Spirit of Britain First*. First flown 18-5-93. ARCO.	03-94
☐ Z7015	G-BKTH	Sea Hurricane I	ex Staverton, Old Warden, Loughborough, Yeovilton, 759, 880. Under restoration to flying condition. IWM/Shuttleworth. 880 Sqn c/s.	03-94
☐ 'Z7381'	G-HURI	Hurricane XII Δ	ex Coningsby, Coventry, Canada. 'XR-T', 71 *Eagle* Sqn c/s . TFC.	03-94
☐ AR614*	C-FDUY	Spitfire V	ex Canada, Dishforth, Bridgnorth, Hednesford, West Kirby, Padgate, 7555M, St Athan, 5378M, 53 OTU, 222, 130, 610, 312. Arrived 10-92. Stored, off-site. OFMC.	03-94
☐ EP120*	8070M	Spitfire V	ex St Athan, Wattisham, Boulmer, Wilmslow, St Athan, 5377M, 53 OTU, 402, 501. Arrived 1-93. 'QV-H', 19 Sqn c/s. TFC.	05-93
☐ FE992	G-BDAM	Harvard IIB Δ	ex North Weald, LN-MAA, Fv16047, FE992, 42-12479. Euan English - Norman Lees - Radial Pair. IWM-L.	03-94
☐ 'FR870'	NL1009N	P-40N	ex N1233N, Wright Patterson, RCAF 840, 43-5802. 'GA-S', 112 Sqn c/s. TFC.	03-94

☐	HM580	G-ACUU	Cierva C.30A	ex Staverton, HM580, 529, 1448 Flt, G-ACUU. CoA expired 30-4-60. IWM.	03-94
☐	KB889	G-LANC	Lancaster X	ex Bitteswell, Blackbushe, Niagara Falls, RCAF 107 MRU, 428. Restn. 'NA-I', 428 Sqn c/s. IWM.	03-94
☐	KF487		Harvard IIB	ex Sandhurst, Avex, 1 FTS, 66 GCF. Spares. ARCO.	11-93
☐	KL161	N88972	B-25D-30-ND Δ	ex CF-OGQ, KL161 5 OTU (RCAF), 43-3318. *Grumpy* 'VO-B'. 98 Sqn c/s. TFC.	03-94
☐	KZ321	G-HURY	Hurricane IV	ex Biggin Hill, Bitteswell, Blackbushe, Israel, Yugoslav AF, RAF. Frame only. TFC.	
☐	LZ766	G-ALCK	Proctor III	ex Staverton, Tamworth, HQ Bomber Command, 21 EFTS. CoA expired 19-6-63. IWM.	03-94
☐	MH434	G-ASJV	Spitfire IX Δ	ex Booker, COGEA Nouvelle OO-ARA, Belgian AF SM-41, Fokker B-13, Netherlands H-68, and H-105 322, MH434 , 349, 84 GSU, 222, 350, 222. OFMC.	09-93
☐	ML407*	G-LFIX	Spitfire Tr IX Δ	ex Audley End, Goodwood, St Merryn, Strathallan, IAAC 162, G-15-175, ML407, 29 MU, 332, 485, 349, 341, 485. 'OU-V' 485 Sqn c/s. Carolyn S Grace. Based from 1992.	03-94
☐	ML417	G-BJSG	Spitfire IX Δ	ex Booker, USA, Indian AF Tr IX HS543, G-15-11, ML417, High Ercall, 411, 442, 443. '21-T'. TFC.	03-94
☐	ML796		Sunderland MR.5	ex La Baule, Maisden-le-Riviere, *Aéronavale* 27F, 7FE, RAF 230, 4 OTU, 228. Restn. IWM.	03-94
☐	MV293	G-SPIT	Spitfire XIV Δ	ex Sleaford, Blackbushe, G-BGHB ntu, Bangalore, Indian inst T20, Indian AF, ACSEA, 215 MU, 33 MU. TFC. F/f 15-8-92 'OI-C' 2 Sqn c/s.	03-94
☐	NF370		Swordfish II	ex South Lambeth, Stretton, RAF. IWM	03-94
☐	PL965*	G-MKXI	Spitfire PR.XI Δ	ex Rochester, Overloon, Bruggen, Overloon, Deelen, Twenthe, 16, 1 PP. Flew in 2-2-93. OFMC — see notes above.	03-94
☐	SM832	G-WWII	Spitfire XIV	ex Winchester, Duxford, Bitteswell, Blackbushe, Indian AF, Dehra Dun gate, SM832, ACSEA, 222 MU, 29 MU. TFC.	05-93
☐	TA719	G-ASKC	Mosquito TT.35	ex Staverton, G-ASKC, Shawbury, 3/4 CAACU, 4 CAACU, Shawbury. Crashed 27-7-64. '6T'. IWM.	03-94
☐	TG528		Hastings C.1A	ex Staverton, 24, 24-36, 242 OCU, 53-99, 47. IWM.	03-94
☐	TV959*		Mosquito T.3	ex Hounslow, South Lambeth, Bicester, 3 CAACU, HCEU, 228 OCU, 13 OTU. 'AF-V'. Arrived by 3-91. Stored.	10-93
☐	TX226	7865M	Anson C.19	ex Little Staughton, East Dereham, Colerne, Shawbury, FTCCF, OCTU Jurby, 187, Hemswell SF, Coningsby CF, CBE. Stored. IWM.	11-92
☐	VN485	7326M	Spitfire F.24	ex Kai Tak, RHK Aux AF, 80. IWM.	03-94
☐	VT260*	8813M	Meteor F.4	ex Firbeck, Duxford, Winterbourne Gunner, 49 MU, 12 FTS, 209 AFS, 203 AFS, 226 OCU, 203 AFS. '67'. Arrived 12-93.	03-94
☐	VX653	G-BUCM	Sea Fury FB.11	ex Hendon, Yeovilton, Lee-on-Solent, Lossiemouth, FRU, 811, 738, 736. Restoration. TFC.	03-94
☐	'WF714'	WK914	Meteor F.8	ex Rochester, Manston, 85, CAW, 5 CAACU, 19. Stored, pending restoration. OFMC.	03-94
☐	WH725		Canberra B.2	ex Wroughton, 50, 44. IWM.	03-94
☐	WJ680*	G-BURM	Canberra TT.18	ex Wyton, 100, 7, 59, 103, 104. Flew in early 1993 for CoA work by ARCO.	03-94

☐	WJ945	G-BEDV	Varsity T.1	ex CFS, 5 FTS, AE&AEOS, CFS, 115, 116, 527. CoA expired 15-10-87. '21'. IWM. 03-94
☐	WK991	7825M	Meteor F.8	ex Kemble, 56, 46, 13 GCF, NSF. IWM. 03-94
☐	WM969	A2530	Sea Hawk FB.5	ex Culdrose 'SAH-5', FRU, 806, 811, 898. IWM. 03-94
☐	WZ590		Vampire T.11	ex Woodford, Chester, St Athan, 8 FTS, 5 FTS, 228 OCU. '19'. IWM. 03-94
☐	XB261		Beverley C.1	ex Southend, HAM, A&AEE. Cockpit. DAS. 03-94
☐	XE627		Hunter F.6A	ex Brawdy, 1 TWU, TWU, 229 OCU, 1, 229 OCU, 54, 1, 54, Horsham St Faith SF, 54, 229 OCU, 92, 65. 65 Sqn c/s, 'T'. IWM. 03-94
☐	XF375*	G-BUEZ	Hunter F.6	ex Cranwell, 8736M, ETPS, Warton, AWA, C(A). For restoration to flying condition. '05'. OFMC. First noted 10-93. Stored. 03-94
☐	XF708		Shackleton MR.3/3	ex Kemble, 203, 120, 201. Restn. 203 Sqn c/s 'C' IWM. 03-94
☐	XG613		Sea Ven FAW.21	ex Old Warden, 766, 809. IWM. 03-94
☐	XG797		Gannet ECM.6	ex Arbroath, 831, 700, 810. IWM. '766-BY', 849 Sqn c/s. 03-94
☐	XH648		Victor B.1A(K2P)	ex 57, 55, Honington Wing, 15, 57. IWM. 03-94
☐	XH897		Javelin FAW.9	ex A&AEE, 5, 33, 25. IWM. 03-94
☐	XJ676*	8844M	Hunter F.6A	ex Lyneham, 1 TWU, TWU, 229 OCU, 9, 93. Spares for OFMC. F/n 10-93. Stored. 10-93
☐	XJ824		Vulcan B.2	ex 101, 9-35, 9, 230 OCU, 27. IWM. 03-94
☐	XK936		Whirlwind HAS.7	ex Wroughton, 705, 847, 848, 701, 820, 845. '62'. IWM. 03-94
☐	XM135		Lightning F.1A	ex Leconfield, 60 MU, Leuchars TFF, 226 OCU, 74, A&AEE, AFDS. IWM. 03-94
☐	XN239	8889M	Cadet TX.3	ex CGS. IWM. 03-94
☐	XP281		Auster AOP.9	ex AFWF, Middle Wallop. IWM (on loan from MoAF). 03-94
☐	XP772*	G-BUCJ	Beaver AL.1	ex Middle Wallop, Beverley, Leconfield, Middle Wallop, 15 Flt, 667, 132 Flt, AFWF. Arrived 11-5-93. For restoration by ARCO. 03-94
☐	XR222		TSR-2 XO-4	ex Cranfield, Weybridge. Unflown. IWM. 03-94
☐	XR241*	G-AXRR	Auster AOP.9 ∆	ex Middle Wallop, Duxford, Old Warden, St Athan, 1 Wing HQ, 654, Middle Wallop. Yellow c/s. Returned 6-93. 03-94
☐	XS183*		Jet Provost T.4	ex Hatfield, 2 FTS. Cockpit. First noted 11-92. Stored. See notes above. IWM 11-92
☐	XS567*		Wasp HAS.1	ex Lee-on-Solent, 829 Endurance Flt. '434-E'. First noted 8-92. 03-94
☐	XS576		Sea Vixen FAW.2	ex Sydenham, 899, Brawdy. '125 -E', 899 Sqn c/s. IWM. 03-94
☐	XS863		Wessex HAS.1	ex A&AEE. IWM. 03-94
☐	XV474*		Phantom FGR.2	ex Wattisham, 56, 23, 56, 23, 19, 2, 31, 17. 'T'. Flew in 13-10-92. OFMC. 03-94
☐	XW763*	9041M	Harrier GR.3	ex St Athan, 9002M, 1, 1453 Flt, 3, 4, 3. Fuselage. F/noted 10-93. Stored. 10-93
☐	XZ133*		Harrier GR.3	ex South Lambeth, St Athan, 4, 1, 1417F, 233 OCU. Arrived 2-9-93. 03-94
☐	ZE359		F-4J(UK)	ex Wattisham, 74, USN 155574. 'J'. IWM. 03-94
☐			Beaufighter I	ex Hendon, Cranfield. Nose. Loan to TFC. 03-94
☐			Typhoon	ex South Lambeth. Cockpit section. IWM. 05-93
☐	A-549		FMA Pucara	ex ZD487 ntu, ex Boscombe Down, Yeovilton, Stanley, FAA. IWM. 03-94
☐			Beaufighter XI	ex Australia. Long term restn project. TFC. 03-94

☐	9893		Bolingbroke IVT	ex Canada. Stored. IWM. 11-93
☐	18393	G-BCYK	CF.100 Mk IV	ex Cranfield, RCAF. IWM. 03-94
☐	'20385'	G-BGPB	Harvard IV	ex North Weald, Portuguese AF 1747, WGAF BF+050, AA+050, 53-4619. Damaged 15-6-89. Under restoration by ARCO. 11-93
☐	3794*		MiG-15 (S-102)	ex Czech AF. Arrived 9-93. 10-93
☐	'S4523'	N4727V	SPAD S.XIII	ex Orlando, Florida. IWM. 03-94
☐	57		Mystere IVA	ex Sculthorpe, FAF 8 Esc, 321 GI, 5 Esc. IWM. '8-MT'. 03-94
☐	14286		T-33A-1-LO	ex Sculthorpe, FAF CIFAS 328. IWM. 05-93
☐	42165		F-100D-11-NA	ex Sculthorpe, FAF Esc 2-11, Esc 1-3, USAF. IWM. 03-94
☐	'152/17'*	G-ATJM	Fokker Dr I rep ▲	ex Rendcomb, North Weald, Duxford, N78001, EI-APY, G-ATJM. Arrived 1992. OFMC. 03-94
☐	10639	G-USTV	Bf 109G-2 ▲	ex Benson, Northolt, Lyneham 8478M, Henlow, Wattisham, Stanmore Park, Sealand, CFE-EAF, 1426 (EA) Flt, RN228, Lydda, 3 Sqn 'CV-V', Gambut, III-JG77. IWM/RAF. 03-94
☐	100143		Fa 330A-1	ex Farnborough. IWM. 05-93
☐	191660	AM.214	Me 163B-1	ex South Lambeth, Cranwell, 6 MU, RAE. '3'. IWM. 03-94
☐	'IZ+NK'		Amiot AAC.1	ex Port AF 6316. Luftwaffe c/s. IWM. 03-94
☐	'TA+RC'	G-BPHZ	MS.505 ▲ •	ex F-BJQC, French military. Luftwaffe c/s. ARCO. 03-94
☐	'LG+01'	G-AYSJ	Bü 133C ▲	ex D-EHVP, G-AYSJ, HB-MIW, Swiss AF U-91. Luftwaffe colours. TFC. 03-94
☐			Tempest II	ex Indian AF. For restn. TFC. 11-91 [Thought to be HA580 from Chichester, W Sussex.]
☐	'MM53211'*	B'79	Fiat G.46-IV	ex Lydd, Southend, Shoreham, Italian AF. ARCO. Arrived 8-92. See notes above. 03-94
☐	B-168		Harvard IIB	ex North Weald, Amsterdam, Dutch AF, FE984, RCAF, 2 FIS, 42-12471. Spares. ARCO. 03-94
☐	NZ5648	NX55JP	FG-1D Corsair ▲	ex TFC. Bournemouth Airport, Biggin Hill, USA, Canada, MoTAT Auckland, NZ, RNZAF NZ5648, USN 88391. RNZAF c/s by 3-94. OFMC. 03-94
☐	'20'*		Lavochkin La-11	ex Monino, CIS, USSR. TFC. Arrived 5-93, for restoration. See notes above. 03-94
☐	'53'*		P-40B	ex CIS, USSR. TFC. First noted 6-92. 03-94
☐	'69'	G-BTZB	Yak 50 ▲	ex USSR. TFC. 03-94
☐	RK858*		Spitfire IX ▲	ex CIS, USSR, no RAF service. TFC. First noted 9-92. 05-93
☐	E3B-153	G-BPTS	CASA 1-131E •	ex Spanish AF. OFMC. 03-94
☐	Fv16105	G-BTXI	Harvard IIB	ex Vasteras, RSwAF, RCAF, 6 SFTS, RAF FE695, 42-892. Restoration. TFC. 05-93
☐	Fv 35075		J35A Draken	ex RSwAF F16. IWM. 03-94
☐	'1164'	G-BKGL	Beech 18 3TM ▲	ex Prestwick, CF-QPD, RCAF 5193, RCAF 1564. USAAC colours. ARCO. 03-94
☐	8178*	G-SABR	F-86A Sabre ▲	ex Bournemouth, N178, N68388, 48-0178. Golden Apple Trust. OFMC. Arrived by 3-94. 03-94
☐	0-17899		VT-29B-CO	ex Mildenhall, 513 TAW. IWM. Stored. 03-94
☐	'40467'	G-BTCC	F6F-5K Hellcat ▲	ex N10CN ntu, N100TF, Yankee Air Corps, N80142, USMC Museum, 80141. TFC. 03-94
☐	'42161'	N33VC	T-33A-3 ▲	ex Switzerland, G-JETT, G-OAHB, CF-IHB, CAF 133261, RCAF 21261. OFMC. 03-94
☐	60689		B-52D-40-BW	ex 7 BW Carswell and others, USAF. IWM. 05-93
☐	66692*		U-2CT-LO	ex Alconbury, 5 SRTS - 9 SRW, Beale, U-2C, U-2F, U-2A. Returned to single-seat configuration. Presented to IWM 26-6-92. 03-94

☐	67543*	NX3145X	P-38J-10-LO ▲	ex Chino, Mercedes, CAF, 36th PRS, 37th PRS, 42-67543. See notes. *California Cutie*, 20th FG colours.	03-94
☐	88297	G-FGID	FG-1D Corsair ▲	ex N8297, N9154Z, USN 88297. TFC.	03-94
☐	114526	G-BRWB	T-6G Texan ▲	ex FAF, 51-14526. *Thumper*. F/f -92. ARCO.	03-94
☐	'124485'	G-BEDF	B-17G-105-VE ▲	ex N17TE, IGN F-BGSR, USAAF 44-85784. *Sally B*. B-17 Preservation Ltd.	03-94
☐	126922	G-RAID	AD-4NA ▲	ex F-AZED, La Ferte Alais, Aero Retro, Gabon AF, French AF No 42, USN 126922. TFC.	03-94
☐	'226671'	NX47DD	P-47D-N ▲	ex 45-49192 - composite. *No Guts, No Glory* TFC.	03-94
☐	'231983'	F-BDRS	B-17G-95-DL	ex IGN F-BDRS, N68269, 44-83735. *Mary Alice*. 'IY-G'. IWM.	03-94
☐	315509	G-BHUB	C-47A-85-DL	ex Aces High G-BHUB, *Airline* : 'G-AGIV', 'FD988' and 'KG418', Spanish AF T3-29, N51V, N9985F, SAS SE-BBH, 43-15509. IWM.	03-94
☐	461748	G-BHDK	TB-29A-45-BN	ex China Lake, 307th BG, Okinawa. *Hawg Wild* IWM.	03-94
☐	'463221'	G-BTCD	P-51D-25-NA ▲	ex N51JJ, N6340T, RCAF 9568, USAAF 44-73149. *Candyman/Moose*. TFC.	03-94
☐	'472917'	G-HAEC	Mustang 22 ▲	ex '592', VR-HIU, RP-C651, PI-C651, VH-FCB, RAAF A68-192. *Ding Hao*. OFMC.	03-94
☐	67-0120*		F-111E-CF	ex Upper Heyford, 20th TFW. *The Chief*. Arrived 19-10-93.	03-94
☐	77-0259		A-10A T'bolt II	ex Alconbury, 10th TFW, 11th TASG, 128th TFW. IWM.	03-94
☐	*		PT-17 Kaydet	ex Sudbury. For restoration by ARCO.	11-93
☐	*		Anson I	ex Australia. TFC. Stored.	03-94
☐	*		P-51 Mustang rep	ex London. '88'. *Cowboys in the Sky*. OFMC. Arrived by 9-93. Stored.	03-94
☐		BAPC.90	Colditz Cock rep	ex Higher Blagdon, BBC. Stored.	01-92
☐		BAPC.93	Fi 103 (V-1)	ex Cosford. On original launch ramp. IWM.	03-94

ELY

■ **RAF Ely** : Is no more. Meteor NF.14 WS774/7959M was offered for tender and had moved to Fearn, Highland, by November 1992.

EVERSDEN (On the A603 west of Cambridge)
The store of aircraft here is thought unchanged. DR.1050 G-ATEV has been assigned to *LOST!*

☐	G-ADJJ	Tiger Moth	ex BB819, 25 RFS, 28 EFTS, 1 EFTS, 9 EFTS, G-ADJJ. CoA expired 20-3-75. Stored.	10-91
☐	G-ASBY	Airedale	ex Royston. CoA expired 22-3-80. Stored.	11-90
☐	G-ASRK	Airedale	ex Cambridge, Oakington. CoA exp 29-7-84.	11-90
☐	G-AYBV	Tourbillon	unfinished homebuild project. Stored.	10-91
☐	G-BAXV	Cessna F.150L	ex Bredhurst, Eversden, Sandtoft. Crashed 25-7-82.	11-91
☐	G-BKKS	Mercury Dart	unfinished homebuild project. Stored.	11-90
☐	G-BRLZ	Cessna 150G	ex Liverpool, Prestatyn, C-GASI, N3080S. Damaged 10-3-90. Sectioned.	11-90

GLATTON (on the B660 south of Peterborough)
■ **Classic Aircraft Ltd** : Are to be found at a strip near the village not at the former USAAF airfield, which is on the *other* side of the A1. Beagle E3 G-ASCC was flying again by December 1993. A Luscombe has been added to the **W&R** inmates.

☐	G-BSYF*	Silvaire 8A	ex Abbotsley, N72028, NC72028. Stored.	10-91

☐ G-BSYG   Super Cruiser   ex Abbotsley, N3228M, NC3228M. Restn.   10-91
☐ F-GAIP   G-BKOT   WA.81 Piranha   ex Eversden. Stored.   09-93

HOUGHTON (on the A1123 east of Huntingdon)
■ **Jon Wilson** : Took delivery of a former Wyton Canberra nose on September 18, 1992.
☐ WJ567*   Canberra B.2   ex Wyton, 100, 85, MinTech, 45, RNZAF, 45,
                                            59, 149. Nose. Arrived 18-9-92..   09-92

KIMBOLTON (On the A45 north west of St Neots)
■ **Airfield** : The Cessna hulk — now a very long term resident — can still be found.
☐ G-ARRG   Cessna 175B   ex Gt Yarmouth, N8299T. Dam 3-11-70.   05-91

LITTLE GRANSDEN AERODROME (south of the B1046, south of Great Gransden)
■ **Aerobuild Ltd / Yak UK Ltd** : This lovely airfield, run by Mark Jefferies, has become the centre for importing Yaks into the UK, many via Lithuania. PT-13D G-BTZM has departed, sold in France as F-AZIC.
☐ G-AGYD*   J/1N Alpha   ex Felthorpe. Crashed 25-11-90. F/n 3-94.   03-94
☐ G-AIRI   Tiger Moth   ex N5488, 29 EFTS, 14 EFTS, 20 ERFTS. CoA
                                              expired 9-11-81. Stored.   06-93
☐ G-ASKJ   Terrier 1   ex (EI-AMC), VX926, 664, AOPS, HS. Damaged
                                                20-6-84. Restoration to Auster T.7 guise.   07-91
☐ G-BKXP   Auster AOP.6   ex Royston, Oakington, Belgian AF A-14, VT987.
                                                            07-91
☐ 'XP248' WZ679   Auster AOP.9   ex Cranfield, Wroughton, Marlborough, Old
                                              Sarum, Middle Wallop.
☐ C-558*   EKW C-3605   ex Wycombe AP, Lodrino, Swiss AF. Arrived
                                              by 1-91. Stored.   06-93

LITTLE STAUGHTON AERODROME (south of the A45, west of Eaton Socon)
From a single entry — the Aztec — in the last edition, 'Staughton has expanded as a lightplane store. Cessna G-AVGU was 'written out' in **W&R12** as having gone by August 1989. It is likely that it has been here all the while. For the Swedish Tomahawk, we travel back to **W&R11** and Chessington, Gtr Lon, where it was thought to have been reduced to spares *circa* 1987.
☐ G-ARAU*   Cessna 150   ex Willingham, Sibson, Land's End, N6494T.
                                              Damaged 23-5-82. Dumped. F/n 2-93.   02-93
☐ G-ARSB*   Cessna 150A   ex Willingham, N7237X. CoA expired 10-6-88.
                                              Fuselage, dumped. First noted 2-93.   09-93
☐ G-ASCU*   Super Cub 150   ex VP-JBL. CoA expired 13-9-90. Stored. First
                                              noted 11-92.   11-92
☐ G-AVGU*   Cessna F.150G   ex Cranfield. Cr 25-5-83. Stored. First
                                              noted 5-89. See notes above.   09-93
☐ G-BBVG   Aztec 250C   ex ET-AEB, 5Y-AAT. CoA expired 10-9-88.
                                              Derelict.   03-94
☐ SE-GVH*   Tomahawk 112   ex Chessington. Stored. First noted 04-92.   09-93

MOLESWORTH
■ **USAF Molesworth** : Now boasting Alconbury as a satellite, USAF presence here will remain for the time being. After the disposal of large amounts of scrap hardware noted in **W&R13**, there has been no activity at all to chronicle.

PETERBOROUGH SPORT AERODROME (or Sibson, east of the A1, south of Wansford)
There has been a considerable tidy-up of the Cessna cache here with the result that several airframes have been reduced to spares, with only two hulks, a 172 and a 182, being left in the weeds behind the hangar. Gone are the following : F.150J G-AWSD, last noted July 1993; FA.150L G-AYRP reduced to a rear section only by 1992 and gone entirely by July 1993; F.150M G-BDZC arrived from Tattershall Thorpe by October 1992 but had gone by August 1993; and F.150G G-HUNY, last noted July 1993. Cessna 310B G-BPIL Fast Lady was out to grass here by October 1992, but was up and

about again by March 1994. Adding to **W&R13**, the cabin of F.150M G-BCRA moved to Westley's at Cranfield, Beds, by April 1991 but was scrapped quickly. Provost T.1 WV444 has been consigned to *LOST!* That makes the current situation as follows : —

☐ G-ASHH	Aztec 250	ex N455SL, N4557P. CoA expired 27-9-85. Stored.	09-93
☐ G-AVIE	Cessna F.172H	ex Bristol Airport, N17014. Damaged 4-2-89. Cabin only by 7-93. Dumped.	03-94
☐ G-BABD	Cessna FRA.150L	ex Cranfield. Crashed 16-10-87. Restn.	09-93
☐ G-BEKN*	Cessna FRA.150M	CoA expired 8-10-89. Stored. F/n 5-90.	03-94
☐ G-BFGY	Cessna F.182P	ex D-EJCG. Damaged 4-8-87. Cabin only by 7-93. Dumped.	03-94
☐ G-BFWF	Cessna 421B	ex Staverton, ZS-JCA, N1567G. CoA expired 15-5-80.	03-94

ST IVES

■ **David Collings & John Chillingworth** : Have acquired the former Brooklands Pup prototype and are restoring it to flying condition. John continues to work on his Chipmunk.

☐ G-AVDF*	Pup 200	ex Brooklands, Shoreham, Duxford, Shoreham. CoA exp 22-5-68. Arrived 30-1-93. Restn.	10-93
☐ WD356 7625M	Chipmunk T.10	ex Bushey, Nostell Priory, Aldergrove, QUAS. Restoration.	03-94

ST NEOTS

An unidentified Gnat is to be found in an industrial estate here, under restoration to flying condition. It is hoped it will be airworthy in 1994.

☐ *	Gnat T.1	see notes above.	10-93

SNAILWELL (North of Newmarket)

■ **Mayer & Perry (Recycling) Ltd** : As related in **W&R13**, this yard was the main contender in the let's-scrap-the-Phantom competition, processing the blue-crossed wonders very quickly from late 1991 through to 1992. See under Wattisham, Suffolk, for the aircraft concerned.

WATERBEACH

■ **39 Engineers Regiment** : The Hunter remains as a reminder of the RAF's occupancy. Both Scouts (XP846 and XT643) are thought to have moved on, or been axed. An anonymous Gazelle lies in a compound.

☐ WN904 7544M	Hunter F.2	ex Duxford, Newton, 257. '3'. Gate.	06-93
☐ *	Gazelle AH.1	dumped. See notes above.	06-93

WHITTLESEY (On the A605 east of Peterborough)

Stored on a farm in the area is an Auster.

☐ G-AOGV	J/5R Alpine	CoA expired 17-7-72. Stored.	

WILLINGHAM (South of the A1123, east of Huntingdon)

Cessna 150 G-ARAU, mentioned in **W&R13** as having gone by October 1991 turned up at Little Staughton, Cambs, by February 1993, along with 150A G-ARSB, which had also been stored here for some time. Tiger Moth G-AZDY, listed in **W&R13**, has been flying since 1989!

WISBECH

■ **Fenland Aircraft Preservation Society** (FAPS) : Work continues to establish a display hall for the Vampire and to extend the display space for this enthralling collection of carefully restored and well displayed artefacts. The Grasshopper remains in store. Restoration of Vampire T.11 XE998 on behalf of Aero Consultants of Huntingdon, Cambs, is nearing conclusion — the standard of workmanship being carried out by Murray Flint and team would put de Havilland's to shame! 1994 has seen a lot of heavy metal arriving, first off being the framework for a hangar and fund-raising is well underway to bring this major advance to fruition. The pair of two-seater Lightnings from Narborough were acquired by members of FAPS.

◆ Located at Bamber's Garden Centre, Old Lynn Road, West Walton Highway, near Wisbech — off the A47/B198 junction. The Museum is open every Saturday, Sunday and Bank Holidays, March to September 9.30am to 5pm. ✉ Richard Mason, 63 St Leonard's Road, Leverington, Wisbech, Cambs, PE13 5BA.

☐ XD434	Vampire T.11	ex Marham, Barton, Woodford, Chester, St Athan,	
		5 FTS, 7 FTS. '25'.	12-93
☐ XE998	Vampire T.11	ex Huntingdon, Horley, Charlwood, Biggin Hill,	
		Warmingham, Wigan, Woodford, Chester,	
		St Athan, 8 FTS, 4 FTS, 8 FTS. Off site,	
		restoration. See notes above.	12-93
☐ XP488	Grasshopper TX.1	ex Long Sutton, Halton, West Malling. Stored.	
			12-93
☐ XS420*	Lightning T.5	ex Narborough, Binbrook, LTF, 5, LTF, 226 OCU.	
		Arrived 4-94. See notes above.	04-94
☐ XS459*	Lightning T.5	ex Narborough, Binbrook, 5, LTF, 56, 29, 226	
		OCU. 'AW'. Arrived 4-94. See notes.	04-94

WITTERING AIRFIELD (on the A1 south of Stamford)
■ **RAF Wittering** : The migration to Bentwaters/Woodbridge is no longer on the cards and if anything, Wittering could well fully take on the mantle of the *Home of the Harrier* if Laarbruch is 'evacuated'. The dump and the buildings around it were all cleared/removed by November 1992, but the aircraft parts here were beyond the remit of **W&R**. The hulk of an OCU Harrier GR.3 that crashed on the airfield has been maintained, and receives the occasional attentions of the fire crews. Hunter F.6 XF383, kept in solitary confinement on the Collyweston side of the airfield, was offered for tender during March 1992 and by October 1992 had moved to North Scarle, Lincs.

☐ LA255	6490M	Spitfire F.21	ex West Raynham, Cardington, Tangmere, 1.	
			'JX-U'. 1 Sqn colours. Kept indoors mostly.	09-93
☐ XV279	8566M	Harrier GR.1	ex Farnborough, Culdrose, A&AEE. GR.3	
			mock-up nose. Weapons training.	04-91
☐ XV779	8931M	Harrier GR.3	ex 1. Gate guardian. 'A'	03-94
☐ XW923	8724M	Harrier GR.3	ex 1417 Flt, 1, 233 OCU, 1. Nose. Inst.	04-91
☐ XZ990*		Harrier GR.3	ex 233 OCU, 3, 4, 3. '3D'. Crashed 14-5-92.	
			Hulk on field, first noted 1-93.	09-93

WOODHURST (north of St Ives)
A collector here took on the nose of a former Wyton Canberra during December 1992.

☐ WE113*	Canberra B.2	ex Wyton, 231 OCU, 100, 85, 98, 231 OCU.	
		Nose. Arrived 13-12-92.	12-92

WYTON AIRFIELD (on the B1090 north west of St Ives)
■ **RAF Wyton** : The inevitable wind-down of the Canberra fleet has continued and with the winning of the ECM trainer contract by FRA Aviation with its Falcon 20s in October 1993, the days of 360 Squadron are now severely limited, with the first of their machines appearing on the scrap site by autumn 1993. Wyton Station Flight Canberra B.2T WJ731 'BK' made the last operational flight of a B.2 on July 7, 1993, bringing to an end a momentous era. Other variants will continue to fly, but in ever dwindling numbers. Left flying the Canberra flag is 39 (PRU) Squadron, who moved their PR.9s to Marham, Norfolk, on November 30, 1993. Being categorised as 'bombers' for the purposes of various arms limitation treaties, the scrapping of the fleet here has involved the now-familiar taking off of the tail, a long wait outside in this guise — to pose for the satellites — and the dreaded blue cross. November 1993 saw the 'SALT site' completely clear, following a major 'cull' of Canberras.

Removals have been as follows, those marked * being in-and-out since **W&R13** : —
B.2 : WE113 had its nose off by 12-92, and the hulk was cut up 22-11-93. The nose left by road 13-12-92 to Woodhurst, Cambs; WJ567 scrapping by 8-92, nose to Houghton, Cambs, 18-9-92; WJ731* (B.2T) — see notes above — was moved to the dump 8-10-93 was scrapped during 11-93..
T.4 : WJ879* scrapping by 8-92; WT478 up for tender 3-92 and removed 7-92.
PR.7 : WT538/9142M was in the scrap area by 8-92 and had gone by 5-93; WJ817/8695M was dismantled 10-93.

PR.9 : nose XH174 moved *possibly* to DRA Bedford, Beds, but had certainly appeared on the dump at St Athan, S Glam, by 9-92.

E.15 : WH981 was dismantled by 8-92 and last noted 9-93 and moved to Stock, Essex; WJ756* was dismantled by 7-93, last noted 10-93.

T.17 : WF890* scrapping by 8-92, last noted 10-93; WH664 up for tender 3-92 and removed; WJ630* dismantled by 10-93; WK111* withdrawn 10-93 and to the dump 1-94..

TT.18 : WH718 scrapping by 8-92; WJ680 out in the scrap area by 8-92 but acquired by A R Mitchell and registered as G-BURM 12-92 and flown out to Duxford, Cambs, early in 1993; WJ682 scrapping by 12-92; WJ636 was dismantled by 10-92, last noted 10-93; WJ715 up for tender by 3-92 and removed 7-92; WK118 up for tender 3-92 and removed to Stock, Essex, 7-92; WK127/8985M was under scrapping by 8-92 and was still present 5-93, nose to Bassingbourn, Cambs, the remainder being scrapped.

☐ WH848		Canberra T.4	ex 231 OCU, 7, 13, 100, 85, 231 OCU, CAW, 231 OCU, 232 OCU, Gaydon SF, Binbrook SF, Marham SF. Fuselage with Canberra Servicing School. Up for tender 8-93.	08-93
☐ WK111*		Canberra T.17	ex 360, 73, 32, 202, RAFC. To dump 19-1-94. 'EA'.	01-94
☐ WK119		Canberra B.2	ex St Mawgan, 7, MoA, NECS, 103. Nose on dump.	
☐ XH170	8739M	Canberra PR.9	ex 39, RAE, 58. Gate guardian.	10-93

Cheshire

CHELFORD (on the A537 west of Macclesfield)

■ **Macclesfield Historical Aviation Society** (MHAS) : A major headache hangs over MHAS as these words are processed, a planning problem could see them removed from the site. During June 1993, MHAS took delivery of a Canberra T.4 nose section previously housed at Winsford. This item had previously been in use with the Cheshire Fire Brigade Training School, having been supplied by Lovaux at Macclesfield. Its serial was initially thought to be WE188 — but that aircraft remains firmly at Carlisle, Cumbria, and well out of the argument. Investigation revealed it to be T.4 WE192, last noted at Samlesbury, Lancs, and unaccounted for in **W&R12**. WE192 was exchanged with SYAM at Firbeck, S Yorks, for the Cessna that went to Winsford, Cheshire. (Still with us?) In order that MHAS can complete their Hunter FGA.9 (currently just a nose section), they offered their Canberra nose, plus former Danish T.53 ET-272 in an exchange for the parts they need. (To this end, they have taken on the centre section of F.6 XF383 — see under North Scarle, Lincs.) The nose of ET-272 moved to Firbeck, S Yorks, by December 1993. The tail and centre section moved to Long Marston. The nose of Hunter FGA.9 XE650 was delivered to Kexborough, S Yorks, on November 9, 1991. Peter Smith, Curator of the Biggin Hill Air Museum (see under Sevenoaks, Kent), has loaned several airframes to MHAS. These are marked as follows ‡. (Vampire NF.10 pod WP250 was briefly here during 1993 — ex North Weald, Essex — before moving on to Tamworth, Staffs. for an 'interesting' incarnation.) Three of the somewhat lose film replicas stored in a heap at Coventry Airport, Warks, have come here. The 'Strutter' and the 'Albatros' are quoted as such because of their rough approximation to these types.

◆ Nominally open to the public on Bank Holidays and at other times by prior arrangement, but please note the opening sentence. ✉ Kevin Whittaker, 19, Lyme Green Park, Lyme Green, Macclesfield, Cheshire, SK11 0LD. (Note new address.)

☐ G-BAYV		Noralpha	ex Sevenoaks, Wycombe AP, Hawkinge, Maidstone, Ford, F-BLTN, French AF. Cr 23-2-74. ‡	12-93
☐ VP519*	G-AVVR	Anson C.19/2	ex Dukinfield, Hadfield, Stockport, Peel Green, Cosford, Wigan, Irlam, Shawbury, FCCS, 11 GCF, MCS, 31, Malta CF, TCDU. Nose. TAC.	12-93
☐ WH850		Canberra T.4	ex Samlesbury, St Athan, Laarbruch SF, Wildenrath SF, 14, 88, Marham SF. ‡	12-93

☐ XD535*	Vampire T.11	ex North Weald, Sevenoaks, Preston, Croston, Woodford, Chester, St Athan, 4 FTS, 5 FTS, 1 ANS, 93. Pod, arrived by 10-93.	12-93
☐ XE584	Hunter FGA.9	ex Macclesfield, Bitteswell, G-9-450, 208, 8, 1. Nose, centre section and tail.. Composite. See notes above.	12-93
☐ XG331*	Lightning F.1	ex Long Marston, Innsworth, Gloucester, Dowty, Foulness, A&AEE, EE. Nose. CARG loan. Arrived by 11-93.	11-93
☐ XR654	Jet Provost T.4	ex Macclesfield, Bournemouth, Coventry, Puckeridge, Hatfield, 27 MU, CAW, 3 FTS, 6 FTS. Fuselage.	11-93
☐ 'B9708'*	'1½ Strutter' rep	ex Coventry. Arr during 1992. See notes.	12-93
☐ 'GBH-7'* BAPC.234 Gunbus replica		ex Coventry, Old Warden, White Waltham. Arrived during 1992. Under restoration.	12-93
☐ 'C850'	'Albatros' replica	ex 'Coventry. Arr during 1992. See notes.	12-93
☐ BAPC.190 Spitfire replica		ex 'K5054', Sevenoaks. ‡	12-93

■ **Military Aircraft Preservation Group** (MAPG) : Problems at their previous workshop location in Hadfield, Derbyshire, left MAPG without a site. MHAS offered them space and they moved in during 1992, bringing their two Vampire pods with them.
✉ Phil Maloney, 51 Bleak Hey Road, Peel Hall, Wythenshawe, Manchester, M22 5FS.

☐ XD534	Vampire T.11	ex Hadfield, Wythenshawe, Cheadle Hulme, Woodford, Chester, Shawbury, 7 FTS, CFS, 9 FTS, 10 FTS. '41'. Pod. First noted 7-92.	12-93
☐ 333	Vampire T.55	ex Hadfield, Dukinfield, New Brighton, Chester, Iraqi AF. Pod. First noted 7-92.	12-93

■ **Others** : At the strip, the Centurion is still a hulk.

☐ EI-BRY	Cessna 210M	ex Dublin, G-BMGU, ZS-KRZ, N6262B. Crashed 16-10-86.	

CHESTER
Restoration of the Vampire T.11 is continues in the area.

☐ XH312	Vampire T.11	ex Knutsford, Woodford, Hawarden, St Athan, 8 FTS. '18'.	06-93

CONGLETON
Leopard Moth G-ACOJ was acquired by Roger Fiennes and moved to <u>Hungerford</u>, Berks. G-ACOL is assumed to have been consumed in G-ACOJ and / or G-ACUS or is too small for **W&R** to consider.

HANDFORTH
■ **395 Squadron ATC** : The unit keeps a *Chippax* in the town. 'Parent' is Shawbury, Salop.

☐ WZ869 8019M	Chipmunk T.10	ex 1 FTS, RAFC, Dishforth SF, Benson SF, Oxf UAS, Dur UAS, 64 GCF, Colerne SF. Crashed 20-5-68. PAX.	

HOOTON PARK (south of Junction 6 of the M53, near Eastham Locks)
■ **Griffin Trust** : A new transport museum is being established here using the hangars on the former airfield which is now partially occupied by fuel storage tanks and Vauxhall Motors. The Aeroplane Collection are slowly moving in from Warmingham, Cheshire.

☐ G-BFTZ*	Rallye Club	ex Warmingham, Fownhope, Cardiff-Wales, F-BPAX. CoA exp 19-9-81. Arr by 3-94.	03-94
☐ XT242*	Sioux AH.1	ex Warmingham, Long Marston, Wimborne, Middle Wallop. Composite. Arrived by 3-94.	03-94

KNUTSFORD
■ **Knutsford Fire Brigade** : The Brigade acquired the fuselage of a former Swanton Morley Cessna during 1993 and have displayed it at several events as part of a safety set-piece.

☐ G-AWTX*   Cessna F.150J   ex Swanton Morley. Fuselage. See notes.   11-93

LYMM

Messenger IVA G-ALAH was noted at Sabadella, Barcelona, Spain by February 1992. Following this logic, it would seem most likely that it was exchanged with a former Spanish Air Force CASA 1.131 Jungmann — any ideas? (See under Stretton, Ches, for one possibility!)

MACCLESFIELD

■ **Lovaux / FLS** : The site should be clear and Buccaneer S.2B XV155/8716M scrapped.
■ **Macclesfield College of Further Education** : Should still have the Vampire in Park Street.
☐ XD624   Vampire T.11   ex CATCS, CNCS, Church F' SF, 19. 'O'.   01-92

MALPAS (east of the A41 north west of Whitchurch)

■ **617 Squadron ATC** : Inside Malpas School, 617 *should* still have their Whirlwind HAS.7.
☐ XK944   A2607   Whirlwind HAS.7   ex Brunel Tech Bristol, Lee-on-Solent, Fleetlands,
                                             Arbroath, Fleetlands, Lossiemouth SF, Fleetlands,
                                             Yeovilton, 824, *Ark Royal* Flight.

RISLEY (west of the M6/M62 junction, north east of Warrington)

■ **UK Atomic Energy Authority** : Still have their BAC 1-11 fuselage for trials work.
☐ 5N-AOK   BAC 1-11-320   ex Manchester Airport, Okada Air, G-BKAW,
                                             BCAL, G-AVBY, Laker. Fuselage.   01-92

SAIGHTON (south east of Chester)

■ **Saighton Camp** : Wessex are resilient creatures! **W&R13** wrote-off HU.5 XS521 after a fire practice went wrong during April 1990. However, it is still to be seen, not well, but decidedly still within this mortal coil. Incidentally, it and the Hunter can be seen from the A55/M53 link road.
☐ WT746   7770M   Hunter F.4   ex Halton, St Athan, AFDS.   01-93
☐ XS521   Wessex HU.5   ex Wroughton. See notes above. Poor state.   02-94

STRETTON

■ **John Sykes** : Spitfire IX MH603 was exported to the USA *circa* 1992. John worked on the restoration of former Spanish Air Force CASA 1.131 G-BSFB here during 1991/1992. It had moved to Barton and was flying by May 1993. (See under Lymm, Ches.) A former Spanish Jungmeister arrived in mid-1993 for similar treatment. John owns T R Bitz — see below.
☐ ES.1-16*   CASA 1.133L   ex Spanish AF. Arr mid-1993. Restn.   03-94
■ **TR Bitz** : Located in Lyncastle Way, on the Barley Castle Trading Estate — part of the former Navy airfield — the car yard also boasts a Vampire.
☐ XE864   Vampire T.11   ex Kibworth, Firbeck, Studley, Chester, Woodford,
                                             St Athan, 8 FTS, 7 FTS, 1 ANS, CFS, 4 FTS.
                                             Wings of XD435.   12-90

WARMINGHAM (south of Middlewich in between the A530 and the A533)

■ **The Aeroplane Collection** (TAC) : Problems with the Craft Centre site mean that TAC will have to move from here by the middle of 1994. Warmingham will be open to inspection until mid-year, but only at weekends and readers are urged to check on this before travelling. By March 1994 the first aircraft had started to move to the new site, at the nascent transport museum located on the former Hooton Park airfield, Cheshire : Rallye Club G-BFTZ (ex Fownhope, H&W, arrived by January 1994) and Sioux AH.1 XT242.

    Disposals have been :— Airguard replica 'G-AFIN' moved into storage at Wigan, Gtr Man, during 1993. Cessna 172K G-AZDZ arrived from Southend, Essex, by late 1993, but moved to Fownhope, H&W, exchanged with Ross Aviation Services for Rallye G-BFTZ. Grasshopper TX.1 XK819 moved to Breighton, Humb, by September 1992. Addyman STG BAPC.15 moved to Wigan, Gtr Man, on June 7, 1993.

    TAC aircraft can also be found under the following locations : ☐ Breighton, Humbs, Fa 330A-1 100502. ☐ Chelford, Ches, Anson C.19/2 nose VP519. ☐ East Fortune, Lothian, *Flea*

BAPC.12. ❑ Firbeck, S Yorks, Chipmunk WB624. ❑ Manchester : Avian G-EBZM, Dragon Rapide G-ADAH, Bensen G-APUD, Roe Triplane BAPC.6. ❑ Wigan, TAC's store — *qv*.
◆ The Old Mill, Warmingham. 10am to 6pm at weekends. **See** notes above. ✉ John Davidson, 38 St Mark's Avenue, Oldfield Brow, Altrincham, Cheshire, WA14 4JB.

❑ G-AIJZ*	J/1 Autocrat	ex Southend, Shobdon. Crashed 25-10-70. Arrived 13-8-93.	12-93
❑ G-AJEB	J/1N Alpha	ex Brize Norton, Wigan, Cosford. CoA expired 27-3-69.	12-93
❑ G-AYFA	Twin Pioneer 3	ex Sandbach, Shobdon, Flight One, Prestwick, G-31-5, XM285, SRCU, 225, Odiham SF, 230. Nose.	12-93
❑ G-BAPH*	Cessna FRA.150L	ex Southend. Crashed 12-7-81. Fuselage. First noted 11-93.	12-93
❑ G-BBUW	SA.102.5 Cavalier	ex East Kirkby, Boston, Crowland. Incomplete homebuild.	12-93
❑ G-BLHL	Emeraude	ex Wigan, East Kirkby, Tattershall, Chinnor, Booker, F-BLHL, F-OBLM. Cr 4-8-81.	12-93
❑	Chrislea Super Ace	ex Bristol area. Fuselage frame only.	12-93
❑ 'K2572'	Tiger Moth replica	ex Hereford, Lutterworth, Holme-on-Spalding Moor. Stored.	12-93
❑	BAPC.192 Weedhopper	unflown homebuild.	12-93
❑	BAPC.193 Whing Ding	uncompleted homebuild.	12-93
❑	BAPC.204 McBroom h-g	omitted from **W&R12** and **W&R13**.	12-93

WARRINGTON

■ **1330 Squadron ATC** : The trailered *JP* nose is a frequent attender of events in the area.
❑ XM474 8121M Jet Provost T.3 ex Shrewsbury, Shawbury, MinTech, 6 FTS, MoA, 6 FTS, CFS. 'Parent' is Shawbury. Nose.

■ **Others** : In deep, secure store in this general area is the cache of former Saudi Lightnings acquired from Warton, Lancs, by Wensley Haydon-Baillie (see also under Southampton, Hants). After careful dismantling, each one was placed in a series of ISO containers awaiting a decision on their future.

❑ ZF577*	Lightning F.53	ex Warton, RSAF 53-668, G-27-38. Stored.	04-92
❑ ZF579*	Lightning F.53	ex Warton, RSAF 53-671, G-27-40. Stored.	04-92
❑ ZF581*	Lightning F.53	ex Warton, RSAF 53-675, G-27-45. Stored.	04-92
❑ ZF582*	Lightning F.53	ex Warton, RSAF 53-676, G-27-46. Stored.	04-92
❑ ZF585*	Lightning F.53	ex Warton, RSAF 53-683, G-27-53. Stored.	04-92
❑ ZF586*	Lightning F.53	ex Warton, RSAF 53-688, G-27-58. Stored.	04-92
❑ ZF587*	Lightning F.53	ex Warton, RSAF 53-691, G-27-61. Stored.	04-92
❑ ZF589*	Lightning F.53	ex Warton, RSAF 53-700, G-27-223. Stored.	04-92
❑ ZF590*	Lightning F.53	ex Warton, RSAF 53-679, G-27-49. Stored.	04-92
❑ ZF591*	Lightning F.53	ex Warton, RSAF 53-685, G-27-55. Stored.	04-92
❑ ZF592*	Lightning F.53	ex Warton, RSAF 53-686, G-AWON, G-27-56. Stored.	04-92
❑ ZF595*	Lightning T.55	ex Warton, RSAF 55-714, G-27-73. Stored.	04-92
❑ ZF596*	Lightning T.55	ex Warton, RSAF 55-715, G-27-71. Stored.	04-92
❑ ZF597*	Lightning T.55	ex Warton, RSAF 55-711, G-27-70. Stored.	04-92

WAVERTON (on the A41 south east of Chester)
At a farm in this locality, a former static test Tucano has turned up.
❑ * c/n S45-T42 Tucano T.1 ex Belfast Harbour. Static test airframe. 09-93

WILMSLOW
Meta-Sokol G-APVU moved to <u>Charnock Richard</u>, Lancs, by July 1992.

WINSFORD (on the A54 south of Northwich)
■ **Cheshire Fire Brigade Training School** : During June 1993 Macclesfield Historical Aviation Society acquired a Canberra T.4 nose section that had been used for a number of years for instruction.

It was moved to <u>Chelford</u>, Ches. In exchange, but coming from the direction of Firbeck, S Yorks, was a Cessna.

☐ G-AWFH*   Cessna F.150H   ex Firbeck, Netherthorpe. Crashed 16-12-79.
                                      Fuselage. Here by 12-93.   12-93

■ **Others** : Stored at a farm here is the hulk of a Musketeer.

☐ G-ASFB   Musketeer 23   crashed 23-5-81. Wreck.   04-91

Cleveland

STOCKTON-ON-TEES
Rallye 100T G-BIRB had turned up at <u>Moston</u>, Gtr Man, by December 1992, broaching the question, did it ever come here? The despatch date from Carlisle, Cumbria, (October 1991) is firm enough, but is this when it moved to Moston? Did someone mistake the phonetics of 'Stockton' for 'Stockport'?

TEES-SIDE AIRPORT (or Middleton St George)
It would not be a vintage **W&R** without 'moving' locations around the UK. This time is no exception and, having studied the postal address of the airport, it has been decided to move it lock, stock and barrel to Durham!

THORNABY-ON-TEES
Fewsdale Gyroplane G-ATLH was scrapped here during 1991.

Cornwall

BODMIN AERODROME (east of the A30, north of Bodmin)
Makes a re-entry into the realms of **W&R** with a stripped-out Cessna.

☐ G-BHJA*   Cessna A 152   ex N4954A. Damaged 21-7-90. Fuselage.
                                        First noted 7-92.   11-93

CALLINGTON (on the A390 south west of Tavistock)
A private house here should still boast a Lightning.

☐ XR755   Lightning F.6   ex Binbrook, 5, 5-11 pool.   06-89

CHACEWATER (east of the A30, north east of Redruth)
It is thought that the wreck situation here is unchanged.

☐ G-ARWY   Mooney M.20A   ex Bodmin, N1079B. CoA exp 6-8-80. Wreck.

☐ G-BTSC   Evans VP-2   CoA exp 18-7-84. *Spirit of Truro*. Stored.   05-93

CULDROSE AIRFIELD (on the A3083 south of Helston)
■ HMS *Sea Hawk* : The School of Aircraft Handling (SAH) has taken on more Hunter T.7s, despite having received Harriers earlier and another in September 1993. Harrier GR.3 XV783 moved to <u>Lee-on-Solent,</u> Hants, August 10, 1993. By May 1993, three airframes from here had gone to the fire school at <u>Predannack</u>, Cornwall : Canberra B(I).6 WT308; Wessex HU.5 XT481 and Phantom FG.1 XV588 nose. In early August 1993 two more airframes, Hunter T.7 XX466 and GA.11 XE668 also made the move to <u>Predannack</u>, Cornwall. Wasp HAS.1 XS538/A2725 arrived from Lee-on-Solent, Hants, on October 12, 1993, but moved on to <u>Predannack</u>, Cornwall, during late November 1993. By November 1993, Harrier GR.3 XV786 had adopted a split personality, with the nose remaining here for rescue training, and the remainder travelling to <u>Predannack</u>, Cornwall, for a more limited life. Three airframes have left, for destinations unknown : Wessex HAS.3 XM870 left by road on July 27, 1993; Wessex HU.5 XT760 during January 1993 and Kestrel FGA.1 XS695 on May 11, 1993 to <u>Lee-on-Solent</u>, Hants. Harrier GR.3 XV760 left by road for <u>Yeovilton</u>, Somerset, on

September 29, 1992. During September 1993, Hunter GA.11s WT711 and WW654 were offered for tender and acquired by the Portsmouth scrapman, Harry Pound. WW654 left on December 15, 1993 for Portsmouth, Hants. WT711 is thought to have been acquired from Pounds' by Ed Stead of Manchester, New Hampshire and was being dismantled during January 1994. WV267 left by road on January 13, 1994 bound for temporary transit through North Weald, Essex, and on to the USA, it is reported to have been acquired for £3,500. Former SAH Wessex HAS.1 XS877/A2687 joined the dump by June 1993 but moved to Predannack, Corn, on January 18, 1994. The Engineering Training School (ETS) also has a handful of airframes here.

Thanks to those stalwarts at *British Aviation Review*, the lid has come off the latest ground airframe numbering craziness. The simulator 'farm' here also 'grows' serials. A full-blown Sea King HAS.6 flight simulator (wholly synthetic and all-axis) has been allocated the serial ZF630. Tolerable, but the full flight crew procedure simulator and the *backseater* simulator have also been allocated serial numbers. These are substantial pieces of kit, but it is the *kit* that is the problem! Each of these *two* has no less than *three* serial numbers allocated, relating to the major avionics workstations within! (Respectively, ZF634, ZF635 & ZF636 and ZG461, ZG462 & ZG463. Another simulator, *possibly* at Prestwick, is *simultaneously* ZF631, ZF632 & ZF633 — another neat trick!) A Jetstream T.3 radar procedures trainer here (*possibly* 'production' Jetstream fuselage based) has also been allocated ZE402. At this stage, it is thought that all of these — and their split personalities — are synthetic (purpose-built simulators nothing to do with 'flight' airframes) and therefore beyond the scope of **W&R**, interesting/crazy though they may be!

☐ WF225	A2645	Sea Hawk F.1	ex FRU, 738, 802. Gate guard. 'CU'.	11-93
☐ WJ677*		Canberra B.2	ex Yeovilton, St Mawgan, 7, 231 OCU, 50, 40, 103. Nose. Arr 15-12-92. Fire pits.	12-92
☐ WT723*		Hunter PR.11	ex FRADU, Lossie SF, 14. Arr 19-3-93.	11-93
☐ WT804		Hunter GA.11	ex Shawbury, FRADU, Lossiemouth, 247. SAH. '831-DD'.	11-93
☐ WV372*		Hunter T.7	ex FRADU, 237 OCU, 208, Laarbruch SF, 4 FTS, RAE, 222. Flew in 19-3-93. '877-VL'.	11-93
☐ XF310*		Hunter T.7	ex FRADU, Laarbruch SF, 2 TWU, TWU, 58, 45, RN loan, MinTech, 20, Faireys, Hawkers. Flew in 25-3-93. '869-VL'.	11-93
☐ XL601*		Hunter T.7	ex FRADU, 237 OCU, 208, 237 OCU, 4 FTS, 229 OCU, 4 FTS,1, West Raynham SF, 1. Flew in 25-3-93. '874-VL'.	11-93
☐ XM328		Wessex HAS.3	ex Wroughton, 737. SAH.	11-93
☐ XP137		Wessex HAS.3	ex SAH, Lee-on-Solent, Wroughton, 737. 'CU'. With ETS by 6-93.	11-93
☐ XP158*	A2688	Wessex HAS.1	ex Lee-on-Solent, 737. '522-CU'. Arrived 15-12-92. ETS, but to the dump 6-93.	01-94
☐ XS866	A2705	Wessex HAS.1	ex Lee, Wroughton, 771. SAH. '520-CU'.	11-93
☐ XS876	A2695	Wessex HAS.1	ex Lee, Wroughton, 771. SAH. '523-CU'.	11-93
☐ XS885	A2668	Wessex HAS.1	ex 772. SAH. '12-CU'.	11-93
☐ XT762		Wessex HU.5	ex Lee-on-Solent, Wroughton, RAE. SAH.	11-93
☐ XV359*		Buccaneer S.2B	ex Lossiemouth, 208, 237 OCU, 12, 208, 12. Flew in 29-3-94. Crash rescue.	11-93
☐ XV669	A2659	Sea King HAS.1	ex Lee-on-Solent, 820. ETS. *Mr Walter*. Crashed 31-3-76. '10'.	11-93
☐ XV741		Harrier GR.3	ex Cosford, 233 OCU, 3, 233 OCU, 3. SAH. Thought to be bound for the gate.	11-93
☐ XV786		Harrier GR.3	ex St Athan, 3, 4, 1, 4. SAH. 'S'. Nose section only by 11-93 for rescue trg. See notes.	01-94
☐ XV806		Harrier GR.3	ex Cosford, 4, 3, 233 OCU. SAH. 'E'.	11-93
☐ XW891		Gazelle HT.2	ex 705. Cr 25-11-87. Pod. Dump. '49'.	11-91
☐ XW919		Harrier GR.3	ex Cosford, 4, 1, 233 OCU. SAH. 'W'.	11-93
☐ XZ996*		Harrier GR.3	ex 1417 Flt, 4, 1417 Flt, 233 OCU, 1417 Flt, 233 OCU. 'G'. First noted 11-93.	11-93
☐ ZD667*		Harrier GR.3	ex 1417 Flt, 233 OCU. '3B'. Flew in 30-7-93. SAH.	11-93

HELSTON

■ **Flambards Village Theme Park — Cornwall Aero Park:** A tale of further contraction of the airframes held at the park. On May 1, 1993, auction house Sotheby's included Buccaneer S.1 XN967, founder-member Sycamore HR.14 XJ917 and SE.5A replica 'F5459' in their sale of the Lamanva Military Vehicle collection at Falmouth, Cornwall. The *Brick* was reported to be moving to the motor museum at Donington Circuit, Leics, but the deal is thought to have fallen through. It was scrapped on site during January 1994, with the nose going to a collector while the rest went to a yard in Bodmin, Cornwall. Bearing in mind the date of the auction, Sycamore HR.14 XJ917 moved by road to Banwell, Avon, on April 30, 1993! Since then, the SE.5 has also moved on, destination unknown. Two helicopters were acquired by the North East Aircraft Museum at Sunderland, T&W :— Widgeon G-APTW and Whirlwind HAR.9 XN258. Sea Hawk FB.3 'WN105'/WF299 moved to Birlingham, H&W, by March 1993. Blackburn 1911 replica BAPC.130 moved to Stoke-on-Trent, Staffs, during June 1993. Also moved on, again with no 'forwarding addresses' are Demoiselle replica BAPC.116 and Blackburn 1911 replica BAPC.129.

◆ Open every day Easter to end of October 10am to 5pm. ✉ Flambards Village Theme Park, Clodgey Lane, Helston, Cornwall, TR13 0GA. Tel 0326 573404 or '574549. **Fax** 0326 573344.

☐	G-BDDX		Excalibur	only flight 1-7-76, built at Bodmin.	12-93
☐	WF122	A2673	Sea Prince T.1	ex Culdrose, 750, Sydenham SF, Arbroath SF, Lossiemouth SF, 700Z Flt, Lossie SF, FOFT, 750, Eglinton SF, 744. '575-CU'.	12-93
☐	WG511		Shackleton T.4	ex Colerne, St Mawgan, MOTU, Kinloss Wing, MOTU, 120, 42. Nose.	12-93
☐	'WG754'	WG725	Dragonfly HR.5	ex Southend, N9987Q, Middle Wallop, Odiham, Colerne, Weeton 7703M, RAE. '912-CU'.	12-93
☐	WK122		Canberra TT.18	ex Samlesbury, 7, 15, 61. '22'.	12-93
☐	WV106		Skyraider AEW.1	ex Culdrose, 849, Donibristle, Abbotsinch, USN 124086. '427 - C'. FAAM loan.	12-93
☐	XA870	A2543	Whirlwind HAS.1	ex Predannack, Lee-on-Solent, *Protector* Flt, 705, *Protector* Flt, 155, 848. Sectioned.	12-93
☐	XD332	A2574	Scimitar F.1	ex Culdrose SAH-19, Lee-on-Solent, 764B, 736, 807, 804. '194-C'.	12-93
☐	XE368	A2534	Sea Hawk FGA.6	ex Culdrose SAH-3, Shotley, 738, 806, 803, 899. '200-J'.	12-93
☐	XG691		Sea Ven FAW.22	ex Chilton Cantello, Yeovilton, FRU, 891, 894. '493-J'.	11-91
☐	XG831	A2539	Gannet ECM.6	ex Culdrose SAH-8, 831. '396'.	12-93
☐	XN647	A2610	Sea Vixen FAW.2	ex Culdrose SAH-10, 766, 899. '707-VL'.	12-93
☐	XP350		W'wind HAR.10	ex Chivenor, 22, 225.	12-93
☐	XS887	A2690	Wessex HAS.1	ex Culdrose, Wroughton, 771. '403-FI'.	12-93
☐	XT427		Wasp HAS.1	ex Yeovilton, Wroughton. '606'. FAAM loan.	12-93

LAND'S END

■ **Theme Park:** Suspended at a dramatic angle at the main entrance is a Bolkow 105. See under Bourn, Cambs, for a possible complication (or addition!) to its pedigree.

☐	'G-BOND'*		MBB Bo 105D	G-BCXO, ex D-HDCE. Cancelled as wfu 4-3-92. Pole mounted.	08-92

[The real G-BOND is a Sikorsky S-76A II Plus and flies with Bond in Scotland. G-BCXO was rebuilt with a new pod and flies on as G-THLS.]

LAND'S END AERODROME (or St Just, on the B3306 south of St Just)

The replica fuselage mentioned in **W&R13** was still to be seen into 1992 and was substantial — hence its inclusion in the listing below, could this be the Dr. I replica G-BVGZ for the Museum of Army Flying, Middle Wallop, Hants?

☐	G-ARZD		Cessna 175C	ex N1689Y. Crashed 28-5-77.. Wreck.	11-93
☐	G-AYMF		Airtourer	crashed 9-6-72. Wreck.	11-93
☐	G-AZTN		Airtourer	ex Exeter. Crashed 27-6-77. Wreck.	11-93

| ☐ G-BFNU | BN-2B-21 | CoA expired 18-8-89. Fuselage, stored. | 11-93 |
| ☐ '124' | -?- replica | fuselage, German markings. Stored. | 11-92 |

LELANT (on the A3074 south of St Ives)
Peter Channon's Swift is still stored in the area.

| ☐ G-ABTC | Comper Swift | CoA expired 18-7-84. *Spirit of Butler*. | 11-93 |

LISKEARD

◙ **Castle Motors** : Guarding the garage — the helipad of Castle Air is adjacent, correcting **W&R13** — in dramatic pose, is a Lightning.

| ☐ XS936 | Lightning F.6 | ex Binbrook, 5, LTF, 5, LTF, 5, 11, 23. | 11-93 |

LOWER TREMAR (near Liskeard)
A private collector here still has his Lightnings and Sycamore.

☐ XG544	Sycamore HR.14	ex Higher Blagdon, 32, MCS, 228, 275.	
☐ XR751	Lightning F.3	ex Binbrook, 11, LTF, 29, 226 OCU, EE.	
☐ XS919	Lightning F.6	ex Binbrook, 11, 5, 11, 5, 56, 11.	

PENZANCE HELIPORT (on the A30 east of Penzance)
The two stored WG.30s G-KATE and G-OGAS (plus the previously operational G-BKGD) had all moved to Yeovil, Somerset, by March 1993.

PREDANNACK AIRFIELD (off the A3083 south of Helston)

▉ **Fleet Air Arm Fire School** : Throughput of airframes here has increased considerably. A comprehensive inspection in May 1993 means that the following can be listed as 'perished' : — Lynx HAS.2 XZ249; Jet Provost T.3 XN635; Wasp HAS.1 XT441; Wessex HAS.1 XM841, XP107, XP149, XS125; Wessex HAS.3 XM331, XS119; Wessex HU.5 XT757; Whirlwind HAS.7 XL836, XL846, XM667, XN314; Whirlwind HAR.9 XL899.

☐ WF125	A2674	Sea Prince T.1	ex 750, Brawdy SF, 750, Lossiemouth SF, Brawdy SF, Yeovilton SF, Lossiemouth SF, 700Z Flt, 750. '576'.	05-93
☐ WT308*		Canberra B(I).6	ex Culdrose, DRA Farnborough, A&AEE. Arrived 1-10-92.	05-93
☐ XE668*		Hunter GA.11	ex Culdrose SAH, Yeovilton, FRADU, 738, 26, 4. '832-DD'. Arrived 11-8-93.	08-93
☐ XE712		Hunter GA.11	ex Lee-on-Solent, Shawbury, FRADU, 738, 43, 222. '708'.	05-93
☐ XM329	A2609	Wessex HAS.1	ex Lee-on-Solent, Arbroath, 771. '533-PO'.	05-93
☐ XM838		Wessex HAS.1	ex Lee-on-Solent, Wroughton, 737. '405'.	05-93
☐ XM868*	A2711	Wessex HAS.1	ex Lee-on-Solent, Wroughton, 737. '517'. Arrived 10-92.	05-93
☐ XM874*	A2689	Wessex HAS.1	ex Lee-on-Solent, Culdrose, Wroughton, 771. '521-CU'. Arrived 10-92.	05-93
☐ XN934	A2600	Buccaneer S.1	ex Culdrose, Lee-on-Solent, 736. '631'. Fuselage.	05-93
☐ XN953	A2655	Buccaneer S.1	ex Culdrose SAH-23, St Athan 8182M, Lossiemouth, 736.	05-93
☐ XP160*	A2650	Wessex HAS.1	ex Lee-on-Solent, Culdrose, SAH-24. '521-CU'. Arrived 10-92.	05-93
☐ XS538*	A2725	Wasp HAS.1	ex Culdrose, Lee-on-Solent, 829 *Lowestoft* Flt. '451' and 'FIR2'. Arrived 11-93.	11-93
☐ XS873	A2686	Wessex HAS.1	ex Lee-on-Solent, Wroughton, 771. '525-CU'. Poor state.	05-93
☐ XS877*	A2687	Wessex HAS.1	ex Culdrose, SAH, Wroughton, 771. Arrived 18-1-94.	01-94
☐ XT450		Wessex HU.5	ex 845. 'YV'. Poor state.	05-93
☐ XT481*		Wessex HU.5	ex Culdrose, Wroughton, 846. 'XF'. Arrived 17-11-92.	05-93

☐ XV588*		Phantom FG.1	ex Culdrose, Leuchars, 892. Crashed 18-5-77. Nose section . '007'. First noted 10-92.	05-93
☐ XV644*	A2664	Sea King HAS.1	ex Lee-on-Solent, Farnborough. Crashed 19-11-74. '664'. Arrived 28-10-92.	05-93
☐ XV786*		Harrier GR.3	ex St Athan, 3, 4, 1, 4. SAH. 'S'. Noseless hulk. Arrived by 11-93. [Nose at Culdrose, Cornwall.]	11-93
☐ XX466*		Hunter T.7	ex Culdrose SAH, Shawbury, FRADU, 1 TWU, Jordan AF, R Saudi AF 70-616, HSA, XL620, 74, 66. SAH. '830-DD'. Arrived 10-8-93.	08-93

ST AUSTELL
A scrap dealer here took on the Short SC-9 and Nimrod from St Mawgan, Corn, during 1992. The Nimrod (MR.2 XV237) was too sectioned and fragmented to consider as having a 'forwarding address' here, but the dealer has high hopes for the retail value of the forward fuselage of the SC-9. Hope springs eternal...

☐ XH132*	8915M	Short SC-9	ex St Athan, RAE Bedford. See notes above.	03-94

ST MAWGAN AIRFIELD (off the A3059, north east of Newquay)
■ **RAF St Mawgan** : With the Nimrods having migrated north, thankfully the base remains active as the home of the Sea King Training Flight and frequent maritime exercises. Short SC-9 XH132 was broken up on May 19, 1992 — what a crying shame. The hulk of Nimrod MR.2 XV237 had gone, assumed scrapped, by August 1992. Both moved to a yard near <u>St Austell</u>, Corn. Victor K.2 XL190 flew in on October 19, 1993 as a new candidate for the dump.

☐ WL756	9101M	Shackleton AEW.2	ex 8, 204, 205, 37, 38. Dump.	08-91
☐ WL795	8753M	Shackleton AEW.2	ex 8, 205, 38, 204, 210, 269, 204. MR.2 guise on gate. 'T'.	11-93
☐ XL190*	9216M	Victor K.2	ex 55, 232 OCU, Witt Wing, 139. Flew in 19-10-93. For the dump.	10-93

ST MERRYN AERODROME (on the B3276 west of Padstow)
The airfield remains a haven for *gyronuts* and two examples are to found in the **W&R** category. Stampe SV-4A G-STMP moved to <u>Ivybridge</u>, Devon, by May 1993.

☐ G-ARTZ {2}		McCandless M4	Stored. CoA expired 13.10.69. [Second aircraft with these marks, see Cultra Manor, Northern Ireland.]	05-91
☐ G-AWIF*		Mosquito gyro	ex Husbands Bosworth, Shipdham, Tattershall Thorpe, Clitheroe. CoA expired 7-1-82. First noted 5-93.	05-93
☐ G-MLAS		Cessna 182E	ex Bodmin, OO-HPE, D-EGPE, N2826Y. Damaged 14-12-80. Para-trainer.	08-92

Cumbria

CARK AERODROME (south west of Grange-over-Sands)
An extensive search here during May 1993 failed to find any trace of the para-trainer Cessna F.172H G-AWMZ. Fate?

CARLISLE (Kingstown, on the A7 north of the City)
■ **RAF Carlisle** : Hunter F.1 WT660 left for <u>New Byth</u>, Grampian, on July 9, 1992. The base is scheduled for closure in the near future.

☐ XT255	8751M	Wessex HAS.3	ex ETPS. Fire/crash rescue.	11-93
☐ XV406	9098M	Phantom FGR.2	ex St Athan, 29, 23, 111, HSA, A&AEE, HSA. 'CK'. Gate.	11-93

■ **Others** : The much-travelled nose of Comet C.2R XK655 moved again, this time to <u>Maryport</u>, Cumbria, by July 1992. A Luscombe has arrived to lick its wounds.

☐ G-AKTT*   Luscombe 8A   ex N71852, NC71852. Crashed 6-7-91.   11-93

CARLISLE AIRPORT (or Crosby-on-Eden, off the B6264 east of Carlisle)

■ **Solway Aviation Society** (SAS) : Fund raising towards permanent display facilities continue. An addition to the fleet is Whirlwind HAR.21 WV198 on loan. This will be restored to 848 Squadron colours from the Operation *Firedog* era. SAS's Chairman is David Price, who is restoring the nose of Comet C.2R XK655 — see under Maryport, Cumbria. SAS have a close relationship with Tom Stoddart, who owns Vulcan XJ823 — see below for Tom's latest project.

◆ The aircraft are open to inspection on Sundays 2pm to 4pm, other times, by prior arrangement..

✉ Paul Wiggins, Solway Aviation Society Ltd, c/o Carlisle Airport, Crosby-on-Eden, Carlisle, Cumbria, CA6 4NW.

☐ WE188		Canberra T.4	ex Samlesbury, 231 OCU, 360, 231 OCU, 360, 100, 56, 231 OCU, Upwood SF, 231 OCU, Upwood SF, Waddington SF, Hemswell SF. 11-93
☐ WS832		Meteor NF.14	ex RRE Pershore, Llanbedr, 12 MU, 8 MU. 11-93
☐ WV198*	G-BJWY	W'wind HAR.21	ex Firbeck, Warmingham, Chorley, Blackpool Airport, Heysham, Carnforth, Gosport, Lee-on-Solent A2576, Arbroath, 781, 848, USN 130191. Loan Dave Charles. Arrived 13-11-92. 11-93
☐ WZ515		Vampire T.11	ex Duxford, Staverton, Woodford, Chester, St Athan, 4 FTS, 8 FTS, 56, 253, 16. '60'. 11-93
☐ XJ823		Vulcan B.2	ex 50, Wadd Wing, 35, 27, 9/35, Wadd Wing, 230 OCU, MoA. Owned by Tom Stoddart. 11-93
☐ ZF583		Lightning F.53	ex Warton, RSaudiAF 53-681, G-27-51. 11-93

■ **Others** : Two Cubs and a Chipmunk arrived from Glasgow Airport during 1993 for restoration by Cormack Air Services. Tom Stoddart has acquired the former Preston, Humb, Sea Prince and intends to restore it to airworthy condition. Relating to this entry in **W&R13** and the removal of Rallye G-BIRB to 'Stockton-on-Tees', Cleveland — see under that heading for a further complication! A cache of Tomahawks arrived by September 1993, one flyer is expected to emerge from this. The Gannet remains stored but Moth Minor G-AFPN was flying again during 1992.

☐ G-BAYY		Cessna 310C	ex Hinton-in-the-Hedges, N1782H. CoA expired 6-12-85. Dump. 11-93
☐ G-BGZE*		Tomahawk 112	ex Tees-Side, Tattershall Thorpe, Breighton. Damaged 16-10-87. Cockpit. Arr by 9-93. 11-93
☐ G-BGZH*		Tomahawk 112	ex Tees-side, Tattershall Thorpe, Breighton. Damaged 16-10-87. Cockpit. Arr by 9-93. 11-93
☐ G-BNGS*		Tomahawk 112	ex Tees-side, Carlisle, N2463A. Damaged 5-87. For restoration. Arrived by 9-93. 11-93
☐ G-CCUB*		J3C-65 Cub	ex Glasgow, N33528, NC33528. Arrived 23-4-93 for restoration. 11-93
☐ N5073E*	G-APPA	Chipmunk 22	ex Glasgow, WP917, Glas UAS, 11 RFS, 8 RFS. Arrived 23-4-93 for restoration. 11-93
☐ NC25793*		J3C Cub	ex Glasgow, USA. For restoration. First noted 5-93. 11-93
☐ WP314*	8634M	Sea Prince T.1	ex Preston, Hull, Syerston, Halton, Kemble, 750, Sydenham SF, 750, Lossiemouth SF, Shorts FU, Brawdy SF, Lossie SF, 750. '573-CU'. Arrived 2-94. For restoration. See above. 02-94
☐ XL502	G-BMYP	Gannet AEW.3	ex Leuchars 8610M, 849, MinTech Pershore, 849. CoA expired 29-9-89. Stored. 11-93

HAVERIGG (south of Millom)

■ **RAF Millom Museum Project** : Run by the South Copeland Aviation Group in co-operation with the HM Prison Service, this small, but flourishing, airfield museum is located adjacent to HMP Haverigg, both on the site of the former RAF Millom. A wide array of exhibits devoted to the airfield have been collected, including items salvaged from the waters surrounding the airfield. Hopefully, the premises — original RAF Millom buildings — will be expanded during 1994. SCAG took delivery of *Flea* BAPC.231 from Torver, Cumbria, on March 12, 1994 and restoration is underway *inside* the prison — the *Flea* is consequently *not* available for viewing!

◆ On the Bankhead Estate, North Lane, Haverigg, adjacent to HMP Haverigg. Open every Sunday afternoon from 12.30pm to 5.30pm April to early September. Other times by prior arrangement. ✉ South Copeland Aviation Group, c/o John Nixon, RAF Millom Museum Project, HMP Haverigg, Millom, Cumbria, LA18 4NA.

☐	*	BAPC.231 HM.14 *Flea*	ex Torver, Ulverston. Arrived 12-3-94. For restoration. See notes above.	03-94

MARYPORT (on the A596 north of Workington)

■ **David Price** : By July 1992, the Comet nose section had settled here. David is also Chairman of SAS at Carlisle Airport, *qv*.

☐	XK655*	Comet C.2R	ex Carlisle, Lutterworth, Strathallan, 51, BOAC, G-AMXA. Nose. First noted 7-92. 11-93

SPADEADAM (north of the B6318, north east of Carlisle)

■ **RAF Ranges** : As with other ranges mentioned in this edition, little in the way of new material to report here. The site is split into two areas : — the Electronic Warfare Site where all of the aggression is of the 'virtual reality' style and the full-blown weapons range, where targets really face the 'sharp end'. The latter is, naturally, remote from the public gaze, so assessing what survives there is problematical. Local 'word on the streets' is that by June 1993 one of the T-33As had disappeared and that this was either FT-02, FT-06 or FT-10. From this the safest deduction is that six out of seven could be seen! (Going back further into the range's history, Gnat T.1s XP506 and XP537 were allocated here from Valley on March 23, 1978 and Gnat T.1 XP500 was allocated here from St Athan the same date. XP500 and XP537 both moved on to Sennybridge, Powys.)

☐	XN387	8564M	Whirlwind HAR.9	ex Odiham, Wroughton, Lee-on-Solent SAR Flt, Lossiemouth SF, 846, 719. 06-93
☐	FT-01		T-33A-1-LO	ex Prestwick, Belgian AF, 51-4041. Range target. See notes above. 05-90
☐	FT-02		T-33A-1-LO	ex Prestwick, Belgian AF, 51-4043. See notes.
☐	FT-06		T-33A-1-LO	ex Prestwick, Belgian AF, Neth AF M-44, 51-4231. See notes above.
☐	FT-07		T-33A-1-LO	ex Prestwick, Belgian AF, Neth AF M-45, 51-4233. See notes above.
☐	FT-10		T-33A-1-LO	ex Prestwick, Belgian AF, 51-6664. See notes.
☐	FT-11		T-33A-1-LO	ex Prestwick, Belgian AF, Neth AF M-47, 51-6661. See notes above.
☐	FT-29		T-33A-1-LO	ex Prestwick, Belgian AF, 53-5753. Range target. See notes above. 05-90
☐	61		Mystere IVA	ex Sculthorpe, FAF. 06-93
☐	64		Mystere IVA	ex Sculthorpe, FAF. 06-93
☐	81		Mystere IVA	ex Sculthorpe, FAF. 06-93
☐	139		Mystere IVA	ex Sculthorpe, FAF. 06-93
☐	180		Mystere IVA	ex Sculthorpe, FAF. 06-93
☐			Mystere IVA	} likely to be 06-93
☐			Mystere IVA	} No 184, 207, 262, 06-93
☐			Mystere IVA	} but unconfirmed. 06-93

TORVER

A more precise location can be given for the Pennington *Flea* in this edition. On March 12, 1994, thanks to the kindness of Mrs Doreen Pennington, BAPC.231 made the short journey to <u>Haverigg</u>, Cumb. The move was an excellent example of co-operation, with the Dumfries & Galloway Aviation Group providing the motive power, the *Flying Flea* Archive 'rediscovering' the craft and sorting out the loan details, and the South Copeland Aviation Group for undertaking the restoration.

WINDERMERE

■ **Windermere Steamboat Museum** : Houses the Falcon water-glider — it celebrated its 50th anniversary during February 1993.

◆ Open Easter to October, Mon-Sat 10am to 6pm and 2pm to 6pm on Sundays. ✉ WSM, Rayrigg Road, Windermere, Cumbria, LA23 1BN. ☎ 096 62 5565.

☐ BGA.266   T.1 Falcon   Modified by T C Pattison 1943.   08-93

■ **Locally:** See under Torver above for details of the Pennington *Flea*.

Derbyshire

BUXTON

Confirmation of the continued existence of the Fauvel flying wing glider would be appreciated.

☐ DCB   BGA.1999 Fauvel AV.36CR   ex RNGSA, F-CBSH. Stored.   03-88

DERBY

■ **Derby Industrial Museum** : The Museum has a staggering array of aero engines (mainly Rolls-Royce) going from the Eagle to the RB.211 and is a must to visit. The phenomenal Rolls-Royce gallery will undergo redevelopment during 1994.

◆ Open Monday-Saturday 11am to 5pm, Sundays and Bank Holidays 2pm to 5pm. ✉ Silk Mill Lane, off Full Street, Derby, DE1 3AR. ☎ : 0332 255308.

          Two other BAPC member groups can be listed under this heading : —

■ **Derbyshire Historical Aviation Society** : Works in support of the Museum and stages regular meetings at the venue.

✉ Peter Kirk, 263 Birchover Way, Allestree, Derby, DE22 2RS.

■ **Rolls-Royce Heritage Trust, Derby Branch** : Unlike the other two Branches listed in **W&R** (Bristol and Coventry), Derby does not have its own collection of aero engines as such — as many of them are on show at the Museum.

✉ Laurie Fletcher, 40 Quarn Drive, Allestree, Derby, DE22 2NQ.

HADFIELD (on the A628 east of Manchester)

■ **Military Aircraft Preservation Group** (MAPG) : Continued problems with the site at Hadfield led MAPG to move their artefacts and airframes to (the pods of Vampire T.11 XD534 and T.55 333.) Chelford, Cheshire, by July 1992 in a co-operative effort with the Macclesfield Historical Aviation Society.

MICKLEOVER

The restoration of Auster G-AIBR will give it a Gipsy Major 10, making it effectively a J/1S.

☐ G-AIBR   J/1 Autocrat   ex Cranfield, Bushey, Duxford, Sywell,
                                              Gamston. Crashed 5-9-70. Restoration.   04-91

RIPLEY

■ **Anchor Surplus** : In Peasehill Road, a Vampire and an armoured car tempt passers by inside.

☐ XD382   8033M   Vampire T.11   ex Shawbury, Syerston, CATCS, CNCS,
                                              RAFC, 5 FTS, 206 AFS, 208 AFS.   03-92

SHARDLOW (on the A6 south east of Derby)

The gyroplane is thought still stored here.

☐ G-ATGZ   Griffiths GH.4   stored. Unflown.   07-91

WILLINGTON (on the A5132 south of Derby)

■ **Derby World War Two Avionics Museum** : Colin Baker's growing collection of electronics, radio and radar gear gained a whole airframe during late 1992 with the acquisition of Meteor T.7 WA662 in kit-of-parts form from Martin Baker. It is currently stored within the grounds of the power station. Plans for a site for the collection are underway. At present visits to the aircraft are not possible. The collection also held the centre section of a Barracuda, acquired from Whernside, but this has moved on to the FAAM at Yeovilton, Som, to act as a source of spares for their project.

✉ Colin Baker, 16, Wroxham Close, Shelton Lock, Derby, DE24 9DW.

☐ WA662*		Meteor T.7	ex Chalgrove, Llanbedr, Farnborough, FCCS, 3, Wildenrath SF, Gutersloh SF, 3. Stored.	12-93

Devon

CHIVENOR AIRFIELD (on the A361 south of Braunton)

■ **RAF Chivenor** : The base will be put into Care & Maintenance from October 1995, when all flying training on Hawks will be done from Valley, Gwynedd. No 22 Squadron 'A' Flight will remains and will take on Sea Kings, so a RAF presence will remain here. Whirlwind HAR.10 XD186/8730M was put up for tender during September 1993 and removed by road on December 15, 1993 — thought exported. Canberra TT.18 WJ629/8747M was removed by lorry on March 9. 1994 — destination unknown..

☐ XF509	8708M	Hunter F.6A	ex Thurleigh, 4 FTS, MoA, AFDS, 54. Gate.	02-94
☐ XN632	8352M	Jet Provost T.3	ex St Athan, Kemble, Shawbury, 3 FTS. Dump.	02-94
☐ XX257*		Hawk T.1	ex Halton, CFS. Ditched 31-7-84. Fuselage. Arrived 8-5-87.	02-94

CHUDLEIGH (east of the A38, south west of Exeter)
The motor museum gave up Bird Gyrocopter G-AXIY. It went to "Wales". That narrows it down!

CREDITON
A scrap dealer here was successful in tendering for all of the BDR airframes at Upper Heyford, Oxon. The hulks arrived here by March 1994.

☐ 36*	Mystere IVA	ex Upper Heyford, Chateaudun, French AF. Once EABDR.8.	03-94
☐ 46*	Mystere IVA	ex Upper Heyford, Chateaudun, French AF. *Assumed* once EABDR.9.	03-94
☐ 127*	Mystere IVA	ex Upper Heyford, Sculthorpe, Chateaudun, French AF. Once EABDR.7.	03-94
☐ 129*	Mystere IVA	ex Upper Heyford, Sculthorpe, Chateaudun, French AF. Once EABDR.6.	03-94
☐ 63-7449*	F-4C-17-MC	ex Upper Heyford, 182 TFS, Texas ANG. '05'.	03-94

DUNKESWELL AERODROME (north of Honiton)
The Vampire and Turbulent continue to uphold the **W&R** front here.

☐ G-ASSY	Turbulent	ex Redhill. Damaged 8-5-83. Restoration.		01-92
☐ XE982	7564M	Vampire T.11	ex Hereford, St Athan, RAFC.	01-92

EAGLESCOTT AERODROME (west of the A377, north of Ashreigney)
Further changes within the **W&R** population here to record. A wrecked Tomahawk fuselage had arrived by July 1992, by which date Currie Wot G-ARZW had moved on. The forward fuselage (at least) of Grob G.109B G-ROBB had moved to <u>Nympsfield</u>, Glos, by June 1991. Cessna F.150L G-BMXJ had moved off site by January 1993, but will remain listed under this heading.

☐ G-AJCP (2)		Turbulent	CoA expired 4-9-78. Stored.	11-93
☐ G-BMXJ	F-BUBA	Cessna F.150L	ex Haverfordwest, Tredegar. Fuselage. Moved off site 1-93.	01-93
☐ N24730*		Tomahawk	fuselage. Stored. First noted 7-92.	07-93
☐ WT867		Cadet TX.3	ex Syerston, 626 VGS. Stored.	11-93
☐ XA289		Cadet TX.3	ex Syerston, 636 VGS. Stored.	11-93

EXETER

The late Bertram Arden's famous cache of aircraft is still stored in the general area.

☐ G-AALP	Surrey AL.1	CoA expired 17-5-40. Stored.	04-92
☐ G-AFGC	BA Swallow II	ex BK893, GTS, CLE, RAE, G-AFGC. CoA expired 20-3-51. Stored.	04-92
☐ G-AFHC	BA Swallow II	CoA expired 20-3-51. Stored.	04-92

EXETER AIRPORT (on the A30, east of the city at Clyst Honiton)

The 'mini-Mojave' that developed here is distinctly on the wane — so perhaps there are 'green shoots' out there after all. Departures have been as follows (those marked * being in-and-out since **W&R13**) :— Short 330-100 G-BEEO became VP-LVR by July 1992; HS.748-2A G-BGMO was flying again by May 1993; HS.748-2A G-BGMN* left during October 1992 for Singapore; Short 330-100 G-BITW joined Celtic Airways early in 1992; Short SD.330-100 G-BJFK became 4X-CSP; Short 330-100 G-BJLK joined Celtic Airways by early 1992; Short 330-100 G-BKMU* became EI-EXP during August 1992; Short 330-100 G-BNYA joined Streamline Aviation (hardly a good title for a *Shoebox* operator!) by February 1993; HS.748-2A G-BPDA joined Janes Aviation, 1993; Short 360-100 G-BPFS* joined BA Express by October 1993; Short 360-100 G-CPTL became G-ZAPG of Titan by May 1993; HS.748-2A G-JHLN became C-GTAD during 1992; Short 360-100 G-OEEC joined BA Express by October 1993; Short 360-100 G-OLBA was sold in Germany February 1993; Short 360-100 G-OLGW became G-ZAPD of Titan during August 1992; Short 360-100 G-OLTN became G-ZAPF by May 1993. An auction of somewhat 'poorly' aircraft was staged here on August 20, 1993. This included Navajo Chieftain G-GTAX, see below. See *Appendix D* for what scant details are available.

☐ G-AHAT	J/1N Alpha	ex Taunton, Old Sarum, HB-EOK ntu. Crashed 31-8-74. Stored.	
☐ G-AYTC	Aztec 250C	ex E Midlands, 5Y-ABL, 5X-UUZ, 5Y-ABL. CoA expired 16-11-79. Spares.	
☐ G-BASU	Navajo 350	ex E Budleigh, N7693L. Cr 12-5-87. Dump.	11-93
☐ G-BJUK	Short 330-100	ex Gill Aviation, G-OCAS, G-BJUK. CoA expired 9-4-90. Stored.	12-93
☐ G-BMLZ*	Cessna 421C	ex G-OTAD, G-BEVL, N5476G. CoA expired 14-2-89. Stored. First noted 5-93.	05-93
☐ G-BNTX	Short 330-100	ex Fairflight, G-BKDN. CoA exp 2-6-90.	12-93
☐ G-BNTY*	Short 330-100	ex Fairflight, G-BKDO. CoA expired 15-5-90. Stored. First noted 7-92.	12-93
☐ G-BORM	HS.748-2B	ex RP-C1043, V2-LAA, VP-LAA, 9Y-TDH. To fire crews by mid-1992.	11-93
☐ G-GTAX*	Navajo 350	ex G-OIAS, OY-CBF, D-IGSA, N54322. CoA expired 25-5-89. First noted 5-93. Stored. See notes above.	05-93

■ **Lightning Flying Club** (LFC) : The two Lightnings that flew in on December 23, 1992 were early Christmas presents for Barry Pover and the Lightning Flying Club. Both are kept in a purpose-built hangar and are being maintained in airworthy condition — see under Plymouth City Airport, Devon. It will be one of these that should join the UK show circuit in 1994. The two Hunters are to act as continuation trainers and chase planes. *Golf Hotel* should be flying by mid-1994.

☐ XL573*	G-BVGH	Hunter T.7	ex Shawbury, 237 OCU, Laarbruch SF, 237 OCU, 4 FTS, 229 OCU, FCS. Arrived by 12-93. See notes above.	12-93
☐ XL613*		Hunter T.7A	ex Shawbury, 237 OCU, Laarbruch SF, 237 OCU, 4 FTS, 45, 8, 208, 1417F, 8 1417F, 8, 208, 8. See notes above.	12-93
☐ XP693*	G-FSIX	Lightning F.6	ex BAe, A&AEE. Flew in 23-12-92. LFC.	05-93
☐ XR773*	G-OPIB	Lightning F.6	ex BAe, 5, LTF, 11, LTF, 5-11 pool, LTF, 5, 11, 5, 56, 74. 'BR'. Flew in 23-12-92. LFC.	05-93

HIGHER BLAGDON

■ **Torbay Aircraft Museum** : After spending much time and effort in an attempt to find a 'new' home for his collection, Keith Fordyce, announced in August 1993 that the massive collection of artefacts would be disposed of and a new 'home' was to be established through the good offices of the BAPC. Fa 330A-1 100545 moved to Yeovilton, Somerset, on May 19, 1992. The nose of Sea Hawk FGA.4 WV843 moved to Salisbury, Wilts, during March 1994.

IVYBRIDGE (on the A38 east of Plymouth)

During May 1993 the former St Merryn Stampe arrived in the locality for restoration.

☐ G-STMP*	SNCAN SV-4A	ex St Merryn, F-BCKB. Restn. Arr 5-93.		05-93

MANADON (near Plymouth)

■ **HMS *Thunderer* - Royal Navy Engineering College** (RNEC) : Wessex HU.5 XT760 stayed but briefly, moving on to Culdrose, Cornwall, by January 1993. Referring back to **W&R13**, the cockpit section of Whirlwind HAS.7 XL879, is reported to have been burnt at the 1990 open day!

☐ XF321		Hunter T.7	ex RAE, 56, 130.	07-91
☐ XP984	A2658	Hawker P.1127	ex RAE Bedford.	07-91
☐ XS122	A2707	Wessex HAS.3	ex Wroughton, 737. '655-PO'.	07-91
☐ XV625		Wasp HAS.1	ex 815. '471'.	07-91
☐ XW839		Lynx 00-05	ex Rolls-Royce, Filton.	07-91
☐ XZ969		Harrier GR.3	ex St Athan, 4, 1, 3. 'D'.	06-91

PLYMOUTH CITY AIRPORT (or Roborough, on the A386 north of Plymouth)

■ **Lightning Flying Club** (LFC) : Barry Pover and team continue to make excellent progress towards the goal of putting a Lightning back into the air. There are *no* engineering hurdles remaining, all obstacles being of the 'paper' variety, and these are dimishing rapidly. Joining G-LTNG at Plymouth has been a former Rossington F.6 nose which is used as a travelling demonstrator. Meanwhile, December 1992 saw the 'second force' drop into Exeter Airport, Devon. One of the single-seaters will beat G-LTNG back into the air. *November Golf* should fly before the end of 1994. The prospect of not just one, but a couple of the breed back in the air is wonderful!

♦ Visits by prior arrangement only. ✉ Lightning Flying Club, Plymouth City Airport, Crownhill, Plymouth, Devon PL6 8BW.

☐ XR747*		Lightning F.6	ex Rossington, Binbrook, 5, 11, 5, 11, 5, 111, 23. 'TVI747'. Nose. Arr 5-6-92. See notes.	12-93
☐ XS451	G-LTNG	Lightning T.5	ex Cranfield, Newton 8503M, St Athan, Binbrook, LTF, 11, 226 OCU, 5, AFDS. Restoration.	12-93

Dorset

BLANDFORD FORUM

Unless a physical sighting is made of the Nord reported to be under rebuild in the area, it looks set to be on finals for the *LOST!* section in **W&R15**.

☐ G-BIUP	NC.854S	ex Henstridge, (G-AMPE), G-BIUP, F-BFSC. CoA expired 24-4-84.	

BOURNEMOUTH

■ **Bill Hamblen** : This *private* collection is thought unchanged since the last edition.

☐ G-AJPZ	J/1 Autocrat	ex Wimborne, New Milton, Thruxton, F-BFPE, G-AJPZ. Damaged.	12-93
☐ 5Y-AYR	Britannia 307F	ex Bournemouth Airport, Air Faisel, G-ANCD, Gemini, Lloyd, BUA, Air Charter, El Al 4X-AGE, (N6595C), G-ANCD, G-18-3. Nose.	12-93
☐ FX442	Harvard II	ex Sandhurst, Avex, 501, 226 OCU, 203 AFS, 61 OTU. Restoration.	12-93

| ☐ | KF488 | Harvard II | ex Wimborne, Sandhurst, Avex. Cockpit. | 12-93 |
| ☐ | | Harvard II | ex Sandhurst. Frame. | 12-93 |

■ **Martin Emery** : Morava G-ASFD settled upon <u>Chessington</u>, Gtr Lon, for its rebuild.

BOURNEMOUTH AIRPORT (or Hurn, west of the A338, north of the city)
■ **Airport** : The influx of former British Airways One-Elevens, and the complexities thereof, is best treated as a separate entry — see under 'Airliner Store' below. Of the light aircraft inmates, Cessna 182F G-ASLH, described in **W&R13** as possibly having been scrapped, was much more fortunate and moved to revived <u>Old Sarum</u>, Wilts, by May 1992. Hurricane replica 'V7767'/BAPC.72 moved to <u>Sopley</u>, Hants, during July 1993. Cessna FR.172G G-AYJW was flying again by 1991. The hulk of Cessna 150G G-BRTC left by road during early 1993, destination unknown. Boeing 727-30 flew out in early 1993. Derek Johnson is restoring Hunter F.51 E-402 to static condition, it will revert to Royal Danish Air Force colours. That makes the current situation :—

☐	G-ATDS	Herald 209	ex Channel Express, 4X-AHT, G-ATDS. CoA expired 19-4-91. To the fire dump 15-2-93.	12-93
☐	G-AYEY	Cessna F.150K	damaged 24-6-88. Stored.	06-92
☐	G-AYMG*	Herald 213	ex Channel Express, D-BEBE. Last flight 7-7-92. Spares use.	12-93
☐	G-AYUW	BAC 111-476FM	ex Luton, Faucett OB-R-953, BAC G-AYUW, G-16-17. Fuselage, sprinkler system trials.	09-92
☐	G-BTER*	Cessna 150J	ex N60713. Wreck. Arrived by road 6-7-93. Fire crews.	12-93
☐	G-HPVC*	Partenavia P.68	ex OH-PVC. Engine fire 9-5-92. Stored.	12-93
☐	G-OCBA*	HS.125-3B	ex G-MRFB, G-AZVS, OY-DKP. Flew in 1-3-92. Stored.	12-93
☐	5N-AOG*	HS.125-3B/RA	ex G-AVXK. Arrived by road 16-6-93. Spares use.	12-93
☐	E-402	Hunter F.51	ex Lovaux - Bournemouth, Macclesfield, Dunsfold, G-9-433, Aalborg, Danish AF *Esk*.724. Restoration. See notes above.	11-93
☐	1190	Bf 109E	ex Buckfastleigh, Canada, II/JG.26. Force-landed Sussex 9-9-40. Stored.	12-93

■ **Airliner Store** : Hurn became the chosen site for storage of the former BA Series 510EDs. Initial hopes that they would be sold in Africa — partly at least — were dashed and instead they were sold on to European Aviation at <u>Filton</u>, Avon, although they may well find themselves staying there for a long time. Cambridge is another destination for further storage.

Transitory examples have been as follows, with arrival and departure dates (all to Filton unless noted) :— G-AVMH 24-11-92 — 25-6-93; G-AVMI 18-11-92 — 1-7-93; G-AVMJ 13-1-92 — 25-5-93; G-AVMK 4-12-92 — 3-6-93; G-AVML 13-1-92 — 13-5-93; G-AVMM 13-1-92 — 25-5-93; G-AVMN 10-8-92 to <u>Cambridge</u>, Cambs, 11-8-93; G-AVMO 29-12-92 to <u>Cosford</u>, Salop, 22-3-93; G-AVMR 13-1-92 — 25-5-93; G-AVMT 1-10-92 — 1-7-93; G-AVMU 29-10-92, to <u>Duxford</u>, Cambs, 4-3-93; G-AVMW 1-8-92 to <u>Cambridge</u>, Cambs, 11-8-93; G-AVMW 30-12-92 — 3-6-93; G-AVMX 13-1-92 — 13-5-93; G-AVMY 13-1-92 — 13-5-93; G-AVMZ 4-11-91 — 13-5-93.

Another long-term One-Eleven was Series 410AK HZ-MAA which arrived 20-12-89. It left 15-6-93 as HZ-ABM2. Also staying long enough in store to merit inclusion in **W&R** were the former Aer Lingus Shorts 360s all of which eventually went to Gill Air :— EI-BEL arrived 17-6-91, left as G-SBAC 5-2-92; EI-BPD arrived 28-8-91, left as G-RMCT 26-11-92; EI-BSP arrived 15-7-91, left as G-UBAC 15-4-93; EI-BVM arrived 28-8-91, left as G-TBAC 2-10-92.

☐	G-AVMP*	BAC 111-510ED	ex BA, BEA. Flew in 9-10-92. Stored.	12-93
☐	G-AXLL*	BAC 111-523FJ	ex BA, OB-R1173, OB-R1137, PP-SDT, G-AXLL, G-16-8. Flew in 1-12-92. Stored. Fuselage to go to a fire school in the Midlands.	12-93
☐	G-AYOP*	BAC 111-530FX	ex BA. Flew in 9-10-92. Stored.	12-93
☐	G-AZMF*	BAC 111-530FX	ex BA, 7Q-YKJ, G-AZF, PT-TYY, G-AZMF. Flew in 31-12-92. Stored.	12-93

■ **Jet Heritage Ltd** (JHL) / **Hunter Wing Ltd** (HWL) : JHL continue to operate in the forefront of the UK's jet 'warbird' world with restoration work continuing and their active aircraft being seen at several displays, including the 50th anniversary of the first flight of the Gloster Meteor and DH Vampire prototypes, held at Staverton and Hurn respectively.

The market for such aircraft has been naturally depressed and accordingly JHL/HWL aircraft have featured in several sales since **W&R13**. JHL and HWL entered the following aircraft into Sotheby's Billingshurst auction of September 19, 1992 : Provost T.1 G-AWVF (flies from Goodwood) £15,000; Sea Hawk FGA.4 WV795 £2,000; Jet Provost T.52A G-JETP £69,000; Hunter T.7 G-BOOM £70,000; Gnat T.1 G-NAAT £10,000. Only G-JETP sold, as noted below. WV795 sold later, going yet again to Savvas Constantinides, but has yet to move. The following year, another attempt was made to go 'under the hammer' again at Billingshurst and again with Sotheby's, on November 27, 1993. Entered were the following, with high bids indicated :— Gnat T.1 G-NAAT £4,200, Provost T.1 G-AWVF £24,000, Hunter F.4 G-HHUN £55,000, Hunter T.53 G-BOOM £130,000. Only G-BOOM sold, and was due to relocate to North Weald, Essex, during 1994.

Departures have been as follows : the nose section of Hunter T.8C WT745/8893M was acquired by Ed Stead of Manchester, New Hampshire, USA, the remainder was scrapped; as noted above, Jet Provost T.52A G-JETP was sold to Savvas Constantinides of Cyprus at auction September 19, 1992, and departed on May 27, 1993; fellow *JP* T.52A G-PROV was sold to a new owner and it flew off to its new home, Leavesden, March 12, 1993. (Only to be displaced with the closure of Leavesden in the spring of 1994, when it moved to <u>North Weald</u>, Essex.) On January 21, 1994 Hunter F.4 (but now with F.6 type tail parachute mods) made its first flight post restoration. JHL also helped to handle Whirlwind HAS.7 XN385, previously held at Wroughton, Wilts, also bought by Savvas Constantinides. It came through Hurn during March 1993 bound eventually for Cyprus. F-86A Sabre 8178/G-SABR made its first flight in the UK on May 21, 1992 and became a popular item on the airshow circuit. It moved to the custodianship of OFMC at <u>Duxford</u>, Cambs, during March 1994. Hunter F.51 E-402 is under restoration by Derek Johnson and is listed under 'Airport', above.

◆ Visits by members of the general public are not possible as the JHL facility is very much a 'working' collection. There are plans to make all of JHL open to public inspection on a regular basis, but readers will have to be patient for a little longer. General enquiries can be made as follows : ✉ JHL, Hangar 600, Bournemouth International Airport, Christchurch, Dorset, BH23 7DQ.

☐ G-BOOM		Hunter T.7 ▲	ex Hunter One Collection (HOC), Stansted, Leavesden, Hatfield, G-9-432, Dunsfold, Aalborg, Danish AF ET-274, *Esk*-724, Dutch AF N-307. HWL. See notes above.	11-93
☐ G-GONE		Venom FB.50 ▲	ex Swiss AF J-1452. J E Davies.	11-93
☐ G-SEAH	WM994	Sea Hawk FB.5	ex HOC, Southend, Swansea, Cranfield, Arbroath A2503, Abbotsinch, Hal Far SAR Flt, 806, 767, 764, 800. Restn. Sark International AW.	11-93
☐ G-SWIS		Vampire FB.6 ▲	ex Sion, Swiss AF J-1149. HWL	11-93
☐ WM167	G-LOSM	Meteor TT.20 ▲	ex HOC, Blackbushe, RAE Llanbedr, 228, Colerne CS, 228 OCU. HWL.	11-93
☐ WV795	A2661	Sea Hawk FGA.6	ex Bath, Cardiff-Wales, Culdrose, Halton 8151M, Sydenham, 738, 806, 700. Restn. See notes.	11-93
☐ XE677	G-HHUN	Hunter F.4 ▲	ex East Kirkby, Loughborough, Dunsfold, 229 OCU, 111, 93, 4. HWL. F/f 21-1-94.	01-94
☐ XF114	G-SWIF	Swift F.7	ex Connah's Quay, Aston Down, CS(A), Cranfield. Restoration. JHL.	11-93
☐ XG290	8711M	Hunter F.6	ex Bruntingthorpe, Swanton Morley, Bentley Priory, Halton, Laarbruch SF, A&AEE. Front and centre fuselage only, for spares.	11-93
☐ XH328		Vampire T.11	ex Cranfield, Hemel Hempstead, Croxley Green, Bushey, Keevil, Exeter, 3 CAACU, 60.	09-93
☐ XM697	G-NAAT	Gnat T.1	ex Woking, HSA, A&AEE, HSA. Restoration. HWL. See notes above.	11-93
☐ XN385*		Whirlwind HAS.7	ex Wroughton, Culdrose, Wroughton, HS, A&AEE, 771, 824, 825, 824. Arrived by 14-1-93. Stored. See notes above.	09-93
☐ XR537	G-NATY	Gnat T.1	ex Cosford 8642M, Red Arrows, 4 FTS. JHL. Restoration.	09-93

☐ '215'   G-HELV*   Vampire T.55 ▲   ex Sion, Swiss AF U-1215. First noted 6-92.
                                        First flown in UK guise 13-10-92. RAF c/s.   11-93
☐ ET-273   Hunter T.7   ex Biggin Hill, Macclesfield, Elsham Hall,
                                        Hatfield, G-9-431, Aalborg, Danish AF *Esk*.724.
                                        Composite, with single-seater nose. 'Gate'.
                                        Original nose also present.   11-93

■ **Lovaux / FLS Aerospace** : Production of the Optica is now underway and the shapely FLS
Sprint (*née* SAH-1) is also nearing production. Lovaux remains a major contractor for the MoD and to
the airline industry, and it is support of MoD and export support for Hunter operators that explain their
W&R 'fodder'. On the Optica front, **W&R13** speculated that G-BGMW and G-TRAK from Old
Sarum, Wilts, would move through to the new plant. This may well have been so, but they are too
small to be considered for an entry. The three Hunters listed in the last edition have been joined by a
former Cosford Canberra, for spares recovery.

☐ G-BNCX XL621   Hunter T.7   ex RAE Bedford, 238 OCU, RAE. Stored.   06-92
☐ WT532* 8890M   Canberra PR.7   ex Cosford, 8728M, RAE Bedford, 13, Wyton
                                      SF, 58, 31, 13, 80. Arr 5-4-92. Spares.   09-92
☐ XJ690   Hunter FGA.9   ex Macclesfield, Bitteswell, G-9-453, 208, 19, 1.
                                      Composite, with nose of XG195.
☐ QA-12   Hunter FGA.78   ex Qatar AF, G-9-286, Dutch AF N-268. Stored.
                                                                                   11-93

■ **Source Classic Jet Flight / Lindsay Wood Promotions Ltd** : On June 1, 1993 all four
Vampires ferried over from Southampton Airport to the new base here. On June 21, 1993 they were
joined by the Venom and on August 19, 1993 by the former DRA Bedford Buccaneer S.2B acquired
from the MoD sale held in London on July 8, 1993. Source announced their intention to operate the
Brick on the civilian register, but it was being advertised on the US market by March 1994.

☐ G-DHVV*   Vampire T.55 ▲   ex Southampton, Sion, Swiss Air Force U-1214.
                                      Flew in 1-6-93.   06-93
☐ G-DHWW*   Vampire T.55 ▲   ex Southampton, Sion, Swiss Air Force U-1219.
                                      Flew in 1-6-93.   06-93
☐ G-DHXX*   Vampire FB.6 ▲   ex Southampton, Payerne, Swiss Air Force
                                      J-1173. Flew in 1-6-93.   06-93
☐ G-DHZZ*   Vampire T.55 ▲   ex Southampton, Sion, Swiss Air Force U-1230.
                                      Flew in 1-6-93.   06-93
☐ 'WE402'*G-VENI   Venom FB.50 ▲   ex Southampton, Cranfield, Swiss Air Force
                                      U-1230. Flew in 21-6-93.   06-93
☐ XX897*   Buccaneer S.2B   ex DRA Bedford, RAE, RRE. Tornado nose.
                                      Flew in 19-8-93. See notes above.   12-93
☐ J-1601* G-VIDI   Venom FB.50   ex Dunsfold, Cranfield, Swiss Air Force Arrived
                                      by 6-93. Stored.   06-93

■ **Warbirds of Great Britain** (WoGB) - **Precious Metals Ltd** : With the death of Doug Arnold
in November 1992 there was a hurried removal of aircraft from the WoGB facility at Hurn — more
details of the background to this can be found under Biggin Hill, Gtr Lon, and these notes should be
read in conjunction with what is given there. It will be some time before the dust settles and the exact
disposition of the fleet can be confirmed. In the meantime, herewith a first stab at what-went-where.
Unless noted, all had gone from the hangar by February and were airworthy : —
¶ F4U-5N Corsair N179PT* flew in from Biggin Hill 28-3-91 and flew to Lelystad, Netherlands, 23-
11-92; ¶ P-51D-25-NA NL314BG *Petie 2nd*; ¶ P-51D-25-NA N513PA *Shangri La*; arrived 19-3-92 ¶
F8F-2 Bearcat NX800H* flew in from Biggin Hill 25-9-91 and flew to Lelystad, 23-11-92; ¶ FM-2
Wildcat N909WJ flew to Lelystad, Netherlands 23-11-92; ¶ F-6F-5K N79863 ex US Navy Museum,
Pensacola, and BuNo 79863 was due to join the collection, but it is thought it did not transit the
Atlantic; ¶ P-40N N9950; ¶ Lancaster B.X KB976*/G-BCOH arrived by road from Biggin Hill 8-10-
92 and sold to Kermit Weeks, Tamiami, Florida, USA, crated 4-93 and cancelled as sold in the USA
23-2-93; ¶ Lancaster B.X KB994* sections *thought* arrived 8-10-92 with KB976 from Biggin Hill
much of this (though not necessarily all, had moved on to <u>North Weald</u>, Essex, by 4-93; ¶ Spitfire IX
NH238/G-MKIX; ¶ Spitfire PR.XI PL983/G-PRXI; ¶ Spitfire XVIII SM969*/G-BRAF flew from
Bournemouth to Biggin Hill 20-11-92; ¶ Pilatus P.3 A-804 exported to the USA by 9-92, becoming
N321RD; ¶ Pilatus P.3 A-811 reported leaving by road 6-4-91 to USA, becoming N328RD.
(Although this machine was also reported *road-running* on the M25 — anti-clockwise 9-7-92, which

fits in much better with the others); ⁋ Pilatus P.3 A-849 exported to the USA leaving 6-7-92, becoming N487RD; ⁋ Pilatus P.3 A-862 exported to the USA by 9-92, becoming N500K; ⁋ T-34A Mentor 33340/N34AB shuttled between Biggin Hill and Hurn 20-23-11-92; ⁋ TF-51D '473871'/N7097V (note amended identity) arrived 16-4-92, last noted in dismantled condition at Hurn 11-92.

BOVINGTON (off the A352 near Wool, west of Wareham)

■ **Royal Armoured Corps and Royal Tank Regiment Tank Museum** : The Skeeter has been on display inside the museum for a numbers of years and is no longer on the charge of the Junior Leaders Regiment. Over 200 armoured fighting vehicles are on display. During 1992, the museum took on the Hamilcar section from Beverley, Humbs, and it will be used as a centre-piece with a Tetrarch air portable tank.

◆ Open daily (with some exceptions) 10am to 5pm. ✉ The Tank Museum, Bovington, Dorset, BH20 6JG. ☎ : 0929 462721 ext 329 or 463 or 0929 463953..

☐ TK718*	Hamilcar I	ex Beverley, Christian Malford. Arr 1992.	07-93
☐ XM564	Skeeter AOP.12	ex 652, CFS, 12 Flt, 652. See notes above.	07-93

CHRISTCHURCH

■ **Sea Vixen Society** : More accurately, the 'Vixen can be found on the B3059 Somerford Road, at the entrance to the Somerford Road Retail Park, near MFI. A plaque explains that the 'Vixen is a tribute to aviation history in Christchurch 1932-1962 and that it was presented by Troika Developments on April 28, 1985.

☐ XJ580	Sea Vixen FAW.2	ex Bournemouth Airport, FRL, RAE Farnborough, Llanbedr, 899. '131-E'. Displayed.	12-93

COMPTON ABBAS AERODROME (south east of Shaftesbury)

Recapping on **W&R13**, Chipmunk 22 composite G-BDBL, owned by Richard Fox, made its first flight during June 1992. The rear fuselages of G-BDBL and G-AOSN moved to Houghton-on-the-Hill, Leics, for use in another project. A Rallye Club keeps the entry going.

☐ G-AWYX*	Rallye Club	CoA expired 27-6-86. Stored.	12-93

DORCHESTER

■ **Wessex Aviation & Transport** : Brian Woodford's largely Moth-dominated collection is based at a private strip in the area, with the large material using Henstridge, Somerset. On June 19, 1993, PT-13D N4712V, Stampe G-BMNV, Lysander G-BCWL and MS.500 G-AZMH were entered in the Brooks auction at Goodwood (see Appendix D). The Lysander was withdrawn prior to sale and none of the others were sold. Brian Woodford purchased DH.60 G-AAVJ at the sale.

◆ Occasional open days are held, but, otherwise, enthusiasts can see the aircraft attending airshows and fly-ins.

☐ G-AAVJ*(2)	DH.60GM Moth ▲	ex N573N, NC573N. Acquired 6-93. See notes above.	06-93
☐ G-ABEV	DH.60G Moth ▲	ex N4203E, G-ABEV, HB-OKI, CH-217.	
☐ G-ACZE	Dragon Rapide ▲	ex G-AJGS, G-ACZE, Z7266, 3 FP, 6 AONS, G-ACZE.	
☐ G-ADHA	Fox Moth ▲	ex N83DH, ZK-ASP, NZ566, ZK-ADI.	
☐ G-ADPS	BA Swallow II ▲	ex Hungerford, Dorchester, Strathallan, Sandown.	
☐ G-ADUR	Hornet Moth ▲	ex Cuckfield.	
☐ G-AEDT	Dragonfly ▲	ex Southampton, N2034, G-AEDT, VH-AAD, G-AEDT.	
☐ G-AFOB	Moth Minor ▲	ex Old Warden, X5117, 10 OAFU, St A UAS, 613, G-AFOB.	
☐ G-AGAT	J3F-50 Cub ▲	ex NC26126.	
☐ G-AIYS	Leopard Moth ▲	ex YI-ABI, SU-ABM.	
☐ G-ANLH	Tiger Moth ▲	ex Hamble, N3744F, OO-EVO, G-ANLH, PG637, Honiley SF,1 RS.	
☐ G-AZMH	MS.500 ▲	ex Booker, EI-AUU ntu, F-BJQG, Fr mil. *Luftwaffe* c/s. See notes above.	06-93

☐ G-BMNV		SNCAN SV-4L △	ex Booker, F-BBNI. See notes above.	06-93
☐ G-BTCU		Antonov An-2T △	ex SP-FDS, Polish AF. Soviet AF colours.	06-92
☐ N4712V		PT-13D Kaydet △	ex 42-16931. See notes above.	06-93
☐ '5964'	G-BFVH	DH.2 replica	ex Duxford, *Gunbus*, 'GBH-7', '4589', Land's End, Chertsey. CoA exp 31-8-86. [Serial worn amended from **W&R13**.]	07-91
☐ T5672	G-ALRI	Tiger Moth △	ex ZK-BAB, G-ALRI, T5672, 7 FTS, 21 EFTS, 7 FTS, RAFC, 4 EFTS.	
☐ 'V9281'	G-BCWL	Lysander IIIA △	ex Booker, Hamble, Blackbushe, Booker, Canada, RCAF. 414 Sqn c/s, 'RU-M'. See notes above.	06-93

PORTLAND AIRFIELD (on the A354 south of Weymouth)

■ **HMS** *Osprey* : By February 1994, a former Lee Wessex HAS.1 had taken up duties on the dump. Previous occupant, Wasp HAS.1 XV623/A2724 is thought to have perished.

☐ XS870*	A2697	Wessex HAS.1	ex Lee-on-Solent, Wroughton. 'PO'. Dump. First noted 2-94.	02-94
☐ XZ243		Lynx HAS.3	ex Lee-on-Solent. '635'. Cr 10-3-88. Inst.	06-93

SOPLEY (on the B3347 north of Christchurch)

■ **Sopley Camp** : This former domestic site is being restored to its former glory, and to act as part of the huge *D-Day* celebrations. During July 1993 it took on the former Bournemouth Hurricane replica as an exhibit.

☐ 'V7767'*	BAPC.72	Hurricane replica	ex Bournemouth, Brooklands, North Weald, Coventry, *Battle of Britain*. Arrived 7-93.	07-93

WEST MOORS (on the B3072 north of Bournemouth)

■ **RAOC Depot** : The fire section *should* still have their Wasp.

☐ XS535		Wasp HAS.1	ex Wroughton, 703. '432'. Fire training.	

Durham

STANLEY

■ **Harry Dodd** : The restoration of a long-forgotten Cherokee in underway.

☐ G-AVWE*		Cherokee 140	ex Biggin Hill. CoA exp 22-4-82. Restn.	04-93

TEES-SIDE AIRPORT (or Middleton St George)

(Previously listed under 'Cleveland', the Airport, admittedly a large chunk of land, actually has its postal address in Durham.)

■ **Civil Aviation Authority International Fire Training Centre** : (Note change of name.) A Viscount-oriented visit during March 1993 found no less than *three* Viscounts in use on the airport for fire training. As well as the two on the airfield perimeter, a third serves within the group of CAA buildings, and is painted in olive drab. This machine is *not* a CAA IFTC airframe and is used by local emergency services and the airport firemen — see below. Only Trident 1C G-ARPW is confirmed as 'passing on'. Its burnt remains were removed by a hopeful scrapman prior to July 1991. Of passing interest is the construction, during much of 1994, of a series of 'synthetic' fire rigs, including a full-size oil rig, complete with helicopter pad, oil storage tanks and — what every well-equipped oil rig needs — a section of Boeing 747.

☐ G-ARPO		Trident 1C	ex BA, BEA. CoA exp 12-1-86. Whole.	05-93
☐ G-AVFJ		Trident 2E	ex BA, BEA. CoA exp 18-9-83. Rear end perished.	05-93
☐ G-AWZR		Trident 3B-101	ex BA, BEA. CoA exp 9-4-86. Poor state.	05-93
☐ G-AWZS		Trident 3B-101	ex BA, BEA. CoA exp 9-9-86. Whole.	05-93

☐ G-AZLP		Viscount 813	ex BMA, SAA ZS-CDT. CoA expired 3-4-82. Whole. 05-93
☐ G-AZLS		Viscount 813	ex BMA, SAA ZS-CDV. CoA expired 9-6-83. Fuselage. 05-93
☐ XP330		Whirlwind HAR10	ex Stansted, 21, 32, 230, 110, 225. Gutted, on its side. 05-93

■ **Others** : Two more Tomahawks, in the shape of G-BGZE and 'ZH, both from Tattershall Thorpe, Lincs, arrived for spares use by October 1992. However, they and the more intact G-BNGS moved on to <u>Carlisle Airport</u>, Cumbria, by September 1993. The rebuild of Noel Robinson's P-51D continues at a location on the airport. Briefly transiting through here was Anson C.21 WD413/G-BFIR which *flew* in from Strathallan, Tayside, during February 1992. It flew on to Enstone, Oxon, by December 1992. The olive drab painted Viscount fuselage — see notes above — is confirmed as being G-AZNC, thought long since scrapped at East Midlands Airport. The arrival of the Lightning is centred around 30th birthday of the airport and it will be restored and placed on display.

☐ G-AZNC*		Viscount 813	ex East Midlands, BMA, G-AZLW ntu, SAA, ZS-SBZ, ZS-CDZ. Fuselage - see notes. 05-93
☐ XR749*	8934M	Lightning F.3	ex Chop Gate, Leuchars, 11, LTF, 11, LTF, Binbrook pool,29, 226 OCU, 56, EE. Overstressed 17-2-87. Arrived 3-94. See notes above. 03-94
☐ 41	44-72028	P-51D-20-NA	ex Duxford, N22B (?), Israel DF/AF, Swedish AF, USAAF. Restoration for Noel Robinson.

Essex

ANDREWSFIELD AERODROME (or Great Saling, north of the A120, west of Braintree)
A pair of Cessnas have appeared for rebuild.

☐ G-ATAT*		Cessna 150E	ex Southend, N3041J. CoA expired 29-7-85. Stored. First noted 12-91. 07-92
☐ G-ATMN*		Cessna F.150F	ex Southend. Cr 11-5-84. Wreck. F/n 1-92. 07-92
☐ XP241		Auster AOP.9	ex Rabley Heath, St Athan, 653, Aden. 07-92
☐ 319		Mystere IVA	ex Sculthorpe, French Air Force. '8-ND'. 12-93

AUDLEY END AERODROME (off the B1383, west of Saffron Walden)
■ **Historic Flying Ltd** (HFL) : A lot of changes within the Spitfire world here, mostly additions to the world stock of 'flyers'. Mk XVI RW382/G-OXVI is stored here, awaiting export to the USA to its *new* owner, John Breit. Mk XVI TD248/G-OXVI made its first flight on November 10, 1992 in stunning 41 Squadron colours, for Eddie Coventry. Mk IX TE566/G-BLCK first flew on July 2, 1992 for the Historic Aircraft Collection of Jersey and adopted Czech Air Force markings. Mk XVIII TP280/G-BTXE first flew on July 5, 1992. After several airshow appearances it was crated and exported to the USA by December 1992, for Rudy Frasca. Additionally Mk XVI RW386/G-BXVI had arrived here from Biggin Hill during 1991 for restoration on behalf of Warbirds of Great Britain — it joined the 'export drive' of 1992 — more details under Biggin Hill, Gtr Lon, and Bournemouth Airport, Dorset. By July 1993 Mk XIV NH799/G-BUZU had arrived from Duxford, Cambs, for completion of restoration on behalf of The Fighter Collection. It made its first flight in 130 Squadron colours as 'AP-V' on January 21, 1994. It was shipped to New Zealand and the Tim Wallis collection on February 14, 1994. The former Spanhoe, Northants, Tempest project arrived here on October 25, 1993 for storage by HFL. It was auctioned by Sotheby's on November 27, 1993, but failed to reach its reserve, reaching a high bid of £80,000. (See *Appendix D*.)

☐ N30228	G-BPUR	J3L-65 Cub	ex Raveningham, F'horpe, NC30228. Frame. 05-93
☐ BM597	G-MKVB	Spitfire Vb	ex Fulbourne, Church Fenton, Linton-on-Ouse, 'Fenton, St Athan, 5713M, 58 OTU, 317. Restoration for HAC. 03-94
☐ RW382*	G-XVIA	Spitfire XVI ∆	ex Braintree, 8075M, Uxbridge, Leconfield, Church Fenton, 7245M, C&RS, 3 CAACU, 604. See notes. Stored. 03-94

☐	SM845*	G-BUOS	Spitfire XVIII	ex Witney, USA, Kalaikunda, Indian AF HS687, SM845. Restn. Arrived early 1993. 03-94
☐	TB252	G-XVIE	Spitfire XVI	ex Braintree, Bentley Priory 8073M, Leuchars, Boulmer, Acklington, Odiham, 7281M, 7257M, 61 OTU, 350, 341, 329, 84 GSU. Stored. 03-94
☐	HA564*	G-BSHW	Tempest II	ex Spanhoe, Chichester, Indian AF, RAF MW376. Stored. Arrived 25-10-93. See notes. 12-93

■ **Ragwing Aviation** Chipmunk 22A G-ARMF was used in the rebuild of Mk 22 G-BCIW and was flying again (as G-ARMF) by January 1993, but with 'IW's previous identity, WZ868. The remains of G-BCIW moved to Fownhope, H&W, on January 13, 1993, for rebuild — this looks set to be a good plot! Another example has arrived for attention.

☐	G-AOSK*	Chipmunk 22A	ex Little Burstead, WB726, 11 FTS. CoA expired 10-6-78. Restoration. 11-93
☐	G-ARMD	Chipmunk 22A	ex Holbeach, WD297, 666, 1 BFTS. CoA expired 5-6-76. 01-92

■ **Others** Silvaire G-BNIO was flying by July 1993. A Tiger Moth has arrived for storage.

☐	F-BGCJ* G-BTOG	Tiger Moth	ex France, French AF, NM192. Stored. First noted 9-92. 12-93

BASILDON

■ **2243 Squadron ATC** : *Should* still have their Airtourer.

☐	G-AWVH	Airtourer T.2	ex Southchurch, Goodwood. Crashed 15-3-81.

BOXTED (north of Colchester, between the A134 and A12)

■ **Colchester Military & Aviation Museum** Located close to the *Wig and Figget* public house, photographic evidence of the state of the Cessna 'exhibit' would imply visitors need more than a few *stiffeners* before venturing further! The Museum is reported to be "open most weekends".

☐	9J-RGH	Cessna F.150F	ex Lexden, Martlesham Heath. Cockpit. 04-93

CHELMSFORD

■ **276 Squadron ATC** : In Meteor Way, maintain their T.7.

☐	WH132 7906M	Meteor T.7	ex Kemble, CAW, CFS, CAW, 8 FTS, 207 AFS. 'J'. 12-93

■ **Fire Station** : Queen Air fuselage G-ASRX moved to Stock, Essex, by February 1993.

CLACTON

■ **East Essex Aviation Museum** (EEAM) Located within one of the fine Martello towers that dot the coastline, the EEAM includes a fine array of recovery items and other memorabilia. Dominating the contents is the fuselage of a P-51D. Less substantial, but very interesting, are the recently recovered remains of Glen Eagleston's 354th FS P-51B and several items from 501 Squadron Tempests.
◆ Point Clear caravan park, opening times vary. ✉ M Gadd, 32 Key Road, Clacton, CO15 3DA.

☐	44-14574	P-51D-10-NA	ex 479th FG *Little Zippie*. Crashed off-shore 13-1-45. Salvaged 8-87. 01-94

CLACTON AERODROME (west of Clacton, east of Jaywick)

[The machinations as to why this entire aerodrome was moved to 'Suffolk' in **W&R13** could produce many papers on behavioural analogies in book compilers but it's best just to put it back where it belongs and hope that nobody notices!] Two Cessnas now inhabit the aerodrome.

☐	G-ASUH	Cessna F.172E	ex *LOST!*, Felthorpe, Norwich. CoA exp 14-4-78. Fuselage. 12-91
☐	G-BKRB*	Cessna 172N	ex EI-BKR, G-BHKZ, N1207F. CoA expired 15-5-89. Stored.

CLAVERING (on the B1038 south west of Saffron Walden)

Nothing new on the contents of the scrapyard at Starling's Green.

☐	G-AXWF	Cessna F.172H	ex Clacton, Andrewsfield. Dbr 26/27-11-83. Fuselage. 04-90

COLCHESTER

■ **Craig Charleston** : Two Bf 109s have arrived at the workshop, having been salvaged on behalf of the Museum of Flying at Santa Monica, California, from the CIS. One aircraft will be used for spares for the other, which is known to have served with JG51 *Green Hearts*. Another Bf 109, this time slavaged from France, arrived during 1993. The Sea Fury and Seafire projects continue when time permits. Gnat T,1 XP532/8615M has been exported to the USA.

☐	Sea Fury FB.11	composite, parts from G-AGHB, G-FURY and *possibly* T.20S D-CIBO. Restn.	03-94
☐ LA546	Seafire F.46	ex Newport Pagnell, Newark. Restn project.	03-94
☐ 1342*	Bf 109E	ex France. Arrived during 1993.	03-94
☐ 3579*	Bf 109E-1	ex Lancing, CIS, 4/JG51. Arrived 12-92. See notes above.	
☐ 8147*	Bf 109F-4	ex Lancing, CIS, JG54. Arrived 1993. See notes above.	03-94
			03-94

■ **Others** : Glenn Mitchell is *thought* still to have his Canberra nose section in the area. The Gnat mentioned in **W&R13** was in the care of Craig Charleston — see above.

☐ WE168 8049M	Canberra PR.3	ex Manston, 231 OCU, 39, 69, 540. Nose.	04-90

EARLS COLNE AERODROME (on the B1024 south of Earls Colne, east of Halstead)

■ **Rebel Air Museum** (RAM) / **Earls Colne Aviation Museum** : Leading light at RAM, Dave Brett sadly died during mid-1993 and his passing has placed a sad cloud over the collection. Determined to carry on in Dave's (and his late father, Stan's) name, the members of RAM are hard at work establishing a format for 1994 and the Museum will open again from Easter. Dave's attention to detail and his rapport with re-union organisations in the US (particularly those that operated his beloved B-26) had turned RAM into a shrine for the 8th and 9th Air Force friends and fanatics. He is dearly missed. The Museum provides a fine testament to the determination of the Brett family and their friends.

◆ Open Saturdays, Sundays and Bank Holidays April to October 10am to 6pm and other times by appointment. ✉ RAM, c/o Earls Colne Aerodrome, Earls Colne, Halstead, Essex.

☐ N9606H	PT-26 Cornell II	ex Andrewsfield, Southend, FH768, 42-14361. Restoration.	07-93
☐ EE425	Meteor F.3	ex Andrewsfield, Foulness, MoS, 206 AFS, 210 AFS, 206 AFS, 63, 266, 1, 222. Nose.	07-93
☐	BAPC.115 HM.14 *Flea*	ex Andrewsfield, Balham, South Wales.	07-93

■ **Others** : Pup 100 G-AXTZ moved to <u>Lancing</u>, W Sussex, on March 6, 1993. The late Peter Treadaway's Naval Aircraft Factory N3N is stored here.

☐ G-ONAF*	NAF N3N-3	ex Audley End, North Weald, N45192, BuNo4406. Stored.	11-93

EAST TILBURY

■ **Thameside Aviation Museum** (TAM) / **Essex Historical Aircraft Society** : Gordon King's Harvard project arrived during July 1992. It will be restored to the colours of an SNJ. The Southend-based Historic Aircraft Society keep their Scion frame here.

◆ Located at Coalhouse Fort. Open on the last Sunday of the month from 12.30pm and at other times by arrangement. ✉ TAM, 80 Elm Road, Grays, Essex RM17 6LD.

☐ G-ADXS	HM.14 *Flea*	ex Andrewsfield, Southend, Staverton, Southend. CoA expired 1-12-36.	06-92
☐ G-AEZF	Scion II	ex Southend, Southend Airport. CoA expired 5-5-54. Stored.	
☐ G-AVZO	Pup 100	ex Southend Airport, Benendon. CoA expired 12-7-75. Fuselage.	
☐ B-163*	Harvard IIB	ex Windsor, North Weald, Amsterdam, Dutch AF, RCAF FE930, 42-12417. Arrived by 7-92. Loan from Gordon King. For restoration to SNJ guise.	07-92

FOULNESS ISLAND

■ **Proof & Experimental Establishment** (PEE) : Underlining still further that there are less things to shoot at in the world (sure??) Tender No T1025 was issued with bids due for return on November 25, 1993 for no less than 73 tonnes of scrap. The recognisable airframes in this cull are denoted in the list below with a ∞ — the nature of bidding these days is that all will go to one contractor and will have moved well before this tome sees the printer. W&R13 was a bit quick in allocating some airframes to the Mayer & Perry clean-out of April 1991 — the following airframes survived that, although the bulk of them were in T1025 : Canberra B.2 WH673; Canberra B.2 'WJ642'/WH723; Canberra B.2 WJ990; Canberra B.2E WK164; Harrier GR.1 XV280; a Canberra cockpit on a trailer, possibly WT205 and a Buccaneer fuselage, possibly XN972. Of the aircraft that 'survived' the tender, they were located in two places, either the famed 'White City' (∏) or at 'Half Way' (¥). Two airframes were not to be seen during April 1991 and again during January 1994 and therefore should be deleted : — Sea Vixen FAW.2 XS580 and the Lynx rotor rig.

☐ WH673		Canberra B.2	ex Farnborough, 7, CAW, RAFC. Tail-less fuselage, see notes above. ∞	01-94
☐ 'WJ642'	WH723	Canberra B.2	ex Upwood, Weeton, 7628M, BAC, 231 OCU. Tail-less fuselage, see notes above. ∞	01-94
☐ WJ990		Canberra B.2	ex RAE, RRE, RAE, 40. Tail-less fuselage, see notes above. ∞	01-94
☐ WK164*		Canberra B.2E	ex 100. Tail-less fuselage, see notes above. ∞	01-94
☐ XA937		Victor K.1	ex St Athan, 214, 57, A&AEE, 10. Sectioned fuselage. ∞	01-94
☐ XK525		Buccaneer S.1	ex Holme-on-Spalding Moor, Brough, West Freugh, RAE. ∞	01-94
☐ XN726	8545M	Lightning F.2A	ex Farnborough, Gutersloh, 92, 19, CFE. ¥	01-94
☐ XN771		Lightning F.2A	ex Farnborough, Gutersloh, 19, CFE. ¥	01-94
☐ XN795		Lightning F.2A	ex RAE Bedford, A&AEE, BAC. ¥	01-94
☐ XN955		Buccaneer S.1	ex RAE. ∞	01-94
☐ XN960		Buccaneer S.1	ex Farnborough, RAE. ∞	01-94
☐ XR756		Lightning F.6	ex Binbrook, 5, 11, LTF, 5, LTF, 5-11 pool, 23, 11, 23, 11, 23, 5. ∞	01-94
☐ XS421		Lightning T.5	ex RAE, 23, 111, 226 OCU. ¥	01-94
☐ XS927		Lightning F.6	ex Binbrook, 5-11 pool, 23, 11, 74. ∞	01-94
☐ XV280*		Harrier GR.1	ex Boscombe Down, A&AEE, HSA. Noseless fuselage, see notes above. ∞	01-94
☐ XV357		Buccaneer S.2A	ex St Athan, 237 OCU, 208. Less nose. ∞	01-94
☐ XV373		Sea King HAS.1	ex Boscombe Down, A&AEE. ∏	01-94
☐ XV417		Phantom FGR.2	ex 29, 17, 14, 17, 14, 2, 228 OCU. Crashed 23-3-76. Noseless. ¥	01-94
☐ XV798		Harrier GR.1	ex Dunsfold. Composite airframe - nose from XP832, wings from XW264. Ex PCB rig. ∏	01-94
☐ XW541	8858M	Buccaneer S.2B	ex Honington, St Athan, 12, 16, 15. ∏	01-94
☐ XX153		Lynx AH.1	ex Westlands. ∏	01-94
☐ *		Buccaneer S.2	less rear fuselage. Location unconfirmed. *Possibly* XN972. See notes above.	01-94
☐ *		Canberra	*Possibly* WT205. ∏ See notes above.	01-94

FYFIELD (on the B184 west of Chelmsford)

Nothing on the Cherokee hulk at the strip — it is hurtling towards *LOST!*

☐ N3850K	Cherokee 140	battered fuselage. See notes above.

GREAT WALTHAM (on the A130 north of Chelmsford)

■ **P G Lee** : Work continues on the Messengers here.

☐ G-AJWB	Messenger 2A	ex Blackpool Airport, Woodvale. CoA expired 13-11-69. Restoration.
☐ G-AKEZ	Messenger 2A	ex 'RG333', Higher Blagdon, Bristol Airport. CoA expired 15-11-68. Spares.

HALSTEAD (north east of Braintree)
Work on the Tiger restoration is assumed to continue.
☐ G-APBI   Tiger Moth   ex Audley End, EM903, 2 FIS, 26. Crashed
                                           7-7-80. Restoration.

LAINDON (north of the A127, near Basildon)
J/1N Alpha G-AIGT moved initially to <u>Wickenby</u>, Lincs, early 1992, leaving just the Autocar.
☐ G-AOBV   J/5P Autocar   ex Stapleford Tawney, Benington. CoA
                                           expired 7-4-71. Open store, poor state.   11-92

NORTH WEALD AERODROME (off the A414, junction 7, M11 east of Harlow)
■ **Aces High Flying Museum** : Despite being in the teeth of a recession that has all but vaporised the film industry — aircraft-wise at least — Mike Woodley and team at Aces High have managed to build a second hangar, putting a lot of the collection under cover. (One hangar being more or less permanently occupied by the set for the TV series *Crystal Maze*.) An ambitious joint production and marketing arrangement with the CIS design bureau Ilyushin will see the Il-103 light aircraft assembled here in due course. The Aces High 'fleet' remains much the same and readers are reminded that Aces look after some Butane Buzzard Aviation (BBA) airframes. The story of the former Southend and Charles Church Lincoln is convoluted and readers are best to refer to both Biggin Hill, Gtr Lon, and Bournemouth Airport, Dorset, for more of the saga. Definitely moving in that direction was BT-15 Valiant 121821/N513L which was exported to Florida in April 1993. AT-6D Harvard '483009'/G-BPSE was exported to the USA during 1992. The former Lasham Dakota 'G-AMSU' was dismantled and exported to France in late 1992 having been acquired as an attraction for the *Euro-Dismal* theme park.
◆ Visits by prior appointment *only*. ✉ Aces High Flying Museum (NW) Ltd, *The Ford*, Ford Road, Chobham, Surrey, GU24 8SS. ☎ 034 882 2949.

☐ G-AWHB		CASA 2-111	ex Royston, Southend, Spanish AF B2I-57. Under restoration. 03-94
☐ G-PROV*		Jet Prov T.52A ▲	ex Leavesden, Bournemouth, Biggin, Singapore AD 352, Yemen AF 104, G-27-7, XS228. Flew in 2-94. Rory McCarthy. 02-94
☐ G-29-1*	RF342	Lincoln 2	ex Bournemouth, Bedford, North Weald, Bitteswell, Blackbushe, Southend, Cranfield, G-APRJ/G-36-3, Napiers G-29-1, G-APRJ, RF342. Along with sections of Lancaster X KB994/G-BVBP. See notes above. 03-94
☐ N232J		Sea Fury FB.11 ▲	ex N232, N54M, CF-OYF, RCN TG114. For sale 10-93. 10-93
☐ N2700	G-BLSW	C-119G-FA	ex Manston, 3C-ABA, Belgian AF CP-9, 51-2700. Engineless. Available for disposal. 03-94
☐ N3455	G-AMSN	Dakota 4	ex Exeter, G-AMSN, EI-BSI, N3455, SU-BFZ, N3455, G-AMSN, KN673, 240 OCU, 1382 TCU, 45 GCF, 44-77047. *Ian Drury*. 03-94
☐ WF877	G-BPOA	Meteor T.7 (mod)	ex Higher Blagdon, Tarrant Rushton, Chilbolton, 96, 11. 03-94
☐ WP321*	G-BRFC	Sea Prince T.1	ex Bourn, Kemble, 750, 744, Stretton. Flew in 20-11-93. '750-CU'. 12-93
☐ XN691	8143M	Sea Vixen FAW.2	ex Coventry, Cosford, Halton, Sydenham, 893, 899. Stored. BBA. For sale 10-93. 03-94
☐ XR674*	9030M	Jet Provost T.4	ex Halton, Shawbury, CATCS, 6 FTS, 1 FTS. 'D'. Arrived 27-10-93, for Rory McCarthy. 03-94
☐ MT-11*	G-BRFU	CM-170-2	ex Cranfield, USA N219DM, IAI Israel, Belgian AF. Arrived 6-93. 06-93
☐ 'VK+AZ'	G-BFHG	CASA 352L	ex Duxford, Fairoaks, Blackbushe, Spanish AF T2B-262. CoA exp 30-10-90. 03-94
☐ 503	G-BRAM	MiG-21PF	ex Hungarian AF. 04-94
☐ J-1758	G-BLSD	Venom FB.54	ex N203DM, Cranfield, G-BLSD, Dubendorf, Swiss AF. 03-94

☐ U-123<u>4</u>		Vampire T.55	ex Swiss AF, HSA, RAF XH308, RAFC. Stored. <u>NB</u> amended Swiss serial. 03-94
☐ 100884	G-DAKS	Dakota 3	ex Duxford, 'KG374', *Airline* 'G-AGHY', TS423, RAE, Ferranti, Airwork, Gatow SF, 436, 1 HGSU, 42-100884. CoA exp 20-12-90. 03-94
☐ 114700		T-6G-NT Texan	ex Coventry Airport, *Empire of the Sun*, La Ferte Alais, French AF. Hulk. 03-94
☐ '122351'	G-BKRG	Beech C-45G	ex Duxford, N75WB, *Octopussy*, N9072Z, 51-11665. 03-94
☐ 430823	N1042B	TB-25N	ex Tallmantz Aviation, 44-30823. *Dolly*. 03-94
☐ 430861	N9089Z	TB-25J	ex Duxford, 'HD368', G-BKXW ntu, Southend, Biggin Hill, N9089Z, 44-30861. *Bedsheet Bomber*. Under restoration. 03-94

■ **Harvard Formation Team** (HFT) / **Great War Combat Team** (GWCT) / **North Weald Flying Services** (NWFS) / *The Squadron* : The population of airworthy 'historics' is growing all the time here. Only those likely to stay on the ground, or under long term maintenance, or part of a reasonably well-defined collection, are listed here. Pilatus P.2-05 U-110/G-PTWO moved on to fly from Earls Colne, Essex, during 1992. P-51D Mustang 472773/G-SUSY moved to Northampton Airport, Northants, during 1992, but is a regular visitor. The amazing Alaparma Baldo 75 G-BCRH moved out during late 1992, to the Chelmsford, Essex, area.

◆ Visits by prior permission *only*. ✉ *The Squadron*, North Weald Airfield, Epping, Essex, CM16, 6AA. ☎ 0992 52 4510, **fax** 0992 52 2238.

☐ G-ALFM*		Devon C.2/2 ▲	ex VP961, 32, Northolt SF, Bangkok *attaché*, 207, 60, MoA, Pretoria *attaché*, 38 GCF, QF, HCCS, 31, NEAFCF, FCCS, Bangkok *attaché*. Dove Group. 10-93
☐ G-ARDE		Dove 6	ex Cranfield, I-TONY. CoA exp 25-8-91. 10-93
☐ G-BFPL		Fokker D.VII ▲	ex Duxford, Lower Upham, Sandown, Land's End, Chertsey, D-EAWM. GWCT. 06-93
☐ G-BRKC		J/1 Autocrat	ex F-BFYT. For restn. *Austerix the Gaulle*. 10-93
☐ G-BSFD*		J3C-65 Cub	ex N88419, NC88419. Euan English. 11-93
☐ G-BTNY*		PT-19-FA Cornell	ex N33870, USAAF. Chris Parr. Arrived 1991 — adding to **W&R13**. Restoration. 11-93
☐ 'P5865'	G-BKCK	Harvard IV ▲	ex N13631, G-BKCK, 13631, RCAF 20286. Eric Webster - HFT. 'LE-W'. 10-93
☐ 'EX280'	G-TEAC	Harvard IIA ▲	ex Portuguese AF 1523, SAAF 7333, EX688, 41-33253. Euan English - HFT. 10-93
☐ 'FT239'	G-BIWX	Harvard IV ▲	ex MM53846, USAF 51-17xxxx. Anthony Hutton - HFT. 10-93
☐ 'HB275'	N5063N	Beech D.18S ▲	ex G-BKGM, CF-SUQ, RCAF 2324. Anthony Hutton - HFT. US Navy colours. 10-93
☐ '152/17'	G-BTYV	Fokker Dr I rep ▲	ex N152JS. GWCT.
☐ 6247*	G-OMIG	SBLim-2A ▲	ex Shoreham, Polish Air Force. Graham Hinkley. Flew in 20-11-93. 10-93
☐ 53319	G-BTDP	TBM-3E ▲	ex N3966A, Ipswich, USN 53319. Anthony Haig Thomas. 10-93
☐ '93542'	G-BRLV	Harvard IV ▲	ex N90448, RCAF 20403. Barbel Abela. *Texan Belle*. 10-93

■ **Intrepid Aviation** : Dave Gilmour's collection of aircraft has grown to the extent that it deserves its own entry, having been previously listed under HFT etc.

☐ G-BKBK*		SNCAN SV-4A ▲	ex OO-CLR, F-BCLR. 10-93
☐ G-BRVE		Beech D.17S ▲	ex N1139V, NC1139V, FT475, 44-67724, USN 23689 ntu. 10-93
☐ G-BRVG		SNJ-7 ▲	ex Gloucester-Cheltenham, N830X, N4134A, Bu90678, 42-85895. 10-93
☐ N4596N		PT-13D ▲	ex 42-17782. *US Mail* colours. 10-93
☐ 'XR991'	G-MOUR	Gnat T.1 ▲	ex Leavesden, Halton 8624M, 4 FTS, XS102. *Yellowjacks* colours. 10-93

☐ 474008   N51RR   P-51D-25-NA ▲   ex N151MC ntu, N76AF, N8676E, RCAF 9274,
                                   44-74008.   10-93

■ **Robs Lamplough / Fighter Wing Display Team**   There have been few changes on this side of 'Weald, although the Albatros is now sufficiently immobile to be included. Sea Fury N232J was offered for sale during October 1993 and now resides with Aces High (*qv*) but is again available for sale. C.18M G-BMJY was entered in the Onslows sale at Rendcomb, Glos, on September 13, 1993 (see *Appendix* D), reached £29,000, but failed to sell. Fokker Dr. I 152/17 (G-ATJM) moved on to Vic Norman at Rendcomb, Glos, during the summer of 1991, but settled upon OFMC at Duxford, Cambs, by mid-1992. See also Filton, Avon; Hungerford, Berks and Lower Upham, Hants, for other aircraft.

☐	G-BMJY		SPP C.18M ▲	ex La Ferte Alais, Egyptian AF 627. '07'.	10-93
☐	LV-RIE		Nord 1002	ex Duxford, Kersey, Argentina.	10-90
☐	N159JC*		L.39ZO Albatros	ex N4312X ntu, Chad, Libyan AF 3227. Stored.	10-93
☐	N999PJ		Paris 2 ▲	ex F-BJLY.	10-93
☐	'EN398'	BAPC.184	Spitfire IX replica	ex Duxford, Huntingdon. 'JE-J'. Stored.	10-93
☐	KZ191		Hurricane IV	ex Fowlmere, Israel, 351, 1695F, AFDU. Centre section, mid fuselage. (Likely identity)	10-93
☐	'628'	N18V	Beech D.17S	ex NC18, Bu32898, FAA FT507, 44-67761. Stored.	10-93
☐	72216	G-BIXL	P-51D-20-NA ▲	ex Duxford, Ein-Gedi, Israeli AF/DF 43, Swedish AF Fv 26116, 44-72216. 'AJ-L'. *Miss L.*	6-93

■ **39 Restoration Group**   The three Vampire pods held here have moved on : Peter Smith's Vampire NF.10 WP250 and Vampire T.11 XD535 to Chelford, Cheshire; and T.11 WZ450 to Lashenden, Kent, on August 7, 1993. Inbound have been the long-lost Powick Meteor NF.13 nose, the TT.20 from Birmingham, W Mids, and an anonymous Auster frame. Restoration work is underway on both of the whole Meteors and there has been much work undertaken on the site and its buildings. Two interesting projects are the restoration of a David Brown aircraft tug and an Austin Mobile Control vehicle.
◆ Visits by prior arrangement. ✉ 39 Restoration Group, Neil Griggs, 16 Dukes Close, North Weald, Epping, Essex, CM16 6DA.

☐	WD646*	8189M	Meteor TT.20	ex Birmingham, 5 CAACU, 3/4 CAACU, CSE. 'R'. Arrived by 4-93.	12-93
☐	WE122*		Canberra TT.18	ex Stock, St Athan, FRADU, 7, 98, 245, 231 OCU. '845'. Nose, arrived 6-92.	12-93
☐	'WM311'	WM224	Meteor TT.20	ex East Dereham, CSDE Swanton Morley 8177M, 5 CAACU, 3 CAACU, 228 OCU. Restn.	12-93
☐	WM367*		Meteor NF.13	ex Powick, Boscombe Down, AWA, MoA. Nose section. Stored. Arrived 1992.	12-93
☐	WV499	7698M	Provost T.1	ex St Athan, Weeton, 6 FTS. Restn. 'G'.	12-93
☐	*		Auster	frame, marked 'TAY/R.695E'. First noted 04-92. Restoration.	12-93

PAGLESHAM (north east of Rochford)
The unfortunate Bell G-BFOI moved out during August 1993, moving to East Winch, Norfolk.

RAYLEIGH
■ **The Cockpit Collection** : The two Valiants will be used to produce one good one. Nigel Towler's collection is placed under this heading as a 'holding point'. The cockpits are scattered in various locations and accordingly, visits are not possible.

☐	WD954	Canberra B.2	ex East Kirkby, Tattershall, Bicester, 76, Upwood, Hemswell. Nose.	01-94
☐	WZ608	Vampire T.11	ex Market Harborough, Lutterworth, Bitteswell, Woodford, St Athan, 3 CAACU, 5 FTS, 266, Fassberg SF, 11 Vampire Flt, 5, Wunsdorf SF, 266.	01-94

☐	'WZ826'* XD826	Valiant BK.1	ex Cardiff-Wales, Abingdon, Stratford, Cosford, 7872M, 543, 232 OCU, 138, 90, 7. Nose. See notes above. Arrived by 4-93. 01-94
☐	XD857	Valiant BK.1	ex Foulness, 49. Nose. See notes above. 01-94
☐	XH560	Vulcan B.2	ex Marham, Waddington, 50, Wadd Wing, 27, Akrotiri Wing, Cott Wing, Wadd Wing, Cott Wing, 230 OCU, 12, MoA, 230 OCU. 01-94
☐	XH670	Victor B.2	ex East Kirkby, Tattershall, Woodford, Radlett, MoA. Nose. 01-94

RAYNE (on the A120 west of Braintree)
The hulk of a Cherokee is stored at the strip here.
☐ G-BEEV*   Cherokee 140F   ex PH-NSG. Cr 16-4-91. Wreck. F/n 2-93.   02-93

SOUTHEND AIRPORT (or Rochford, on the B1013 north of Southend-on-Sea)
■ **Airport** : A continued mixture of airliners and general aviation in terms of both the healthy population and the **W&R** inmates. Another Belfast has been retired and this location is another host to surplus HS.748s. The former Libyan L 39 has remained motionless and now merits an entry, as does its cousin at North Weald, Essex. As ever with the light aircraft wrecks here, please keep an eye on the 'last noted' dates for an indication of 'currency' — as with every element of **W&R**, all updates very welcome. Vulcan XL426 now merits its own entry — see below — as the legal clouds have vaporised from around it. The two Andovers were acquired for their engines, but took the unusual step of being ferried to Southend, perhaps because a ferry flight was within the purchase amount!
        Departures have been as follows : Auster J/1 G-AIJZ to <u>Warmingham</u>, Cheshire, on August 13, 1993; Viscount 806 G-AOYG, first noted as withdrawn by June 1993 had moved on to <u>Stock</u>, Essex, by March 1994; Viscount 806 G-AOYL was broken up and moved to <u>Stock</u>, Essex, by March 1993; Herald 100 G-APWA made the move (by road) to <u>Woodley</u>, Berks, August 29, 1992; Cessna F.150F G-ATMN moved to <u>Andrewsfield</u>, Essex, by January 1992; Fournier RF-3 G-AYJD moved to South Scarle, Lincs, and was flying by 1990; Cessna 172K G-AZDZ moved to <u>Warmingham</u>, Ches, by November 1993; Viscount 813 G-AZNA was removed by road on September 15, 1992, for export to Antwerp, Belgium for a new life as a night club; Viscount 814 G-BAPF to the fire school at <u>Moreton-in-Marsh</u>, Glos, on February 15, 1992; Cessna F.177RG G-BFAC was flying by 1991; former Air Cymru BAC 111-304 G-BPNX became 5N-MZE during 1992; likewise -304 G-WLAD became 5N-OVE; Viscount 806 G-LOND was scrapped and moved to <u>Stock</u>, Essex, by March 1993; CL-44J EI-BRP was broken up and moved to <u>Stock</u>, Essex, by March 1993; during February 1994 Belfast C.1 XR363/G-OHCA and G-BEPE were scrapped and work was likely to start on G-BFYU before too long.

☐	G-AOHL	Viscount 802	ex BAF, BA, BEA. CoA exp 11-4-80. Fuse. 01-93
☐	G-APEX	Viscount 806	ex BAF, BA, BEA. CoA exp 12-5-84. Fuselage.
☐	G-ASYN	Terrier 2	ex Sibson, VF519, 661. Dam 2-1-76. Spares.
☐	G-ATGG	Super Rallye	ex F-BKLR. CoA expired 14-10-83. Stored.
☐	G-AWAV	Cessna F.150F	ex OY-DKL. Crashed 10-10-83. 12-93
☐	G-AWCK	Cessna F.150H	crashed 30-9-75. Wreck. 01-93
☐	G-AWJI	Rallye Club	CoA expired 26-11-84. Stored.
☐	G-AWLJ	Cessna F.150H	crashed 20-11-84. Wreck. 01-93
☐	G-AWOC	MS.892A Rallye	crashed 13-6-74. Wreck.
☐	G-AXFH	Heron 1B/C	ex J6-LBD, G-AXFH, JA6161, PK-GHG. CoA expired 28-1-83. Stored. 12-90
☐	G-AXTK	Cherokee 140B	ex Andrewsfield. Crashed 6-9-81. 10-89
☐	G-AYRK	Cessna 150J	ex 5N-AII, N61170. CoA expired 25-4-76. Fuselage. 07-90
☐	G-AYYE	Cessna F.150L	crashed 26-4-78. Wreck, spares use. 01-93
☐	G-AZRW	Cessna T.337C	ex 9XR-DB, N2614S. CoA expired 7-6-82. Stored.
☐	G-BAPG	Viscount 814	ex SE-KBN ntu, G-BAPG, 4X-AVH, G-BAPG, D-ANIZ. CoA expired 23-3-90. Stored. 01-93
☐	G-BCAB	MS.894A Rallye	crashed 25-2-77. Wreck, spares use. 07-90

[Was in use for spares for MS.894A G-STOL, which went to the yard at Caterham, Surrey - see **W&R13**.]

□ G-BCTH	Cherokee 140	ex PH-VRN, N6661J. Cr 14-11-76. Wreck.
□ G-BCWA*	BAC 111-518FG	ex British World, G-OBWI ntu, G-AXMK, VP-LAK, G-AXMK, TG-ARA, G-AXMK. Last flight 1992. Spares use by 3-93. 11-93
□ G-BCXR*	BAC 111-517FE	ex British World, G-OBWK ntu, G-BCCV, VP-LAN, VP-BCQ, G-16-12. Last flight 26-6-92. Spares use by 3-93. 11-93
□ G-BDOZ	Fournier RF-5	ex Chinnor, 5Y-AOZ, D-KCIQ. CoA expired 5-9-83. Stored. Spares for G-BLAA. 12-93
		[RF-5 G-BLAA currently airworthy.]
□ G-BFYU*	Belfast	ex Heavylift, G-52-15, XR367, 53. Last flight 27-6-92. Stored. See notes above. 02-94
□ G-BLOA*	Viscount 806	ex BAF, G-AOYJ. *Viscount Jock Bryce OBE*. CoA expired 31-8-92. Stored. 10-93
□ G-BOHY*	HS.748-2B-378	ex D-AHSA. CoA expired 1-4-92. Stored. First noted 6-93. 06-93
□ G-BOHZ*	HS.748-2B-378	ex D-AHSB, G-11-17. CoA expired 3-4-92. Stored. First noted 6-93. 06-93
□ G-HDBC*	HS.748-2B-378	ex D-AHSC, G-11-18. CoA expired 28-7-92. Stored. First noted 6-93. 06-93
□ G-MAST	Cherokee 180	crashed 14-7-81. Wreck.
□ EI-BWI G-ASJC	BAC 111-201	ex N101EX, G-ASJC. CoA expired 29-8-90. 11-93
□ N162JC*	L 39 Albatros	ex Tchad, Libyan AF. F/n 10-91. Stored. 01-93
□ XS597*	Andover C.1	ex Shawbury, 60, 32, Brize Norton SF, 32, 46, Thorney Island SF, Abingdon SF, A&AEE. Flew in 11-11-93. 02-94
□ XS637*	Andover C.1	ex Shawbury, 60, 115, 32, AFN Oslo, Brize Norton SF, 32, Thorney Island SF, 52, 46. Flew in 1-11-93. Stored. 02-94

■ **Vulcan Restoration Trust** (VRT) : On July 28, 1993 ownership of Vulcan XL426 was transferred to the Vulcan Memorial Flight Supporters Club (VMFSC) which has been campaigning long and hard — often in the background — over the years to formalise the preservation of the aircraft. At the same time as ownership was transferred from Roy Jacobsen, the VMFSC settled all the outstanding debts on parking the delta with the Southend Airport Authorities. The spectre of the ever-increasing debt was always a problem with the stability of the project and with this wiped away VMFSC renamed itself on October 30, 1993 as the VRT to better underline its aims. A conservation programme is in hand with a long term view of achieving airworthy status.

◆ Visits to the aircraft are possible only by prior arrangement. ✉ Richard Clarkson, VRT, 39 Breakspears Drive, St Pauls Cray, Orpington, Kent, BR5 2RX.

□ XL426 G-VJET	Vulcan B.2	ex Waddington, VDF , Waddington SF, 50, 617, 27, 617, 230 OCU, 617, 230 OCU, 617, 230 OCU, 617, 230 OCU, Scampton Wing, 83. See notes. 12-92

■ **1312 Squadron ATC** : Keep their two airframes on the Airport site.

□ WB670 8361M	Chipmunk T.10	ex MoS, 5 FTS, LAS, 12 RFS, 5 RFS. PAX 2-92
□ XG325	Lightning F.1	ex Wattisham, Foulness, A&AEE. Nose.

■ **Locality** : Two Nigerian registered Chipmunk 22As (5N-AEE and 5N-AGP) moved into the area during 1991 from Shoreham, W Sussex, but moved again to <u>Gamston</u>, Notts, late 1991.

SOUTH WOODHAM FERRERS

The nose of a Canberra TT.22 came here from Stock, Essex, during February 1994.

□ WT525*	Canberra T.22	ex Stock, St Athan, FRADU, 17, 80. '855'. Nose. Arrived 12-2-94. 02-94

STANSTED AIRPORT (north of the A120 east of Bishop's Stortford and the M11, junction 8)

The Trident continues to serve the firemen in a non-destructive capacity, while the Dove labours on helping to teach electronics to apprentices.

□ G-ANUW	Dove 6	ex CAA CAFU. CoA exp 22-7-81. Inst. ʼ11-93
□ G-AWZU	Trident 3B-101	ex Heathrow, BA, BEA. CoA exp 3-7-85. 12-93

STAPLEFORD TAWNEY AERODROME (on the A113 south of the M11/M25 junction)
There has been a major increase in **W&R**-style inmates here.

☐ G-AREE*	Aztec 250	ex Biggin Hill. CoA expired 6-6-81. Stored. First noted 12-90.	12-90
☐ G-AXGD	MS.880B Rallye	CoA expired 8-7-85. Restoration.	
☐ G-AZTO*	Seneca 200-2	ex Linley Hill, N4516T. Crashed 27-8-92. Arrived 1-93. Spares.	07-93
☐ G-BHUP	Cessna F.152	ex Tattershall Thorpe. Cr 17-5-89. Fuse.	07-93
☐ G-BOIP*	Cessna 152 II	ex Tattershall Thorpe, Staverton, N49264. Damaged 11-1-90. Restn. First noted 11-92.	07-93

STOCK (on the B1007 south of Chelmsford)

■ **Hanningfield Metals** Took on a large batch of Phantoms from Wattisham, Suffolk, and St Athan, S Glam, in April 1993 and April 1992 respectively. The growing fascination with nose sections has not passed the owners of the yard by and the cockpit sections remain long after the remainder have been 'processed' in the hope of selling on the nose/cockpit. The wonderful Tiger-schemed Phantom FGR.2 XV404 came here in three sections during April 1993 and the company hoped to put it on display as a gate guardian. Keeping it intact was technically a breach of an arms treaty and XV404 was axed in front of MoD observers during the middle of April 1994. At least the nose of Canberra B.2 WJ676 came here from Wroughton, Wilts, but by mid-1993 it had moved on to <u>Liverpool</u>, Merseyside. Of the aircraft listed in **W&R13**, the following had passed on by February 1993 : — Canberra PR.7 WH796, Canberra T.22 WH803, Canberra B.2 WJ603, Canberra T.22 WT510, Canberra TT.22 WT525 nose moved to <u>South Woodham Ferrers</u>, Essex, on February 12, 1994; Victor K.2 XL163, Vulcan B.2 XM656, Buccaneer S.2A XN930. The nose of Canberra TT.18 WE122 moved to <u>North Weald</u>, Essex, by June 1992. Canberra PR.9 XH175 arrived here from St Athan, Mid Glam, by November 1991, and is used as a travelling exhibit. Canberra PR.9 nose XH165 also arrived from St Athan, S Glam, by November 1991 but by mid-1993 had gone to <u>Walpole</u>, Suffolk. Viscount 838 nose section XT661 arrived from DRA Bedford during August 1993. The nose section was presented on permanent loan to Cockpits for Hire and moved to <u>Bruntingthorpe</u>, Leics, during February 1994. Canadair CL-44J EI-BRP arrived from Southend, Essex, by March 1993 but was very quickly cut up into small pieces. Canberra TT.18 WK118 came here from Wyton, Cambs, with the nose section going on to <u>Worcester</u>, H&W. (The remainder was processed very quickly.) Jet Provost T.3 XM468/8081M arrived here from St Athan, S Glam, by June 1993 but moved to <u>King's Lynn</u>, Norfolk, by August 1993. Lightning F.6 XR754/8972M came here from Honington, Suffolk, by June 1993, but February 1994 the nose had moved on to <u>Lowestoft</u>, Suffolk. Buccaneer S.2B XW550 came in from St Athan, S Glam during 1992 and was quickly scrapped. The nose section went to <u>West Horndon</u>, Essex. See under Manston, Kent, for details of a clear out there.

Readers are reminded that it is always a difficult task listing the contents of a 'working' yard. During the putting together of this list, a lot of 'wishful thinking' needed editing out. For example, three *Bricks* from Shawbury, were 'reliably' noted here during December 1993 — probably as they had been covered in several enthusiast magazines as *due* here. They actually arrived during February 1994! The camouflaged Queen Air brought a flurry of U-8 Seminole sightings — including likely identities! And there are others... This puts the situation as follows.

☐ G-AOHT	Viscount 802	ex Southend, ZS-SKY, G-AOHT, BAF, BEA. CoA expired 16-5-86. Cockpit.	02-94
☐ G-AOYG*	Viscount 806	ex Southend, BAF, BA, BEA. *Sir Peter Masefield.* CoA expired 18-6-92. First noted 3-94.	03-94
☐ G-AOYL*	Viscount 806	ex Southend, BAF, BA, BEA. CoA expired 2-8-88. First noted 3-94.	02-94
☐ G-ASRX*	Queen Air A80	ex Chelmsford, Manston, Exeter. CoA expired 30-4-84. Fuselage, camouflaged. F/n 2-93.	02-94
☐ G-BDES*	Sikorsky S-61N II	ex Farnborough, BIH. Wreck. F/n 8-93.	02-94
☐ G-BEID*	Sikorsky S-61N	ex Farnborough, BIH, N317Y, JA9507, N317Y. Wreck. F/n 8-93.	02-94
☐ G-BNAA	Viscount 806	ex Southend, BAF, C-GWPY, G-AOYH, BAF, BA, BEA. CoA expired 22-3-88. Cockpit.	02-94
☐ G-LOND*	Viscount 806	ex Southend, BAF, G-AOYI, G-LOND, G-AOYI, BA, BEA. CoA exp 20-6-88. F/n 3-93.	02-94

☐ G-SOFS*		F-27-200	ex Southend, BAF, G-BLML, P2-ANC, P2-TFJ, VH-TFJ, PH-FBC. F/n 12-92. Sectioned. 02-94
☐ 4X-AVB		Viscount 833	ex Coggleshall, Tel Aviv, Arkia, BUA, G-APTB. Cockpit. 02-94
☐ 6V-AFX		HS.748-222	ex Southend, Air Senegal, CS-TAV, G-ATEK, RP-C1041, V2-LIV, VP-LIV, G-ATEK. Nose only by 12-91. 02-94
☐ 5N-xxx*		JetRanger	fuselage shell. Bristows colours with flying horse motif. First noted 8-93. 02-94
☐ WE173*		Canberra PR.3	ex Coltishall, Farnborough, 231 OCU, 39, RAE, 39, 69, 82. *Thought* arrived 18/2/92. Nose only by 6-93. 02-94
☐ WF425*		Varsity T.1	ex Duxford, RAE Met Flt, RAE, CFS, 1 ANS, 2 ANS. Sectioned. First noted 10-93. 02-94
☐ WH780*		Canberra T.22	ex St Athan, FRADU, 81, 82, 527, 58, 542. Nose. Arrived 2-93. 02-94
☐ WH797*		Canberra T.22	ex St Athan, FRADU, 81, 58, 542. '851'. Cockpit. First noted 8-92. 02-94
☐ WH801		Canberra T.22	ex St Athan, FRADU, 17, 31, 13, 58, 540. '850'. Nose only by 2-93. 02-94
☐ WH981*		Canberra E.15	ex Wyton, 100, MoD(PE), 100, 98, 45, Akrotiri, 73, 9. 'CN'. Sectioned. Here by 5-93. 02-94
☐ WJ861*		Canberra T.4	ex St Athan, 231 OCU, PRU, 39, 7, 100, 85, 231 OCU, 31, Laarbruch SF, Wyton SF, Weston Zoyland SF, Marham SF. 'BF'. Arr 1-2-94. 02-94
☐ WK144	8689M	Canberra B.2	ex St Athan, 85, 98, 245, 527. Fuselage. 02-94
☐ WT301*		Canberra B.6 (m)	ex Chattenden, 51, 192. Arrived by 11-93. 02-94
☐ WT518*	8691M	Canberra PR.7	ex St Athan, 8133M, 31, 80, 31. Nose and mid-fuselage. Arrived 8-93. 02-94
☐ XA801*	7739M	Javelin FAW.2	ex Stafford, St Athan, 46. Arrived 10-94. 02-94
☐ XH133*		Canberra PR.9	ex St Athan, 1 PRU, 39, 13, MinTech, 13, MoA. First noted 6-93. Nose. 02-94
☐ XH175*		Canberra PR.9	ex St Athan, 1 PRU, 39, 58. Arrived 11-91. Nose, travelling exhibit. 02-94
☐ XH177*		Canberra PR.9	ex Cardiff-Wales, Boscombe Down, 13, 58. Nose. Arrived 1-2-94. 02-94
☐ XN769*	8402M	Lightning F.2	ex West Drayton, Leconfield, 92, 19, 92. 'Z'. Arrived 16-1-94. 02-94
☐ XN983*		Buccaneer S.2B	ex Shawbury, 12, 208, 12, 15, 12. F/n 02-94 02-94
☐ XR519		Wessex HC.2	ex Shawbury, 2 FTS, 18. Sectioned. First noted 3-93. 02-94
☐ XS506*		Wessex HU.5	ex Shawbury, Wroughton, 845. Sectioned. First noted 3-93. 02-94
☐ XS922*		Lightning F.6	ex Wattisham, Binbrook, 5-11 pool, 56, 5. 'BJ'. Nose. First noted 6-93. 02-94
☐ XT451*		Wessex HU.5	ex Shawbury, Wroughton, 845. 'N'. First noted 3-93. 02-94
☐ XT575*		Viscount 837	ex DRA Bedford, OE-LAG. Arr 8-93. 02-94
☐ XT874*	9068M	Phantom FG.1	ex Bruntingthorpe, Wattisham, 111, 43. Arrived by 2-94. Sectioned. 02-94
☐ XT898*		Phantom FGR.2	ex Wattisham, 56, 228 OCU, 29, 228 OCU, 19, 2, 228 OCU. See notes. Fuselage. 02-94
☐ XV165*		Buccaneer S.2B	ex Shawbury, 12. First noted 02-94. 02-94
☐ XV398*		Phantom FGR.2	ex Wattisham, 56, 228 OCU 'CI'. See notes. 02-94
☐ XV399*		Phantom FGR.2	ex Wattisham, 56, 228 OCU, 29, 41, 2 See notes. Nose. 02-94
☐ XV402*		Phantom FGR.2	ex Wattisham, 56, 29, 23, 228 OCU, 23, 92, 41 See notes. Nose. 02-94

☐ XV495*		Phantom FGR.2	ex Wattisham, 23, 29, 56, 228 OCU, 29, 41, 6.
			See notes. Fuselage.	02-94
☐ XV869*		Buccaneer S.2B	ex Shawbury, 12, 208. First noted 12-93.	02-94
☐ XW298*	9013M	Jet Provost T.5	ex Abingdon, Scampton, 6 FTS, 1 FTS. Arrived
			by 5-92.	02-94
☐ *		Harrier	ex Stafford, Abingdon, Hamble. Arrived *circa*
			11-92. See notes under Abingdon, Oxon.	02-94

STONDON (off the A128 south east of Chipping Ongar)
■ **Thurston Engineering** : The Tawney Owl is still stored here.
☐ G-APWU   Tawney Owl   Crashed on its first and only flight at Stapleford
                                22-4-60. Stored.

WEST HANNINGFIELD (west of the A130, south of Chelmsford)
The Blackburn B-2 hulk *is* still listed here, but shows no signs of having been worked on.
☐ G-ACBH 2895M   Blackburn B-2   ex Wickham Bishops, Downham, Ramsden Heath,
                                         Brentwood. Fuse. CoA exp 27-11-41.   01-94

WEST HORNDON (west of Basildon, south of the A127)
■ **Project XW550** : Broderick Kelley acquired the nose section of a former Stock, Essex,
Buccaneer and is actively restoring it.
✉ Broderick Kelley, 47 Freshwell Gardens, West Horndon, Essex, CM13 3NE.
☐ XW550*   Buccaneer S.2B   ex Stock, St Athan, 16, 15. Nose. Restn.   12-93

Gloucestershire

ASTON DOWN AIRFIELD (south of the A419 west of Cirencester)
■ **Cotswold Gliding Club** : Two gliders of a long term nature deserve mention.
☐ FMD*   BGA.3362 Ka 7 Rhonadler   ex D-2877, HB-603. Damaged 6-5-92. Stored.
                                          First noted 5-92.   10-93
☐ XP493*   Grasshopper TX.1   first noted 7-91. Stored.   10-93
■ **MoD (PE)** : Phantom FG.1 XT858 was offered for tender during June 1993. The deal fell
through and it was re-offered in February 1994.
☐ XT858   Phantom FG.1   ex Brough, Holme-on-Spalding Moor, Leuchars,
                                 Aldergrove, Hucknall, A&AEE, RAE, Hucknall,
                                 700P, RAE. See notes above.   02-94

CHELTENHAM
■ **Geoff Lewis:** Is working hard on the former Long Marston *Flying Flea*. It will be fitted with a
425cc Citroen engine with the aim of taxying it..
☐ 'G-ADRY'* BAPC.77 HM.14 *Flea*   ex Long Marston, Innsworth, Ross-on-Wye,
                                       Staverton. Restoration - see notes above.   10-93
■ **Nick Parker** : Took delivery of a Scimitar nose during February 1994.
☐ XD215* A2573   Scimitar F.1   ex Ottershaw, Foulness, Culdrose, 764B, 800, 803,
                                        A&AEE. Nose. Arrived 19-2-94.   02-94

CIRENCESTER
Still kept (along with a fire engine) in the garden of a house on the A417/A419 eastern bypass is the
former WAM Gannet.
☐ XA459 A2608   Gannet AS.4   ex Cardiff-Wales, Culdrose SAH-7,
                                      Lee-on-Solent, 831.   11-93

GLOUCESTERSHIRE AIRPORT (or Staverton, on the B4063 west of Cheltenham)

W&R13 reported Twin Pioneer G-ACWF as being taken on by a "well-known operator". This was indeed Air Atlantique from Coventry Airport. *Primrose* (as she is known) was used for a geophysical survey then returned for temporary storage at Staverton. The *Twin Pin* was back at Coventry by mid-1993 and was being prepared for a full-blown Public Transport Category Certificate of Airworthiness. Heron 'G-ODLG'/G-ORSJ was a fixture on the skyline here since at least 1991. It was sold to Heron Airlines of Australia, becoming VH-NJP, departing on the great trek September 9, 1993. Clarifying **W&R13**, the DH.88 Comet project is still to be found stored here. Stored here since 1989 is Fiat G.46 G-BBII.

☐ G-ACSP	DH.88 Comet	ex Bodmin, Chirk, Portugal, CS-AAJ, E-1. Black Magic Ltd. See notes above.	03-92
☐ G-AJOE	Messenger 2A	ex Innsworth, 'RH378'. CoA expired 4-3-77. CARG — see under Innsworth, Glos.	
☐ G-AVVF	Dove 8	CoA expired 11-2-88. Dump.	10-93
☐ G-AWEK*	Fournier RF-4D	ex Biggin Hill. Crashed 25-10-72. Fuselage. First noted 12-91.	12-91
☐ G-BBII*	Fiat G.46-3B	ex I-AEHU, MM52801. '14', *Luftwaffe* c/s. CoA expired 19-7-89. Stored.	07-93
☐ WL349	Meteor T.7	ex Kemble, 1 ANS, 2 ANS, CFE, 229 OCU. 'Z'. Placed in store by 10-93.	10-93
☐ XK896 G-RNAS	Sea Devon C.20	ex 781, Hal Far SF, 781. CoA expired 3-7-84. Stored.	05-93

■ **Locally** : Without information to the contrary, the two 'off-site' Tigers are still listed.

☐ G-ANOM	Tiger Moth	ex airfield, Maidens Green, N6837, Finningley SF, 1 GU, 2 GS, 11 RFS, 11 EFTS, 217. Crashed 17-12-61.
☐ G-BNDW	Tiger Moth	ex airfield, Cranfield. Composite, mostly N6638 in which case ex Fairford CF, 27 GCF, St Mawgan CF, Prestwick CF, 25 PFTS, 22 ERFTS.

HUCCLECOTE (close to the M5 east of Gloucester)

■ **Gloucestershire Aviation Collection** (GAC) : The store of airframes waiting patiently for a museum site has expanded somewhat. A business plan has been drawn up for a museum building and fund raising for the £1.2million project is underway. Included in the latter exercise is an excellent series of commemorative plates marking the 75th anniversary of the founding of the Gloster Aircraft Company. GAC are committed to the building of a full-scale Gloster Gamecock replica and this major project may well see a 'flyer' come out of the deal as well. The former Innsworth Javelin is now on site and the former Batley, W Yorks, Hunter T.7 is also stored here on behalf of a GAC member. Awaiting collection at Innsworth, Glos, is the forward fuselage of a Harrier T.2.

◆ By prior arrangement only. ✉ GAC, Unit 2B, Gloucester Trading Estate, Hucclecote, Gloucester GL3 4AA. ☎ 0242 515533 or '577240.

☐ WL360	7920M	Meteor T.7	ex Locking, 229 OCU, 1, Wattisham SF, 211 AFS, 210 AFS, 215 AFS. 'G'. Restn.	12-93
☐ XH903*	7938M	Javelin FAW.9	ex Innsworth, Shawbury, 5, 33, 29, 33, 23. First noted 10-93.	12-93
☐ N-315*		Hunter T.7	ex Batley, Amsterdam, NLS spares, Dutch AF, XM121. Arrived 8-9-93. See notes.	12-93

INNSWORTH (west of the B4063, near Parton, north east of Gloucester)

■ **Cotswold Aircraft Restoration Group** (CARG) : 'Supply missions' large and small continue to be CARG's forte. Work continues on their own restoration projects — their Messenger at Gloucestershire Airport, Glos, progresses with first flight anticipated during 1994. Tiger Moth G-AMBB and Auster 6A G-ASIP are 'lodgers', being stored for their owner and are likely to move during 1994. Another Tiger Moth needs 'unveiling' here; 'G-MAZY' being readied to go on display at the Newark Air Museum, Winthorpe, Notts. This originated as a collection of parts (including no less than seven wings, originating from DH.60, DH.82 and Jackaroo sources). The airframe — which will be displayed partially covered so as to reveal its structure — came from Neville Franklin and is expected to travel to Newark during 1994, its previous identity has yet to be established. The forward fuselage of Harrier T.2 XW264 is due for collection by the Gloucestershire Aviation Collection — see under Hucclecote, Glos. CARG's excellent restoration of the Meteor T.7 came to fruition during mid-1993 and was due to be placed on the gate of their host, RAF Innsworth, by January 1994 — see below.

◆ Visits to the workshop are possible only by prior application. ✉ Steve Thompson, CARG, *Kia-Ora*, Risbury, Leominster, Herefordshire, HR6 0NQ.

☐ G-AMBB		Tiger Moth	ex Staverton. Composite, mostly T6801, ex Scampton SF, 6 FTS, 18 EFTS. See notes.	12-93
☐ G-ASIP		Auster 6A	ex Gloucestershire, Nympsfield, Heathrow, VF608, 12 Flt, 652,1904 Flt, Hague Air Attaché. Damaged 7-5-73. See notes above.	12-93
☐ 'G-MAZY'		Tiger Moth	composite. See notes above.	12-93
☐ R9371		Halifax II	ex local, 10. Cr 9-3-42. Cockpit section.	12-93
☐ XN412		Auster AOP.9	ex Swindon, Dorchester, Middle Wallop, 6 Flt, C(A). Stored for future rebuild.	12-93
☐ XR267	G-BJXR	Auster AOP.9	ex Staverton, Congresbury, St Athan, 655, 652. Under restoration to flying status.	12-93
☐ XW264		Harrier T.2	ex Dowty, Boscombe Down, HSA. Damaged 11-7-70. Forward fuselage. See Notes.	12-93

■ **RAF Innsworth** : Javelin FAW.9 XH903 finally left the site by October 1993, going to storage at Hucclecote, Glos. CARG's Meteor T.7 restoration was unveiled on the gate on March 5, 1994.

☐ VW453	8703M	Meteor T.7	ex Salisbury Plain, Hullavington, Takali, 604, 226 OCU, 203 AFS. Gate.	03-94

KEMBLE AIRFIELD (on the A429 south west of Cirencester)

■ **RAF Kemble / Army Sub Depot** : The joint RAF/USAF presence here ceased on July 31, 1992 and the base was transferred to the Army for use as a temporary storage facility. The long term future of the base/airfield has yet to be decided. Meteor F.8 WH364 was taken off the gate on April 10, 1992 and was subsequently acquired by the Avon Air Museum / Meteor Flight and moved to Yatesbury, Wilts. Interestingly, Harrier GR.3 XV810 arrived from Abingdon, Oxon, by May 1992, just in time for the closure!

☐ XV810*	9038M	Harrier GR.3	ex Abingdon, St Athan, 233 OCU, 4, 20. 'K'. Arrived by 5-92.	05-92

MORETON-IN-MARSH (on the A44 north east of Cheltenham)

■ **Home Office Fire Training College** : Located on the former airfield, the school has managed to collect a number of airframes and has announced plans for expansion. Further details much appreciated, the information given here being gleaned mostly from a fly-by! Also out on the airfield is a large airliner fuselage — this is a purpose-built mock-up. (See also under Bournemouth Airport, Dorset, for a possible inmate.)

☐ G-BAPF*		Viscount 814	ex Southend, Hot-Air-Baltic, SE-FOY, G-BAPF, D-ANUN. CoA exp 13-6-90. Arr 15-2-92.	04-93
☐ XM404*	8055BM	Jet Provost T.3	ex Halton, Newton, Shawbury, 3 FTS, 2 FTS. Arrived by 4-93.	04-93
☐ *		Wessex HAS.3	See notes above.	04-93
☐ *		Jet Provost T.5	See notes above.	04-93
☐ *		Jet Provost	nose section. See notes above.	04-93

■ **Wellington Aviation Art** : Gerry Tyack's superb aviation art and print gallery is always worth a visit. Among the impressive array of artefacts lie the substantial remains of Wellington L7775. Most of the memorabilia centre around the local airfield, home of 21 OTU, and the Wellington.

◆ Open 10am to 12am and 2.30pm to 5.30pm daily. On the A44 east of the town. ✉ British School House, Moreton-in-the-Marsh, Glos GL56 0BG. ☎ 0608 50323

☐ L7775		Wellington I	ex Firbeck, Braemar, 20 OTU. Crashed 23-10-40. Substantial sections.	06-92

NYMPSFIELD AERODROME (off the B4066, south west of Stroud)
A Grob has joined the store of motorgliders and gliders here. Grasshopper TX.1 WZ831 was last noted here during July 1992.

☐ G-AXIW	SF.25B Falke	ex D-KABJ ntu. Crashed 27-4-91. Stored	07-93
☐ G-ROBB*	Grob G.109B	ex Eaglescott. Crashed 4-7-88. Forward fuselage. First noted 6-91	07-93
☐ WZ796	Grasshopper TX.1	ex Halton, Eastbourne. Stored	07-93
☐	Grasshopper TX.1	stored.	07-93

QUEDGELEY
■ **RAF Quedgeley** : The Meteor is still displayed on No 1 site of the large storage facility. Also here is the centre-section of Britannia 308F G-ANCF — the bulk of which is now at Banwell, Avon.

☐ WF784	7895M	Meteor T.7	ex Kemble, 5 CAACU, CAW, FTU, 130, 26. Gate.	05-93

STROUD
■ **1329 Squadron ATC** : Chipmunk T.10 WP845 was acquired by Sandy Topen and left here 28-5-92, eventually moving to <u>Cranfield</u>, Beds.

Hampshire

ALDERSHOT
■ **Airborne Forces Museum** : With the 50th anniversaries of the Normandy and Arnhem operations, the Museum will be staging special displays and there is a full-blown open day on June 3, 1994. Conservation work on the Dakota has been successfully carried out and it is hoped that it will be open to internal inspection on occasions during 1994.
◆ Open every day, except Mondays and Christmas, 10am to 4.30pm. Special group visits by prior arrangement. ✉ Browning Barracks, Aldershot, Hampshire, GU11 2DS. ☎ 0252 349619 (Note, *new* number.)

☐ KP208	Dakota IV	ex Kemble, AFNE, Air Adviser New Delhi, AFNE, HCCF, 24, MEAF, USAAF 44-77087. Displayed outside. 'YS'.	11-93
☐	Hotspur II	full nose section and part of troop bay.	11-93
☐	Horsa II	full nose section.	11-93

ANDOVER
■ **Viv Bellamy-Hampshire Aeroplane Company** : Work on the Barracuda DP872 was suspended and it moved back to <u>Yeovilton</u>, Som, by September 1992.
■ **Durney Collection** : Work on the restoration of the Dragon Rapide project continues.

☐ G-ALAX	Dragon Rapide	ex Old Warden, Luton, RL948, ERS, 27 GCF. CoA expired 8-3-67. Composite, including parts from G-AFRK, G-AHGC, G-AHJS and G-ASRJ.

■ **Spitfire Society** : During late 1992 the Spitfire prototype replica 'K5054' (BAPC.214) moved to AeroFab's workshop at <u>Thruxton</u>, Hants, in readiness for its debut at the RAF Museum.

CALSHOT
Edward Hulton sold Sunderland V G-BJHS in March 1993 to well-known US collector and operator Kermit Weeks. The flying-boat departed on a ferry flight that took it to stardom at Oshkosh on July 20, 1993. The end of an era.

CHILBOLTON AERODROME (east of the A3057, south of Andover)
Another one bites the dust... The aerodrome is no more, the runways have all but gone. Chilbolton Aviation ceased trading and biplanes no more grace the airfield. Clearing up the reference in **W&R13**, Tiger Moth G-ANDE was flying from Redhill, Surrey, by 1992. Canuck CS-ACQ turned up at

Atherstone, Warks. Wessex Air Contracts have also gone, with only one of the Hillers surviving in a forlorn manner near what was their hangar — now a dried flower workshop! All the others, several of which were to be found stored inside the old control tower, are believed to have been scrapped : — Hiller UH-12Es G-AVKY, G-AZSV, G-BBLD, G-BDFO and AP-AWQ; Westland-Bell 47Gs G-BGFS and G-BGOZ.

☐ G-BEDK Hiller UH-12E ex XS706, 705. CoA exp 14-6-85. Cabin. 08-93

FARLEY (on the A27 north of Southampton)
No news on the C.336/337 gathering here.

☐ G-ASLL	Cessna 336	ex Bournemouth, Doncaster, N1774Z. CoA expired 6-1-74. Stored.	02-90
☐ G-ATAH	Cessna 336	ex Bournemouth, N1707Z. CoA exp 5-12-76. Stored.	02-90
☐ G-ATSM	Cessna 337A	ex Exeter, N5334S. CoA exp 29-7-88. Stored.	
☐ G-BBBL	Cessna 337B	ex EI-AVF, 5H-MNL, N5455S. CoA expired 12-2-77. Stored.	
☐ G-BNNG	Cessna T.337D	ex Bournemouth, G-COLD, PH-NOS, N86147. CoA expired 15-7-85.	01-90
☐ N1721Z	Cessna 336	ex Bournemouth, Isle of Mull. Cr 10-7-74.	02-90

FARNBOROUGH

■ **Prince's Mead Shopping Centre** : The SE.5A replica is due to move to Tangmere, W Sussex, early in 1994.
☐ 'D2700' BAPC.208 SE.5A replica built by AJD Engineering. See notes above. 11-93
■ **Locally** : Tiger Moth G-APMX moved to Hungerford, Berks, by November 1990. No news on the Swiss Pup thought to be in the area.
☐ HB-NBA Pup 150 ex Redhill, Elstree.

FARNBOROUGH AIRFIELD (east of the A325, north of Aldershot)
■ **Defence Research Agency (Aerospace Division)** (DRA) : Far from there being a wind-down of airframes here, as predicted in **W&R13**, there has been a decided increase — although this will only be a fleeting state. The removal of DRA (other than the wind tunnel site) from here to Boscombe Down, Wilts, continues, with several buildings having been demolished. DRA flying was due to cease here on March 25, 1994. The SBAC show will certainly be staged in 1994 and the organisers say that it will go on "indefinitely" after that. The civil enclave has expanded and along with its twee-looking industrial estate should keep an aviation interest alive on the site. Greatest influx of airframes has come from the appearance of a whole host of Soviet made hardware which has been in the country for a long time, but only recently surfaced. All the tests and evaluations must have been made for the material to be dumped so publicly. Of these, the nose of MiG-21UM *Mongol* 0446 was first noted on the dump during September 1992, but moved to Salisbury, Wilts, in March 1994. Likewise, the nose of Su-7 Fitter 7907 was first seen on the dump during September 1992 and moved to Robertsbridge, East Sussex during March 1994. Many of the RAE airframes listed below lack up-to-date 'last seen' dates, so the situation might not be as fulsome as the list implies. Disposals have been as follows : — long, long term resident, the Broburn Wanderlust sailplane, moved to Woodley, Berks (its birthplace) by October 1992; Varsity T.1 WL679 flew to Cosford, Salop, on July 27, 1992 making the last flight ever by the type; Canberra B(I).6 WT308 moved to Culdrose, Cornwall, on September 19, 1992; Nimrod prototype XV147, in sections since at least October 1992 was removed by road on December 11 and 12, 1993, going to Warton, Lancs. The anonymous Sea Vixen FAW.2 nose on the dump turned out to be XJ579 and it moved to Coventry Airport, Warks, during September 1992. The TSR-2 nose section moved to Brooklands, Surrey, during August 1992.

☐ G-ANNG		Tiger Moth	ex DE524, 15 EFTS. CoA expired 29-11-67. Restoration.	09-93
☐ APW	BGA.562	Olympia 1	ex G-ALJZ. Crashed 20-7-58. Stored.	
☐ WE146		Canberra PR.3	ex RAE. Nose section only. Dump.	04-91
☐ WJ865		Canberra T.4	ex ETPS. Apprentices.	01-94
☐ WT333*		Canberra B(I).8	ex DRA Bedford, RAE, C(A). Last flight 9-2-94. Pending disposal.	02-94
☐ WV276	7847M	Hunter F.4	ex Halton, Horsham St Faith, A&AEE, R-R.	12-93

☐ XD860		Valiant BK.1	ex 214, 138, 214. Nose section.	
☐ XF844		Provost T.1	ex RAE, 6 FTS. '70'. Apprentices.	10-92
☐ XJ396		W'wind HAR.10	ex RAE Lasham, XD776 ntu. Derelict.	
☐ XL563*		Hunter T.7	ex IAM, MoA, Hawkers. Withdrawn from use by 2-94. For display.	01-94
☐ XM330*		Wessex HAS.1	ex RAE. Stored.	12-93
☐ XN688	8141M	Sea Vixen FAW.2	ex Halton, 893, 899, 890. Dump, poor state	10-92
☐ XP166		Scout AH.1	ex RAE, G-APVL. Apprentices.	10-92
☐ XP393		W'wind HAR.10	ex Wroughton, RAE, 28, 103, 225. Derelict.	
☐ XP516	8580M	Gnat T.1	ex 4 FTS. Structures Laboratory.	12-93
☐ XP925		Sea Vixen FAW.2	ex Tarrant Rushton, ADS, 899. '752'. Nose section. Dump.	10-92
☐ XS482		Wessex HU.5	ex A&AEE. RAE Apprentices.	10-92
☐ XT272		Buccaneer S.2	ex RAE Bedford. Dismantled.	01-94
☐ XV631		Wasp HAS.1	ex Wroughton, *Endurance* Flt.	
☐ XW241		SA.330E Puma	ex RAE Bedford, F-ZJUX. Stored.	12-93
☐ XW428*		Jet Provost T.5A	ex 3 FTS, RAFC, 1 FTS, 3 FTS. '39'. Apprentices. Arrived 18-6-91.	10-92
☐ XW566		Jaguar T.2	ex RAE, A&AEE. Stored.	12-93
☐ XW930 *		HS.125-1B	ex DRA Bedford, RAE, G-ATPC. Arrived 20-5-92. Stored.	12-92
☐ XX344*	8847M	Hawk T.1	ex Abingdon, Dunsfold, RAE. Crashed 7-1-82. Arrived by 9-92. Dump.	09-92
☐ XX907		Lynx AH.1	ex RAE. Stored.	
☐ XX910		Lynx HAS.2	ex RAE. Stored.	
☐ 2684*		MiG-19	ex Egyptian AF. Nose. First noted 9-92.	10-92
☐ 702*	20+48	MiG-23BN	ex Boscombe Down (?), *Luftwaffe*, LSK-LV. First noted 10-92.	10-92
☐ 98+10*		Su-22M-4	ex Boscombe Down, LSK-LV 820. F/n 9-92.	10-92
☐ *		Mil Mi-24 *Hind*	ex Boscombe Down, Afghanistan (?). First noted 10-92.	10-92
☐ *		Su-7	ex Egyptian AF. Fuselage. First noted 9-92.	09-92

■ **Civil enclave** : Gulfstream II VR-BRM gathered dust here from at least early 1992 as a monument to that memorable Atlantic non-swimmer and pensions consultant, Robert Maxwell. It became N194WA and quickly N57HJ during August 1993 and is thought to have moved on.

FLEET

■ *Dakotas* : The bistro continues to serve good food while those noshing are surrounded by large chunks of C-47A N9050T. The tail was removed from Fleet Pond during July 1992 — rescue services kept being called out! — and thought scrapped.

☐ N9050T		C-47A	ex Thruxton, Hal Safi, 5N-ATA, PH-MAG, G-AGYX, KG437, 42-92656. Sections with bistro, including nose.	07-92

FLEETLANDS (on the B3334 south of Fareham)

■ **RNAY Fleetlands Museum** : Two of the airframes previously held here have moved on, both to Middle Wallop, Hants, by May 1992 :— Whirlwind HAR.10 XK988/A2646 and Skeeter AOP.12 XL738/7860M. As well as the airframes, there is a large display on the history of the 'Yard.
◆ By prior arrangement only. ✉ Curator, RNAY Fleetlands Museum, Gosport, Hants. ☎ 0707 822351, ext 44391.

☐ WV783	7841M	Sycamore HR.12	ex Henlow, HDU Old Sarum, CFS, ASWDU.	01-94
☐ XJ481		Sea Vixen FAW.1	ex Southampton, Ilkeston, Yeovilton, Portland, Yeovilton, Boscombe Down, LRWE Woomera. On FAAM charge.	01-94
☐ XL853	A2630	Whirlwind HAS.7	ex Southampton, Middle Wallop, Lee-on-Solent, Wroughton, Yeovilton SF, 824.	01-94
☐		Gannet AS.?	nose section.	

■ **Royal Naval Aircraft Yard** (RNAY) : A considerable influx of airframes here. Readers are reminded that the 'meat' of the work undertaken at the RNAY is of the 'in-and-out' nature and therefore beyond the scope of **W&R**. Airframes listed here are instructional and long-term stored. There have been a couple of departures :— Hunter T.7 XL600 was put up for tender during March 1992 and left by road for Southall, Gtr Lon, on June 5, 1992. Wessex HAS.3 XM923 had served on the dump, but had gone by March 1992 — in its place was an ornamental fishpond! CH-47C Chinook AE-520/ZH257 arrived by road from Wroughton, Wilts, by August 1992. It left by road on September 28, 1993 and was noted running clockwise on the M25 (at Junction 13, no less) that day. Destination is thought to be Boeing-Vertol in the 'States, either to add to the HC.2 conversion line, or — more likely — to act as an installation trials airframe. A cache of Wasp HAS.1s (XS541, XS562, XT420, XT793 & XV639) arrived from Wroughton, Wilts, during 1992 but were offered for tender during November 1993. Three (XS541, XS562 and XV639) were sold to a dealer in New York — where there is an historic and buoyant market for Wasps! They were shipped out in April 1994. XT793 moved to Bruntingthorpe, Leics, and XT420 went to Ipswich, Suffolk. Wasp HAS.1 XT795 arrived on August 5, 1992 (from Wroughton) but left by road on April 19, 1993 bound for De Kooy in the Netherlands and preservation.

☐ XP110	A2714 (2)	Wessex HAS.3	ex Wroughton, 737. '55-FL'. Apprentices.	06-92
☐ XS523		Wessex HU.5	ex Wroughton, 781. '824-CU'.	06-92
☐ XS539*	A2718 (3)	Wasp HAS.1	ex Lee-on-Solent, 829 *Endurance* Flt. '461'. Arrived by 8-92.	08-92
☐ XS568		Wasp HAS.1	ex 829. '441'. Boom of XS539. Apps.	06-92
☐ XS569		Wasp HAS.1	ex Wroughton. Apprentices.	06-92
☐ XS868	A2706	Wessex HAS.1	ex A2691, Wroughton. Gate guardian.	06-92
☐ XT434*		Wasp HAS.1	ex Lee-on-Solent, 829. '455'. Arr by 8-92.	06-92
☐ XT480		Wessex HU.5	ex Wroughton, 847. 'XQ'.	06-92
☐ XT759*		Wessex HU.5	ex Wroughton, 847, 771, 846, 848. 'XY'. Arrived 2-9-92.	12-93
☐ XT780		Wasp HAS.1	ex Wroughton, 703. '636'. Apprentices.	06-92
☐ XV127*		Scout AH.1	ex Chelsea, Wroughton, Army Recruiting, Wroughton, 655. Arrived by 1-93. Stored.	07-93
☐ XV657*		Sea King HAS.5	ex Wroughton, 826. '132'. Arr 20-5-92.	12-93
☐ XW860*		Gazelle HT.2	ex Wroughton, 705. Arrived 22-5-92.	05-92
☐ XW890*		Gazelle HT.2	ex Wroughton, 705. '53-CU'. 'Pod' only. Arrived 27-7-92.	12-93
☐ XZ671*		Lynx AH.7	ex Yeovil, Wroughton. Crashed 24-1-85. Arr by 4-93. Stripped shell. Under conversion to AH.9 ground trainer, using boom of ZE377.	11-93
☐ QP30*		Lynx Mk 28	ex Almondbank, Wroughton, Qatar Police, G-BFDV. Arr by 3-93, conv to ground tnr.	03-93
☐ QP31*		Lynx Mk 28	ex Almondbank, Wroughton, Qatar Police. Arrived by 11-93. See QP30 above.	01-94

GOSPORT

■ **Gosport Aviation Society** : Work continues on the restoration of the Dragonfly.
✉ Gosport Aviation Society, 38 Wycote Road, Bridgemary, Fareham, Hants.

☐ VX595	Dragonfly HR.1	ex Fleetlands, Henlow, Fleetlands. Restn.	06-91

■ **Bernie Salter** : No news on the arrival of the nose of Lancaster X FM118 from Shilo, Manitoba.

HAMBLE

■ **British Aerospace** : The Gnat still guards the former Folland plant.

☐ XM693	7891M	Gnat T.1	ex Abingdon, Bicester, A&AEE.	10-91

HAVANT

■ **Military Vehicle Conservation Group** (MVCG) : Restoration of the Auster should continue.
✉ MVCG, 86 Priorsdean Crescent, Leigh Park, Havant, Hants, TO9 3AU.

☐ G-AGYL	J/1 Autocrat	ex Lasham, White Waltham. Cr 6-7-64. Fitted with wings of VF505 and VX110. Restn.	

HEDGE END (on the A334 east of Southampton)

■ **British Classic Aircraft Restorations** (BCAR) : BCAR acquired the nose section of Hunter F.5 WN980 from Boscombe Down, Wilts, on September 12, 1992. They exchanged it for a Grasshopper TX.1 and this can be found at <u>Hatch</u>, Beds, by February 1993. The Hunter travelled to <u>Hatch</u>, Beds, by February 1993. Auster J/1N Alpha G-AGXT moved to <u>Shoreham</u>, W Sussex, for Terry McCrae. Terry is also looking after BCAR's Cadet TX.2 at the same location. The identity of Auster 6A G-ARDX is now doubted, certainly in terms of the BCAR example, which is thought given more correctly below.

◆ Visits are possible only by prior application. ✉ BCAR, Steve Challis, 40 Peverells Wood Avenue, Chandlers Ford, Hants.

☐	G-ANLU	TW448	Auster 5	ex Elvington. CoA expired 8-8-68. Restn. 11-92
☐	G-ARLO		Terrier 1	ex Slinfold, TW642, 663, deH. Cr 10-7-79. 11-92
☐			Auster 6	ex Warmingham, Rearsby. Undrilled frame. 11-92
☐	*		Spitfire V cockpit	ex Salisbury. Replica, built by TDL, Lowestoft. Travelling exhibit. Arrived 3-93. 03-93
☐	XK421*	8365M	Auster AOP.9	ex Fownhope, Long Marston, Innsworth, Bristol, Caldicote, St Athan, Detmold, 'Wallop. Frame. Arrived during mid-1993. 12-93

HOOK (north of the M3, near Junction 5)

Rebuild of the Auster continues at the strip.

☐	G-AJXC		Auster 5	ex TJ343, 652, 655. CoA exp 2-8-82. Restn. 08-93

LASHAM AERODROME (west of Golden Pot, north west of Alton)

■ **Airfield** : With FLS Aerospace, the hulk of HS.748 G-ARAY had moved to a compound on the south side by February 1993 and its days are thought to be numbered. With the Lasham Gliding Society on the north side, a Cessna 150 wreck is stored.

☐	G-ARAY		HS.748-1A-200	ex Dan-Air, OY-DFV, G-11, G-ARAY, PI-C784, G-ARAY, VP-LIO, G-ARAY, PP-VJQ, G-ARAY, YV-C-AMC, G-ARAY. CoA expired 16-6-90. Scrap compound by 2-93. 02-93
☐	G-BBNY*		Cessna FRA.150L	ex Blackbushe. Cr 8-6-86. Wreck, stored. 11-92

■ **DRA enclave** : The Comet serves on at the telecommunications and radar site on the south east side of the airfield. During 1993 a battered and very patched up Lynx fuselage had arrived here.

☐	G-ALYX		Comet 1	ex Farnborough. CoA expired 21-7-54. Noseless fuselage. 02-93
☐	XW836*		Westland 606	ex Lee-on-Solent, Middle Wallop, Yeovil, Sherborne, Yeovil. Arrived by 6-93. 06-93

■ **Second World War Aircraft Preservation Society** (SWWAPS) : Expansion of the buildings on site have meant an enlarged shop and other facilities. As well as the aircraft and artefact collection, SWWAPS offers a commanding view of the intensive gliding activity on the airfield. After a long struggle the Meteor composite is now whole having found a radome and nose extension. The radome, a *pukka* NF.14 type, was another Cotswold Aircraft Restoration Group 'supply mission', the radome having been previously in use as a dog kennel! SWWAPS are happy and so it seems is the dog, which now gets to sleep in the garage! Correcting **W&R13**, Wessex HAS.3 XM833 did *not* journey to the ill-fated collection at Long Marston, and is still to be found here. It is owned by group member Clive Forshaw.

◆ Located to the east of the gliding headquarters, on the north side of the airfield. Open Sundays and Bank Holidays 10am to 6pm (or dusk if first) and other times by arrangement. ✉ Bob Coles, 8 Barracane Drive, Crowthorne, Berks, RG11 7NU.

☐	'VH-FDT'	G-APXX	Drover II	ex Blackbushe, S'end, G-APXX, VH-EAS. 12-93
☐	4X-FNA		Meteor NF.13	ex Israel, IDF-AF, WM366, A&AEE, RRE. Centre section, wings and tailplane; nose from TT.20 WM234 ex Arborfield, 5 MU, 3 CAACU, 151, Odiham; rear fuselage (F.8?) ex Biggin Hill. See notes above. 12-93

☐ VR192	G-APIT	Prentice 1	ex Biggin Hill, Southend, VR192, 1 ASS, 6 FTS, CFS, 2 FTS, Blackburn's. CoA exp 7-9-67.	12-93
☐ WF137		Sea Prince C.1	ex Yeovilton, Culdrose SF, Shorts FU, Arbroath SF, 781.	12-93
☐ WH291		Meteor F.8	ex Kemble, 229 OCU, 85, CAW, 257.	12-93
☐ WV798	A2557	Sea Hawk FGA.6	ex Chertsey, Culdrose, FRU, 801, 803, 787. '026'.	12-93
☐ XK418	7976M	Auster AOP.9	ex Basingstoke, Thruxton, 'Wallop, 654.	12-93
☐ XM833		Wessex HAS.3	ex Lasham, Wroughton. See notes above.	12-93
☐ E-423		Hunter F.51	ex Bitteswell, Dunsfold G-9-444, Danish AF, Aalborg store, Esk-724.	12-93
☐ 22+35		F-104G	ex Manching, JbG34, KE+413, DD+105.	12-93

LEE-ON-SOLENT AIRFIELD (on the B3333 south of Fareham)

■ HMS *Daedalus* : As the base prepares for closure, it is interesting to note that airframes are still being allocated here, although the inevitable flow will be outwards as the pace towards shut down builds. The Air Engineering School (AES) will move to Gosport, Hants, *circa* 1996. The base also continues to be a storage centre for the FAA Museum, Yeovilton, Somerset. Delete reference to Sea Fury FB.11 VR930 in **W&R13**, this can be found at Yeovilton, Som. Fascinating arrival by October 1993 was the Fraser Aviation Anson, from Enstone, Oxon, for completion of its restoration. Back to **W&R12**, where the disposal of Hunter GA.11 WV382 was noted without a destination. This went to *another* Staravia yard, this time at <u>Smethwick</u>, W Mids. Kestrel FGA.1 XS695 arrived from Culdrose, Corn, on May 11, 1993 for work prior to its removal to <u>Cardington</u>, Beds, by February 1994. Departures have been as follows : —

Sea King HAS.1 XV644 to <u>Predannack</u>, Cornwall, on 28-10-92.

Wasp HAS.1 XS538/A2725 to <u>Culdrose</u>, Cornwall, on 12-10-93; XS539 to <u>Fleetlands</u>, Hants, by 8-92; XS567 to <u>Duxford</u>, Cambs, 1992; XT434 to <u>Fleetlands</u>, Hants, by 8-92; XT795 left as long ago as 16-1-89 for Wroughton, Wilts, then moving to <u>Fleetlands</u>, Hants, on 5-8-92.

Wessex HAS.1 XM868 to <u>Predannack</u>, Cornwall, by 5-93; XM874 to <u>Predannack</u>, Cornwall, by 5-93; XP157 to <u>Yeovilton</u>, Somerset 3-11-92; XP158 to <u>Culdrose</u>, Cornwall, by 1-93; XP160 to <u>Predannack</u>, Cornwall, by 5-93; XS865/A2694 was last noted on the dump in 1988 and is assumed to have expired; likewise XS867/A2671, last noted on the dump 1988; XS870/A2697 moved to Portland, Dorset, by 2-94; XS878/A2683 last noted on the dump 8-90 and thought demised.

Wessex HAS.3 XS153 moved out to the Sennelager training area, near Paderborn, Germany by October 1991; XS862 had gone by 4-92, to <u>Winterbourne Gunner</u>, Wilts.

Wessex HU.5 XS508 to <u>Yeovilton</u>, Somerset, 28-6-93; XT453 to <u>Yeovilton</u>, Som, 13-9-93; XT487/A2723 last noted on the dump during 7-86 and assumed demised; XT769 arrived from Wroughton, Wilts, 9-7-92, but moved to <u>Yeovilton</u>, Somerset, on 7-9-93.

Westland 606 : XW836 moved to <u>Lasham</u>, Hants, by mid-1993.

Additionally, Wessex HAS.1 XS888 arrived from Wroughton, Wilts, July 7, 1992. It stayed only until April 19, 1993 when it was airlifted care of Chinook HC.1 ZA862 to <u>Guernsey</u>, Channel Islands.

☐ T8191		Tiger Moth T.2	ex FAAHAF, Yeovilton SF, Culdrose SF, Y'ton SF, BRNC, Lossie SF, Arbroath SF, Culdrose SF, Bramcote, Gosport, 3 FF, 22 EFTS, 4 FIS, 3 EFTS. FAAM store.	11-93
☐ EZ407		Harvard III	ex Yeovilton, Portuguese AF 1656, EZ407, 42-84931. FAAM store.	11-93
☐ VV106	7175M	Supermarine 517	ex Cosford, St Athan, Colerne, Yatesbury. FAAM. Stored.	11-93
☐ VX272	7174M	Hawker P.1052	ex Cosford, St Athan, Colerne. FAAM store.	11-93
☐ WD413*	G-BFIR	Anson C.21	ex Enstone, Tees-side, Strathallan, Bournemouth, East Midlands, Aldergrove, 7881M, TCCS, BCCS, 1 ANS. Flew in by 10-93. Restoration.	10-93
☐ WV903	A2632	Sea Hawk FGA.4	ex Culdrose, Halton 8153M, Sydenham. '128-C'. FAAM store.	11-93
☐ WV911	A2526	Sea Hawk FGA.6	ex Fleetlands, Lee-on-Solent. '115-C'. FAAM store.	11-93

☐	XE339	A2635	Sea Hawk FGA.6	ex Culdrose, Halton 8156M. '149-E'. FAAM store. 11-93
☐	XG888		Gannet T.5	ex Culdrose, Lossie, 849. 'LM'. FAAM store. 11-93
☐	XL500	A2701	Gannet AEW.3	ex Culdrose, Dowty-Rotol, Culdrose, Lossie, 849. 'LM'. FAAM store. 04-92
☐	XL880	A2714	Whirlwind HAR.9	ex Wroughton, *Endurance* Flt, *Protector* Flt, 847, 848, 815. '35'. Dump. 12-92
☐	XM843	A2693	Wessex HAS.1	ex Wroughton, 771. '527-LS'. Gate. 04-92
☐	XM917	A2692	Wessex HAS.1	ex AES, Wroughton, 771. Dump.
☐	XN359	A2712	Whirlwind HAR.9	ex Wroughton, *Endurance* Flt, Fleetlands, Arbroath, *Protector* Flt, 847, 719. BDR. 06-91
☐	XP116	A2618	Wessex HAS.3	ex AES, 737. Cr 15-11-71. Metalwork School.
☐	XP150		Wessex HAS.3	ex W'ton, 829, *Antrim* Flt. '406-AN'. AES. 04-92
☐	XP151	A2684	Wessex HAS.1	ex AES, Wroughton, *Ark Royal* Flt. Dump. 10-92
☐	XS483		Wessex HU.5	ex Wroughton, 845. 'T'. AES. Dump. 10-92
☐	XS496		Wessex HU.5	ex 772. '625-PO'. AES. 11-93
☐	XS507		Wessex HU.5	ex 772. '627-PO'. AES. 11-93
☐	XS510		Wessex HU.5	ex 772. '626-PO'. AES. 11-93
☐	XS511		Wessex HU.5	ex 845. 'YM'. AES. 11-93
☐	XS513		Wessex HU.5	ex AES, 772. '419-PO'. BDRF. 04-92
☐	XS514		Wessex HU.5	ex 845. 'YL'. AES. 11-92
☐	XS515		Wessex HU.5	ex 845. 'YN'. AES. 11-92
☐	XS516		Wessex HU.5	ex 845. 'YQ'. AES. 11-92
☐	XS520		Wessex HU.5	ex 845. 'YF'. AES. 11-92
☐	XS522		Wessex HU.5	ex Wroughton, 848. 'ZL-VL'. AES. 11-92
☐	XS529		Wasp HAS.1	ex 829 *Galatea* Flt. AES. '461'. 04-92
☐	XS545	A2702	Wasp HAS.1	ex AES, Wroughton. '635'. *Willy-never-Fly*. BDRF. 04-92
☐	XT437	A2721 (2)	Wasp HAS.1	ex 829 *Diomede* Flt. '423'. AES. 11-92
☐	XT449		Wessex HU.5	ex AES, Wroughton, 845. 'C'. Dump. 11-92
☐	XT455		Wessex HU.5	ex 845. 'U'. AES. Dump by 10-92. 11-92
☐	XT458		Wessex HU.5	ex 772. '622'. AES. 11-92
☐	XT460		Wessex HU.5	ex Wroughton, 845. 'YK'. AES. 11-92
☐	XT468		Wessex HU.5	ex Wroughton, 772. '628-PO'. AES. 11-92
☐	XT482		Wessex HU.5	ex Wroughton, 848. 'ZM-VL' & '19'. AES. 11-92
☐	XT484		Wessex HU.5	ex 845. 'H'. AES. 11-92
☐	XT485		Wessex HU.5	ex 772. '621-PO'. AES. 11-92
☐	XT752		Gannet T.5	ex Culdrose, Lossiemouth, 849, Indonesian Navy AS-14, G-APYO, WN365. 'LM'. FAAM store. 04-92
☐	XT756*		Wessex HU.5	ex Wroughton. 'ZJ-VL'. AES. Arr 7-7-92. 07-92
☐	XT761		Wessex HU.5	ex Wroughton. AES. 11-92
☐	XT765		Wessex HU.5	ex 845. 'J'. AES. 11-92
☐	XT778	A2722 (2)	Wasp HAS.1	ex 772. '430'. AES. 11-92
☐	XV370*		SH-3D Sea King	ex Yeovil, G-ATYU. AES. Arrived 22-2-90. 11-92
☐	XV642*		Sea King HAS.2A	ex Yeovil, A&AEE, Yeovil, A&AEE, Yeovil. Arrived early 1991. BDR. 04-92
☐	XV751		Harrier GR.3	ex 3, 1, 3, 20, 233 OCU. AES. 06-91
☐	XV783*		Harrier GR.3	ex Culdrose SAH, Cosford, 233 OCU, 4, 3, 233 OCU, 1, 233 OCU, 1, 233 OCU, 1417 Flt, 233 OCU, 4, 20, 4. 'N'. Arrived 10-8-93. 08-93
☐	XW630		Harrier GR.3	ex 3, 4, 3, 20. AES. FAA colours. 11-92
☐	XX510		Lynx HAS.2	ex Foulness, Boscombe D. '69-LS'. AES. 09-93
☐			Lynx TA	built by RNAW Almondbank. AES.
☐			Lynx TA	built by RNAW Almondbank. AES.

LOWER UPHAM (on the A333 near Bishop's Waltham)
Robs Lamplough (see under North Weald, Essex) has a small store here.

☐ G-AHUF	Tiger Moth	ex Yeovilton, A2123, Arbroath, NL750, Coimbatoire. Stored.	12-91
☐ G-BILA	DM-165L Viking	ex F-PPZE. CoA expired 14-9-83. Stored.	

MIDDLE WALLOP AIRFIELD (on the A343 south west of Andover)

■ **Army Air Corps Historic Aircraft Flight** : The 'core' fleet of the Flight remains unchanged. But a 'Reserve Flight', with civil 'cover' registrations appears to be evolving. As part of a decided shuffle of Beavers to and from ARCO, Beaver AL.1 XP772/G-BUCJ moved to Duxford, Cambs, on May 11, 1993. While on the subject of Beavers, note that the Flight has had XP820 on charge since May 1989 — **W&R** has now caught up with it! Stored, courtesy of the Flight, is Flycatcher G-BEYB.
◆ Please note that the Flight is *not* available for public inspection, but does 'do the rounds' of the airshow circuit.

☐ 'S1287'* G-BEYB		Flycatcher rep ⚠	ex Duxford, Middle Wallop, Yeovilton. Returned 1993. CoA expired 8-4-93. Stored.	03-94
☐ XL814		Skeeter AOP.12 ⚠	ex 1 Wing, 2 Wing, 651.	03-94
☐ XP242	G-BUCI	Auster AOP.9 ⚠	Reserve Flight.	03-94
☐ XP820		Beaver AL.1 ⚠	ex 7 Regt, 667, 132 Flt RCT, 130 Flt RCT, 30 Flt RASC, 11 Flt, 656. See notes.	03-94
☐ XR244		Auster AOP.9 ⚠	ex AFWF.	03-94
☐ XT131		Sioux AH.1 ⚠	ex D&T Flight.	03-94
☐ XT827		Sioux AH.1	ex Arborfield, 654. Spares use.	07-93

■ **Military Auster Flight** (MAF) : Also well-known at airshows, MAF really does deserve a mention within **W&R**, although its siting under Middle Wallop is really a 'paperwork' allocation as they are based at various locations, coming together for displays and training. Current members are : —

☐ LB375	G-AHGW	Auster I ⚠	ex 451, 43 OTU, 653. Carl Butler.	07-93
☐ MT438	G-AREI	Auster III ⚠	ex 9M-ALB, VR-RBM, VR-SCJ, MT438, Malaya CS. J A Vetch.	07-93
☐ NX534	G-BUDL	Auster III ⚠	ex PH-POL, RNeth AF R-17, NX534, 84 GCS, 4, 130 AF, 658. M Pocock.	07-93
☐ TW467	G-ANIE	Auster 5 ⚠	ex 664. 'ROD-F' 664 Sqn c/s. S J Partridge.	07-93
☐ TW536	G-BNGE	Auster AOP.6 ⚠	ex 7704M, TW536, 652, 1912 Flt, 657, Eastern Sector. 'TS-V', 657 Sqn c/s. Ron Eastman.	07-93
☐ VF526	G-ARXU	Auster 6A ⚠	ex Keevil, 664, CS(A). E C Tait.	07-93
☐ WE569	G-ASAJ	Terrier 2 ⚠	ex 652, CFS, 2 FTS, CFS. V M Howard, R Skingley, S J B White.	07-93
☐ WZ662	G-BKVK	Auster AOP.9 ⚠	ex Auster, HS, A&AEE, Auster. J D Butcher.	07-93
☐ WZ706	G-BURR	Auster AOP.9 ⚠	ex 656. R P D Folkes.	07-93

■ **Museum of Army Flying** (MoAF) : The Museum continues to prosper and to widen its scope to all aspects of army-bound military aviation. Recent exhibits well reflect this variety, the Avro 504K from the Science Museum and an Alouette II. Registered to the Museum on December 20, 1993 was Fokker Dr I replica G-BVGZ, built/being built by Viv Bellamy — it has yet to appear here. 1994 sees a whole series of major anniversaries with the 50th anniversary of *D-Day* taking the largest slice of the cake. Within can be found the excellent *Skeeters* cafe which offers commanding views of the activity on the airfield.

The three Prospectors (G-APWZ, G-APXW and G-ARDG) have moved to a workshop at Durrington, West Sussex, from which it is hoped at least one display EP.9 will emerge. Otherwise the principal place of migration would appear to be Duxford. Part of the 'Beaver shuffle' (see above) also involved MoAF. XP822 left in May 1990 to join ARCO at Duxford, Cambs, but returned on May 11, 1993. During February 1994, Beaver AL.1 XP806 was put up for tender. Also taking that route (but this time by air) was Auster AOP.9 XR241/G-AXRR going to Duxford, Cambs, during June 1993. Loaned SE.5E 'B4863'/G-BLXT left by late 1991, initially to Vic Norman's fabulous airfield at Rendcomb, Glos, before joining OFMC at Duxford, Cambs, by late 1992. Pucara A-528 moved to Sunderland, T&W, by October 1993. The Peter Pyket/AeroFab taxiable Hurricane replica 'L1679' 'JX-G' was here on loan from about July 1993 while it was advertised for sale, it had moved on by March 1994 — the Netherlands as originally intended?

MoAF aircraft out on loan are as follows : ❏ Gazelle XW276 and Pucara A-528 at Sunderland, Tyne & Wear; ❏ Skeeter AOP.12 XL770 at Southampton, Hants and ❏ Whirlwind HAS.7 XL853 at Fleetlands, Hants.

◆ MoAF is open 10am to 4.30pm every day. Please note that the workshops are dispersed and not all of the aircraft listed below will be on public display.

✉ MoAF, Middle Wallop, Stockbridge, Hampshire SO20 8DY. ☎ 0264 384421 or '4428.

❏	G-AXKS		W-Bell 47G-4A	ex Bristows, ARWF, G-17-8. CoA expired 21-9-82. 03-94
❏	ACH	BGA 285	T.6 Kite I △	ex G-ALNH, BGA.285. Colours of 'E', 1 GTS. On loan from E B Scott. Flown occasionally. 07-93
❏	'B-415'	BAPC.163	AFEE 10/42 rep	ex Wimborne. 'Flying Jeep'. On loan from Wessex Aviation Society. 03-94
❏	P-5	8381M	Rotachute III	ex Henlow. On loan from RAFM. 03-94
❏	'5964'	BAPC.112	DH.2 replica	ex Chertsey. 07-93
❏	D7560*		Avro 504K	ex South Kensington, Waddon. ScM loan. Arrived by 10-92. 03-94
❏	'N5195'	G-ABOX	Sopwith Pup	ex Redhill. On loan. CoA expired 18-6-90. 03-94
❏	N6985	G-AHMN	Tiger Moth △	ex 2 EFTS, 22 EFTS, Andover SF. On loan. 07-93
❏	'KJ351'	BAPC.80	Horsa II	fuselage, composite, inc parts from TL659, 8569M & LH208. I/d changed from **W&R13**. 03-94 [Note that another nose and other Horsa bits are to be found in various displays within Hayward Hall here.]
❏	TJ569	G-AKOW	Auster 5	ex G-AKOW, PH-NAD, PH-NEG, TJ569. CoA exp 26-6-82. I/d amended from **W&R13**. 03-94
❏	TK777		Hamilcar I	ex Christian Malford. Forward fuselage, also parts from TK718 and NX836, ex Henlow. 03-94
❏	WJ358	G-ARYD	Auster AOP.6	ex Perth, WJ358, 651, 657, 1913 Flt. 07-93
❏	WZ721		Auster AOP.9	ex 4 RTR, 656, 6 Flt. *Dragon*. 03-94
❏	XG502		Sycamore HR.14	ex gate, Wroughton, Bristols, JEHU. 03-94
❏	XK776		ML Utility Mk 1	ex Cardington. Wings for *Clouy, Delta* and *Gadfly* configurations stored. On loan. 03-94
❏	XK988*	A2646	Whirlwind HAR10	ex Fleetlands, Middle Wallop, Ilkeston, Middle Wallop, Lee-on-Solent, 103, 110, 103, CFS, JEHU. First noted 5-92. 07-93
❏	XL738*	7860M	Skeeter AOP.12	ex Fleetlands, Middle Wallop, Southampton, Middle Wallop. Composite airframe, boom from XM565/7861M. First noted 5-92. 07-93
❏	XL813		Skeeter AOP.12	ex ARWF, 4 Regt, 9 Flt. 03-94
❏	XP806		Beaver AL.1	ex Arborfield, Middle Wallop, 668, 13F, 15F, 131F, 6F. Composite. Up for tender 2-94. 03-94
❏	XP821		Beaver AL.1	ex Shawbury, Kemble, St Athan, Defence Attaché, Laos, 130 Flt, 30 Flt RASC, 656. White/grey colour scheme. 03-94
❏	XP822*		Beaver AL.1	ex Duxford, Middle Wallop, Shawbury, Kemble, 132 Flt, 667, 18 Flt. Arrived 11-5-93. 03-94
❏	XP847		Scout AH.1	ex AETW. 03-94
❏	XR232*		Alouette AH.2	ex Historic Flight, Wroughton, Boscombe Down, Middle Wallop, EW&AU, 656, Boscombe Down, 16 Flt, 6 Flt. First noted 5-92. 03-94
❏	XR458*	8662M	W'wind HAR.10	ex Netheravon, Halton, 2 FTS, CFS, 28, 110, 103. 'H'. Arrived by 9-92. 03-94
❏	XT108		Sioux AH.1	ex Duxford, Yeovilton, Middle Wallop, D&T Flt, Middle Wallop. 03-94
❏			Scout CIM	ex AETW. 03-94
❏	A-533	ZD486	FMA Pucara	ex Boscombe Down, Abingdon, Finningley, Portsmouth, Stanley Airport, Argentine AF. 03-94
❏	AE-406		UH-1H Iroquois	ex Fleetlands, Stanley Racecourse, Argentine Army, 72-21491. 03-94

☐	AE-409		UH-1H Iroquois	ex Duxford, Middle Wallop, 656, Stanley Racecourse, Argentine Army, 72-21506. 03-94
☐	51-111989 N33600		L-19A Bird Dog	ex Fort Rucker, Alabama. 03-94
☐	'243809' BAPC.185		WACO CG-4A	ex Burtonwood, Shrewsbury. Fuse. '10'. 03-94
☐		BAPC.10	Hafner R-II	ex Locking, Weston-s-M, Old Warden, Yeovil. On loan. 03-94

■ **School of Aeronautical Engineering** (SAE) / **70 Aircraft Workshops** (AC) : Plans are afoot to move SAE to Arborfield, Berks, in 1994. This move may well help to re-assess just what airframes are held by SAE, as a scan down the 'last noted' column shows that some of the sightings are now very long-in-the-tooth. (The usual comments also apply relating to the much more amorphous Classroom Instructional Modules — CIMs.) Scouts from Wroughton and even a former Navy Gazelle HT.2, also from Wroughton, have been noted inbound. Scout AH.1 XP907 moved to <u>Netheravon</u>, Wilts, by May 1993. Scout AH.1 XR627 arrived from Wroughton, Wilts, on June 19, 1992, but moved to <u>Dishforth</u>, N Yorks, by April 1993. Scout AH.1 XR632 was active with 658 Squadron by 1992. Gazelle AH.1 XW912 moved to Fleetlands, Hants, by January 1993 for return to service. Clearly the able Lynx has been deemed as too valuable an asset for use with SAE and most (other than the CIMs) have been 'called up'. Lynx AH.1 XZ205 moved to Fleetlands, Hants, by April 1993 for upgrade into an AH.7 and active duty. Lynx AH.1 XZ213/TAD.213 left on November 15, 1990 for Wroughton, Wilts, then moving on to Fleetlands, Hants, on June 11, 1992 and then back into service. Lynx AH.1 XZ323 moved to Wroughton, Wilts, on June 20, 1991, only to return to the SAE on July 17, 1991. Having learned the route, it moved back to Wroughton, Wilts, on February 10, 1992 and then to Fleetlands on August 6, 1992 for return to active duty. Lynx AH.1 XZ641 moved to Fleetlands, Hants, by December 1993, again for return to duty. By late 1993 two *Chippies* with the BFWF were being used for spares for the remainder of the fleet — now on their own in UK on basic flying training within the military. Unless noted, the aircraft below all belong to the SAE fleet.

☐	WG403*		Chipmunk T.10	ex BFWF, EM UAS, 6 AEF, CFS, Bri UAS, W UAS, South Cerney SF, Leeds UAS, FTCCS, HCCS, Ed UAS, 11 RFS, 2 BFTS. 'O'. Spares recovery by 11-93. 03-94
☐	WK620*		Chipmunk T.10	ex BFWF, Hull UAS, Mcr UAS, QUAS, Bri UAS, 22 RFS. 'T'. Spares use by 11-93. 03-94
☐	WZ724	7432M	Auster AOP.9	ex 'WZ670', 656, FEAF. Gate guardian. 03-94
☐	XL847	A2626	Whirlwind HAS.7	ex BDR, AETW, MoAF, Lee-on-Solent, Lossiemouth SF, 771, 829, 820. Dump. 05-92
☐	XN494*	9012M	Jet Provost T.3A	ex Halton, 1 FTS, RAFC. '43' and 'R'. First noted 7-93. Dump. 03-94
☐	XP191		Scout AH.1	ex Shrivenham, Wroughton. BDR. Boom of XW799. 07-90
☐	XP848		Scout AH.1	ex Wroughton. 05-92
☐	XP853		Scout AH.1	ex 655. 05-92
☐	XP854	7898M	Scout AH.1	TAD.043. Crashed 15-5-65. Hydraulic rig. 07-90
☐	XP856		Scout AH.1	BDR. 07-90
☐	XP857		Scout AH.1	ex Yeovil. Dump. 05-92
☐	XP884		Scout AH.1	ex ARWS. 05-92
☐	XP888		Scout AH.1	ex Wroughton, 651. 05-92
☐	XP893*		Scout AH.1	ex Wroughton, Garrison Air Sqn, 3 CBAS, 655, 666, 656. 70 AC. Arrived 29-7-92. 11-93
☐	XP905		Scout AH.1	ex Wroughton, 656. 05-92
☐	XR436		SARO P.531-2	ex MoAF, A&AEE. BDR. 07-90
☐	XR597		Scout AH.1	ex travelling display, Wroughton, 654. 07-90
☐	XR635		Scout AH.1	ex 653. 05-92
☐	XT640		Scout AH.1	ex Wroughton, 640. 07-90
☐	XV124*		Scout AH.1	ex Wroughton, 656, 653, 654. Arr 19-6-92. 06-92
☐	XV131*		Scout AH.1	ex Wroughton, 660, 665,.653, D&TS. Arrived 3-7-92. 70 AC. 11-93
☐	XV629		Wasp HAS.1	ex Wroughton. BDR. 07-90
☐	XW796*		Scout AH.1	ex Wroughton, 660, 659. Arrived 3-7-92. 07-92
☐	XW838	TAD.009	Lynx 1-03	ex Yeovil. 03-<u>88</u>

☐	XW863*		Gazelle HT.2	ex Wroughton, 705. Arrived 10-1-92.	01-92
☐	XW888		Gazelle AH.1	ex ARWF.	07-90
☐	XW889		Gazelle AH.1	ex ARWF.	05-91
☐	XW900	TAD.900	Gazelle AH.1	crashed 25-5-76.	07-88
☐	XX411		Gazelle AH.1	ex Falklands, 3 CBAS. Shot down 21-5-82. BDR. Pod only.	03-88
☐	XX452		Gazelle AH.1	crashed 24-8-82. Pod only. Dump.	02-85
☐	XZ654		Lynx AH.1	-	07-90
☐		TAD.01	Gazelle CIM	or *possibly* TAU.01.	
☐		TAD.02	Gazelle CIM	-	
☐		TAD.04	Gazelle CIM	-	
☐		TAD.08	Gazelle CIM	-	
☐		TAD.007	Lynx CIM	fuselage number TO.42.	
☐		TAD.010	Lynx CIM	-	
☐		TAD.011	Lynx CIM	-	
☐		TAD.012	Lynx CIM	-	
☐		TAD.018	Lynx CIM	-	
☐		TAU.3	Gazelle CIM	ex Arborfield, Middle Wallop.	

NEW MILTON

■ **Peter Burton** : The Buccaneer nose — which is nearly 80% complete — has been joined by that of a Sea Vixen. The Sea Vixen, now identified, was last heard of in poor state at Boscombe Down during 1975. It was the Martel development aircraft.

☐	XJ488*		Sea Vixen FAW.1	ex Portsmouth, Boscombe Down, 22 JSTU, A&AEE. Nose. Stored. Arrived 10-10-93.	10-93
☐	XK527	8818M	Buccaneer S.2B	ex Lutterworth, Brough. Nose.	12-93

ODIHAM AIRFIELD (on the A32 south of Odiham)

■ **RAF Odiham** : The base 'parents' Chipmunk T.10 PAX Trainer WK570, currently located at Southampton, Hants, and *JP* T.4 cockpit XP677 at Headley, Surrey. Jet Provost T.4 XR681/8588M was held here on charge with 1349 Sqn ATC but moved to 1218 Sqn ATC at Manston, Kent, by March 1993. Gazelle 1 G-RALE became G-GAZA during June 1992 and presumably left. Other airframes here are thought unchanged.

☐	XR453	8883M	W'wind HAR.10	ex Foulness, 2 AFTS, CFS, 230, 1563 Flt, CFS. 'A'. Gate.	04-93
☐	XR670	8498M	Jet Provost T.4	ex Brize Norton, Halton, SoRF, CATCS, 3 FTS, 1 FTS, 2 FTS, 7 FTS, CFS. Dump.	07-93
☐	XS489		Wessex HU.5	ex Wroughton, 845. 'R'. For tender 7-93.	07-93
☐	XS871	8457M	Wessex HAS.1	ex Wroughton. 72 Sqn colours, 'AI'. Inst.	
☐	ZE449	9017M	SA.330L Puma	ex Sherborne, Weston-s-M, Fleetlands, Portsmouth, Port Stanley, Argentine PNA PA-12. BDR.	06-91
☐	61-2414		CH-47A	ex Boeing. Instructional airframe.	

■ **Locally** : Steve Markham is thought still to store his SIPA pair locally.

☐	G-AMSG		SIPA 903	ex OO-VBL, F-BGHB.	
☐	G-AWLG		SIPA 903	ex F-BGHG. CoA expired 22-8-79.	

PETERSFIELD

■ **Churchers College** : On June 20, 1988, the college bought 'their' Grasshopper TX.1 from the MoD. It should still be here.

☐	XA225*		Grasshopper TX.1	see notes above.	06-88

POPHAM AERODROME (on the A303 west of North Waltham)

This very pleasant 'drome makes a re-appearance in **W&R**. An Auster AOP.9 is under restoration.

☐	XP279*	G-BWKK	Auster AOP.9	CoA expired 19-8-92. Restoration.	01-94

PORTSMOUTH

■ **Harry Pounds** : The ARV hulk G-OARV in the scrapyard had moved on to the Ipswich area by early 1991. A Hunter arrived at the yard during December 1993 and was followed by a Gnat from the former DRA Bedford. See under Culdrose, Devon, for one acquisition 'diverted' elsewhere.

☐ WW654*	Hunter GA.11	ex Culdrose, SAH, FRADU, 738, 229 OU, 98, 4, 98. '83-DD'. Arrive 15-12-93.	12-93
☐ XM694*	Gnat T.1	ex Bedford, Filton, Dunsfold, A&AEE. Arrived by early 1993.	04-93

■ **Others** : The Sea Vixen nose moved to New Milton, Hants, during October 1993.

SOUTHAMPTON

■ **Antique Aeroplane Company / Aero Antiques**: DH.60GMW G-AANO moved to Comberton, Cambs, by November 1991. Cub G-AISX moved to the Milton Keynes, Bucks, area by December 1990 and was flying by June 1993. That leaves two 'long-termers' with Ron Souch.

☐ G-AFSW		Chilton DW.2	ex Chilton Manor. Unflown. Stored.
☐ EI-ABU	G-ABYN	Spartan II	ex Abbeyshrule, Cloughjordan, G-ABYN.

10-91

■ **Crofton Aeroplane Services** : Super Cub 18-1528 became G-WGCS as long ago as 1984 so can be safely deleted from this reference! Status of the three other airframes welcomed.

☐ G-AHHU	J/1N Alpha	ex Sandown. Crashed 10-6-63. Stored.	
☐ G-APAA	J/5R Alpine	crashed 9-8-75. Stored.	
☐ 9M-ANN	Chipmunk 22	ex N70727 ntu, R Malaysian AF FM1026, WP909, 19 RFS, 8 RFS. Stored.	

■ **Hall of Aviation** : The Museum's policy of showing the aviation heritage of the Solent area continues with the acquisition of the SARO SR.A.1 jet flying-boat fighter on loan from the IWM at Duxford, Cambs. The anonymous Gnat T.1 nose section moved to Salisbury, Wilts, during 1993. The Museum has an excellent relationship with 424 Squadron ATC and their airframes are listed within the main section, although some may not be on public view.

◆ Open daily except Mondays and over Christmas, 10am to 5pm (Tuesday to Saturday) and 2pm to 5pm (Sundays). ✉ Southampton Hall of Aviation, Albert Road South, Southampton, SO1 1FR. ☎ 0703 635830.

☐ G-ALZE		BN-1F	ex Cosford, Kemble, Bembridge. On loan.	02-94
☐ VH-BRC		Sandringham 4	ex Lee-on-Solent, VP-LVE *Southern Cross*, N158C Antilles Air Boats VH-BRC Ansett *Beachcomber*, TEAL ZK-AMH *Auckland*, Sunderland III JM715.	02-94
☐ N248		Supermarine S.6A	ex Cowes, Southampton, Henlow, Southampton Pier, 'S1596' in *First of the Few*, Calshot, RAFHSF.	02-94
☐ 'N546'	BAPC.164	Wight Quadruplane	ex Wimborne.	02-94
☐ 'C4451'	BAPC.210	Avro 504J	static replica. Built by AJD.	02-94
☐ BB807	G-ADWO	Tiger Moth	ex Wimborne. Composite with G-AOAC and G-AOJJ.	02-94
☐ PK683	7150M	Spitfire F.24	ex Kingsbridge Lane, Kemble, Colerne, Changi, Singapore Aux AF.	02-94
☐ TG263*		SARO SR.A.1	ex Duxford, Staverton, Cranfield, G-12-1, TG263. Loan from IWM. Arrived by 12-93.	02-94
☐ WK570	8211M	Chipmunk T.10	ex Bournemouth Airport, Hamble, 663, Hull UAS, 663, RAFC. PAX ATC.	10-91
☐ WM571		S'Venom FAW.22	ex Wimborne, Staverton, ADS, 831B, HS.	02-94
☐ WZ753		Grasshopper TX.1	ex Halton, Emanuel School, London.	02-94
☐ XD235*		Scimitar F.1	ex Ottershaw, Foulness, FRU, 803. Nose. ATC.	04-92
☐ XD596	7939M	Vampire T.11	ex Calmore, St Athan, CATCS, CNCS, 5 FTS, 4 FTS. ATC.	02-94
☐ XJ476		Sea Vixen FAW.1	ex Boscombe Down, A&AEE. Nose. ATC.	02-94
☐ XK740	8396M	Gnat F.1	ex Hamble, Cosford, Bicester, Church Fenton, MoS, Filton.	02-94

☐	XL770	8046M	Skeeter AOP.12	ex Middle Wallop, Shrivenham, Wroughton,	
				15/19 Hussars, 652, 654.	02-94
☐	XN246		Cadet TX.3	ex Syerston.	02-94
☐		BAPC.7	SUMPAC	ex Old Warden, Southampton.	02-94
☐		BAPC.215	Airwave HG	prototype.	12-90

■ **Spitfire Society** : After display at the RAF Museum, Hendon, Gtr Lon, the Society's Spitfire prototype replica came for brief display at Southampton Airport and then to storage in the area. ✉ The Spitfire Society, 141 Albert Road South, Southampton, SO1 1FR. ☎ 227343.

| ☐ | 'K5054'* | BAPC.214 | Spitfire proto rep | ex Hendon, Thruxton, Middle Wallop, Thruxton, | |
| | | | | Andover. Stored. Arrived by 9-93. | 01-94 |

■ **Wensley Haydon-Baillie** : A store of several airframes is believed to still be held within the dock area. The former Saudi Lightnings purchased by Mr Haydon-Baillie from Warton, Lancs, are stored in the Warrington, Cheshire, area.

☐	G-WGHB		T-33A-N	ex Coventry Airport, Duxford, Southend,	
				CF-EHB, 21640, 133640.	
☐	XA847	8371M	EE P.1B	ex Hendon, Farnborough, A&AEE, makers.	
☐	XS422		Lightning T.5	ex Boscombe Down, A&AEE, 56, 29, 111, 29,	
				111, 226 OCU.	

■ **Others** : The status of Terrier 1 G-ARLH, here or anywhere, is now doubted and it has been banished to *LOST!* The Cub rebuild in the area has been joined by that of a Tiger Moth. A collector is still has a Gannet fuselage and a Vampire pod in his garden. The identity long given to the Vampire pod, XD614 is now strongly doubted. Favoured identity is WZ572.

☐	G-ALJL*		Tiger Moth	ex T6311, Fairford SF, 38 GCF, Tarrant Rushton	
				SF, 11 OTU, 25 PEFTS. CoA expired 28-9-50.	
				Long term restoration. First noted 11-92.	11-92
☐	G-BDMS		J-3C-65 Cub	ex F-BEGZ, 44-80753. Stored.	
☐	WN411		Gannet AS.1	ex Abbotsinch, 820. Fuselage.	03-94
☐	XD614 (?)	8124M	Vampire T.11	ex Southampton ATC, Chilean AF spares, 3 FTS,	
				7 FTS, 1 FTS, CFS, RAFC. '65'. Pod.	
				See notes above.	03-94

SOUTHAMPTON AIRPORT (or Eastleigh, at the A335/M27 junction north of the City)
■ **Lindsay Wood Promotions** : Listed in **W&R13** as under Cranfield, Beds, the fleet of airworthy Vampires were actually based here from 1991 with the entire fleet then making a migration to Bournemouth, Dorset. The Vampires and Venom flew in to Southampton direct from Switzerland, and not via Cranfield, Beds, as given in **W&R13**. The comings are goings are best charted as follows: —

Type	Identity	From	On	F/f in UK	To Bournemouth
Vampire FB.6	J-1173/G-DHXX	Payerne	7-8-91	—	1-6-93
Vampire T.55	U-1214/G-DHVV	Sion	6-8-91	4-12-92	1-6-93
Vampire T.55	U-1219/G-DHWW	Sion	6-8-91	23-9-92	1-6-93
Vampire T.55	U-1230/G-DHZZ	Sion	7-8-91	12-6-92	1-6-93
Venom FB.50	'WE402'/G-VENI	Cranfield	24-10-92	—	21-6-93

■ **Others** : As the airport undergoes massive redevelopment, the dump appears to be enjoying a considerable renaissance. Joining the anonymous single-engine Cessna have been a 421 and another early series HS.125.

☐	G-DBAL*		HS.125-3B	ex G-BSAA, 5N-AKT, 5N-AET. CoA	
				expired 16-9-92. On dump by 7-93.	09-93
☐	G-SHOE*		Cessna 421C II	ex Oxford, G-BHGD, D-IASC, OE-FLR, N3862C.	
				Cr 8-11-85. Fuselage. Dump by 7-93.	09-93
☐	*		Cessna	fuse, minus tail & wings. Dump by 4-92.	07-93

SOUTHSEA (on the extreme tip of the Portsmouth 'peninsula')
■ **Royal Marines Museum** : Certainly the Whirlwind on show here is a former Torbay Aircraft Museum example, but it is *not* the one that has been listed in the last two editions! Given here, erroneously, was HAR.3 XJ393, this is not the case, the example here is the famous *Iron Chicken*,

HAS.7 XN299. (XJ393 can be found under Pulborough, West Sussex.) Another museum adopting a heavy *D-Day* theme.

◆ Open all year except Xmas. Whitsun to August 9.30am to 5.30pm, September to May 10am to 4.30pm. ✉ Royal Marines Eastney, Southsea, Hants, PO4 9PX. ☎ 0705 819385. **Fax** 0705 838420.

☐ XN299		Whirlwind HAR.3	ex Higher Blagdon, *The Iron Chicken*, Culdrose, JWE Old Sarum, Fleetlands, 847 'B' Flt, 847, Culdrose, 848. 848 Sqn c/s 'ZZ', *Bulwark*. 04-93

THRUXTON AERODROME (north of the A303 west of Andover)

■ **Aeronautical Engineers and Fabricators** (AeroFab) : By the end of 1992 the Spitfire prototype replica for the Spitfire Society had moved here for final assembly and checking. The Spitfire was moved to Hendon, Gtr Lon, and unveiled at the RAF Museum on April 24, 1993. It was displayed briefly at the Museum of Army Flying, Middle Wallop, Hants, prior to its move to Hendon. During 1992, AeroFab built a Hurricane and Spitfire replica for export to the Netherlands during the spring of 1993. The Hurricane, 'L1679' moved to Middle Wallop, Hants, by July 1993 on loan to MoAF. Auster 5 F-BGOO had gone from here by 1992, having moved to 'Yorkshire' for rebuild. Work continues on the Spitfire Vb restoration.

☐ BL628	G-BTTN	Spitfire Vb	ex Winchester, Australia, St Merryn, 719, 610, 401. Restoration, off site. 03-94

■ **Flying Services** : By July 1992 Texan G-BSBD and Harvard IVs G-BSBB, G-BSBE and G-BSBF had moved to Shoreham Airport, W Sussex, for storage and sale. Harvard IV G-BSBC moved to Wellesbourne Mountford, Warks, about the same time.

■ **Heliwork** : Continue to specialise in rebuilding mostly Bell helicopters. Most of their work is far too short term for **W&R**, and determining 'long-termers' can be quite difficult. Of those listed in **W&R13**, Sioux G-BCYY and the pod of Hiller UH-12E c/n 4463 are thought long gone. These have been joined by two other entries :—

☐ G-BRMF	Bell 206B	ex 5Y-KPC. Long term rebuild.	12-91
☐ G-ICRU	Bell 206A	ex Carlisle, C-GXVE ntu, N7845S. Crashed 23-5-84. Wreck.	
☐ G-TPTR*	AB 206B	ex Fairoaks, G-LOCK. Crashed 13-3-89. Wreck. Arrived by 2-90.	12-91
☐ D-HEAS G-BPIC	AB.206B	ex I-CELT. Damaged 23-5-87. Wreck.	04-89
☐ 5N-AQS*	Bell 222B	ex N3205T. Major rebuild, first noted 3-91.	08-93

WARSASH (south of the A27 west of Fareham)

■ **Naval College of Nautical Studies** : *Should* still have their Wessex.

☐ XM327		Wessex HAS.3	ex 829 *Kent* Flt. 06-91

WHITCHURCH

■ **Ron Eastman** : Ron is currently at work on a Plus D for the Museum of Army Flying at Middle Wallop, Hants, and an Auster 5D.

☐ G-AHWJ	Taylorcraft Plus D	ex Kingsclere, Wincanton, LB294, W Raynham SF, Millfield SF, 43 OTU, 653. CoA exp 30-6-71. Restoration.	07-93
☐ G-ANIJ	Auster 5D	ex Swanton Morley, TJ672, 227 OCU, 657. CoA expired 5-5-71. Restoration.	

WINCHESTER

■ **Dick Melton Aviation** (DMA) - **Charles Church Collection** (CC) : Dick's predominantly piston-powered workshop entered the 'jet-age' briefly during 1992/1993 when Jet Provost T.1 G-AOBU arrived by road from Thatcham, Berks, for restoration to flying condition for Kennet Aircraft. By September 1993 it had moved to Kennet's base at Cranfield, Beds, for flight trials. The wonderful Walrus project makes good progress towards flying condition. Three Spitfire projects from the estate of the late Charles Church were acquired by Kermit Weeks and moved to Wycombe Air Park, Bucks to be restored by PPS :— Mk XIV MV262/G-CCVV; Mk IX PL344/G-IXCC (airworthy) and Mk IX TE517/G-CCIX. The two-seater G-CTIX is up for disposal.

☐	W2718	G-RNLI	Walrus I	ex Southampton, 276, 751, 764. Former motorised caravan. Restoration.	01-94
☐	PT462	G-CTIX	Spitfire Tr IX Δ	ex Nailsworth, Israel, Israel AF-DF 2067-0607, Italian AF MM4100, RAF PT462 73 (?), 253.	02-93
☐			Spitfire Tr IX	new-build project.	02-93

Hereford & Worcester

BIRLINGHAM (east of the B4080 to the west of Evesham)
■ **Graham Revill** : Has doubled the size of his collection.

☐	WH166	8052M	Meteor T.7	ex Digby, CFS, 5 CAACU, CAW, 4 FTS, 205 AFS, 210 AFS, 208 AFS.	06-93
☐	'WN105'*	WF299	Sea Hawk FB.3	ex Helston, St Agnes, Topcliffe, Catterick 8164M, Lee-on-Solent, A2662, A2509, Culdrose SAH-8, 802, 738, 736. Composite. F/n 3-93.	06-93
☐	WZ425*		Vampire T.11	ex Cardiff-Wales, Woodford, Chester, St Athan, 5 FTS, RAFC, 229 OCU, CGS. F/n 3-93.	06-93
☐	XE979		Vampire T.11	ex Stonehouse, Woodford, Chester, St Athan, 1 FTS, 8 FTS, RAFC.	06-93

BROMSGROVE
During October 1993, a Tiger Moth arrived from Scotland for restoration.

| ☐ | G-ALWS* | | Tiger Moth | ex Rothesay, Strathallan, Perth, N9328, Upwood SF, 6 FTS, 15 EFTS, 17 EFTS, 15 EFTS, 19 EFTS, Duxford SF, Farnborough SF. Arrived 10-93. Restoration. | 10-93 |

DEFFORD (on the A4104 south west of Pershore)
A 'vintage' Rallye is under restoration at a farm nearby.

| ☐ | G-ASAT* | | MS.880B Rallye | CoA exp 18-11-90. Restn. First noted 3-93. | 03-93 |

DROITWICH
■ **Rotorspan** : Visits in December 1993 and January 1994 failed to find trace of the wreck of Bell 47G-5 G-AWRZ. Assumed scrapped.

EVESHAM
■ **HMS** *Explorer* : Located close to the high security prison, in Honeybourne Road, South Littleton, the Sea Cadets have a Wessex HAS.1. It was delivered here on June 26, 1992.

| ☐ | XS886* | A2685 | Wessex HAS.1 | ex Birmingham, Lee-on-Solent, Wroughton, 771. '27-CU'. See notes above. | 11-93 |

EWYAS HAROLD (on the A465 south west of Hereford)
■ **22 Regiment Special Air Service** : The 'Hereford Gun Club' are due to give up their somewhat forlorn Trident. It is reported to be the centre of yet another restaurant project (*not* at its current location!) and something like a 707 is reputed to be replacing it with the SAS.

| ☐ | G-AVYB | | Trident 1E-140 | ex BA, BEA, Channel. Fuselage. CoA expired 21-6-82. See notes above. | 11-93 |

FOWNHOPE (on the B4224 south east of Hereford)
■ **Ross Aviation Services** : Mark Biggs acquired the former Wales Aircraft Museum (WAM) Venom FB.4 WR539 and it was stored here during 1992. In an exchange with the Mosquito Aircraft Museum, it moved on to <u>London Colney</u>, Herts, by November 1992, with a Tiger Moth coming the other way. Mark's Rallye Club G-BFTZ was briefly on display at WAM (see under Cardiff-Wales Airport, S Glam) and after a short period of storage here moved on to TAC at <u>Warmingham</u>, Cheshire,

in exchange for Cessna G-AZDZ. The remains of Chipmunk G-BCIW arrived from Audley End, Essex, on January 13, 1994 for rebuild. G-BCIW is fast taking on a dual life — see under Audley End for the plot! Former Long Marston, Warks, Auster AOP.9 frame XK421 came here briefly, before joining BCAR at <u>Hedge End</u>, Hants, during 1993.

☐ G-ANFP*		Tiger Moth	ex London Colney, Denham, Rush Green, N9503, 2 RFS, 7 RFS, 2 RFS, 4 RFS, 4 EFTS. CoA exp 1-7-63. Frame. See notes. Arr by 11-92. 12-93
☐ G-AVCT		Cessna F.150G	ex Shobdon, Southend. CoA exp 3-3-79. 12-93
☐ G-AZDZ*		Cessna 172K	ex Warmingham, Southend, 5N-AIH, N1647C, N84508. Cr 19-9-81. Arr by 1-94. 01-94
☐ G-BCIW*		Chipmunk 22	ex Audley End, WZ868, PFTS, Birm UAS, 1 FTS, Birm UAS, 8 AEF, Birm UAS, 15 RFS. Crashed 26-11-91. Arrived 13-1-94. See notes. 01-94

HEREFORD

■ **RAF Hereford** (or Credenhill) : The base was due to close in April 1994.

☐ XG252	8840M	Hunter FGA.9	ex Cosford, 1 TWU, 2 TWU, 1 TWU, TWU, 45, 8, Wittering SF, MoA, 54, 66. 'U'. 11-93

POWICK

The nose, rear fuselage and outer wings of Meteor NF.13 WM367 was rescued and moved to <u>North Weald</u>, Essex, by June 1993.

SHOBDON AERODROME (north of the A44 west of Leominster)

■ **Shobdon Aircraft Maintenance** (SAM) : Clive Hardiman's company here provides the bulk of the airframe listing. Please note that some of the airframes have not been sighted for some time and are therefore subject to the usual warnings. Clive has developed a speciality of supplying time-ex airframes to pubs and clubs and, as ever, details of just where these items have ended up would be much appreciated. Harker Hawk G-BDNE is just such an example, having last been noted here during January 1992. Not all of SAM's airframes are to be found within the confines of the airfield. Cessna FA.150K G-AXVC was cancelled as sold in the USA during 1992.

☐ G-ADWJ		Tiger Moth	ex Land's End (?), BB803, 9 EFTS, 20 EFTS, 12 EFTS, G-ADWJ. 05-91
☐ G-AOHY		Tiger Moth	ex N6537, Dyce SF, Ringway SF, 11 RFS, 11 EFTS, 35 ERFTS. CoA expired 20-8-60. Restoration. 12-93
☐ G-AWEO		Cessna F.150H	ex Tattershall Thorpe. Damaged 22-11-89. For a pub/club. 01-92
☐ G-AWFF		Cessna F.150H	ex Bredhurst, Leavesden. Damaged 12-2-85. Fuselage. Restoration. 12-93
☐ G-AYSZ		Cessna FA.150L	ex Dubai. CoA exp 28-5-88. Restn. SAM.
☐ N9191	G-ALND	Tiger Moth	ex Shipdham, N9191, 5 SoTT, 19 EFTS, Duxford CF, 6 CPF. Crashed 8-3-81. 01-90
☐		Tiger Moth	ex Fownhope. Frame. 03-91
☐		Tiger Moth	ex Fownhope. Frame. 03-91

■ **Others** : Westland-Bell 47G-3B1 G-BFVM had moved on by late 1993, destination unknown. The long-term Dove and Pawnee are still here.

☐ G-APSO		Dove 5	ex N1046T ntu. CoA exp 8-7-78. Stored. 12-93
☐ G-BEPN		Pawnee 235D	ex N54877. Cr 11-2-78. Fuselage frame. 12-93

UPPER HILL (between the A4110 and the A49 south of Leominster)

■ **Lion Motors — Sheppards Crane Hire** : In late 1992 the long-standing Swift was joined by a Whirlwind HAR.10 from NEAM at Sunderland, T&W.

☐ WK275		Swift F.4	ex Hatfield, Filton, C(A). 12-93
☐ XP360*		W'wind HAR.10	ex Sunderland, Warmingham, Lasham, Fawkham Green, CFS, 225. 'V'. First noted 12-92. 12-93

VOWCHURCH (on the B4348 west of Hereford)
Stored in the area since 1989 has been a Jodel.
☐ G-AYXP   SAN D.117A   CoA expired 24-5-90.   04-89

WORCESTER
■ **John Hancock** : Took delivery of the nose of a Canberra TT.18 during 1993.
☐ WK118*   Canberra TT.18   ex Stock, Wyton, 100, 7, 59, 103. Nose.   12-93

Hertfordshire

BERKHAMSTED
The store in the area is thought undisturbed.
☐ G-AMTK   Tiger Moth   ex Cranfield, Bushey, Rochester, Croydon, N6709, 2 GS, 6 EFTS, 1 EFTS, 34 ERFTS. CoA expired 27-5-66. Stored.
☐ G-AVPD   Jodel D.9 Bebe   ex Langley. CoA expired 6-6-75. Stored.
☐ G-AWDW   Bensen CB-8M   CoA expired 7-10-71. Stored.
☐ G-AZZZ   Tiger Moth   ex Langley, Maidenhead, F-BGJE, French mil, NL864. Wings from G-BABA. Stored.
☐ G-BBGP   Berg Cricket   damaged 21-9-73. Stored.

BISHOP'S STORTFORD
■ **Russavia / The Aviation Heritage Collection** (TAHC) : Previously announced plans to re-organise as TAHC in early 1992 were not proceeded with following prolonged negotiations. Work on Dragon Rapide G-AGTM (at Rush Green, Herts) was suspended; various factors caused this, not least the prevailing economic conditions. Resuming, therefore, its 'Russavia' title, early in 1993 the collection took on a new tack. Now approaching his mid-60s Mike Russell decided once-and-for-all to discontinue attempts to re-establish anything approaching the scale of the previously very successful AOC pleasure flying operation, and continue purely in the role of "an enthusiast restorer and operator of historic aircraft". All but one of his historic sailplanes were disposed of, the unique archive of glider plans passed into the hands of the Vintage Glider Club and the Dragon Rapide placed for sale. By kind courtesy of Paul Szluha of Ragwing Aviation at Audley End, Essex, Mike himself completed restoration of Gemini G-AKKH and it was flying again during February 1994, ready for the new season. No additions to the collection are contemplated in the future.
          Disposals have been as follows :— Willow Wren BGA.162 and Lippisch Falke FCZ/BGA.3166 moved to Brooklands, Surrey, during 1993; Petrel ATR/BGA.651 sold during 1993 for restoration in the High Wycombe, Bucks, area. Additionally, Dagling BGA.493, under restoration by Peer Underwood at Eaton Bray, Beds, has been transferred to him. See under Rush Green, Herts, for the disposal of the Dragon Rapide G-AGTM.
◆ Visits are not possible, as aircraft are dispersed. General enquiries can be made to : ✉ Russavia, Woodend Green, Henham, Bishop's Stortford, Herts, CM22 6AY.
☐ G-EBQP   DH.53 H' Bird   composite, using wings of G-AEYY. Stored.   12-93
                              [See under Hitchin, Herts, for the fuselage of G-AEYY.]
☐ G-ACET   DH.84 Dragon   ex AW171, Ringway SF, 6 AACU, G-ACET. Major restoration project, stored.   12-93
☐ G-AEDB   BAC Drone 2   ex Duxford, BGA.2731. CoA expired 26-5-87. Stored. Aim to fly again 1994.   12-93
☐ G-AKKH   Gemini 1A   ex Duxford. *Gemima.* CoA expired 21-9-89. Completing restoration.   12-93
☐ BQJ   BGA 1147 Kranich II   ex RAFGSA.215 and probably D-11-0442. Planned to fly during 1994/1995.   12-93
☐ 'K2567' G-MOTH   Tiger Moth ▲   ex Duxford. Composite. Airworthy.   12-93

BUSHEY

■ **Breakers** : The car breakers' yard here still has its broken aircraft on show.

☐ G-BARI | Sundowner | crashed 23-4-75. Battered fuselage only. | 01-94

■ **Others** : Clearing up the question posed in **W&R13**, Vampire FB.5 VZ304 was indeed scrapped, *circa* February 1991. (Vampire FB.6 G-MKVI, formerly Swiss Air Force J-1167 flew from Cranfield, Beds, during 1993 as 'VZ304' either as a wry reminder of the real thing, or just to spread headaches!) The anonymous Venom FB.4 pod and the Mystery Jet MJ-1 mock-up were also burnt at the same time.

CLOTHALL COMMON (on the A507 south east of Baldock)

Both the Auster and Aeronca are *believed* still stored at a farm here.

☐ G-AIJS | J/4 Arrow | ex Compton. CoA expired 14-12-71. Stored.
☐ G-APYU | Tri-Traveler | ex Moreton-in-the-Marsh. Cr 23-4-72. Stored.

ELSTREE AERODROME (north of Junction 4, M1)

The **W&R** population here has increased, including the arrival of two Queen Airs. Navajo 300 ST-AHZ which was last noted in July 1988 — fate?

☐ G-ASON* | Twin Comanche | ex N7273Y ntu. CoA exp 30-11-91. Stored. | 04-93
☐ G-BHLK | GA-7 Cougar | ex N749G. CoA expired 12-5-89. Derelict. | 12-91
☐ G-CHTT | Varga Kachina | crashed 27-4-86. Fuselage. | 03-92
☐ G-JLTB | Varga Kachina | ex OO-RTV, N8373J. Cr 11-12-84. Wreck. | 03-92
☐ G-KEAA* | Queen Air 70 | ex Manston, G-REXP, G-AYPC. CoA exp 6-11-89. Arrived by 8-93. Stored. | 08-93
☐ G-KEAC* | Queen Air A80 | ex Biggin Hill, Manston, G-REXY, G-AVNG, D-ILBO. CoA expired 18-9-89. Ferried in by 6-92. Stored. | 06-92
☐ G-SARA* | Archer II | ex Shoreham, N21270. CoA exp 27-3-88. | 11-93

GOFF'S OAK (on the B156 west of Cheshunt)

The Hiller UH-12 is thought to be still stored at a farm here.

☐ G-ATKG | Hiller UH-12B | ex Brandis Corner, Thornicombe, Redhill, Thai AF 103. CoA expired 28-11-69. Stored.

HATFIELD

■ **Gerry Atwell** & **Frank Telling** : The Auster and an anonymous HM.21 are here.

☐ G-AKXP | Auster 5 | ex Claygate, NJ633, 29 EFTS, 22 EFTS, 659, HS. Crashed 9-4-70. Under restoration.
☐ | Mignet HM.21 | ex France. Stored. | 01-92

■ **University of Hertfordshire** : The Jetstream test-shell is still to be found on the campus of what used to be called Hatfield Polytechnic.

☐ | Jetstream | fuselage. Test-shell. | 11-92

HATFIELD AIRFIELD (west of the A1 at Hatfield)

■ **British Aerospace** : The airfield itself closed on April 8, 1993. The retreat by BAe from here is understandable, but the destruction of a fine regional general and executive aviation airfield is unforgivable. The Shuttleworth DH.88 Comet continues to be based here, but will be moving by road to Old Warden, Beds, in due course. BAe's airworthy Moth G-EBLV is now based at Old Warden, Beds. Trident G-AWZO was painted up as '5C-399' with 'Interactive Airways' titles for a film during July 1992. By August 1993 it had been presented to the Mosquito Aircraft Museum at nearby London Colney, Herts, but will be staying here. Midland Air Museum acquired HS.125 G-ARYB and it moved to Coventry Airport, Warks, on December 2, 1993. During January 1994 the BAe test facility on the north side was being demolished and from out of it appeared a fuselage on a low loader. (This *may* have been HS.125-1B/522 G-BOCB (ex Luton with CoA expired 16-10-90). The HS.125 (sorry, Corporate Jets 800 and 1000), ATP and Jetstream travelling 'roadshow' airframes are still *technically* based here, but must surely move in due course.

☐ G-ACSS | DH.88 Comet ▲ | ex Farnborough, Old Warden, Leavesden, K5084, G-ACSS. See notes above. | 08-93
☐ G-AREA | Dove 8 | CoA expired 18-9-87. Stored for MAM. | 12-93

☐	G-AVYE		Trident 1E-140	ex Wroughton, BA, Northeast, BEA, Channel. CoA expired 13-7-82. Fuselage. Fire trials. 09-92
☐	G-AWZO		Trident 3B-101	ex Heathrow, BA, BEA. CoA expired 13-2-86. Presented to MAM by 8-93. See notes above. 12-93
☐	G-TACE*		HS.125-403B	ex G-AYIZ, F-BSSL, PJ-SLB, G-AYIZ, G-5-15. CoA expired 16-7-86. External storage. 06-92
☐		c/n 1808	HS.748-2B	ex Woodford, Set 289. Static tests. 01-94
☐			ATP mock-up	ex Woodford. Based on Andover C.1 XS647 ex Kemble, St Athan, Kemble, 84, HS. Travelling demonstrator.
☐			HS.125-800	ex Chester Airport. Based on HS.125-600A fuselage ex IAAC 236, G-AYBH. Crashed 27-11-79. Travelling demonstrator.
☐			Jetstream 31	ex East Midlands. Based upon Jetstream 1 fuselage N14234.
☐			Jetstream 41	ex Prestwick. Based on Jetstream 200 G-ATXJ. CoA expired 8-2-71. 07-91

■ **Corporate Jets** : The glossy headquarters of what is now a Raytheon-Beech company is located in Bishop Square, part of the inevitable redevelopment of the historic airfield. During early July Vanguard Engineering succeeded in installing a mock-up Corporate Jets 1000 (*née* BAe 125-1000) into the lobby of the building. Some 30ft long and around six tons in weight, it is nevertheless, wholly a fibre glass mock-up.

| ☐ | * | | Corporate Jets 1000 | see notes above. 07-93 |

HERTFORD
Stored in the area is an L.200 Morava, used by Martin Emery as a source of spares for G-ASFD (see under Chessington, Gtr Lon) and the airworthy G-BNBZ.

| ☐ | OE-FBC | L.200 Morava | stored. Spares use — see above. |

HITCHIN
The Martin Monoplane project is thought still to be underway here. Super Cub G-BKEZ moved on to the "Southampton area" — can we be more specific?

| ☐ | G-AEYY | Martin Mono | ex Bishop's Stortford, Meir. Restoration project . |
| | | | [Wings are at Bishop's Stortford, Herts.] |

HODDESDON (on the A41 south of Ware)
■ **1239 Squadron ATC** : Vampire T.11 XD616 moved to <u>London Colney</u>, Herts, in March 1994. In the John Warner School, on the Old Highway, is the unit's Vampire.

KINGS LANGLEY (on the A41 north of Watford)
■ **'Trout Lake Air Force'** : Graham Gayward's personal collection, located at Trout Lake, Home Park, is viewable most weekends. The DH.88 replica 'tours' so may not always be on site.

☐	'G-ACSS'	BAPC. 216	DH.88 replica	ex Wroughton, Australia. Taxiable. 11-93
☐	WW442	7618M	Provost T.1	ex Leverstock Green, Cranfield, Booker, St Merryn, Houghton-on-the-Hill, Kidlington, Halton, CNCS, 3 FTS. 'N'. 11-93
☐	XE327	A2556	Sea Hawk FGA.6	ex Llangennech, Sydenham, 738. '644-LH'. 11-93
☐	XJ494		Sea Vixen FAW.2	ex Farnborough, FRL, A&AEE, HSA, Sydenham, 899, Sydenham, 892. 11-93

LEAVESDEN AERODROME (south of Abbots Langley, north of the A41)
■ **Aerodrome** : And another one bites the dust... It was announced in January 1994 that the aerodrome would close that April. Doubtless it is doomed to become another 'trading estate' and a all of the locals will suddenly discover just how nice it was aircraft flew from there! Goose N4575C was taxying again by January 1993 and flying by July 1993. Gnat XP504/G-TIMM was completed and made its first flight on December 13, 1993, ferrying to its new base at <u>Cranfield</u>, Beds. A Tomahawk has arrived for spares recovery.

☐ G-AJPR   Dove 1B   ex Biggin Hill. CoA expired 14-9-68. Forward fuselage. Dump.   01-93

☐ N2535T* G-BPHI   Tomahawk 112   ex Southall. Damaged --90. Spares.   01-93

■ **2(F) Squadron ATC** : On the northern boundary of the airfield, they have two Vampire pods.

☐ WZ415   Vampire T.11   ex Croxley Green, Bushey, Keevil, Exeter, 3/4 CAACU, 226 OCU, CS(A). '72'. Pod.

☐ XK632   Vampire T.11   ex Hemel Hempstead, Bushey, Keevil, Exeter, 3/4 CAACU, CFS. '67'. Pod.   08-91

LONDON COLNEY (off the A6 between London Colney and South Mimms)

■ **Mosquito Aircraft Museum** (MAM) : BAe at Hatfield donated Trident 3B G-AWZO during August 1993 and it is now on show close to the St Albans Road, with MAM's Dove 8 G-AREA (*qv*). Clearly the Trident will prove difficult if not impossible to move to London Colney and instead MAM are looking intently on the possibilities of the Museum moving to it! With the removal of BAe from the Hatfield site, possibilities are appearing, but these are of a tenuous nature at present. Tiger Moth G-ANFP was exchanged for the former Wales Aircraft Museum Venom FB.4 WR539, with the former going to <u>Ross-on-Wye</u>, H&W. The latter is in very poor shape and is a long, long term restoration project. MAM came to a conclusion about their BE.2e project A1325 during 1993. The conclusion was that it was really beyond their restorative prowess and that it could be used in a three-cornered exchange that would bring them a Dragon Rapide — something that has been on their 'shopping list' for a very long time. The BE.2e was acquired by the Historic Aircraft Collection and moved to <u>Hatch</u>, Beds, by October 1993. Alan Allen's Vampire NF.10 pod was due to arrive during April/May 1994 and will be amalgamated with parts from the former Hoddesdon T.11 to make a complete NF.10. The arrival of the former Brooklands Technical College Vampire T.11 XE985 means that MAM's own composite T.11 XE985 will be disposed of.

◆ Open from March to the end of October, Saturdays and Sundays 10.30am to 5.30pm, Thursdays 2pm to 5.30pm and Bank Holidays. ✉ MAM, PO Box 107, Salisbury Hall, London Colney, near St Albans, Herts, AL2 1BU. ☎ 0727 822051.

☐ G-ABLM   Cierva C.24   ex Hatfield. CoA exp 16-1-35. ScM loan.   12-93

☐ G-ADOT   Hornet Moth   ex Hatfield, Old Warden, Stoke Ferry, Stapleford Tawney, Houghton-on-the-Hill, X9326, 5 GCF, 23 OTU, 24 GCF, 6 AONS, Halton SF, 2 CPF, G-ADOT. CoA exp 15-10-59.   12-93

☐ G-AFOJ   Moth Minor   ex Navestock, E-1, E-0236, G-AFOJ. CoA expired 27-8-69.   12-93

☐ G-ANRX   Tiger Moth   ex Belchamp Walter, N6550, SLAW, 25 EFTS, 18 EFTS, 241, 14 EFTS, 56 ERFTS. CoA expired 20-6-61. Crop duster.   12-93

☐ G-AOJT   Comet 1XB   ex Farnborough, Air France F-BGNX. Fuse.   12-93

☐ G-ARYC   HS.125 Srs 1   ex Hatfield, Filton, Rolls-Royce. CoA expired 1-8-73. Restoration.   12-93

☐ G-AVFH   Trident 2   ex Heathrow, BA, BEA. Forward fuselage.   12-93

☐ D-IFSB   Dove 6   ex Hatfield, BFS, D-CFSB, Panshanger, G-AMXR, N4280X.   12-93

☐ F-BCDB*   Dragon Rapide   ex Aviodome, Amsterdam store, G-AKDW, YI-ABD, NR833. Arr by 3-94. See notes.   03-94

☐ W4050   Mosquito I proto   ex Hatfield, Chester, Radlett, E-0234.   12-93

☐ LF789   BAPC.186   Queen Bee   ex 'K3584', Hadfield, Droylsden, Redhill, St Athan, Pilotless Aircraft Unit, Manorbier, St Athan. Identity now 99% certain. Restn.   12-93

☐ TA122   Mosquito FB.6   ex Soesterberg, 4, 2 GCS, 48, 4, 605, 417 ARF. Fuselage, being rebuilt with the wing of TR.33 TW233 ex Israel. 'UP-G', 605 Sqn c/s.   12-93

☐ TA634   Mosquito TT.35   ex Liverpool, G-AWJV, Aldergrove, 3 CAACU, APS Schleswigland, APS, Ahlorn, APS Sylt, 4 CAACU. '8K-K', 571 Sqn colours.   12-93

☐ TJ118   Mosquito TT.35   ex Elstree, Exeter, 3/4 CAACU, 3 CAACU. Nose.   12-93

☐	WM729*		Vampire NF.10	ex Ruislip, Bingley, Bradford, Church Fenton, CNCS, 2 ANS, 25, 151. Nose. Due 4/5-94. See notes above.	04-94
☐	WP790	G-BBNC	Chipmunk T.10	ex Rush Green, WP790, Bir UAS, Wales UAS, PFTS, AOTS, 1 ITS, RAFC, Man UAS, G&S UAS Stn UAS, 24 GCF, 5 RFS, 17 RFS. 'T'.	12-93
☐	WR539*	8399M	Venom FB.4	ex Fownhope, Cardiff-Wales, 'Midlands', Cosford, Kai Tak, 28, 60. 'F'. Stored. Pod arrived 11-92.	12-93
☐	WX853	7443M	Venom NF.3	ex Debden, Shawbury, 23. Restoration.	12-93
☐	XD616*		Vampire T.11	ex Hoddesdon, Old Warden, Woodford, Chester, St Athan, 8 FTS, 1 FTS, 8 FTS, 65. '56'. Arr 3-94. See notes above.	03-94
☐	XE985		Vampire T.11	ex Woodford, Chester, St Athan, 5 FTS. Wings of WZ476. See notes above.	03-94
☐	XG730		Sea Ven FAW.22	ex Southwick, ADS, 893, 894, 891. '499-A'.	12-93
☐	XJ565		Sea Vixen FAW.2	ex RAE Bedford, 899, 893, 766B. '127-E'.	12-93
☐	XJ772*		Vampire T.11	ex Brooklands, Wisley, Shawbury, CATCS, 1 FTS, 8 FTS, RAFC, RNorAF 15018 'XP-G'. 'H'. Arrived 29-3-94.	03-94
☐	J-1008		Vampire FB.6	ex Hatfield, Swiss AF.	12-93
☐		BAPC.146	Toucan MPA	ex Hitchin, Old Warden, Radlett. Centre body plus props.	12-93
☐		BAPC.232	Horsa I / II	composite fuselage.	12-93

PANSHANGER AERODROME (south of the B1000 east of Welwyn Garden City)
The aerodrome closed early in 1992, only to re-open in 1993! It is thought that all of the former Autair cache was cleared out of here prior to the closure. Bell 47D-1 G-ASOL and Sioux AH.1s XT148 and XT803 are unaccounted for. The wreck of Bell 212 G-BARJ had gone by early 1991. Some (at *least*) of Sikorsky S-55 S-885 — unaccounted for in **W&R13** — has been tracked down, the boom being in the yard at Stock, Essex, along with the boom of Bell 205 U-705, also a 'long-termer' here. On the fixed-wing front, Comanche 180 N5052P was flying April 1991.

PATMORE (north west of Bishop's Stortford)
Although not reported for some time, the Cricket is thought still to be stored here.
☐ G-AYDJ   Cricket   CoA expired 13-4-72. Stored.

RUSH GREEN AERODROME (west of the A1(M) west of Stevenage)
Work on the Victor Gauntlett Dragon Rapide G-AEML *Proteus* came to fruition on April 16, 1993 when Colin Dodds performed its post-restoration test flight. It has since been seen at several events. The Russavia (see under Bishop's Stortford, Herts) example, G-AGTM left by road on March 1, 1994 for Reading, Berks.. Coates Swalesong G-AYDV was flying again by 1991. The Pawnee frame noted as being present in **W&R13** was most likely G-BILL, which was flying again by July 1990. Also previously present, until mid-1989, was the cockpit section of G-BFBP, which can now be found under Wainfleet, Lincs.
☐ G-ARNP*   Airedale   Damaged 20-10-90. Restoration.   06-93
☐ WT899   Cadet TX.3   ex Benington. Stored.   06-93

ST ALBANS
■ **College of Further Education** : One of the three Vampires was up for sale during July 1992. This turned out to be WZ584 which moved to Bridgend, M Glam.
☐ XE956   Vampire T.11   ex Hatfield, CATCS, 1 FTS, 8 FTS, 3 CAACU, APS, 67.   07-92
☐ XH313   Vampire T.11   ex Hatfield, CATCS, Wattisham SF, 111. 'E' 07-92

BEVERLEY

■ **Museum of Army Transport** (MoAT) : Work on the only surviving Beverley continues at the museum. Geoff Simmons and team have made exceptional progress on the restoration and fitting out of the interior. Thanks to sterling support from the RAF Museum's Restoration and Storage centre at Cardington, Beds, a large amount of spares have 'appeared', especially in the vital area of undercarriage, wheels and tyres. Additionally, enough parachute seats have been found to bedeck the rear boom as it should be. The cockpit is now almost completely restored, including a brand new' pilot's seat — again from Cardington. Concentration of efforts on the Beverley and a rethink of internal exhibits meant that the Hamilcar I section TK718 became surplus to requirements and it moved to the tank museum at <u>Bovington</u>, Dorset. Fund raising continues on putting a roof over the *Bev's* head, but it has a long way to go. MoAT has 211 vehicles of all description on charge — not all on show at any one time.

◆ Located in Flemingate, Beverley, and well signed within the town, close to the Minster. Open 10am to 5pm every day except Mondays in November, December, January and is closed December 24-26. ✉ MoAT, Flemingate, Beverley, North Humberside, HU17 0NG. ☎ 0482 860445.

☐ XB259   Beverley C.1   ex Paull, Luton, RAE, Blackburns, G-AOAI.   11-93

BREIGHTON AERODROME (in between Bubwith and Breighton, east of Selby)

■ **Real Aeroplane Company** (RAC) : With Nigel Ponsford at the helm as "unpaid, overworked and totally happy" curator, RAC are making great strides with a 'museum' hangar and hope to be able to extend visits here by taking a 'peek' into the 'live' hangars. Nigel's collection of aircraft is being supplemented with aircraft from other owners, not least of whom is the owner and operator of the aerodrome, Tony *Taff* Smith. Nigel's aircraft can also be found under Wigan, Gtr Man and Leeds, W Yorks. OH-7 Coupe G-ARIF and Cadet TX.1 RA854 are both due here from Wigan. His aircraft are marked § here. Not all of the aircraft that reside at this lovely aerodrome are listed below, but *Taff's* gorgeous machines — the superb Magister, the Jungmann and Jungmeister flying at airshows as the *Vintage Trio* — are listed, marked RAC. M.1C Sokol G-AIXN has left, going to the Bradford, W Yorks, area for rebuild. Cessna 150F G-ATKY has not been noted since 1988 — fate? Not yet large enough to merit a place in the listings, during January 1994 the Museum of Berkshire Aviation's Miles Master 'starter kit' arrived here from Woodley, Berks, for long term attention.

◆ Visits are by prior appointment at present, but there are plans to open on a regular basis. ✉ The Real Aeroplane Club, The Aerodrome, Breighton, near Selby, North Yorks. ☎ 0757 289065.

☐	G-ADFV* 2893M	Blackburn B-2	ex East Kirkby, Tattershall, Wigan, Caterham, 4 EFTS, Hanworth. CoA expired 26-6-41. Forward fuselage. Arrived 10-93.	04-94
☐	G-ADPJ*	BAC Drone II	ex Wigan, Bristol, Benson, Thetford. Damaged 3-4-55. Also parts from G-AEKU. Restoration. Arrived 8-4-93. §	04-94
☐	G-AEFG* BAPC 75	HM.14 *Flea*	ex Leeds, Harrogate, Kirkby Overblow, Wigan. Arrived 15-8-93. Restoration. §	04-94
☐	'G-AEKR'* B'.121	HM.14 *Flea*	ex Firbeck, Nostell Priory, Crowle, Finningley. Arrived by 2-93.	04-94
☐	G-AEVS*	Aeronca 100 ∆	Composite, inc parts from G-AEXD. §	04-94
☐	G-AOBG	Somers-K SK.1	ex Benington, 'Sussex', Eaton Bray, Cranfield. wfu 11-7-57. Stored.	04-94
☐	G-AXEI*	Ward Gnome	ex East Kirkby, Tattershall. RAC. Stored. Arrived by 10-93.	04-94
☐	G-BMDS*	Wassmer D.120	ex F-BMOS. CoA exp 29-5-91. Restoration.	06-93
☐	G-BUTX*	CASA Jungmeister	ex Spanish AF ES1-4. Restoration.	04-94
☐	G-TAFF*	CASA Jungmann ∆	ex G-BFNE, Span AF E3B-148. RAC.	04-94
☐	G-TAFI*	Bü 133 Jungm'r ∆	ex N2210, HB-MIF, Swiss AF U-77. RAC.	04-94
☐	BVM* BGA.1269	Dart 17R	ex Rufforth. '150'. § Arrived 7-4-93.	04-94
☐	CBK* BGA.1410	Grunau Baby III	ex Stoke-on-Trent, Firbeck, RAFGSA 378, D-4676. Arrived by 9-93. Stored.	12-93

☐ 'F50'		HM.14 *Flea*	taxiable. Built by Mick Ward. Citroen Ami engine. RAC. 04-94
☐ T9738	G-AKAT	Magister Δ	ex Sherburn area, Winthorpe, Leicester East, 24 EFTS, 15 EFTS. Flown by 3-93. RAC. 04-94
☐ XK819*		Grasshopper TX.1	ex Warmingham, Stoke-on-Trent. § Restn. 04-94
☐ 100502*		Fa 330A-1	ex East Kirkby, Tattershall, Wigan. On loan from TAC. Arrived 10-93. 04-94

BROUGH AIRFIELD (south of the A63 west of Hull)

■ **British Aerospace** : Swordfish II W5856/G-BMGC was completed in 810 Squadron colours and made its first flight on May 12, 1993, being handed over to the Fleet Air Arm on May 22 and now operates from Yeovilton, Som. Buccaneer S.2C XN982, previously in a fatigue rig, was scrapped during July 1992. Recent inspections have revealed a whole stack of fatigue airframes and it is felt that the unique airworthy Blackburn B-2 deserves listing. The first and last *Brick* to use the runway at Brough was XV168 when it flew in on October 15, 1993 for display.

☐ G-AEBJ*		Blackburn B-2 Δ	airworthy. Operated by BAe. 12-93
☐ NF389		Swordfish III	ex Lee-on-Solent. Stored. 12-93
☐ XL572	G-HNTR	Hunter T.7	ex Bournemouth, Cosford 8834M, 1 TWU, 2 TWU, TWU, 229 OCU. '83'. Inst. 12-93
☐ XV168*		Buccaneer S.2B	ex Lossiemouth, 12, 208, 12, FAA. Flew in 15-10-93. 12 Sqn c/s. On display 27-2-94. 02-94
☐		Hawk	fatigue rig. T.1A life extension test. 12-93
☐ *		Hawk 203	forward fuselage. Fatigue rig. 12-93
☐ *		T-45 Goshawk	fatigue rig. 12-93
☐ *		Eurofighter 2000	fatigue rig, two-seater variant. 12-93
☐ *		Eurofighter 2000	fatigue rig, single-seater cockpit only. 12-93
☐ *		Harrier GR.5	fatigue rig. 12-93
☐ *		Harrier T.2 or '4	forward fuselage. 12-93

GRINDALE

■ **British Skysports** : Not the original Grindale airfield, but a new strip nearby. A para-trainer arrived in May 1992 to help train people for the big drop.

☐ G-BRID*		Cessna U.206A	ex N4874F. Arrived 16-5-92. Para-trainer. 12-93

HAXEY (off the A161, north west of Gainsborough)

■ **Andrew Exton** : Took on the nose of a former Rossington Lightning during 1993.

☐ XR759*		Lightning F.6	ex Rossington, Binbrook, 5-11 pool, 56, 74, 5. 'TVI759'. Nose section. 12-93

LECONFIELD AIRFIELD (on the A164 north of Beverley)

■ **RAF Leconfield - School of Army Driving** : The Whirlwind serves on with the firemen.

☐ XG577	9050M	Whirlwind HAS.7	ex Duxford, Waterbeach, Duxford, East Midlands, Duxford, Lee-on-Solent A2571, Arbroath, 705, 737, 815, 705, 701, *Albion* Flt. '752-PO'. 10-90

NEW WALTHAM (on the A1098 west of Cleethorpes)

■ **Museum of Weapon Technology** : The cache of Lightnings here has been increased.

◆ Open Tuesday to Saturday 10am to 5pm at Peak's Top Farm. ✉ Museum of Weapon Technology, 31, Montgomery Road, Cleethorpes, Humberside, DN35 9JG.

☐ XR757		Lightning F.6	ex Rossington, 'TVI757', Binbrook, 5-11 pool, 23, 5. Nose. 05-93
☐ XR770		Lightning F.6	ex Laceby, Binbrook, 11, 5-11 pool, 56, 23, 74. 'AA'. 05-93
☐ XS416*		Lightning T.5	ex Rossington, Binbrook, 5, LTF, 11, 74, 226 OCU, MoA. 'TVI416'. Arrived 12-12-92. 05-93
☐ XS457		Lightning T.5	ex Laceby, Binbrook, 5, 11, 5, LTF, 11, 226 OCU. Nose. 05-93

☐ S-884		S-55C	ex Panshanger, Elstree, Danish AF Esk.722.	05-93
☐ 22+57		F-104G	ex Skegness, Laceby, Binbrook, Manching, JbG34, DD+239, KE+438.	05-93

POCKLINGTON AERODROME
The EoN Primary (not Eton TX.1 as given in **W&R13**) with loyalties to Croydon is still stored here and no longer anonymous. It has been joined by a Capstan.

☐ BSK*	BGA.1196	T.49B Capstan	stored, dismantled. First noted 10-92.	10-92
☐ DYW	BGA.2493	EoN Primary	BAPC.35. Ex Bishop's Stortford, Old Warden, Higher Blagdon, Old Warden, Sunderland. *Verna Flo*, '42nd Croydon'. Stored.	07-91

PRESTON (on the B1239 north of Hedon)
During February 1994, Sea Prince T.1 WP314 made to the move to <u>Carlisle</u>, Cumbria, for restoration by Tom Stoddart and team. The status of the Varsity nose is unconfirmed.

☐ WL627	8488M	Varsity T.1	ex Hull, Newton, 6 FTS, 2 ANS, 1 ANS, BCBS. Nose.	02-92

SANDTOFT AERODROME (south of the M180, between Sandtoft and Westgate)
First entry for this pleasant airfield. Two Cessnas are dumped here. On the apron is a Cessna 152 marked 'G-B'. This is reported to have used parts from the unfortunate G-BRWC, but the remainder of its pedigree is more bashful.

☐ G-BKRD*		Cessna 320	ex D-IACB, HB-LDN, N2201Q. Dumped. Crashed 5-11-90. First noted 2-92.	02-94
☐ G-BRWC*		Cessna 152 II	ex TF-GMT, N67569. Cr 29-8-90. F/n 3-93.	02-94
☐ *		Cessna 152	see notes above.	10-93

STORWOOD (south east of York)
■ **Melbourne Autos** : Within the scrapyard, three helicopters can still be found, in fair condition.

☐ WH991		Dragonfly HR.3	ex Tattershall T, Tattershall, Wisbech, Taunton, Fleetlands, Culdrose SF, 705, 700, Eglinton SF, *Centaur* Flt, 705, *Illustrious* Flt. 03-92
☐ WP503		Dragonfly HR.3	ex Cleethorpes, Elsham Hall, Stansted, RAE Bedford, North Coates, Lee-on-Solent, Lossiemouth SF. '901'. 03-92
☐ XP345	8792M	W'wind HAR.10	ex Tattershall Thorpe, Lee-on-Solent, Cyprus, Alexander Barracks, 84 'B' Flt, 1563 Flt, 202, CFS. 03-92

Isle of Man

ISLE OF MAN AIRPORT (or Ronaldsway, north east of Castletown)
■ **Aeroservice (IoM) Ltd** : With no reports to the contrary, it is assumed that the contents of the Aeroservice hangar are unchanged.

☐ G-AFFD		Percival Q6	ex Sutton Coldfield, Duxford, Redhill, G-AIEY ntu, X9407, MCS, 510, Old Sarum SF, Halton SF, Heston SF, Northolt SF, 6 AACU, G-AFFD. CoA expired 31-8-56. Restoration. 04-91
☐ G-AJEE		J/1 Autocrat	ex Compton Abbas. CoA exp 10-7-89. Restn. 04-91
☐ G-APSZ		Cessna 172	ex Barton, N6372E. Dam 2-3-84. Stored. 04-91
☐ G-AYVV		ST-10 Diplomate	ex Cippenham. Crashed 30-9-79. Stored. 04-91
☐ G-BAEO		Cessna F.172M	ex Manchester, Barton. Cr 7-5-78. Restn. 04-91
☐ G-BCGA		Seneca 200-2	ex Panshanger, N41975. Crashed 18-12-77. Fuselage. 04-91

JURBY AERODROME (west of Andreas)
The Island's other airfield makes an appearance in the pages of **W&R**. Within the main hangar a Jet Provost fuselage was noted by August 1992. It is *thought* to be the one acquired by Mr R MacGregor Muir of Ramsey from Halton, Bucks.

☐ XP672*   G-RAFI   Jet Provost T.4   ex Halton, 8458M, SoRF, CAW, CATCS, CAW,
2 FTS. '27'. F/n 8-92. See notes above.   08-92

Isle of Wight

BEMBRIDGE AERODROME (south west of Bembridge)
■ **Pilatus Britten-Norman** : An Islander is being converted into a static mock-up for a new military observation version. Going back to **W&R12**, the remains of BN-2A A40-CT were removed during 1992. A 'green' Gosselies fuselage is reported to have left here for a technical college in London.

☐ G-BCWR*   BN-2A-20   ex OY-RPZ, G-BCWR. Under conversion to Pilot's
Extended View configuration.   06-93

COWES
By October 1992, the nose section (at least) of a former Abingdon Phantom had appeared at a scrapyard here. The yard is also known to have taken a large amount of the scrap from Abingdon (if not all of it), certainly the Nimrods.

☐ XT863*   Phantom FG.1   ex Abingdon, 43, 111, 892, 767. 'AS'. Nose.
See above. First noted 10-92.   10-92

NEWPORT
Stored in the area in two separate places are two homebuilds.

☐ G-AZJE   JB.01 Minicab   ex Sandown. CoA expired 7-7-82. Stored.
☐ G-BCMF   Levi Go-Plane   one and only flight 16-11-74. Stored.   11-93

SANDOWN
■ **Airframe Assemblies** : The substantial fuselage section and assorted other parts of Spitfire IX TA805 arrived here for storage on behalf of Steve Atkins during January 1992.

☐ TA805*   Spitfire IX   ex Battle, South Africa, SAAF, 234, 183.
Arrived 1-92. See notes above.   12-93

SANDOWN AERODROME (east of Sandown)
■ **Aeronotec / The Norman Aeroplane Company** : Freelance G-NACI was flying again by early 1993 with renewed hopes of production. Fellow G-NACA is also being worked on.

☐ G-NACA   Freelance 180   ex Cardiff. Restoration.   12-93
☐ G-NACL*   Firemaster 65   ex G-BNEG. CoA exp 5-12-90. Stored.   12-93
☐ G-NDNI   Firecracker   ex Carlisle area. CoA exp 11-8-83. Stored.   12-93
☐ G-NRDC   Fieldmaster   ex Old Sarum. CoA exp 17-10-87. Fuse.   12-93
☐   Fieldmaster   ex Old Sarum. Test airframe. Stored.   12-93

■ **Others** : Rallye Minerva G-BCAC had gone by May 1992, moving to <u>Tattershall Thorpe</u>, Lincs, and then greater things. A Stinson 108 and a Ryan PT-21 have arrived for storage.

☐ G-AGYY*   Ryan PT-21-RY   ex N56792, 41-1942. Stored.   06-93
☐ G-AMXT   Dove 6   ex G-BJXI ntu, XJ347, G-AMXT, N1561V.
CoA expired 5-12-86. Stored.   12-93
☐ G-BHMR*   Stinson 108-3   ex F-BABO, F-DABO, NC6352M. CoA expired
23-11-90. Stored.   06-93

ASHFORD
Work is believed to continue on the restoration of Brian Knock's Jackaroo.
☐ G-ANFY   Jackaroo   ex NL906, 9 RFS, 23 EFTS, 9 FTS. CoA
expired 25-5-68.

BRAND'S HATCH CIRCUIT
A visit to the circuit during 1993 could find no trace of Vampire T.11 pod XD602, Wessex HAS.1 XP159 and Whirlwind HAR.10 XP353. Any ideas?

BREDHURST (south of Junction 4 of the M2, south of Gillingham)
SAN DR.1050 G-AXVS was flying again by early 1991. It sadly crashed on a (or *the*) test flight, on February 17, 1991, but has not been noted since. Other **W&R** inmates are thought unchanged.
☐ G-ARWH   Cessna 172C   ex Golders Green, Fenland, N1466Y. CoA
expired 28-4-86. Spares use.   08-92
☐ G-BEYT   Cherokee 140   ex West Germany, D-EBWO, N6280W.
Crashed 17-2-91.
☐ G-BEZA   Zlin Z.226T   ex D-EMUD, OK-MUA. Stored.   07-92

BRENZETT (on the A2070 north west of New Romney)
■ **Brenzett Aeronautical Museum Trust** : Disposal of the Avro XIX has proved to be fruitless job, the airframe remaining on site. A Canberra nose has been acquired from Cardiff-Wales Airport and restoration work is underway on it — please see under Cardiff-Wales Airport, S Glam, for the plot relating to its provenance! A large amount of artefacts showing both the history of the former airfield and military aviation in Kent in general are displayed within the buildings.
◆ Open Sundays and Bank Holidays from Easter to October, 11am to 5.30pm and additionally Tuesdays, Wednesdays and Thursdays, July to September from 2pm to 5pm. ✉ Brenzett Aeronautical Museum, Ivychurch Road, Brenzett, Romney Marsh, Kent TN29 0EE.
☐ G-AGPG   Avro XIX Srs 2   ex Southend, Pye, Ekco, Avro. CoA exp 13-12-71.
Poor state, available for disposal.   11-93
☐ G-AMSM   Dakota 4   ex Booker, Brenzett, Duxford, Brenzett, Lydd,
Skyways, Eagle, Starways, KN274, TCDU, 77,
St Eval SF, Azores SF, 43-49948. Damaged
17-8-78. Nose.   11-93
☐ V7350   Hurricane I   ex Robertsbridge, 85. Cr 29-8-40. Cockpit.   11-93
☐ WH657   Canberra B.2   ex Godalming, RAE, 231 OCU.   11-93
☐ XK625   Vampire T.11   ex Firbeck, North Weald, Southend, Woodford,
St Athan, 8 FTS, 7 FTS. '12'   11-93
☐ *   Canberra PR.7   ex Cardiff-Wales, WAM, CTTS St Athan. Nose.
Arr by 10-92. *Possibly* WJ581. See notes.   11-93

CANTERBURY
■ **Tired Iron Ltd** : B-26C N4806E should still be in a workshop in the locality..
☐ N4806E   B-26C Invader   ex Southend Airport, Rockford (Illinois), 44-34172,
Davis-M, 3 BW, 17 BW, 7 ADW. Restn.   04-91

CHALLOCK LEES (on the A251 north of Ashford)
Turbulent G-AWWT was flying again by 1991. A visit here during December 1993 failed to find Cadet TX.3 XN198, or any other **W&R** fodder.

CHATHAM
■ **Royal Engineers Museum** : A Harrier has gone on display. The Sioux is still in store off-site.
◆ On the B2004 to the north of Chatham. Open Tuesday to Friday and Spring-Summer Bank Holidays 10am to 5pm and Sundays 11.30am to 5pm. ✉ Royal Engineers Museum, Brompton Barracks, Chatham, Kent ME4 4UG. ☎ 0634 406397

☐ XT133	7923M	Sioux AH.1	ex Arborfield, Middle Wallop. Stored.	01-94
☐ XZ964*		Harrier GR.3	ex St Athan, 1417F, 233 OCU, 3, 233 OCU, 1.	01-94
			'D'. First noted 06-92.	

■ **1404 Squadron ATC** : In Boundary Road have a *Chippax*.

☐ WZ846	8439M	Chipmunk T.10	ex G-BCSC, Bicester, Manston, Wales UAS, AOTS,
			202, 228, CFE, West Raynham SF, G&S UAS,
			Bri UAS, 1 AEF, St Athan, Nott UAS, 63 GCF,
			Edn UAS, S'tn UAS.

■ **Others** : Three light aircraft are held in store in the area.

☐ G-AXDB		J-3C-65 Cub	ex Whitwell, Bembridge, F-BMSJ, 43-29929.
			Identity confirmed. Damaged 13-12-72. Stored.
☐ G-AYVP		Woody Pusher	unfinished homebuild project.
☐ G-BCNC		GY-201 Minicab	ex F-BICF. Restoration.

CHATTENDEN (on the A228 north of Rochester)

■ **Defence Ordnance Disposal School** : Within Lodge Hill Camp can be found the DODS. Amending **W&R13**, the *Doodlebug* and the Ohka have not been displayed outside for many years and instead are within an impressive display of *squibs* inside. Likewise, the Canberra was not a gate guardian, but an instructional airframe. It was replaced by a Phantom in January 1993, and moved to Stock, Essex, by October 1993.

☐ XT907*	9151M	Phantom FGR.2	ex 74, 228 OCU. 'W'. EOD. Arrived 1-93.	09-93
☐	BAPC.158	Fieseler Fi 103	held inside the camp.	09-92
☐	BAPC.159	Ohka 11	held inside the camp.	09-92

CHISLET

The strip returns to the fold with the arrival of a long out-of-use Super Cruiser by January 1993.

| ☐ G-AXUC* | | Super Cruiser | ex Canterbury area, 5Y-KFR, VP-KFR, ZS-BIN. | |
| | | | CoA expired 4-5-81. Stored. F/n 1-93. | 01-93 |

HAWKINGE (on the A260 north of Folkestone)

■ **Kent Battle of Britain Museum** : The astounding collection of artefacts, backed-up by dioramas centred upon *Battle of Britain* replicas continues to prosper.

◆ Open seven days a week Easter to September 30 10am to 5pm and October all week 11am to 2pm.

✉ Aerodrome Road, Hawkinge Airfield, Folkestone, CT18 7AG. ☎ 0303 89 3140.

☐ 'D-3-340'		Grunau Baby	true identity unknown.	08-90
☐ 'L1592'	BAPC.63	Hurricane rep	ex Higher Blagdon, *Battle of Britain*. 'KW-Z',
			615 Sqn colours.
☐ 'N3289'	BAPC.65	Spitfire replica	ex Chilham Castle, *Battle of Britain*. 'QV-K',
			19 Sqn colours.
☐ 'N3313'	BAPC.69	Spitfire replica	ex Higher Blagdon, Stoneleigh, *Battle of Britain*.
			'BO-D', film codes.
☐ 'P3059'	BAPC.64	Hurricane rep	ex Chilham Castle, *Battle of Britain*. 'SD-N',
			501 Sqn colours.
☐ '1480'	BAPC.66	'Bf 109' replica	ex Chilham Castle, *Battle of Britain*. '6'.
☐ '6357'	BAPC.74	'Bf 109' replica	ex Higher Blagdon, *Battle of Britain*. '6'.
☐	BAPC.36	Fi 103 (V-1) rep	ex Old Warden, Duxford, Old Warden.
☐	BAPC.67	'Bf 109' replica	ex Coventry Airport, North Weald, Newark,
			Battle of Britain. '14', JG52 colours.

HEADCORN AERODROME

From this edition, the opportunity has been taken to list the aerodrome under its official title — see under Lashenden, Kent.

HIGH HALDEN (on the A28 south west of Ashford)

■ **Trevor Hukins** : Acquired the former Tonbridge Vampire T.11 during early 1992.

| ☐ XE995* | | Vampire T.11 | ex Tonbridge, Higher Blagdon, Woodford, 19 MU, |
| | | | 8 FTS, 5 FTS, 32. '53'. Restoration. | 04-92 |

LASHENDEN AERODROME (or Headcorn, on the A247 south of Headcorn)

■ **Lashenden Air Warfare Museum** (LAWM) : Plans for the enlarged museum are at present on the 'back burner' as a more pressing need was addressed — campaigning to keep this lovely airfield open. Thankfully, sense has prevailed and the airfield's future is much more secure. However, the campaign cost a lot of money and time and expansion of LAWM will have to wait a while. In association with Gull Wing Aviation, LAWM are offering pleasure flights, using a resident Auster. Vampire T.11 WZ589 is well into its restoration programme with most of the woodwork completed. The acquisition of the pod of WZ450 was planned to provide LAWM with a travelling exhibit, but they took delivery of a much more readily mobile exhibit during March 1994!.

◆ Open Sundays and Bank Holidays 10.30am to 6pm from Easter until the end of October. Parties at other times by prior arrangement. ✉ LAWM, Lashenden Aerodrome, Ashford, Kent TN27 9HX.

☐ WZ450*	Vampire T.11	ex North Weald, Birmingham, Sealand, Wrexham, Woodford, Chester, Shawbury, RAFC, 233 OCU, 202 AFS. Pod. Arr 7-8-93. See notes.	12-93
☐ WZ589	Vampire T.11	ex Woodford, Chester, St Athan, 56. For restoration — see notes above. '19'.	12-93
☐ XN380	Whirlwind HAS.7	ex Wroughton, 705, 771, 829, 824, 825. '67'.	12-93
☐ 84	Mystere IVA	ex Sculthorpe, French AF. On loan from Robertsbridge AS. '8-NF'.	12-93
☐ 63938	F-100F-16-NA	ex Sculthorpe, French AF. '11-MU'.	12-93
☐ 100549*	Fa 330A-1	ex Manchester, Liverpool, Blackpool, Lavenham, Hullavington, Biggin Hill, Farnborough. Arrived 22-3-94.	03-94
☐	BAPC.91 Fi 103R-IV	ex Horsham, Farnborough.	12-93

[*Possibly* a genuine 'R-IV.]

■ **Airfield** : J/1 Autocrat G-AGYK was flying by mid-1990. During February 1994 the B-25 from Coventry Airport, Warks, started to arrive here. It will be refurbished by a private collector.

☐ G-AHAV	J/1 Autocrat	ex HB-EOM ntu. CoA exp 21-6-75. Stored.	05-90
☐ G-AWGJ*	Cessna F.172H	damaged 16-10-87. Stored. F/n 11-92.	12-93
☐ G-BSPC	SAN D.140C	ex F-BMFN. CoA exp 31-10-85. Stored.	12-92
☐ G-OTVS	BN-2T	ex G-BPBN, G-BCMY. Damaged 11-3-89. Stored.	12-93
☐ '151632'* NL9494Z	TB-25N-NC	ex Coventry, Blackbushe, USAAF 44-30925. *Gorgeous George-Ann.* Arrived 2-94.	02-94

LYMPNE AERODROME (on the A261 north west of Hythe)

Fiat G.46 BAPC.79 was rescued by The Aircraft Restoration Co and moved to <u>Duxford</u>, Cambs, during August 1992. It may be beyond restoration however.

MANSTON AIRFIELD (or Kent International Airport, on the A253 west of Ramsgate)

■ **Airport** : The VIP-configured Saudi Boeing 707 was partially scrapped during 1992 with the view (at that stage) of turning it into a restaurant or even conference centre. This plan has since been shelved, but the fuselage has been held in store by Jet Support in the hope that the sumptuous interior will attract a buyer. Former Angolan Air Charter Boeing 707 D2-TOU has joined the fire school — see below. Queen Air 70 G-KEAA fled to <u>Elstree</u>, Herts, by August 1993.

☐ D2-TOG	Boeing 707-373	ex Angolan Air Charter, D2-TAG, HZ-ACF, N374WA. Scrapping, sectioned by 1-93.	01-93
☐ HB-IEI	Boeing 707-328	ex 5Y-ANA ntu, XT-BBF, SU-DAB, ST-AKR, SU-DAB, F-BLCG. Stored.	06-92
☐ HZ-TAS	Boeing 707-321	ex Stansted, N98WS, N111MF, N763W, N763PA. Stored. Fuselage only 9-92. See notes.	12-93

■ **Central Training Establishment** (CTE) : There has been a clear-out (or burn-out) of airframes at the CTE and the question of what-lives-on remains vague. Bearing this in mind the following are thought to be firmly in the 'ashes-to-ashes' category, most by November 1992 :— Devon C.2/2s VP953, VP956, VP963 and VP965; Whirlwind HAR.10s XJ430, XK969 (but see under Otterburn, Northumberland), XP333, XP394 and XP400.

During August 1993 Hanningfield Metals of Stock, Essex, cleared more airframes from the CTE, all in a well deceased state :— Viscount 724 G-BDRC; Lightning F.1 XG327/8188M; Victor K.1A XH590; Vulcan B.2 XL386/8760M; Vulcan B.2 XM657/8734M; Argosy E.1 XN855/8556M and Whirlwind HAR.10 XP357.

☐	D2-TOU		Boeing 707-351	ex airfield, Angolan Air Charter, 5Y-BFB, 5A-DJS, TF-VLP, N88TF, VR-HGQ, VR-HGR ntu, N363US. Reasonably complete. 08-93
☐	VP971	8824M	Devon C.2/2	ex Catterick, Northolt, 207, 60, 207, SCCS, SCS, AAFCE, SCS, HS, MoA, SCS, MCS, MCCS, MCCF, BCCF. 08-93
☐	WK124	9093M	Canberra TT.18	ex Wyton, 100, 7, 213, 59, 103. 'C'. 12-93
☐	XJ695	8738M	Hunter FGA.9	ex 8677M, Kemble, 1 TWU, TWU, 229 OCU, 58, 45, 20, 14, 20. With tail of XF519. 08-93
☐	XK968	8445M	W'wind HAR.10	ex Wroughton, 28, 103, 110, 22, JEHU. 'E'. On side. 08-93
☐	XL162	9114M	Victor K.2	ex Marham, 55, 57, 55, 57, Wittering Wing, 139, MoA. 12-93
☐	XM475*	9112M	Jet Provost T.3A	ex 1 FTS, 7 FTS, RAFC, TWU, RAFC, 7 FTS, 2 FTS. '44'. 08-93
☐	XN602	8088M	Jet Provost T.3	ex Brize Norton, Halton, Brampton, Shawbury, 6 FTS. On its back. 08-93
☐	XP741	8939M	Lightning F.3	ex 5, LTF, 11, 5, 111, Wattisham TFF, 111, Wattisham TFF, 111. 'AR'. 12-93
☐	XT475	9108M	Wessex HU.5	ex Wroughton, 772. '624-PO'. On side. 08-93
☐	XV411	9103M	Phantom FGR.2	ex 56, 92, 19, 92, 14. 'L'. 12-93
☐	XV864*		Buccaneer S.2B	ex 12, 237 OCU, 16. Flew in 5-4-94. Dump. 04-94
☐	ZD239	G-ASGK	Super VC-10	ex Abingdon, Prestwick, BA, BOAC. With rear fuselage of ZD233/G-ASGC. 08-93
☐	ZE353	9083M	F-4J(UK)	ex 74, USN 153785. 'E'. Airfield fire crews. 12-93
☐	ZE360	9059M	F-4J(UK)	ex 74, USN 155529. 'O'. 12-93

■ **RAF Manston Memorial Building** : The superb Hurricane and Spitfire are still on show.
◆ Open daily, 10am to 4.30pm. ✉ RAF Manston, Ramsgate, Kent, CT12 5BS. ☎ 0843 823351.

☐	'BN230'	LF751	Hurricane II	ex Rochester, Bentley Priory, Waterbeach 5466M, 27 OTU, 1681 BDTF. Composite, parts of Z3687 and PG593. 'FT-A', 43 Sqn c/s. 12-93
☐	TB752	8086M	Spitfire XVI	ex Rochester, Manston 7256M/7279M, Lyneham, 5 CAACU, 103 FRS, 102 FRS, 403, 66. 'KH-Z', 403 Sqn colours. 12-93

■ **1218 Sqn ATC** : A former Odiham, Hants, based *JP* nose was on charge with this unit by March 1993. It *may* be based off-site — any comments? While on the subject, the base 'parents' the Chipmunk T.10 PAX Trainer at Chatham, Kent.

☐	XR681*	8588M	Jet Provost T.4	ex Odiham, Abingdon, RAFEF, CATCS, 6 FTS, RAFC. Nose. See notes above. 03-93

PADDOCK WOOD (on the B2160 north east of Royal Tunbridge Wells)
■ **Aero Vintage** (AV) / **Historic Aircraft Collection Ltd** (HAC) : AV and HAC projects are fairly widespread, but this location will be used as the 'hub' for **W&R** purposes. Omitted from this location in **W&R13** was genuine Fi 156C-3 *Storch* G-FIST which came here from Seaton Ross and Ludham. It moved to Duxford, Cambs, during May 1993. Tiger Moth G-ANOR was flying by 1992 as 'T6991'. AV also have their Hawker Demon project at Hatch, Beds and HAC have a Spitfire IX at Audley End, Essex. The HAC Nieuport was exported via Old Warden, Beds, which see. The Curtiss Jenny listed here in **W&R13** is actually to be found at Sudbury, Suffolk. The Audax parts mentioned in **W&R13** are actually quite substantial and deserve formally listing. See also under Hatch, Beds, for the HAC BE.2 and under St Leonards-on-Sea, E Sussex, for other projects.

☐	VT-DPE*G-BUJY		Tiger Moth	ex Shipdham, Indian AF HU858. Arr 1993. 03-94
☐	MK912	G-BRRA	Spitfire IX	ex Ludham, Saffraanberg, Belgium, Belgian AF SM-29, RNeth AF H-59, H-119, RAF MK912, 84 GSU, 312. HAC. 03-94

☐ RN201	G-BSKP	Spitfire XIV	ex Audley End, Ludham, Beauvechain 'SG-3', Belg AF SG-31, RAF, 350, 83 GSU, RN201. 03-94
☐ 1342	G-BTZD	Yak-1	ex USSR. Arrived 1991. Restoration. HAC. 03-94
☐ *		Audax	substantial airframe. Restn project. HAC. 03-94

ROCHESTER AERODROME (on the A229 south of Rochester)

■ **Medway Aircraft Preservation Society Ltd** (MAPS) : The sweet sound of a Merlin was heard over the aerodrome on December 23, 1992, when Mark Hanna of The Old Flying Machine Company (OFMC) took Spitfire PR.XI PL965/G-MKXI into the air for the first time following restoration. This restoration, on behalf of Tangmere Flight, underlines of the skills of the team here. The project was brought to MAPS by the late Nick Grace — a restorer and engineer of great prowess himself. He would have been well pleased with the final result. PL965 completed its flight tests and flew on to <u>Duxford</u>, Cambs, where it is operated on behalf of Tangmere Flight by OFMC. Coming inbound from Duxford has been the next MAPS project, the restoration of the Short SB.4 SHERPA to display condition. Sadly, the major feature of this aircraft, its aero-isoclinic wings, no longer exist. MAPS is working hard in its own way to make a lasting record of Shorts and their stay on the Medway — the SHERPA being the first large artefact to this end. Work on the restoration of MAPS's own *hack*, the Tri-Pacer, is fast coming to a conclusion. Restoration of the Hurricane for the RAF Museum should be completed during 1994.

◆ The workshop facilities are open to the public on Sunday mornings, but Airport rules must be observed — the threshold of Runway 34 needs negotiating. ✉ Lewis Deal, 15, Amethyst Avenue, Chatham, Kent, ME5 9TX. ☎ / Fax 0634 816492.

☐ G-APXU		Tri-Pacer 150	ex Bredhurst, N1723A. CoA exp 20-2-85. 12-93
☐ G-36-1*		SB.4 SHERPA	ex Duxford, Staverton, Bristol, Cranfield, G-14-1. Arrived 10-3-93. For restoration. 12-93
☐ LF738	5405M	Hurricane II	ex Biggin Hill, Wellesbourne Mountford, 22 OTU, 1682 BDTF. Restoration. 12-93

■ **Others** : The Beech 18 was receiving some attention by late 1993. It is not known what plans there are for it. As the battle hots up for the new attack helicopter for the Army Air Corps, GEC continue to work on the AH-1T as a mock-up for their joint proposal with Bell.

☐ N96240		Beech D.18S	ex Spain, Wellesbourne Mountford, Blackbushe, G-AYAH, N6123, RCAF 1559. See notes. 12-93
☐ 160810		AH-1T Cobra	ex USMC. GEC static trials. 12-93

SEVENOAKS

■ **Biggin Hill Air Museum / Friends of Biggin Hill** : The aim to establish a museum at Biggin Hill is plodding on, but developments relating to the north site at *The Hill* are taking some time to gel, although the local Council is very supportive. The collection has taken on two of the replicas that for a long time were stored at Coventry Airport, Warks. These machines were, to say the least, 'loose' replicas and tying each one down is somewhat difficult — see under Coventry and Chelford, Cheshire. Peter Smith has four airframes on loan to the Macclesfield group :— Spitfire replica BAPC.190, Noralpha G-BAYV, Vampire NF.10 pod WP250 and Vampire T.11 pod XD535 — see under Chelford, Cheshire. Both of the Typhoon cockpit sections were moved to <u>Brooklands</u>, Surrey, by August 1992 on loan. The Typhoon project makes good progress, Curator Peter Smith has an engine and is following up leads on wings. The rear fuselage of Sea Fury FB.11 VW589 was salvaged from Malta, during late 1993, also for the Typhoon project. Coming the other way from Brooklands was the former *Wings* BE.2 replica.

◆ Airframes are stored in a variety of places and visits are not possible. General enquiries can be made to ✉ Peter Smith, Curator, 3, Chatto Road, Battersea, London SW11 6JL.

☐ G-AAXK		Klemm L25	CoA exp 29-11-60. Dam 3-62. Fuselage. 12-93
☐ *		'SE.5A' replica	ex Coventry Airport. Arr 1993. See notes. 12-93
☐ *		'FB.5 Gunbus' rep	ex Coventry Airport. Arr 1993. See notes. 12-93
☐ *	BAPC.117	BE 2c replica	ex Brooklands, North Weald, BBC *Wings*. Arrived -93. Under restoration. 12-93

■ **Locally** : Airedale G-AWGA moved to Biggin Hill, Gtr Man, during December 1993.

☐ G-APJZ		J/1N Alpha	ex St Albans, 5N-ACY, VR-NDR ntu, G-APJZ. Crashed 10-11-75. Restoration.

SHOREHAM
■ **Shoreham Aircraft Preservation Society** (SAPS) : A superb museum based upon SAPS' extensive number of 'digs', all beautifully researched and presented. Centre-piece is the cockpit section and other parts from the former Kenley dump Spitfire XVI TB885.
◆ Last Sunday of the month during the summer, or by prior arrangement. ✉ SAPS, High Street, Shoreham Village, Sevenoaks, Kent, TN14 7TB.
| ☐ TB885 | Spitfire XVI | ex Kenley, *Reach for the Sky* as 'R1247', Cosford. Cockpit section etc, under restoration. | 10-93 |

SHORNCLIFFE (near Lydd)
■ **Sir John Moore Barracks** : The Whirlwind should still be with the Junior Infantry Regiment.
| ☐ XP405 | 8656M | W'wind HAR.10 | ex Halton, 2 FTS, CFS, 228. 'Y'. | 10-89 |

SMEETH (on the A20 east of Ashford)
In a garden here, an Aztec is thought still used as a plaything.
| ☐ G-ASER | Aztec 250B | ex Biggin Hill. Crashed 14-9-72. Hulk. | 10-91 |

TONBRIDGE
■ **Peter Griffiths** : Disposed of his Vampire T.11 to Trevor Hukins at <u>High Halden</u>, Kent.
■ **Chris Jefferson** : During mid-1992 Chris acquired the long-'lost' Kensinger KF from storage at Bobbington, Staffs. Restoration to airworthy condition is underway.
| ☐ G-ASSV* | Kensinger KF | ex Bobbington, N23S. Crashed 2-7-69. See notes above. | 07-93 |

TUNBRIDGE WELLS
■ **David** & **Mollie Wood** : Tiger G-ANOD fled the coop for restoration, thought in the Reading area. The other two remain in place.
| ☐ G-APJO | Tiger Moth | ex Bournemouth, NM126, 16 RFS, 19 FTS. Largely G-APJR, ex T7391, 1 GU, 2 GS, 14 RFS, 6 RFS, 6 EFTS. Cr 28-5-61. Restoration. | |
| ☐ G-ISIS | Tiger Moth | ex G-AODR, Biggin Hill, NL779, Scampton SF, Binbrook SF, 11 RFS, 13 RFS, 8 RFS, 8 EFTS, 10 FIS. Crashed 18-9-61. | |

WEST MALLING AIRFIELD (on the A228 west of Maidstone)
■ **681 VGS** : Two gliders are stored in the VGS hangar.
| ☐ WT910* | Cadet TX.3 | stored. | 10-93 |
| ☐ WZ819* | Grasshopper TX.1 | stored. | 10-93 |

Lancashire

BACUP
■ **Pennine Aviation Museum** (PAM) : Severe problems relating to the site have led PAM to effectively wind down their operation. During mid-1992 most of the airframes were offered again for disposal, with the following results :— Anson T.21 VV901 to <u>Elvington</u>, N Yorks, on January 8, 1993; Balliol T.2 cockpit sections WN149 and WN534 to <u>Wolverhampton</u>, W Mids, May 16, 1993. The rear flying surfaces, tail section, struts etc of Hadrian BAPC.157 also went to Elvington, but the main fuselage section remains at Moorlands Park in Bacup, along with the Albemarle sections and the complete Canberra, all reportedly had to leave very quickly, or face the axe.
✉ PAM, 54 Hillcrest Avenue, Cliviger, Burnley, Lancashire, BB10 4JA.
| ☐ WF911 | Canberra B.2 | ex Preston, Samlesbury G-27-161, 231 OCU. Nose section. Stored off site. | 07-92 |
| ☐ WJ721 | Canberra TT.18 | ex Samlesbury, 7, 50, 40. External store, poor state. See notes above. | 01-93 |

☐	XG297		Hunter FGA.9	ex Macclesfield, Bitteswell, HSA, 20, 28, 20, 4. Nose. Stored, off-site.	07-92
☐	XK627		Vampire T.11	ex Hazel Grove, Woodford, Chester, St Athan, 8 FTS, CFS.	01-93
☐			Albemarle	ex Carlisle, Westnewton. Composite, frames.	
☐		BAPC.157	CG-4A Hadrian	ex Ormskirk. Fuselage frame. See notes.	01-93

BLACKBURN

■ **1262 Squadron ATC** : During 1992, the unit gave up their anonymous *Chippax*, and it moved to Salisbury, Wilts.

BLACKPOOL AIRPORT (or Squires Gate, off the A584 south of Blackpool)

■ **Airport** : There has been an increase in **W&R**-type airframes at the Airport, although it must be noted that some of the others in the list are getting long in the tooth and may have moved on.

☐	G-APOI		Skeeter 8	ex Wilkie, Old Buckenham, Llandegla, Inverness, Blackpool, Southampton. CoA exp 30-3-61.	12-91
☐	G-ARCI		Cessna 310D	ex N6966T. Damaged 22-8-86. Stored.	09-93
☐	G-ATRS		Cherokee 140	crashed 28-7-70. Stored.	
☐	G-AVFS*		Cherokee Six	crashed 28-9-90. Fuselage. F/n 5-92.	05-92
☐	G-AVWG*		Cherokee 140	crashed 11-12-88. Fuselage.	09-93
☐	G-AVPH		Cessna F.150G	ex Woodvale. CoA expired 9-4-86. Stored.	09-93
☐	G-AWUA		Cessna P.206D	ex Thruxton, N8750Z. Damaged 16-10-87.	11-90
☐	G-BBTL*		Aztec 250C	ex N6525Y. CoA expired 14-8-89. Stored.	09-93
☐	G-LYDD*		Navajo 300	ex Lydd, G-BBDU, N6796L. Damaged 17-7-91. Fuselage. First noted 5-92.	09-93
☐	G-RIFF		Gazelle 1	ex Barton, G-BLAN, N6958, F-WTNT. Crashed 7-3-90. Dump.	10-92
☐	G-YIII*		Cessna F.150L	ex PH-CEX. Fuselage, first noted 9-93.	09-93
☐	F-BHMU	G-BHVZ	Cessna 180	ex N4793B. Restoration.	
☐	XL391		Vulcan B.2	ex 44, 101, 44, 9/35, BCDU, MoA. Manchester Vulcan Bomber Society.	09-93

■ **Helicopter Museum of Great Britain** (HMGB) / **Wilkie Helicopters** : A valiant attempt to start an *active* helicopter museum came to a sad end on January 13, 1993, when an auction was held, selling the entire contents of the hangar occupied by the proposed HMGB and Wilkie Helicopters, by the order of Blackpool Airport Ltd in lieu of lease fees relating to Hangar 42. Although there were no reserves and it was said that everything would go, in the end there were ownership disputes reported on all but one of the airframes. Airframes in the auction were as follows : —

Lot 61	Whirlwind HAR.9 XN386	withdrawn
Lot 62	Skeeter AOP.10 XK482	withdrawn
Lot 63	Lynx fuselage shell	£5 (yes, *five* pounds!)
Lot 67	Grasshopper III G-AWRP	withdrawn
Lot 68	Grasshopper III G-AXFM	withdrawn
Lot 69	Grasshopper III G-AZAU	withdrawn

The identity of the Lynx was long doubted and helped to plunge the sale into still further levels of surrealism. XX469 was a naval prototype, therefore having a *wheeled* undercarriage. But the shell sitting in Hangar 42 was with *skids*. The item being auctioned was the rig RG-05 (see under Lancaster, Lancs), but what does that make the Lynx at Lancaster? Lot 63 went to the International Helicopter Museum for a *fiver*! The entire sale netted £810. Eventually, the IHM at Weston-super-Mare, Avon, became the happy owners of the following : — Lynx RG-05 and Grasshoppers G-AWRP, G-AXFM, G-AZAU. Other disposals were as follows : — Widgeon 2 G-ANLW, Hiller UH-12B G-APKY and Whirlwind HAS.7 G-AYXT to Northampton Aerodrome, Northants, by July 1992; Skeeter 8 G-APOI to a local owner on the Airport, see above; Scout 5X-UUW wreckage to East Dereham, Norfolk. That leaves the following either waiting resolution of ownership, or existence!

| ☐ | XK482 | G-BJWC | Skeeter AOP.10 | ex Heysham, Horsham, Ottershaw, Middle Wallop 7840M, HTF, HS, MoS. See notes above. | 01-93 |

☐	XN386	A2713	Whirlwind HAR.9	ex Wroughton, Yeovilton, F'lands, *Endurance* Flt,
				846, 814. '435-ED'. See notes above.	01-93
☐	XX469	G-BNCL	Lynx 1-07	ex Lancaster, Sherborne A2657, Westlands.
				Identity doubted — see notes above.

CHARNOCK RICHARD (on the A49, south west of Chorley)
Meta-Sokol G-APVU has moved on again, settling here.
| ☐ | G-APVU* | | Meta-Sokol | ex Wilmslow, Manchester Airport, OK-NMI. |
| | | | | Accident 12-9-78. Stored. First noted 7-92. | 07-92 |

CHORLEY
■ **International Fire Training Centre**: At Washington Hall, should still have their Whirlwind.
☐	XN298		Whirlwind HAR.9	ex Warmingham, Stoke-on-Trent, Bournemouth,
				Yeovilton, Wroughton, Lee-on-Solent SAR Flt,
				Fleetlands, Lee, 846, 848.	04-90

COCKERHAM (or Banks End, on the A588 between Lancaster and Fleetwood)
■ **Black Knight Parachute Centre** : Should still have their para-trainer.
| ☐ | G-ARZE | | Cessna 172C | ex Blackpool. Dam 11-9-76. Para-tnr. | 03-90 |

ECCLESTON (on the B5250 south of Leyland)
■ **Bygone Times Antique Warehouse** : The incredible warehouse (open daily) continues to supply a throughput of full size replicas — to attract passing *punters* looking for that off-the-wall impulse buy. Avro 504K replica 'E373' (BAPC.178) has not been noted since September 1988. It was replaced by a Fokker D.VII replica, but this was sold *circa* early 1993. In its turn, the Fokker was replaced by a Bristol Monoplane.
| ☐ | 'C4940'* | | Bristol M.1C rep | see notes above. | 04-93 |

LANCASTER
■ **Lancashire Fire Brigade Headquarters** : See under Blackpool Airport for a puzzle. It looks most likely that Lynx rig RG-05 either went to Blackpool Airport, or never came here. They may (or may not) have Lynx XX469.

PRESTON
Mr Conroy's Sycamore may still be located in Oswald Road.
| ☐ | XG540 | 8354M | Sycamore HR.14 | ex Drighlington, Shawbury 'XJ385', Ternhill, |
| | | | | 7899M, MCS, CFS. 'Y-S'. | 06-91 |

RAMSGREAVE (between the A59 and the A6119 north of Blackburn)
An up-to-date report on the Dragonfly here would be welcome.
| ☐ | WG751 | | Dragonfly HR.3 | ex Ancoats, Wisbech, Blackbushe, Fleetlands, 705. |
| | | | | | 05-90 |

SAMLESBURY AIRFIELD (on the A59 east of Preston)
■ **British Aerospace** : The notes given in **W&R13** relating to the former Argentinian Canberras still hold, ie they *may* or *may not* still be here. The gate still has its Canberra and Lightning.
☐	WH914	G-27-373	Canberra B.2	ex frustrated Argentine AF B.62, 231 OCU, 35,
				76, 50, 61, 100. Dismantled and stored.	09-91
☐	WT537		Canberra PR.7	ex 13, 31, 17. Gate guardian.	10-93
☐	XH583	G-27-374	Canberra T.4	ex frustrated Argentine AF T.64, St Athan, 231
				OCU. Dismantled and stored.	09-91
☐	ZF580		Lightning F.53	ex RSAF 53-672, G-27-42. On plinth.	10-93

WARTON AIRFIELD (on the A584 west of Preston)
■ **British Aerospace** : The much-troubled EFA makes an entry into the realms of **W&R** by way of static test airframes etc (see also Brough, Humberside) and the pioneering EAP is now long enough out of use to list also. BAe here acquired a Jet Provost T.5A from Cranwell on January 11, 1991. This

may be a flyer, or otherwise. The former Farnborough Nimrod is in use for trials work while BAe limbers up for its replacement Nimrod bid — in the form of refurbished Nimrods. The last of the BAe 'Tornado Flight' Lightnings, XS928, remains here for the gate. (The others went as follows :— XP693 and XR773 to Exeter, Devon, on December 23, 1992, and XS904 to Bruntingthorpe, Leics, on January 21, 1993 — the latter making the last ever flight by a Lightning under military aegis.) The nose sections of Canberra T.4 WJ857 and Buccaneer S.1 XN973 have not been sighted for a long time and are assumed to have expired.

☐ XS928*		Lightning F.6	ex BAe, Binbrook, 5-11, 56, 11, 56, 74, 5, 11. See notes above. 03-94
☐ XV147*		Nimrod prototype	ex Farnborough, Woodford, A&AEE. Sections. Arrived 12-93. See notes above. 03-94
☐ XW363*		Jet Provost T.5A	ex RAFC, 6 FTS, 1 FTS. '36'. See notes. 03-94
☐ ZA597		Tornado GR.1	ex Honington. Cat 4 8-11-83. Spares use. 07-92
☐ ZD939*		Tornado F.2	ex St Athan, 229 OCU. 'AS'. Arrived by 10-91. Saudi Support Unit. 03-94
☐ ZF534*		EAP	withdrawn. Stored. 03-94
☐ Q497		Canberra T.4	ex Samlesbury, frustrated Indian AF B.52, Bracebridge Heath, Samlesbury, Kemble, WE191, 231 OCU, 237 OCU, 231 OCU, 245. Fuselage. Dump. 03-94
☐		Strikemaster	ex SSU, dump. Nose spare BAC.167, centre section mock-up, rear end from *JP* 3 XN634, one wing *JP* 3 other *JP* 5! 03-94
☐	AV.023	Tornado ADV	fatigue rig, built in between ZE154 & ZE155. 07-92
☐	BN96	Eurofighter 2000	fatigue rig.. (JP003) 07-92
☐	BN94	Eurofighter 2000	two-seater, crew escape rig. 07-92

Leicestershire

BRUNTINGTHORPE AERODROME (between the M1 and the A50 south of Leicester)
■ **British Aviation Heritage** (BAH) / **C Walton** (**Aviation Division**) **Ltd** : In the persona of David Walton and the rest of his energetic family, C Walton Ltd were the successful bidders for the last flying Vulcan, B.2 XH558. It made an emotional arrival here on March 23, 1993 and since has been kept in ground-running status, including two fast runs at the *Big Thunder* air display in July 1993, with more planned for the 1994 event. A huge quantity of spares have been acquired to maintain XH558 in 'live', if not airworthy, condition and the commitment in hardware, space, personnel (the aircraft has a full time engineer on site) and determination is huge. On November 19, 1993, the Vulcan was joined by a former 55 Squadron Victor K.2. As XM715 reported the field in sight, a first for radio telegraphy was scored when the aircraft called, "Bruntingthorpe, this is Victor *Meldrew* One..." It being correct that at that moment the type certainly had *One Foot in the Grave*! Completing the V-Bomber trio, the nose of Valiant XD875 is here on loan from Ken Ward, it came here from its brief display at Marham, Norfolk, for the RAF's 75th anniversary *bash*. On the same day as the Victor arrived, a former DRA Canberra also flew in to join the collection, owned Frances and Peter Gill — another example of the 'co-operative' nature of the historic aircraft at Bruntingthorpe. A 'Friends of' organisation is being formed and there are wider plans to build a display/maintenance hangar under the BAH logo initially started by the late Nick Grace during his brief operation from this airfield. BAH/C Walton maintain close relations with Phoenix Aviation and with the Lightning Preservation Group. Sandy Topen's Vintage Aircraft Team is in the throes of moving in here from Cranfield, Beds. For the time being, VAT will also continue to be 'placed' under the latter heading while the already clouded situation settles down with this 'fleet' of aircraft. As far as the USAF Museum (as custodians of all of the 'museum' former French MAP aircraft in the UK) is concerned, it is C Walton Ltd who are keepers of the Mystere IVA here and it is accordingly listed under this heading. T-33A 19252 was due to arrived here from Tangmere, W Sussex, during December 1993, but had yet to arrive.

◆ Open days for the Vulcan and Victor are planned, but nothing is confirmed as **W&R14** goes to press. Visits by prior permission only. ✉ C Walton (Aviation Division) Ltd, Bruntingthorpe Airfield, Bruntingthorpe, Lutterworth, Leics, LE17 5QH. ☎ 0533 478030.

☐ XD875*		Valiant B.1	ex Marham, Firbeck, Coventry, Cosford, 7, 138, 207, SAC Bombing Sqn, 207, 49, 207. Nose. Loan NYARC, Chop Gate.. Arr by 12-93. 01-94
☐ XH558*		Vulcan B.2	ex Waddington, VDF, Marham, Waddington, 50, Wadd Wing, A&AEE, Wadd Wing, 27, 230 OCU, 27, Wadd Wing, 230 OCU. Flew in 23-3-93. 01-94
☐ XH568*	G-BVIC	Canberra B.2/6	ex DRA Bedford, RAE, MoA. Flew in 25-11-93. See notes above. 01-94
☐ XM715*		Victor K.2	ex 55, 232 OCU, 543, 232 OCU, 100, 139. Flew in 25-11-93. 01-94
☐ 85		Mystere IVA	ex East Midlands, Sculthorpe, French AF.

■ **Lightning Preservation Group** (LPG) : After a bid by a German museum failed, the LPG became owners of Lightning F.6 XS904. This machine was delivered on January 21, 1993 and marked the end of an era, the last flight by a Lightning under UK military aegis. Hours on this aircraft are quite limited, but it joins XR728 in being regularly kept 'live' by the LPG. During January 1994, LPG were busy moving a QRA shed from Wattisham, Suffolk. It is hoped to erect this and keep the collection in 'period' accommodation. Hugh Trevor's F.6 nose is also best listed under this heading.
◆ Regular running days, all well advertised. Other visits by prior permission only. ✉ LPG, 95, Thornhill, North Weald, Essex, CM16 6DP.

☐ XP703	Lightning F.3	ex Warton, fatigue rig, MoD(PE), 29, 56, 74. Nose. 01-94
☐ XR728	Lightning F.6	ex Binbrook, 11, LTF, 5, 56, 23, 11, 23. Taxiable. 'JS'. 01-94
☐ XS904*	Lightning F.6	ex BAe Warton, Binbrook, 5-11 pool. Flew in 21-1-93. 01-94
☐ XS932	Lightning F.6	ex Rossington 'TVI932', Binbrook, 5, 11, 56, 11. Nose. Owned by Hugh Trevor. 09-93

■ **Phantom Restoration Group** (PRG) / **Cockpits for Hire**: By April 1993 PRG acquired the nose section of an FGR.2 and have had it refurbished to a high standard. The nose section is trailer-mounted and has already appeared at a good number of aviation events. They have another waiting 'in the wings'. Cockpits for Hire is an offshoot of the PRG and their first item is the cockpit section of Viscount XT661, acquired on permanent loan from Hanningfield Metals of Stock, Essex. Work is now underway to convert the cockpit into a walk-through and travelling exhibit. It is possible that Cockpits for Hire at least may relocate during 1994.
◆ Visits possible by prior arrangement only. ✉ PRG, Steve Edwards, 84 Mepham Road, Wootton, Beds, MK43 9EN.

☐ XT661*	Viscount 838	ex Stock, DRA Bedford, 9G-AAV. Arrived 2-94 See notes above. 02-94
☐ XV489*	Phantom FGR.2	ex Stock, Wattisham, 92, 23, 56, 23, 29, 92, 56, 17. 'S'. Nose section only. Arrived by 4-93. 01-94 [Remainder at Stock, Essex.]
☐ XV490*	Phantom FGR.2	ex Wattisham, 228 OCU, 92, 56, 22, 92, 56, 23. Nose only. Stored. 01-94

■ **Phoenix Aviation** : Neville Martin appears to have had spectacular luck in fathoming the 'policy' (or more accurately, the total lack of) followed by the Ministry of Defence when they dispose of retired airframes. Accordingly a large amount of airframes and nose sections have gravitated to Bruntingthorpe and by January 1994 had congregated in a dispersal on the north west side of the airfield. It is difficult to define this assortment as a 'collection' as a glance below will show that a goodly number of airframes move around in 'trades'. A major *coup* was the arrival of almost intact Phantom FG.1 XT874, snatched from destruction at Wattisham, Suffolk. This was too good to last and by February 1994 it had moved to <u>Stock</u>, Essex. The nose of Canberra B.15 WH960 belongs to collector Steve Milnthorpe and is accordingly listed later. For a period Hunter F.51 E-427 was displayed close to the main gate of the airfield site, while the bulk of the other airframes remain closely packed in ranks, or shyly adorning one of the former dispersal sites. Neville Martin also had a store at

Lutterworth, Leics, but this has now closed. **W&R13** described *all* of Hunter F.6 XG290/8711M as going to Bournemouth Airport, Dorset, on January 18, 1992. In fact, only the nose and centre section went south. The rear fuselage and wings are still to be found here.

Departures have been as follows :— Canberra PR.7 nose WH957/8869M to East Kirkby, Lincs, by December 1993; Canberra T.17 nose WK102/8780M moved to Welshpool, Powys, in November 1993; Jet Provost T.3 XM355/8229M moved to Cambridge, Cambs; Jet Provost T.4 XP557 left for Firbeck, S Yorks, on January 29, 1994; Buccaneer S.2A nose XT277/8853M arrived from Cosford, Shrop, by October 1993, but moved the following month to Welshpool, Powys; Wessex HU.5 XT766/9054M came in from Halton, Bucks, on November 25, 1992 but quickly moved on to Shawell, Leics; Harrier GR.3 XV747/8979M moved to Hucknall, Notts, during 1993; the anonymous Gannet fuselage and wings of AEW.3 XL471 were scrapped during 1993.

Additionally, the fuselage of Shorts SD.360 G-ROOM from Charlwood, Surrey, was stored externally for some time during 1993. It was moved during October 1993 to a diving centre, reportedly either in 'Northamptonshire' or 'near The Wash'. Anything more concrete on this? The nose of Canberra B.2 WH775 is known to have come here from Cosford, Shrop, after tendering (for the second time) in November 1992 — fate?

☐ WH964	8870M	Canberra E.15	ex Cosford, St Athan, 100, 98, Akrotiri Wing, 32, 12. Nose.	09-93
☐ WH984	8101M	Canberra B.15	ex Cosford, HS, 9, Binbrook SF, 9. Nose.	09-93
☐ WJ565	8871M	Canberra T.17	ex Cosford, St Athan, 360, CA. Nose.	01-93
☐ WT536	8063M	Canberra PR.7	ex Cosford, 80, 31, 13, 17. Nose. [Remainder at Stock, Essex.]	01-93
☐ XH136*	8782M	Canberra PR.9	ex Cosford, 1 PRU, A&AEE, 39, 13, 58. MoA. Nose only. first noted 10-93.	10-93
☐ XM408	'8233M'	Jet Provost T.3	ex Halton 8333M, Kemble, Shawbury. MoA, 2 FTS. 'D'.	01-93
☐ XP503	8568M	Gnat T.1	ex Halton, 4 FTS. '73'.	09-93
☐ XP540	8608M	Gnat T.1	ex Halton, 4 FTS. '62'.	09-93
☐ XR569*	8560M	Gnat T.1	ex Linton-on-Ouse, Halton, 4 FTS, CFS, 4 FTS, CFS. '08'. First noted 1-93 .	09-93
☐ XS231		Jet Provost T.5	ex Bournemouth, Scampton, Shawbury, A&AEE, G-ATAJ ntu.	09-93
☐ XT755*	9053M	Wessex HU.5	ex Halton, Wroughton, 845. 'V'. F/n 10-93.	01-94
☐ XT793*		Wasp HAS.1	ex Fleetlands, Wroughton. '456'. Arr 4-94.	04-94
☐ XX669	8997M	Bulldog T.1	ex Cosford, Birm UAS. 'B'. Cr 6-9-88.	01-94
☐ E-427		Hunter F.51	ex Brough, Holme-on-Spalding Moor, Brough, Dunsfold, G-9-447, Danish AF, *Esk.*724.	01-94

■ **Vintage Aircraft Team** : The move from Cranfield, Beds, to the new location started in 1992, but the bulk of the 'action' took place during the summer of 1993. The story of what-went-where from Cranfield will take a long time (if not forever) to unravel. During late 1993/early 1994 the construction of a hangar was well underway, located at the extreme end of the northern perimeter track, halfway towards the threshold of Runway 06. Until the hangar is operational, many airframes will remain in the containers they moved from Cranfield in. Only aircraft *known* to have gravitated here are listed.

☐ WP845*		Chipmunk T.10	ex Cranfield, Stroud, Nor UAS, AOTS, PFS, AOTS, ITS, 7 AEF, 2 FTS, HCCS, Lon UAS, RAFC, 14 RFS. Arrived by mid-1993.	11-93
☐ WZ507*	G-VTII	Vampire T.11	ex Cranfield, Carlisle, 60 MU, CATCS, 3/4 CAACU, 5 FTS, 8 FTS, 229 OCU, 22 MU. arrived by mid-1993.	07-93
☐ XL578*		Hunter T.7	ex Cranfield, St Athan, 1 TWU, TWU, 229 OCU. '77'. Arrived 1-2-93.	10-93
☐ XN637*	G-BKOU	Jet Provost T.3 ▲	ex Cranfield, Bushey, Duxford, Winterbourne Gunner, 1 FTS, RAFC.	07-93
☐ '91007'*	G-NASA	T-33A-1-LO	ex G-TJET, Danish AF DT-566, USAF 51-8566. CoA expired 7-5-87. First noted 10-93.	10-93

■ **Others** : The Mystere IVA is now listed under the C Walton (Aviation Division) Ltd heading above. Lightning F.6 XS932 nose has also moved. It can be found under the LPG listing, above. The nose of Canberra B.15 WH960 is owned by Steve Milnthorpe — see also under Hinckley, Leics, but is due to move on. Restoration of the Luscombe continues slowly and an Aztec has entered external storage.

☐ G-BBGE*		Aztec 250D	ex N6137Y. CoA expired 17-8-92. Stored, engineless. First noted 1-93.	01-94.
☐ D-EFYR	G-LUSC	Silvaire 8E	ex LN-PAT, NC1248K ntu. Restoration.	01-94
☐ WH960	8344M	Canberra B.15	ex Cosford, Akrotiri Wing, 32, 9, 12. Nose. Steve Milnthorpe — see notes above.	01-93
☐ XD459		Vampire T.11	ex Long Marston, Bennington, Cranfield, Bushey, Keevil, 3/4 CAACU, 229 OCU, 233 OCU, 151, 253, 56. '63'. Pod. Les Wicks.	03-92

COALVILLE

■ **Snibston Discovery Park** : The park includes a huge display building in which can be found a whole sweep of industrial and technological history — with great emphasis on companies past and present that have operated within the County. The displays are excellent, ranging from an enchanting railway siding and coal yard, to the history of underwear, to all aspects of extractive industries to transport. The only item acknowledging the County's aviation industry is the Auster AOP.9. It may be the Compiler's myopia, but the bland sign saying what the Auster is even neglects to explain that it is a local product. There are no other displays on the aviation industry, or flying within Leicestershire — a great pity. Still, the site offers great potential and it is hoped in time this wide gap in the Museum's coverage will be filled. As with **W&R13**, other 'hopefuls' for display here are listed under this heading, though they are not available for inspection or are off-site. Leicestershire Museums Arts & Records Service maintain an extensive Auster archive, including the original manufacturer's drawings, this is stored in Leicester. (Contact Peter Stoddart on 0533 765532 Monday only, or on 0533 775932.) There is also a large photographic collection on Brush, which is available from the Leicestershire Record Office in Wigston, Leics (more details on 0533 571080). See also under Leicester Aerodrome, Leics.

◆ Daily 10am to 6pm, except December 25-26. Well signed off the A50 Coalville road. ✉ Ashby Road, Coalville, Leicestershire, LE6 2LN. ☎ 0530 510851. 24 hour information line 0530 813256.

☐ G-AIJK		Auster J/4	ex Leicester, Stratford-on-Avon. CoA expired 24-8-68. Under restoration, off site.	11-93
☐ G-AJRH		J/1N Alpha	ex Leicester, Harrogate, Wigan. CoA expired 5-6-69. Stored, off site.	11-93
☐ VZ728	G-AGOS	Desford Trainer	ex Perth, Strathallan, Thruxton, RAE. CoA expired 28-11-80. Stored.	11-93
☐ XP280		Auster AOP.9	ex Leicester, St Athan, 2 Wing, Queen's Dragoon Guards, 2 RTR, 651. On display.	02-94

COTTESMORE AIRFIELD (north of the B668, north east of Oakham)

■ **RAF Cottesmore** : A Harrier GR.3 arrived for the dump during December 1993 and was 'baptised' by the firecrews on the very day of arrival! Otherwise no change here.

☐ WH791	8187M	Canberra PR.7	ex St Athan 8165M, 8176M, 81, 58, 82, 542. Gate.	10-93
☐ XL618	8892M	Hunter T.7	ex Shawbury, Kemble, 1 TWU, 229 OCU, Jever SF, Gutersloh SF. '05'. Dump.	07-92
☐ XM375	8231M	Jet Provost T.3	ex Halton, Shawbury, RAFC, 3 FTS, 2 FTS. 'B'. Dump.	07-92
☐ XR716	8940M	Lightning F.3	ex Binbrook, 5, LTF, 5, 11, 5, LTF, 56, 29, 226 OCU, 111, Wattisham TFF, 111. 'AQ'. Dump.	04-92
☐ XZ966*	9221M	Harrier GR.3	ex St Athan, 1417F, 4, 1417F, 233 OCU, 1, 1417F, 1. 'F'. Arrived 15-12-93. Dump.	12-93

DONINGTON CIRCUIT (or Donington Park, near to East Midlands Airport)

■ **Donington Motor Museum / Donington Circuit** : The museum has a stunning array of racing cars and is well worth a diversion. On the circuit itself, a Spitfire replica had been mounted on a dramatic 'wishbone' plinth overlooking the track as far back as 1988.

◆ Open all year round (except Xmas week) from 10am to 5pm. ✉ Donington Motor Museum, Castle Donington, Derby, DE7 2SA. ☎ 0332 810048.

☐ *   Spitfire replica   'K-W'. See notes above.   07-93

EAST MIDLANDS AIRPORT (or Castle Donington, junction 24 M!, on the A453)
■ **Aeropark Visitors Centre** : The centre gives a commanding view of the activities of most of *EMA* as well and is open daily dawn to dusk. Of the airframes on display, restoration programmes continue at the hands of the EMAVA (see below) and a former Abingdon Hunter T.7 and Warton Buccaneer have arrived. The Visitors Centre itself contains a very well presented history of the Airport and aviation in general, offers educational facilities and has a small shop.
◆ Aeropark is open all year round from dawn to dusk, except for December 25 to January 1. Visitors Centre times vary, enquiries to the number below. ✉ East Midlands Airport Aeropark, Castle Donington, Derby, DE7 2SA. ☎ 0332 810621.
■ **East Midlands Airport Volunteers Association** : (Note change of name.) Maintaining the aircraft held at the Aeropark is the AVA. Aircraft are kept as 'live' as possible, with some having their engines run. Membership enquiries to :
✉ John Bigger, 8 West End, Long Whatton, Loughborough, Leics, LE12 5DW.

☐ G-BEOZ		Argosy 101	ex ABC, N895U, N6502R, G-1-7. CoA expired 28-5-86.	10-93
☐ G-FRJB		SA.1 Sheriff	ex Sandown. Incomplete and unflown.	10-93
☐ VR-BEP		Whirlwind Srs 3	ex Cuckfield, G-BAMH, Bristows, Redhill, XG588, 705, 701, *Warrior* Flt, *Albion* Flt.	07-93
☐ WH740	8762M	Canberra T.17	ex Cosford, 360, RNZAF, Upwood SF, 40, 18. 'X'.	10-93
☐ WL626	G-BHDD	Varsity T.1	ex Coventry, 6 FTS, 1 ANS, 2 ANS, 201 AFS. 'P'.	10-93
☐ XL569*	8833M	Hunter T.7	ex Abingdon, Cosford, 2 TWU, 1 TWU, 12, 216, 237 OCU, Laarbruch SF, 15, 237 OCU, 12, MinTech, 2 TWU, 1 TWU, TWU, 229 OCU. '80'. Arrived 20-2-93.	07-93
☐ XM575	G-BLMC	Vulcan B.2	ex 44, Wadd Wing, Scampton Wing, 617.	10-93
☐ XV350*		Buccaneer S.2B	ex Shawbury, Warton, RAE. Arr 11-12-93.	12-93
☐ ZF588		Lightning F.53	ex Warton, RSAF 53-693, G-27-63.	10-93

■ **Airport** : Hunting Cargo Airlines continue to take on more Lockheed Electras. Accordingly the final flying days for the small Merchantman fleet cannot be far off. G-APEJ and 'M have been withdrawn and G-APET was donated to the fire section during March 1993. The two HS.748s also remain in open store and have been joined by three Meridiana BAe 146s. The hulk of Cessna 404 G-BKTJ has not been noted for a considerable period of time and is assumed to have been scrapped.

☐ G-APEG		Merchantman	ex Airfast, ABC, BEA. CoA expired 18-5-83. Fire training. On belly by 11-93.	12-93
☐ G-APEJ*		Merchantman	ex ABC, BEA. Stored. First noted 2-93.	10-93
☐ G-APEM*		Merchantman	ex Hunting, ABC, BEA. Withdrawn 1-94.	02-94
☐ G-APET		Merchantman	ex ABC, BEA. CoA expired 6-7-91. To fire section by 3-93. Minus tail by 10-93..	12-93
☐ G-AZLR		Viscount 813	ex BMA, ZS-SBU ntu, SAA ZS-CDU. Fire.	12-93
☐ G-BSNR*	EC-FGT	BAe 146-300A	ex Meridiana, EC-807, G-6-165, G-BSNR, N886DV, G-BSNR, N886DV ntu, G-6-165. Flew in 15-7-92. Stored.	11-93
☐ G-BSNS*	EC-FHU	BAe 146-300A	ex Meridiana, EC-839, G-6-169, G-BSNS, N887DV, G-BSNS, N887DV ntu, G-6-169. Flew in 17-9-92. Stored.	11-93
☐ G-BSYT*	EC-FKF	BAe 146-300A	ex Meridiana, EC-899, G-BSYT, G-6-187. Flew in 17-9-92. Stored.	11-93
☐ G-BTJG*	EC-FIU	BAe 146-300A	ex Meridiana, EC-876, G-BTJG, G-6-163, N885DV. First 17-9-92. Stored.	11-93
☐ CS-TAG		HS.748-2A/270	ex SATA, G-AYIM, G-11-5. Stored.	11-93
☐ CS-TAH		HS.748-2A/270	ex SATA. Stored.	11-93

■ **Trent Aero** : Work on the Seafire continues, to the extent that first flight is not far off. (See under Biggin Hill, Gtr Lon, and Bournemouth Airport, Dorset, for more details.) Trent Aero undertook the restoration of the wings of the *Dinah* at the Aerospace Museum, Cosford, Salop, which see.

☐ PP972   G-BUAR   Seafire III   ex Biggin Hill, Thruxton, Biggin Hill, Vannes-
Meucon, Gavres, *Aéronavale* 12F, Bien Hoa,
1F, PP972, FAA, 767, 809. Restoration
for Precious Metals Ltd. See notes.   05-93

HINCKLEY

■ **Douglas Boston-Havoc UK Preservation Trust** : Many years of work by Dick Nutt and friends have produced a full-size replica Boston forward fuselage under construction and working examples of A-20G main landing gear and a Wright Cyclone 14 cylinder double-row radial engine. Also held are the pilot's instrument panels from an early DB-7 Havoc and a late A-20G Boston. The Trust has developed a specialised library of original A-20 drawings, manuals and historical literature.

◆ Visits by prior appointment only. ✉ Dick Nutt, 17 Hinckley Road, Barwell, Leics, LE9 8DL.

■ **Hurricane & Aircrew Collection** : Steve Milnthorpe's amazing collection of aircrew clothing and his restoration of a composite Hurricane fuselage are housed in the area. Steve also has a Canberra nose housed at Bruntingthorpe, Leics, but this was due for disposal during March 1994..

☐   *   Hurricane   forward fuselage. See notes above.   02-94

HOUGHTON-ON-THE-HILL (on the A47 east of Leicester)

Restoration of the Proctor continues in this area. The rear fuselages of two Chipmunks previously at Compton Abbas, Dorset, have joined a cockpit section for possible restoration.

☐ G-AKIU   Proctor V   ex North Weald, Southend, Edenbridge. CoA
expired 24-1-65. Restoration.   11-92
☐   *   Chipmunk   cockpit section, along with rear fuselages of
G-AOSN and G-BDBL. See above.   11-92
                                  [G-BDBL currently airworthy.]

HUSBANDS BOSWORTH AERODROME (south of the A427, south of the village)

Brooklands Mosquito G-AWIF gravitated to that great centre for such thrashing devices, <u>St Merryn</u>, Cornwall, by May 1993. Doppelraab IV ERC/BGA.2882 has moved on, being last noted in August 1991. An anonymous Grasshopper has appeared.

☐   *   Grasshopper TX.1   'fuselage', c/n SSK/FF/2013. Hung on wall.
First noted 11-92.   07-93

LEICESTER AERODROME (or Leicester East or Stoughton, south east of Leicester)

■ **Leicestershire Museums Arts & Records Service** : Leicester Aerodrome is the base for J/1 Autocrat G-AGOH and for their restoration project, Taylorcraft G-AFTN. *Oscar Hotel* is currently facing a monetary problem in renewing its CoA — let's hope a backer can be found to keep her flying. See also under Coalville, Leics.

☐ G-AFTN   T'craft Plus C2   ex Heavitree, HL535, 43 OTU, 652, 651,
G-AFTN. CoA expired 1-11-57. Restoration.
☐ G-AGOH   J/1 Autocrat ▵   see notes above.   03-94

■ **RN Aviation** : Ron Neal continues to look after the interests of Auster lovers everywhere and his cache of rebuilds receives attention whenever time permits.

☐ G-AEXZ   J-2 Cub   CoA expired 2-11-78. Restoration, off-site.
☐ G-AGVG   J/1 Autocrat   ex off-site, Paull. Wrecked 2-1-76. Noted at
airfield 6-91.   06-91
☐ G-APMH   J/1U Workmaster   ex F-OBOA, G-APMH. Cr 22-12-70. Restn   03-94
☐ G-ARDJ   Auster D.6/180   crashed 30-5-86. Stored, pending restoration   03-94
☐ XK417   G-AVXY   Auster AOP.9   ex Tattershall Thorpe, Wisbech, Henstridge,
St Athan, 652, 9 Flt, 18 Flt, Middle Wallop.
Under restoration.   04-92

LOUGHBOROUGH

■ **Classic Jet Aircraft Group** : Work is thought to have come to a halt on the two Meteors here, in preference to the projects of Meteor Flight — see under Yatesbury, Wilts.

| ☐ WE925 | | Meteor F.8 | ex Cardiff-Wales, Tarrant Rushton, FRL, 229 OCU, 34, 43, 92, 64, 63, 64. Composite, with parts from VZ530. Restoration. | 10-93 |
| ☐ WS760 | 7964M | Meteor NF.14 | ex Cranfield, Bushey, Duxford, Brampton, Upwood, 1 ANS, 64, 237 OCU. Restn. | 10-93 |

■ **University** : The Department of Transport Technology uses the fly-by-wire *Jag* as a training aid.

| ☐ XX765 | | Jaguar GR.1 | ex Warton, BAe, RAE, A&AEE, 226 OCU, 14. Instructional airframe. | 07-91 |

LUTTERWORTH

■ **Neville Martin / Phoenix Aviation** : A change of ownership has resulted in the store of aircraft here being dispersed. Bensen B.8M G-AXCI moved to <u>Lichfield</u>, Staffs. Cessna 207 G-BAAK was flying by July 1992. Cessna 152 II G-BGLI cannot be accounted for — scrapped?

MARKET HARBOROUGH

■ **Ian Castle** : Owner and operator of immaculate Tiger Moths, Ian acquired a Moth Major during 1992. It is being restored nearby.

| ☐ G-ABDA* | | DH.60G III | ex Stourbridge, 2595M, DG583 - no service, G-ABDA. Acquired during 1992. Restn. | 02-93 |

NORTH LUFFENHAM (north of the A6121 south west of Stamford)

■ **RAF North Luffenham** : Another base slated to close "in the near term". As can be seen from a scan of the identities below, the *JP*s noted in **W&R13** were *not* T.5s, they did *not* fly in and multiplied from four to *six*! By September 1992 they had been painted olive drab and were dispersed around the airfield. All airframes on the site are for EOD training — the RAF's Explosive Ordnance Disposal unit is located at nearby Wittering and uses 'Luffenham for exercises — frequently cratering what is left of the runway system here. Indeed, all of the airframes are 'parented' by the RAF Armament Support Unit at Wittering. The Hunter received some cosmetic treatment to make it look like a convincing 'MiG' from a distance by September 1992 — with the removal of the extreme nose and the addition red stars! Also sighted during November 1992 was a scale replica Sopwith Camel in one of the hangars. This may be a flying project, so is not listed here — yet. Sea Vixen FAW.2s XJ608, XN699 and XP921 were scrapped at around the time the *JP*s arrived.

☐ WS776	7716M	Meteor NF.14	ex Lyneham, 228 OCU, 85, 25. 'K'. Gate.	07-93
☐ XG194	8839M	Hunter FGA.9	ex Cosford, 1 TWU, TWU, 229 OCU, 1, 92, 111, 43. '55'. Soviet red stars by 11-92.	11-92
☐ XM410*	8054AM	Jet Provost T.3	ex Halton, Shawbury, RAFC, 7 FTS, 2 FTS. 'B'.	09-92
☐ XN554*	8436M	Jet Provost T.3	ex Halton, St Athan, Shawbury, CFS. 'K'.	09-92
☐ XN579*	9137M	Jet Provost T.3A	ex Shawbury, 1 FTS, 7 FTS, 1 FTS, RAFC, TWU, RAFC. Arrived 4-92, see notes above. '14'. EOD airframe.	09-92
☐ XP344	8764M	W'wind HAR.10	ex Cranwell, Finningley, Chivenor, 22, SAR Wing, CFS.	
☐ XP629*	9026M	Jet Provost T.4	ex Halton, Shawbury, CATCS, SoRF, CAW, 2 FTS. 'P'.	09-92
☐ XP686*	8502M	Jet Provost T.4	ex Halton, 8401M, CATCS, 6 FTS, CAW, CATCS, CAW, 3 FTS. 'G'.	09-92
☐ XS186*	8408M	Jet Provost T.4	ex Halton, St Athan, Kemble, Shawbury, CAW. 'M'.	09-92

SHAWELL (south of Lutterworth, east of the A5)

Phoenix Aviation supplied a Wessex HU.5 for use in a civilian assault course/paintball arena here.

| ☐ XT766* | 9054M | Wessex HU.5 | ex Bruntingthorpe, Halton, Wroughton, 781. '822-CU'. See notes above. | 10-93 |

STANFORD (off the B5414 north east of Rugby)

■ **Stanford Hall / Percy Pilcher Museum** : Within the hall is a small display devoted to the life and times of Sir Percy Pilcher, including a replica Hawk. The 'Hawk — although a replica — is probably the most representative of the pioneer craft, including the original which can be found at East Fortune, Lothian.

◆ Open weekends , Easter to September 2.30pm to 6pm and Bank Holidays 12am to 6pm. ✉ Stanford Hall, Lutterworth, Leicestershire, LE17 6DH. ☎ 0788 860250.

☐   BAPC.45   Pilcher Hawk   replica, ex Coventry.   12-92

STONEY STANTON (on the B581 east of Hinckley)

The Wessex immersed in Stoney Cove during February 1992 is now identified. The lake is also *said* to be the final home of a Viscount forward fuselage from East Midlands, also used for similar police training. This is most likely to be Series 814 G-AWXI which was donated by BMA to Leicester Police in *1970*.

☐ XT768   Wessex HU.5   ex Finningley, Wroughton, Westlands. See notes
                                              above.   02-92

UPPINGHAM (on the A6003 north of Corby)

■ **Uppingham School** : The college bought 'their' CCF Grasshopper TX.1 from the MoD during the great sell-off on June 29, 1988. It *should* still be here.

☐ XA230*   Grasshopper TX.1   see notes above.   06-<u>88</u>

Lincolnshire

BARKSTON HEATH AIRFIELD (on the B6403 north of Grantham)

■ **RAF Barkston Heath** : The Canberra still clings to this mortal coil...

☐ WT339   8198M   Canberra B(I).8   ex Cranwell, 16, 3, 14, 88. Dump.   10-93

BINBROOK AIRFIELD (north of the B1203, north of the village)

■ **Lightning Association** (LA) : After the acquisition of Lightning F.6 XR724 at Shawbury, Salop, the LA encountered many problems in their attempts to ferry it to Binbrook. In the end, intervention by BAe allowed the aircraft to position to Binbrook under the aegis of a military ferry flight — the civilian registration, although allocated, having no legal bearing in this instance. LA are working towards the operation of this aircraft, with the goal of flying her. The LA unites all those who love the Lightning — surely countless beings! — and has a much wider remit than just the preservation of an example. As well as regular events, it publishes an exceptional journal covering all aspects of Lightning history and operation.

◆ Annual open day and other times for LA members. Other visits by prior permission only. ✉ Lightning Association, Charles Ross, Binbrook Airfield, Lincs, LN3 6HF.

☐ XR724*   G-BTSY   Lightning F.6   ex Shawbury, BAe Warton, 5, 11, 5, 11, 5,
                                              LTF, 11. Flew in 23-7-92.   07-92

■ **Global Aviation** (GA) : Operating out of some of the former QRA sheds here, Richard Lake's company looks set to become a major entry in this work, through many purchases of Jet Provosts from the MoD. Announced in February 1994 as the "67th largest air force in the world" have purchased a staggering 65 *JPs* of all marks from the RAF. Main source will be the T.5 and T.4 store at Shawbury, Shrop, but the former instructional airframes at Halton, Bucks, will also be involved. Many aircraft are expected to be flown to Binbrook, but as **W&R** was closing for press, the set-up was in its early days. T.3A XM461 was put for tender at Linton-on-Ouse during September 1991 and was stored here until sold in the USA as N6204M in 1992. Two T.3As were handled by VAT at Cranfield, Beds, going on to the USA : — XM466 also acquired from Linton and flew to Cranfield on January 27, 1993 and crated for the USA (becoming N7075V) during February 1993; XN499 from Shawbury arrived at Cranfield by road early February 1993, but moved here on February 19, 1993 then to the USA, becoming N7075X. By August 1993, three T.3As had arrived via the dealer at Colsterworth, Lincs, only one of which has been identified. During March 1994 G-BVEG (and another for spares) was sold only one of which has been identified. During March 1994 XN629/G-BVEG (and another for spares) was sold to Tom Maloney of Transair Pilot Shop fame. *Echo Golf* arrived at 'Weald, on April 2, only to shoot to fame the following day when an apparent ejector seat failure resulted in Tom's brother Des, leaving the aircraft during a roll! Des survived by what can only be termed a miracle.

- ☐ XM479* G-BVEZ   Jet Provost T.3A   ex Linton-on-Ouse, 1 FTS, RAFC. '54'.
- ☐ *   Jet Provost T.3A   ex Colsterworth, Shawbury. See notes.   08-93
- ☐ *   Jet Provost T.3A   ex Colsterworth, Shawbury. See notes.   08-93

■ **Charles Ross** : Charles has moved his Lightning into the grounds of his home nearby and has planted a 'horseshoe' of trees around it to remain in favour with the neighbours!

- ☐ XR725   Lightning F.6   ex Rossington 'TVI725', Binbrook, 11, 5, LTF, 5, 56, 74, 5, 23.   12-93

BOSTON

■ **Lance's Trading** : It is thought that the former Holbeach Chipmunk is still held here..

- ☐ WP784   Chipmunk T.10   ex Holbeach, Wellingborough, Reading, Benson, Abingdon, 6 AEF, Leeds UAS, Abn UAS, 8 FTS, Man UAS, QUB UAS, Air Attaché Paris, 5 RFS, 17 RFS.   01-91

■ **Dick Yates** : The private workshop continues to hold some fascinating aircraft, all of which are 'long-termers' with an over-riding French accent. Note : visits to the workshop are not possible.

- ☐ G-AWUB   Gardan GY-201   ex F-PERX. CoA exp 23-10-80. Fuselage, stored.
- ☐ G-AXDY   Falconar F-11   unfinished homebuild, incorporating parts from Wassmer D.112 G-AYBR. Stored.
  [D.112 G-AYBR, ex F-BMIG is currently airworthy.]
- ☐ G-AXGA   Super Cub 95   ex Tattershall Thorpe, PH-NLE, PH-CUB ntu, RNethAF R-51, 52-2447. Cr 26-12-86.   08-90
- ☐ G-AYVT   Brochet MB.84   ex Tattershall Thorpe, Sunderland, F-BGLI. Damaged 28-6-77.   08-90
- ☐ G-BFDM   Wassmer D.120   ex F-BHYB. CoA exp 26-7-84. Spares use.
- ☐ G-PULL   Super Cub 150   ex Tattershall Thorpe, PH-MBB, ALAT 18-5356. Crashed 13-6-86. Frame.   08-90
- ☐ F-BBGH   Brochet MB.100   ex F-WBGH. Stored.   08-90
- ☐ F-PFUG   Adam RA-14   Stored.   08-90
- ☐ No 37   G-ZARA   Nord 3400   ex Stixwould, Breighton, Coventry, La Ferte Alais, ALAT F-MMAB. Restoration.   08-90

BURGH-LE-MARSH (on the A158 west of Skegness)
Contrary to **W&R13**, the spares ship Apache/Geronimo is *still* to be found at a yard here.

- ☐ PH-NLK*   Geronimo   ex Ipswich. Spares recovery.   10-93

CASTLE BYTHAM (east of the A1, north of Stamford)
J-3C-65 Cub F-BBBN *never* came here, it was to be found 'up the road' at Swayfield until it was exported to Ireland in 1992.

COLSTERWORTH (on the A1 north of Stamford)
Locally, a dealer in military vehicles etc extended his remit into the world of surplus military aircraft during mid-1993. The nose of Canberra B.2(mod) WH660 came through this yard (from Boscombe Down, Wilts) before settling upon <u>Bruntingthorpe</u>, Leics. By July 1993 no less than *seven* Jet Provosts had gravitated here. The first four were T.3As XM464, XN509, XN595 and XN629 which arrived by road from Shawbury, Salop, on January 20, 1993. XN629 moved to Binbrook, Lincs, by August 1993. XN509 is thought to have been sold in the USA. Three more arrived by August 1993, all from Halton, Bucks :— T.3As XM358, XM412 and XM414. Two of these moved quickly on to Binbrook, Lincs. Whirlwind HAR.10 XJ729/8732M arrived here from Finningley, S Yorks, by August 1993. It was registered as G-BVGE to Cricklade, Northants, owners during November 1993. Chronicling comings and goings here can be problematical, as the yard is also used for 'overnighting' lorries carrying aircraft to all corners of the UK!

- ☐ XP354*   8721M   W'wind HAR.10   ex Halton. 22, 202. Arrived by 8-93.   08-93

CONINGSBY AIRFIELD (on the B1192, south of Horncastle)

■ **Battle of Britain Memorial Flight** (BBMF) **and Visitor Centre** : Major milestone for the flight was the arrival of Dakota ZA947 on July 20, 1993. With the demise of 8 Squadron on Shackletons, BBMF has been without a taildragger multi-engined type to provide conversion training for the *Lanc*. The *Dak* acts perfectly in this role and was snapped up when DRA announced it was to be disposed of. In conjunction with the Army, ZA947 will be appearing in its own right at a whole series of events during 1994 as D-Day anniversaries get into swing. The *Dak* will be used to disgorge paratroops using 'period' uniforms and canopies. The Dakota technically replaces the Devon, which may well see 1994 in store. Previously being restored to flying condition for BBMF at Abingdon, Oxon, Spitfire IX MK356 is now underway at St Athan, S Glam. Spitfires P7350 and AB910 plus the *Lanc* have changed their colours for the 1994 season. P7350 was undertaken by Shorts at Sydenham and PA474 at St Athan.

◆ Open Monday to Friday except Bank Holidays 10am to 4.30pm with the last guided tour at 3.30pm. <u>Note</u> : although booking is not required to attend the Visitor Centre, it is advisable as it may be that the Flight in whole or in part are positioning to a show. ✉ BBMF Visits, RAF Coningsby, Lincoln LN4 4SY. ☎ 0526 344041.

■ **Lincolnshire's Lancaster Association** : Supporting the Visitor Centre, the BBMF and PA474 in particular. Membership details from :— ✉ John Ball, 31, Knaton Road, Carlton-in-Lindrick, Worksop, Notts, S81 9HJ.

☐ P7350	Spitfire IIA ▲	ex *Battle of Britain* G-AWIJ, Colerne, John Dale Ltd, Colerne, 57 OTU, CGS, 64, 616, 603, 266. 'RN-S', 72 Sqn c/s, *Enniskillen*. See notes.	01-94
☐ AB910	Spitfire VB ▲	ex *Battle of Britain*, Allen Wheeler G-AISU, 29 MU, RWE, 527, 53 OTU, 402, 242, 133, 130, 222. 'AE-x', 402 Sqn c/s.	01-94
☐ LF363	Hurricane IIC	ex Biggin Hill SF, 41, 41 GCF, Waterbeach SF, Odiham SF, Thorney Island SF, FCCS, Middle Wallop SF, 61 OTU, 41 OTU, 62 OTU, 26, 63, 309, 63. Crashed 11-9-91. Stored, awaiting restoration by contractor.	12-93
☐ PA474	Lancaster I ▲	ex 44, Wroughton, Cranfield College, RAE, Flight Refuelling, 82. 'WS-J' 9 Sqn c/s, *Johnny Walker - Still Going Strong.*	12-93
☐ PM631	Spitfire PR.XIX ▲	ex THUM Flt, Buckeburg SF, 206 OCU, 203 AFS. 'N', *Mary*, SEAC colours.	12-93
☐ PS853	Spitfire PR.XIX ▲	ex West Raynham, CFE, North Weald SF, Biggin Hill SF, THUM Flt, 16, 268, 16. 'C'.	12-93
☐ PS915	Spitfire PR.XIX ▲	ex Samlesbury, Preston, Brawdy, St Athan, Coningsby, Brawdy, Leuchars 7548M/7711M, West Malling, Biggin Hill, THUM Flt, 2, PRDU, 541. Colours of 2nd proto Mk XIV (JF319)	12-93
☐ PZ865	Hurricane II ▲	ex Hawker Siddeley G-AMAU.	12-93
☐ VP981	Devon C.2/2 ▲	ex Northolt, 207, 21, WCS, Wildenrath CF, AAFCE, MinTech, AAFCE, Paris Air Attaché, Hendon SF, AFWE. Flight 'mother ship'.	12-93
☐ WK518	Chipmunk T.10 ▲	ex Man UAS, Lon UAS, Liv UAS, Lee UAS, Hul UAS, Cam UAS, 1 AEF, Coltishall SF, FWS, 63 GCF, RAFC. Flight 'hack'.	12-93
☐ ZA947*	Dakota III ▲	ex DRA, RAE, Farnborough, West Freugh, 'KG661', RCAF 661, 42-24338. Arrived 20-7-93. 'YS'. See notes above.	12-93

■ **RAF Coningsby** : Going back to **W&R13**, page 181 illustrated a dying Lightning, plus equally unwell Citroen, on the dump here. This was *not* T.4 XM987, which had perished by then, but F.2A XN774. Of the Citroen, we have no news! Another long-gone dump occupant is Canberra PR.7 WJ815/8729M which should also be deleted, assumed perished. As will be seen from a scan of the list below, the number of **W&R** airframes has multiplied somewhat, to the tune of five Phantoms, one which adorns the gate.

☐	XN774	8551M	Lightning F.2A	ex 92, 19. Dump. 'F'.	06-93
☐	XT891*	9136M	Phantom FGR.2	ex 74, 228 OCU, 56, 228 OCU. 'S'. Gate by 6-92.	02-94
☐	XT905*		Phantom FGR.2	ex 74, 228 OCU, 29, 228 OCU, 31, 17. 'P'. Arrived 6-10-92. Decoy.	06-93
☐	XV426*		Phantom FGR.2	ex 56, 23, 228 OCU, 111, 31 'P'. Stored. First noted 10-92.	06-93
☐	XV460*		Phantom FGR.2	ex 74, 92, 228 OCU, 29, 228 OCU, 92, 19, 56, 31. 'R'. Flew in 31-10-92. Decoy.	10-92
☐	XV497*		Phantom FGR.2	ex 56, 92, 19, 92, 23, 56, 228 OCU, 17. 'W'. Flew in 31-10-92. Decoy.	06-93
☐	XW528	8861M	Buccaneer S.2B	ex St Athan, 15. Crash rescue.	06-93
☐	ZD935*		Tornado F.2	ex St Athan, 229 OCU, ETPS, 229 OCU. 'AN'. Arrived by 10-93. Operational training rig.	11-93
☐	ZE354	9084M	F-4J(UK)	ex 74, USN 153795. 'R'. Delivered 2-91. BDR.	07-91

CRANWELL AIRFIELD (on the A17/B1429 north west of Sleaford)

■ **RAF Cranwell** : A Phantom has joined the line-up of 'gate' guardians here. Contrary to **W&R13**, the OFMC Hunter XF375/G-BUEZ remained here until making the move to Duxford, Cambs, in October 1993. See under SIF below for details of the Harrier and crash rescue Hunter. Going in the other direction, ie *from* the fire section *to* SIF, has been *JP* T.3 cockpit section XN643. Note that what had previously been referred to as the Engineering Wing here is more properly the ATF and SIF — see below.

☐	'WH699'	WJ637	Canberra B.2	8755M, ex Wyton, 231 OCU, 35. Outside Trenchard Hall.	02-94
☐	XG209	8709M	Hunter F.6	ex SIF, Halton, Kemble, 12, DFLS, 111, 14. '66'. Crash rescue by July 1991.	11-93
☐	XV408*	9165M	Phantom FGR.2	ex Wattisham, 92, 29, 23, 228 OCU. 'Z'. Gate. Directorate of Recruitment & Selection.	11-93
☐	XW353	9090M	Jet Provost T.5A	ex 3 FTS, RAFC, CFS, 3 FTS, RAFC. '3'. Gate.	02-94
☐	XZ138	9040M	Harrier GR.3	ex SIF, St Athan, 1, 233 OCU, 1453F, 1, 4, 3. Cockpit only, Trenchard Hall.	11-93

■ **Airframe Technology Flight** (ATF) : Located in the workshop building adjacent to the SIF (see below), a Harrier and Jaguar serve as instructional airframes.

☐	XX747*	8903M	Jaguar GR.1	ex Halton, Royal Tournament, Shawbury, Gibraltar Det, 6, 20, 31, 226 OCU. '08'. Gulf pink c/s as *Sadman* (XZ364). First noted 11-93.	11-93
☐	XZ132*	9168M	Harrier GR.3	ex St Athan, 4, 1, 1351F, 1, 233 OCU, 1, 3. 'C'.	11-93

■ **Servicing Instruction Flight** (SIF) : The arrival of former *Lossie* two-seat Hunter *Brick-*trainers heralds changes with the SIF fleet. All of the single-seat Hunters will be offered for tender or onward sale. Harrier GR.3 XZ138 was struck off charge during October 1992. The cockpit was moved into Trenchard Hall (see above) as a structural demonstration training aid. The rest was disposed of locally. Hunter F.6 XG209 was demoted to crash rescue duties on the airfield during July 1991 — see above. For training purposes, SIF operates as the fictional "284 (Training) Squadron" and it is frequently referred to as such during the end of each course.

☐	WV322*	9096M	Hunter T.8C	ex 237 OCU, 764, 92. 'Y'. Arr by 7-91.	11-93
☐	XF516	8685M	Hunter F.6A	ex 1 TWU, 229 OCU, 92, 56. 'F'.	10-93
☐	XF967*	9182M	Hunter T.8B	ex 237 OCU, 12, 237 OCU, Honington SF, 237 OCU, 12, FAA, 229 OCU, 3. 'T'. F/n 4-93	11-93
☐	XF995*		Hunter T.8B	ex 208, 12, Laarbruch SF, 237 OCU, Honington SF, 237 OCU, FAA, 229 OCU, 245, 247. Flew in 11-4-94. 'W'.	04-94
☐	XJ634	8684M	Hunter F.6A	ex 1 TWU, TWU, 229 OCU, 92. '29'. For tender 2-94.	02-94
☐	XJ639	8687M	Hunter F.6A	ex 1 TWU, TWU, 229 OCU, 4. 'H'.	10-93

☐ XK149	8714M	Hunter F.6A	ex 1 TWU, TWU, 229 OCU, 54, 1, AFDS. 'L'.	04-94
☐ XL568*	9224M	Hunter T.7A	ex Lossiemouth, 12, 74, MoA, 74, HS. 'C'. Arrived by 4-94.	04-94
☐ XL577	8676M	Hunter T.7	ex 2 TWU, 237 OCU, 1 TWU, TWU, 229 OCU 'W'.	04-94
☐ XL616*	9223M	Hunter T.7A	ex Lossiemouth, 208, Laarbruch SF, MoA, 19, 23, APS Sylt. Arrived by 4-94.	04-94
☐ XN643	8704M	Jet Provost T.3	ex Barkston Heath, Cranwell, Abingdon, RAFEF, 1 FTS, 3 FTS. Cr 30-7-81. Nose. BDR.	11-93
☐ XX821	8896M	Jaguar GR.1	ex Coltishall, 41, 14, 17, 226 OCU, 17. 'P'.	04-94

■ **Cranwell Aviation Heritage Centre** : Located close to the base, it charts the history of Cranwell and gives notes on the other airfields on the Lincolnshire Airfields Trail. There are no airframe or engine exhibits as such, although there remains the possibility of the building taking on small displays. It is an excellent stop-off when visiting Cranwell and/or the trail.
◆ Open 9am to 5pm daily other than Xmas and New Year. Signposted just off the A17 (to the south of RAF Cranwell) on the minor road to North and South Rauceby. ✉ Tourist Information Centre, The Mill, Moneys Yard, Carre Street, Sleaford, Lincs NG34 7TW. ☎ 0529 414294.

CROFT (west of Skegness)
A location near here took on most of the non-airworthy inmates from Skegness Aerodrome.

☐ G-AHCK*		J/1N Alpha	ex Skegness. Dam 14-9-91. F/n 5-93.	05-93
☐ BGA.789* AZK		T.8 Tutor	ex Skegness, VM650. Stored. F/n 5-93.	05-93
☐ NJ703*	G-AKPI	Auster 5	ex Skegness, Humberside, 652, 660. Stored. First noted 5-93.	05-93

CROWLAND
All but the fin and rudder are now on the *JP* in a garden here.

☐ XM383		Jet Provost T.3A	ex Scampton, 7 FTS, 1 FTS, RAFC, 6 FTS, BSE, 2 FTS, A&AEE, 2 FTS. Fuse. '90'.	11-93

DIGBY (east of the B1188 north of Sleaford)
■ **RAF Digby** : Having lost its Meteor T.7, the MoD moved the former Church Fenton plastic Spitfire to guard the base.

☐ 'MJ832'* BAPC.229	Spitfire replica	ex 'L1096', Church Fenton. Gate. 'DN-Y', 416 Sqn colours. First noted 10-93.	11-93

EAST KIRKBY (on the A155 west of Spilsby)
■ **Lincolnshire Aviation Heritage Centre** (LAHC) : The whole centre is run by Fred and Harold Panton as a memorial to their brother Christopher, who was killed on the Nuremberg raid — and as a memorial to Bomber Command as a whole. The *Lanc*, owned by the Pantons, is occasionally rolled out on 'special event' days — giving photographers a bean feast. As well as the aircraft, the control tower is completely restored and an extensive exhibit in its own right. Other displays include the RAF Escaping Society, a blast shelter, Link trainer, air raid shelter and much more. A 'thinning' of the exhibits is due to start here, and this has been reflected in the winding-up of the Lincolnshire Aviation Society's preservation interests. The wind-down of LAS aircraft is being handled by the newly-founded Lincolnshire Aircraft Preservation Society — see below. Disposals have been as follows :— Blackburn B-2 forward fuselage G-ADFV/2893M to <u>Breighton</u>, Humbs by October 1993; Ward Gnome G-AXEI returned to Mick Ward at the Real Aeroplane Company, <u>Breighton</u>, Humb, by October 1993; Skeeter AOP.12 XM561/7980M to Firbeck, S Yorks, early 1993; Fa 330A-1 100502 also made the trek to <u>Breighton</u>, Humb, during October 1993; *Flea* BAPC.43 moved to <u>Winthorpe</u>, Notts, 9-3-94. After much pondering, the 'Supermarine 535' 'VV119' has been deleted. It gives every indication of being a 'synthetic' simulator and not what legend claims it to be. (For those that wish to follow it, it moved to the Southampton Hall of Aviation during November 1993.)
◆ Open Easter to October Monday to Saturday 10am to 5pm and November to Easter Monday to Saturday 10am to 4pm. NB *not* open on Sundays. ✉ LAHC, East Kirkby, near Spilsby, Lincs, PE23 4DE. ☎ 0790 763207 (note, *new* number).

■ **Lincolnshire Aircraft Recovery Group** (LARG) : 'Prize' exhibit is the very substantial Spitfire BL655. LARG have a wide array of artefacts on show at the Heritage Centre.

⊠ LARG, 13 Granville Avenue, Wyberton, Boston, Lincs, PE21 7BY.

■ **Lincolnshire Aircraft Preservation Society** (LAPS) : Is the new group over-seeing what airframes were held by the Lincolnshire Aviation Society.

⊠ LAPS, 154 Park Street, Grimsby, South Humberside, DN32 7NS.

□ G-AJOZ		Argus II	ex Tattershall, Wigan, Market Drayton, Wigan, Southend, Sywell, FK338, Kemble, ATA 2 FP, 42-32142. Crashed 16-8-62. Stored.	12-93
□ AE436		Hampden I	ex Henlow, Sweden, 144. Crashed 4-9-42. Forward fuselage under restoration by Brian Nicholls of LAPS.	12-93
□ BL655		Spitfire V	ex Dorrington Fen, 416, 129, 341, 164, 602, 416. Crashed 1-7-43. Substantial fuselage section recovered by LARG.	12-93
□ NP294		Proctor IV	ex Tattershall, Friskney, Poynton, Andover Down, Cosford, 4 RS, 2 RS. 'TB-M'. LAPS.	02-94
□ NX611	G-ASXX	Lancaster VII	ex Scampton, 8375M, Blackpool Airport, Hullavington, Lavenham, Biggin Hill, *Aéronavale* WU-15, St Athan, Llandow. 'YF-C', Scampton, SF colours. Panton brothers.	02-94
□ WH957*	8869M	Canberra PR.7	ex Bruntingthorpe, Cosford, 100, 98, Akrotiri Wing, 32, Hemswell SF, Upwood SF, 21, 542, 617. Nose. 'Hands-on' exhibit. Panton brothers. First noted 12-93.	02-94
□ WW421	7688M	Provost T.1	ex Tattershall, Lytham St Annes, St Athan, 3 FTS. 'O'. LAPS, awaiting disposal.	02-94
□ XA909		Vulcan B.1	ex Tattershall, Waddington, Wadd Wing, 50, 101. Nose. LAPS. Awaiting disposal.	02-94
□	BAPC.154	Turbulent	ex Tattershall, Friskney, Nottingham. Unfinished, PFA.1654. LAPS. Awaiting disposal.	12-93
□ *		CASA 2-111D	ex Firbeck, Henlow, *Battle of Britain*, Spain. Nose section. With LAPS by 3-93. [Plate gives it as an He 111H-16, w/nr 150].	12-93

FENLAND AERODROME (or Holbeach St Johns, west of the B1168, west of the village) The situation here is unchanged.

□ G-AREL	Caribbean 150	ex N3344Z. CoA exp 16-5-85. Stored.	02-94
□ G-ASTV	Cessna 150D	ex Panshanger, Luton, N6005T. CoA expired 18-10-75. Restn to 'tail-dragger' guise, using 'WAX as spares.	02-94
□ G-AWAX	Cessna 150D	ex OY-TRJ, N4153U. Crashed 3-2-80.	02-94

■ **Locally** : Geoff Hare is working on a tail-dragger Tri-Pacer in the area. The MS.317 is *assumed* to still stored, but please note the 'sell by' date!

□ G-ARGY*	Tri-Pacer 160	ex G-JEST, G-ARGY. Crashed 4-10-91.	10-92
□ G-BPLG	MS.317	ex Boston, N317MS, F-BFAH, French mil.	10-90

GLENTHAM (on A631 west of Market Rasen)

■ **Alan Ellis** : And his Vampire T.11 pod have moved here.

□ XD595*	Vampire T.11	ex Altrincham, Woodford, Chester, St Athan, 1 FTS, Oakington SF, 7 FTS, 4 FTS. Pod.	

HEMSWELL (on the A631, east of Gainsborough)

■ **Bomber County Aviation Museum** (BCAM) : Nestled within the domestic camp of the former bomber base, BCAM — run by the Hemswell Aviation Society — continues to work on both the site and the airframes. Contrary to **W&R13**, Bristol Babe BAPC.87 was not scrapped but was donated to Ken Fern and moved to <u>Stoke-on-Trent</u>, Staffs. Of note is that the Hemswell domestic site is permanently open to the public and that three of the H-blocks are devoted to a huge antique and bric-a-brac centre, well worth visiting in its own right and perhaps somewhere to 'park' the 'other half' while BCAM is sampled!

◆ Antiques centre well signed from the A631, follow them. Open Sundays and Bank Holidays 11am to 6pm and at other times by prior arrangement. ✉ B Pound, Hemswell Aviation Society, 77 Fairway, Waltham, South Humberside DN37 0NB.

☐ G-AEJZ	BAPC.120	HM.14 *Flea*	ex Cleethorpes, Brough. Stored.	02-94
☐ WJ975		Canberra T.19	ex Cleethorpes, Cambridge, 100, 7, 100, 85, West Ray' TFF, 228 OCU, 44, 35, 231 OCU. 'S'.	02-94
☐ XD445		Vampire T.11	ex Cleethorpes, H'field, Woodford, Chester, St Athan, 4 FTS, 5 FTS, Buckeburg SF. '51'.	02-94
☐ XG195	(WT741)	Hunter FGA.9	ex Macclesfield, Bitteswell, HSA G-9-453, 208, 1, 19. Composite, nose of GA.11 WT741, other parts from XG297/G-9-452.	02-94
☐ XG506	7852M	Sycamore HR.14	ex Cleethorpes, Misson, Halton, HDU, MCS, 72, 118, 225, 118, 275. Poor state.	02-94
☐ 101		Mystere IVA	ex Cleethorpes, Sculthorpe, FAF. '8-MN'.	02-94

LITTLE BYTHAM (on the B1176 north of Stamford)

■ **Walnut Lodge** : Acquired a Grasshopper during the large clear out of 1988. It *may* be present.

☐ WZ825*   Grasshopper TX.1   see notes above. Sold 4-2-88.   02-88

NORTH SCARLE (east of the A1133, north of Swinderby)

■ **TM Aviation** : The Stearman *duster* N65501 became G-BTGA and was flying by 1991.

■ **Nigel Spur** : The yard here has a contract to clear various scrap items from RAF airfields. The Harrier cockpit section mentioned in **W&R13** came from Wittering's dump and was in a poor state — too poor for inclusion, please delete. The former Wittering Hunter F.6 came here by January 1993, after problems when it was bought by an American who thought it could be fired up and flown!. It was dispersed as follows : — cockpit to <u>Kidlington</u>, Oxon; wings and tail to Long Marston, Wilts; centre section to Chelford, Ches. For the purposes of **W&R**, only the nose will be 'followed',

SCAMPTON AIRFIELD (on the A15 north of Lincoln)

■ **RAF Scampton** : The anonymous Vulcan on the dump had given up the ghost by May 1993. 'Active' occupant of the fire crash rescue training area is Phantom XT853, since November 1991. Vampire T.11 XE920/8196M moved to <u>Sealand</u>, Clwyd, in October 1992.

☐ XR571	8493M	Gnat T.1	ex Cosford, Kemble, Brampton, Kemble, 4 FTS. Displayed outside Red Arrows HQ.	02-92
☐ XT853	9071M	Phantom FGR.2	ex BAe. Derelict by 11-91.	03-94

■ **Trade Management Training School** (TMTS) : Two former *Lossie* Hunters have joined the fold. Phantom FGR.2 XT853 was not with TMTS going to the dump — see above.

☐ WV318*		Hunter T.7B	ex 12, Laarbruch SF, 237 OCU, Laar' SF, 16, 15, Laar' SF, 12, HS, 74, MoA, CFS, FCIRF, 54, 56, 111, 93, 14. 'A' Flew in 11-4-94.	04-94
☐ XE653	8829M	Hunter F.6A	ex Kemble, 1 TWU, 229 OCU, 111, 43. 'S'.	08-93
☐ XF515	8830M	Hunter F.6A	ex Kemble, 1 TWU, 229 OCU, 43, 247. 'C'.	08-93
☐ XG160	8831M	Hunter F.6A	ex 1 TWU, 229 OCU, 111, 43. 'U'.	08-93
☐ XG172	8832M	Hunter F.6A	ex 1 TWU, 229 OCU, 263, 19. 'A'.	08-93
☐ XL587	8807M	Hunter T.7	ex 208, 237 OCU, 1 TWU, 229 OCU. 'Z'.	08-93
☐ XL592	8836M	Hunter T.7	ex 1 TWU, TWU, 229 OCU. 'Y'.	08-93
☐ XL614*		Hunter T.7A	ex Lossiemouth, 237 OCU, Honington SF, 237 OCU, RAE, 12, RAE, 111, APS Sylt. Flew in 11-4-94.	04-94

SKEGNESS AERODROME (or Ingoldmells, on the A52 north of Skegness)

The Official Receiver was called into Skegness Air Taxi Service on January 18, 1993. The company continued to trade for a month or so, but then closed down. The business was sold off by May 1993 and the resident aircraft told to move on. The site was taken over *post haste* by the landlords — from whom it had been rented since 1948 — *viz* Rank Leisure, *née* Butlins. It was clear that innovative ideas like keeping the airfield going were not in the owner's options as by July 1993 the whole hangar and associated buildings were demolished. Aviation promoter Billy Butlin doubtless spinning in his grave. Skegness Aerodrome therefore ceased to exist. The following **W&R** inmates moved to <u>Croft</u>, Lincs : — J/1N G-AHCK, T.8 Tutor BGA.789 and Auster 5 NJ703/G-AKPI. J/1N Alpha G-AJAB — not mentioned in **W&R13** — is unaccounted for. J/1 Autocrat G-AHAR did not arrive here as stated in **W&R13** but instead went to Pat Miller's place at <u>Spilsby</u>, Lincs.

SPILSBY

■ **Pat Miller** : Moved his growing collection of Austers from Wickenby Aerodrome in early 1993 to a location near here. Also gravitating here have been an AgCat wreck and an Auster previously attributed to Skegness.

☐ G-AHAR*	J/1 Autocrat	ex North Weald, F-BGRZ. Restoration.	03-93
☐ G-AIGT*	J/1N Alpha	ex Wickenby, Laindon, Audley End. CoA expired 22-10-76. Arrived early 1993. Restn.	03-93
☐ G-AIPV*	J/1 Autocrat	ex Wickenby, Cabourne. CoA expired 1-6-68. Arrived early 1993. Stored.	08-93
☐ G-AVOD*	D5/180 Husky	crashed 31-7-92. Wreck. First noted 6-93.	06-93
☐ G-DCAT*	Turbo AgCat	ex Wickenby, N8312X. Crashed 3-7-85. Fuselage plus two wings. Arr early 1993.	03-93

STAMFORD

■ **Stamford School** : The School bought their CCF's Grasshopper TX.1 XP949 on June 16, 1988 and continued to keep it within the grounds. It was acquired by Ken Fern in mid-1993 and moved to <u>Stoke-on-Trent</u>, Staffs.

STRUBBY AIRFIELD (on the A157 west of Mablethorpe)

■ **Lincolnshire Lightning Preservation Society** : Keep their F.3 on the former RAF airfield.
✉ 48 Ryland Road, Dunholme, Lincoln LN2 3NE.
☐ XP706   8925M   Lightning F.3   ex Binbrook, LTF, 11, 5, LTF, 23, 111, 74.   09-92

SUTTON BRIDGE (on the A17 west of King's Lynn)

■ **Lindsey Walton** : The Pingouin is still stored here. Restoration of the other one, G-ASTG, is being carried out at Duxford, Cambs.
☐ G-ASUA   Nord 1002   ex Elstree, F-BFDY. Crashed 30-7-64. Stored.

SWINDERBY AIRFIELD (on the A46 north east of Newark-on-Trent)

■ **RAF Swinderby** : This superb station closed its doors during 1993 with the disbanding of the Elementary Flying Training School. There are rumours that the airfield may yet stay operational — in civilian hands. Fingers crossed! Lightning F.1 XG329 was acquired by Ian Hancock and it moved to <u>Flixton</u>, Suffolk, care of Barry Pover and team during October 1993. Vampire T.11 XD506 was entered into the MoD auction of July 8, 1993 (see *Appendix D*), fetching £2,900, which included the plinth! It had yet to move by October 1993. Gnat T.1 XM706/8572M on the dump was offered for tender during September 1993 and left the following month for an unknown scrappy in Nottingham, Notts. Chipmunk T.10 WG362/8630M PAX trainer is unaccounted for.
☐ XD506   7983M   Vampire T.11   ex Finningley, CATCS, CNCS, 5 FTS, 206 AFS. See notes above.   10-93

TATTERSHALL THORPE (on the B1192 south of Woodhall Spa)

Thanks to considerable clarification of the situation here, this section can be considerably re-jigged.
■ **Lodge Road Flying Services** (LRFS) : This is the name of Roger Windley's company, which deals in the moving and crating of aircraft, restoration etc of helicopters and the occasional fixed-wing type. Roger's well-known Queen's Flight Whirlwind HCC.12 G-RWWW and other aircraft held by the family and friends are based at the strip. The hulk of Scout Series 1 5X-UUX/G-BKLJ moved to <u>East Dereham</u>, Norfolk. Skeeter AOP.12 XL735 had gone by October 1992.

☐	G-BAWI*		Enstrom F-28A	ex Farnborough, N68719. Crashed 26-6-92.	
				Stored.	10-92
☐	G-BDII*		Sikorsky S-61N II	ex Bristow, 9M-ELF, G-BDII. Ditched 17-10-88.	
				Drum. Fuselage, stored. F/n 10-92.	10-92
☐	G-BKAN		Cessna 340 II	ex N68719. Crashed 8-6-91. For rebuild.	10-92
☐	XJ407	N7013H	Whirlwind HAR10	ex Lakenheath, G-BKHB, 32, 103, 110, 22,	
				155. Damaged. Stored.	10-92
☐	XP328*	G-BKHC	Whirlwind HAR10	ex Northolt, 32, 21, 28, 110, 225, 110, 225.	
				Crashed 22-8-88. Cabin recovered to here and	
				in store since.	10-92
☐	XP329	8791M	Whirlwind HAR10	ex Shawbury, Lee-on-Solent, Akrotiri, 84, 230,	
				110, 225. 'V'. Cabin only, external store.	10-92
☐	XP395	8674M	Whirlwind HAR10	ex Halton, SARTS, 22, 230. Cabin & boom.	10-92

■ **F & H (Aircraft) Ltd** : This company, better known in the past for purchases of Chipmunks, Varsities and others from the MoD, is the concern that purchases and dismantles 'insurance' airframes. F & H are agents for the huge US-based Dodson Aviation, who re-cycle vast amounts of aircraft, components etc. Aircraft inbound to Tattershall (more often than not moved by LRFS) tend to lead very fragmented lives as their parts go elsewhere. Accordingly they have very short 'shelf-lives' here and in many cases only small bits may remain. The listing that appears in **W&R** from now on will be much smaller, tending to lie only with substantial machines that may be moving on in an equally substantial manner!

The best method of explaining the work done here, so that readers may appreciate how few 'whole' airframes are present at any one moment, is to present two 'case histories'. Seneca 200T II G-BOGS — page 101 of **W&R13**. Tailplane, engines, props and much of the interior went to Dodson Aviation. Wings to a UK dealer for onward sale to individual Seneca owners. Avionics to various buyers. Gutted fuselage into store. Cherokee 140 G-ATTU — collided with AA-5A G-OCPL at Elstree June 27, 1992. Engines and prop overhauled and now propelling other Cherokees. Instruments, radios, fuel tanks and undercarriage to stock for future use. One aileron to another Elstree-based Cherokee for a repair. Port fuel tank to an operator in the West Country. Fuselage, tail and wings to Geneva, Switzerland, to hang in a hotel foyer!

All this said, the following can be regarded as scrapped/processed/dismantled beyond the realms of **W&R** : — Cessna 150F G-ATHF; Cessna F.172H G-AWRL; Cricket G-AXRC; Musketeer G-AYPB; Rallye Club G-BAOT; AA-1B Trainer G-BDRE; Rallye 150ST G-BFGA; Robin HR.100-210 G-BFWW; Cessna F.152 II G-BGHA; AA-5A Cheetah G-BLHO; Tomahawk 112 G-BOEB; AA-5A Cheetah G-JULY; Tomahawk 112 N23185; and Pembroke C.1 WV703.

The following were sold on, some of which may still be regarded as firmly **W&R** territory, but under other headings : — EAA Biplane G-AYFY thought sold to a pub for exhibition; Cherokee 140C G-AYMN to the Clacton, Lincs, area (ideas?); Arrow 200 G-AZSN to Pleasure World of Great Yarmouth (ideas?); Wilga 35 G-AZYJ to Sudbury, Suffolk; AA-5 Traveler G-BBGH to Caterham, Surrey and quickly processed; Cessna F.150M G-BDZC to Sibson, Cambs; Cessna 180 G-BEOD to the Bournemouth area for rebuild; Tomahawk 112 cockpits G-BGZE and G-BGZH to Tees-side Airport, Durham; Cessna 152 II G-BOHB to Caterham, Surrey and quickly processed; J3C-65 G-TCUB was rebuilt and flying again by 1992; the AgCat fuselage spares and other extensive parts were exported to the USA via East Winch, Norfolk. Additionally Minerva 220 G-BCAC came here from Sandown, IoW, before going on to a new world of stardom at Trafford Park, Gtr Man.

So, bearing all of the above in mind, the long-termers follow. The Pilatus and the Chipmunk arrived during 1993 for sale by F&H.

☐	G-BGNS		Cessna F172N	damaged 16-10-87. Fuselage, stored.	10-92
☐	G-BIPU		AA-5B Tiger	ex N29941. Crashed 17-9-89. Fuse, stored.	10-92
☐	G-BJAX*		Pilatus P2-05	ex Duxford, Leicester, Swiss AF U-108, A-108.	
				CoA exp 28-5-91. Arrived 9-93. For sale.	09-93
☐	G-BMOL*		Aztec 250D	ex Elstree, G-BBSR, N6610Y. CoA expired	
				26-7-87. Stored.	10-92
☐	G-BOGS		Seneca 200T II	ex Exeter, N976GM, C6-BDU, N4969F.	
				Damaged 7-6-90. Fuselage, stored. Gutted.	
☐	'(18)671'*	G-BNZC	Chipmunk 22 ▲	ex Duxford, Hampton, G-ROYS, 7438M, WP905,	
				CFS, 664, RAFC. For sale. Arrived 10-93.	10-93
				See notes above.	10-92

TUMBY WOODSIDE (to the east of Coningsby)
By May 1993 Aviatik replica 'C19/18' (BAPC.118) from Firbeck had joined the other stored airframes, but had moved by October 1993 to <u>Stoke-on-Trent</u>, Staffs. T.8 Tutor AZQ/BGA.795 left during June 1993 for <u>Withern</u>, Lincs. *Flea* fuselage BAPC.101 moved to <u>Winthorpe</u>, Notts, on March 9, 1994.
☐   BAPC.61   Stewart Ornithopter ex East Kirkby, Tattershall, Wigan. Stored.

WADDINGTON AIRFIELD (on the A607 south of Lincoln)
■ **RAF Waddington** : Vulcan B.2 XH558 made its last ever public appearance at the Cranfield *Dreamflight* show on September 20, 1992, and made an emotional flight back to base to await the tender forms. Check flights were carried out to maintain aircrew currency at least every 21 days as the machinations of the MoD continued. It was clear that if the highest bidder was a scrapman, then a revolution was a-brewing! In the end, David Walton from Bruntingthorpe was successful and a hasty press conference was held with a view to hastening the Vulcan out of the air before the 75th Anniversary of the RAF farce at Marham on April 1, 1993. A huge crowd saw XH558 off as she departed for <u>Bruntingthorpe</u>, Leics, via a series of fly-bys at Vulcan-associated bases, and her birthplace at Woodford, on March 23, 1993.

Otherwise, the three airframes listed in **W&R13** live on. Phantom FGR.2 XV473 of 56 Squadron suffered a fuel pump blow within a wing tank during 1992 and it was decided not to repair the aircraft. Instead, she was allocated to the dump and the first 'burn' took place during March 1993. This too was problematical, as the fuel was reported not to have been drained out of her! The first fire practice with the Phantom turned rapidly into the last and the hulk was removed by road on May 5, 1993 to a scrapyard in the Barnsley area.

☐ XH669	9092M	Victor K.2	ex 55, 57, Witt Wing, A&AEE. Emergency landing 6-90. Crash rescue.	03-94
☐ XM607	8779M	Vulcan B.2	ex 44, 101, 35. Display airframe.	03-94
☐ ZE356	9060M	F-4J(UK)	ex 74, USN 153850. 'Q'. Arrived by 2-91. BDR.	10-93

WAINFLEET (south west of Skegness)
■ **Aerial Application Collection** (AAC) : Bill Taylor's growing collection of archive material relating to all forms of aerial application is based here, although the collection's equipment is dispersed widely throughout Norfolk and Lincolnshire undergoing restoration. In addition to many small aircraft components and items of ground support equipment, the collection contains some substantial airframes.
◆ Because of the dispersed nature of the collection, visits are only possible by prior arrangement. ✉
Bill Taylor, *Field House*, Eaudykes, Friskney, Boston, Lincolnshire, PE22 8RT.

☐ G-AVDZ*	Pawnee 235B	ex Sibson. Crashed 10-3-87. Burnt out cockpit section.	11-93
☐ G-BFBP*	Pawnee 235D	ex Rush Green. Crashed 11-5-78. Cockpit frame, to become travelling display exhibit. Collected 5-88.	11-93
☐ G-BFEY*	Pawnee 235D	ex Old Buckenham. Heavily corroded fuselage frame, following immersion in salt water. CoA expired 19-1-87. Collected 8-87.	11-93

■ **Golf Range** : The Lightning T.5 moved from the haulage yard of T A Smith & Co (Farm Produce) Ltd across the road to act as 'gate guardian' for the golf range, which is also run by the family.

☐ XS456	Lightning T.5	ex Binbrook, LTF, 11, LTF, 11, 56, Watt SF, 56. See notes above.	11-93

■ **Others** : In the general area, the following are under restoration.

☐ G-AWLX*	J/2 Arrow	ex Gloucester, F-BGJQ, OO-ABZ. CoA expired 23-4-70. Restoration.	11-93
☐ G-BDPJ*	Pawnee 235B	ex East Winch, PH-VBF, Midden Zeeland, Bredhurst, SE-EPZ. Cr 25-6-80. Arr 11-92.	11-93
☐ G-BENL*	Pawnee 235D	ex Old Buckenham, Sutton Bank, N54893. Crashed 10-7-85. Arrived 7-91.	11-93
☐ G-BHUU*	Pawnee 235D	ex East Winch. Cr 19-5-87. Arr 1-89. Restn.	11-93
☐ RAFGGA 502*	L-Spatz 55	ex Bruggen. Arrived 12-80. Identity subject to confirmation.	11-93

WICKENBY AERODROME

The Miller Aerial Spraying facility finally closed in early 1993. Pat Miller moved on to Spilsby, Lincs, taking with him J/1N Alpha G-AIPV. J/1N Alpha G-AIGT was here briefly, from Laindon, Essex, before it also moved to Spilsby, Lincs, early in 1993. Contrary to **W&R13**, AgCat G-DCAT did not go to the USA, settling also for Spilsby, Lincs.

☐ G-AIGM		J/1N Alpha	damaged in hangar collapse 1-87. Stored, poor shape.	
☐ G-BCTW*		Cessna F.150M	ex Newtownards. Crashed 12-4-89. Fuselage. First noted 2-93.	02-93
☐ G-EWUD*		Cessna F.172F	ex Barton, G-ESSO ntu, G-EWUD, G-ATBK. Ditched 14-8-92. First noted 2-93.	02-93

WITHERN (on the A157 north of Alford)

The former Tumby Woodside Tutor arrived here during June 1993 for restoration to flying condition.

☐ AZQ*	BGA 794	T.8 Tutor	ex Tumby Woodside, East Kirkby, Tattershall. Arrived 6-93. Restoration.	06-93

WOODHALL SPA (on the B1192 south east of Woodhall Spa)

■ **Thorpe Camp Preservation Group** : Opening to the public in the summer of 1994, Thorpe Camp will bring to life hat was Communal Site No 1 of the former Woodhall Spa airfield, towards Tattershall Thorpe. Themes will include life in Lincolnshire during World war Two, the history of Woodhall Spa and the Communal Site, including the history of 617 Squadron. It is planned to eventually display airframes and engines, but the primary aim of establishing the site and the displays has naturally taken priority.

◆ Due to open July 1994, an SAE to the following address will provide details of opening times etc.

✉ Thorpe Camp Preservation Group, Mike Hodgson, *Lancaster Farm*, Tumby Woodside, Mareham-le-Fen, Boston, Lincs, PE22 7SP.

Greater London

BENTLEY PRIORY

■ **RAF Bentley Priory** : Despite Lightning F.1A XM173 being put up for tender during October 1991 (see **W&R13**) it is still to be found within the grounds here. See under Shawbury, Salop, for Spitfire F.21 LA226, which is awaiting covered accommodation before coming here.

☐ 'N9926'	BAPC.217	Spitfire replica	317 Sqn c/s, 'JH-C'. In the grounds.	07-92
☐ 'P3386'	BAPC.218	Hurricane rep	43 Sqn c/s, 'FT-1'. In the grounds.	07-92
☐ XM173	8414M	Lightning F.1A	ex Binbrook, Binbrook TFF, Leuchars TFF, 226 OCU, 56. 'A' See notes above.	11-92

BIGGIN HILL

Both the Proctor and the Tiger Moth are thought still to be in the area.

☐ G-BBRB		Tiger Moth	ex Biggin Hill Airport, Headcorn, OO-EVB, Belgian AF T-8, DF198, Belgian TS. Damaged 16-1-87. Under restoration.	
☐ NP181	G-AOAR	Proctor IV	ex Headcorn, Biggin Hill, NP181, TTCCF, 2 RS. CoA expired 25-10-63. Stored.	

BIGGIN HILL AIRPORT (on the A233 north of Biggin Hill)

■ **Airport** : The number of light aircraft **W&R**-type inmates continues to fluctuate. Note that some of the aircraft listed below are either lacking in 'last noted' dates or have fairly dated entries — confirmation of their continued existence here (or otherwise) appreciated. Moving on since **W&R13** have been the following : Messenger G-AKVZ first flew after a lengthy restoration on January 20, 1994; Aztec 250 G-AREE moved to Stapleford Tawney, Essex, by December 1990; long-standing resident Fournier RF-4D G-AWEK moved to Gloucestershire Airport, Glos, by December 1991, ending a 19-year residency; Cherokee 140 G-BEAC was flying again by 1991; Queen Air A80 G-KEAC was ferried through to <u>Elstree</u>, Herts, by June 1992. Back-tracking to **W&R13**, Cherokee G-AVWE turned up at Stanley, Durham.

☐ G-AAOK	Travel Air	ex Yugoslavia, N370N, NC370N, NC352M. Damaged 21-10-83. Stored.	03-93
☐ G-ABYA	DH.60G Moth	crashed 21-5-72. Stored.	
☐ G-ANUO	Heron 2D	ex Exeter. CoA expired 12-9-86. Stored.	01-94
☐ G-AOGE	Proctor III	ex BV651, Halton SF, 2 GCS, FAA. CoA exp 21-5-84. Stored.	01-94
☐ G-AOKH	Prentice 1	ex VS251, 3 FTS, CFS, 2 FTS. CoA expired 2-8-73. Spares.	01-94
☐ G-AOTI	Heron 2D	ex Exeter, G-5-19. CoA exp 24-6-87. Stored.	01-94
☐ G-APZR	Cessna 150	ex N6461T. Cr 14-1-81. Engine test-bed.	01-94
☐ G-ARWC	Cessna 150B	ex Exeter, N1115Y. Cr 28-4-84. Wreck.	
☐ G-ASDA	Queen Air A80	CoA expired 8-11-79. Broken up by 12-92. Forward fuselage to fire dump.	01-94
☐ G-ASSW*	Cherokee 140	CoA expired 20-7-85. Stored. F/n 10-93.	01-94
☐ G-AVKB	Brochet Pipistrelle	ex Kingsclere, F-PFAL. CoA exp 13-12-83. Stored.	07-91
☐ G-AWCO	Cessna F.150H	CoA expired 29-8-75. Fuselage, poor state.	06-93
☐ G-AWGA*	Airedale	ex Sevenoaks, Biggin Hill, Bicester, EI-ATA, G-AWGA, D-ENRU. CoA exp 3-7-86. Spares for G-ATCC. Arrived 12-93.	12-93
☐ G-AYRM	Cherokee 140D	crashed 12-1-84. Wreck.	01-94
☐ G-BBNO*	Aztec 250E	ex N964PA. CoA exp 18-1-92. Stored.	01-94
☐ G-BCBH*	Argus III	ex VH-AAQ ntu, G-BCBH, ZS-AXH, HB737, 43-15011. Cr 24-6-89. Restn. F/n 7-93.	01-94
☐ G-BHCX	Cessna F.152 II	damaged 16-10-87. Stored.	06-93
☐ G-BHYS	Cherokee 181	ex N8218Y. Crashed 7-12-85. Wreck.	01-94
☐ G-BIFB*	Cherokee 150C	ex Elstree, 4X-AEC. CoA expired 17-12-90. Fuselage. First noted 01-94.	01-94
☐ G-BLDA*	Rallye 110ST	ex F-GDGH. Damaged 16-10-87. Dumped. First noted 6-92.	06-92
☐ G-BMTI*	Robin R3000-120	damaged 16-10-87. Dumped. F/n 6-92.	06-92
☐ G-BNJV*	Cessna 152 II	ex N5333B. Cr 8-3-92. Fuse. F/n 6-93.	06-93

■ **RAF Memorial Chapel** : With the former RAF camp up for sale and looking like a shanty town at present, the two replicas continue to watch over the Chapel.

☐	'L1710'	BAPC.219 Hurricane replica	gate guardian. 'AL-D'.	09-93
☐	'N3194'	BAPC.220 Spitfire replica	gate guardian. 'GR-Z'. 92 Sqn colours.	09-93

■ **Warbirds of Great Britain** (WoGB) / **Precious Metal Ltd** : Amid intense speculation, the story that Doug Arnold had died swept the preservation community in the last weeks of 1992. It transpired that the man did indeed die during the first two weeks of November 1992. During November and December 1992 and then with dramatically lessening degrees beyond that, there was a flurry of activity both at Biggin Hill and at Bournemouth, Dorset. Essentially the entire collection was moved — believed exported. It will be some time before the full story surfaces as sightings are made, at Lelystad in the Netherlands and in Florida. So for now herewith what can only be described as a first stab at the disposition of the WoGB fleet. (This is put together over a year after the 'exodus' and still information is nigh on impossible to find.) Prior to the death of Doug Arnold there had been some sorting of the fleet and generally, Bournemouth was used for the 'flyers' and Biggin for restoration and storage. Disposals are as follows. Unless noted all departed during November 1992 and the airframes were *not* airworthy. This information should be read in conjunction with the material given under Bournemouth Airport, Dorset : — ☐ Lincoln 2 G-29-1/RF342 is, to say the least (!), a complex issue : certainly large chunks of this aircraft moved from North Weald, Essex, to Biggin Hill (with other parts reliably sighted at Bournemouth Airport, Dorset) but by April 1993 the majority — *sans* at least engines, main undercarriage etc — of the aircraft was at <u>North Weald</u>, Essex; ☐ F4U-5N Corsair N179<u>PT</u> flew to <u>Bournemouth</u>, Dorset, March 28, 1991; ☐ F8F-2 Bearcat NX800H flew to <u>Bournemouth</u>, Dorset, September 25, 1991; ☐ F4U-4 Corsair NX49092 moved out by road February 1992 and was exported to the USA; ☐ Spitfire Vc wreck 'EE606'/G-MKVC sold to a 'dealer' in the

Derby, area 1992: ❑ Lancaster X KB976/G-BCOH moved by road to <u>Bournemouth</u>, Dorset, October 8, 1992; ❑ Lancaster X KB994 *thought* moved by road to <u>Bournemouth</u>, Dorset October 8, 1992; ❑ Spitfire IX 'PV260'/BR601, restoration was suspended during 1991; ❑ Spitfire XVI RW386/G-BXVI to <u>Audley End</u>, Essex, *circa* 1991; ❑ Spitfire XVI TE392/8074M and ❑ FW 190A-5 1227 is *thought* to have gone to the Bournemouth, Dorset, area for restoration for another 'warbird' operator.

The Precious Metals Seafire project is listed under East Midlands Airport, Leics. Of note, but only frustratingly so, are B-17G-105-VE Flying Fortress N3509G which was acquired in mid-1992 at San Diego, California, for a ferry flight to the UK and P-63A-6-BE Kingcobra N90805 acquired at Van Nuys, California, for shipping to the UK. Both never made it! That leaves only the Catalina which seems to have been too troublesome to fly out : —

❑ G-BPFY	PBY-6A Catalina ▲	ex North Weald, N212DM, G-BPFY, N212DM, G-BPFY,C-FHNH, F-ZBAV, N5555H, N2846D, BuNo 64017. Stored.	01-93

CATFORD

■ **Catford Independent Air Force** : Under this enchanting title, Alan Partington has established a large and varied collection of aviation artefacts. The search for a full time display venue goes on, but for the meantime items are dispersed in a variety of sites and visits are not possible. The Harrier is thought to be an unused cockpit section and may have come from Richmond ATC. Provenance of the *Flea* is likewise vague, although it carries a plaque saying *Made at Capel*.
✉ Alan Partington, 13 Farley Road, Catford, London SE6 2AA.

❑	*	HM.14 *Flea*	unfinished. See notes above.	12-93
❑	*	Spitfire replica	built by Feggans Brown for *Piece of Cake*. Cockpit section.	12-93
❑	*	Harrier	nose section. See notes above.	12-93
❑ XA571*	7722M	Javelin FAW.1	ex Wycombe Sibson, Aylesbury, Halton 7663M, 87, 46. Nose. Arrived during 1993.	12-93

CHELSEA

■ **National Army Museum** : During March 1992 the Museum took delivery of Scout XV127 from Wroughton, Wilts, to act as a centre-piece for its newly-opened Falklands exhibition. It moved on to <u>Fleetlands</u>, Hants, by January 1993, but the Museum is still worth a visit!
◆ Open Monday to Saturday 10am to 5.30pm and Sunday 2pm to 5.30pm.
✉ National Army Museum, Royal Hospital Road, London SW3 4HT. ☎ 071 730 0717.

CHESSINGTON (on the A243 south of Surbiton)

■ **Geoff Masterton** : Geoff continues to work on a wide variety of airframes, some of which are long term enough to merit listing in **W&R**. Taylorcraft Plus D G-AHUG moved to Panshanger, Herts, early in 1992, ready for flight tests. The much-travelled Morava G-ASFD has settled here, and another Zlin has moved in. Noted here in late 1992 was a nose section, variously described as a Valiant or a Canberra — any offers? The fuselage of the Brooklands Museum Tiger Moth has arrived for restoration to flying condition as part of a student project. It will fly in Brooklands Aero Club colours.

❑ G-ANHR	Auster 5	ex Jersey, MT192, 662. CoA expired 20-7-86. Frame.	
❑ G-ARZM	Turbulent	ex Headcorn. Crashed 23-6-91.	12-91
❑ G-ASAM	Turbulent	ex Headcorn. Crashed 23-6-91.	12-91
❑ G-ASFD*	L-200A Morava	ex Bournemouth area, Bournemouth Airport. CoA expired 12-7-84. F/n 10-92.	10-92
		[Spares for airworthy G-BNBZ. See also Hertford, Herts.]	
❑ G-AWJX	Zlin Z.526	CoA expired 29-5-85. Restoration.	
❑ G-BKKZ	Pitts S-1D	ex G-BIVW ntu. Fuselage frame. Stored.	12-91
❑ EI-BIG*	Zlin Z.526	ex Abbeyshrule, D-EBUP, OO-BUT. Spares. First noted 10-92.	10-92
❑ F-BGEQ*	Tiger Moth	ex Brooklands, Le Mans, French military, NL846. Fuselage. Arr late 1993. See notes above.	11-93
❑	Pitts S-1	fuselage frame. Stored.	12-91

CROYDON

■ **Airport** : On February 26, 1994, a Tiger Moth was 'hung' in the foyer of the former airport terminal, part of the new developments being undertaken by Westmead Business Group. The Tiger (the identity of which is open to debate) was restored for static display by Acebell Aviation at Redhill.

☐ T7793* G-ANKV Tiger Moth ex Redhill. Hung for display 26-2-94. See notes above. 02-94

[G-ANKV was not converted and cancelled 9-56.]

■ **1924 Squadron ATC** : Keep their *Chippax* at the headquarters here.

☐ WP921 Chipmunk T.10 ex Henley-on-Thames, Benson, CoAT G-ATJJ, Colerne SF, Ox UAS, HCMSU, 10 RFS. 04-93

■ **Whitgift School** : Like several other schools, it elected to purchase its Grasshopper TX.1 primary glider (on June 17, 1988) and it may well still be found on the premises.

☐ WZ793* Grasshopper TX.1 see notes above. 06-88

GREENFORD

■ **Vanguard Haulage** : The Hunter has been joined by the nose section of the former Boulmer Lightning. XP745 is used as a travelling demonstrator/attraction.

☐ WT555 7499M Hunter F.1 ex Cosford, Locking, A&AEE, Dunsfold. 09-93
☐ XP745* 8453M Lightning F.3 ex Boulmer, Leconfield, 29, 56. 'H'. Forward fuselage. Arrived 4-93. 09-93

HAMPTON

By July 1992 Tiger Moth 'G-ADNZ' had moved to <u>Duxford</u>, Cambs, and was for sale.

HANWELL (on the A4020 east of Uxbridge)

The famous Aeronca store is intact.

☐ G-AETG Aeronca 100 ex Booker. Crashed 7-4-69. Stored. 12-90
☐ G-AEWV Aeronca 100 substantial components. Stored.
☐ G-AEXD Aeronca 100 CoA exp 20-4-70. Stored. 12-90

[Composite, including parts of G-AESP.]

HANWORTH

Arkle Kittiwake G-AWGM is thought to have moved on — Shropshire?

HAYES (on the A4020 south east of Uxbridge)

■ **Science Museum storage facility**: Changes at South Kensington, Gtr Lon, (qv) have brought three balloon exhibits here for storage, one of them allowing G-ATTN to be re-united.

☐ G-ATTN Piccard HAB ex South Kensington, canopy, joined by basket and burner 1992. 08-92
☐ G-BBGN* Cameron A-375 ex South Kensington. Gondola only. *Daffodil II*. Arrived by 8-92. 08-92
☐ OO-BFH* Piccard Gas ex South Kensington. Gondola. Arr by 8-92. 08-92
☐ BAPC.52 Lilienthal Glider ex South Kensington. Original.
☐ Albatross ex South Kensington. McCready *Gossamer Albatross*, trans-Channel man powered aircraft.

HENDON

■ **Royal Air Force Museum** (RAFM) : The policy of continuing to 'rotate' aircraft exhibits continues to pay dividends as the Museum re-inforces its 'live' image. All of this is backed up by continually changing displays and myriad special events and exhibitions. Turn to Cardington, Beds, for news of the restoration and storage side of things and of course to Cosford, Salop, for the Aerospace Museum. Greatest acquisition has been that of Handley Page Hampden I P1344 — parts of this machine are already on show at Hendon, but it will be a long time before it is displayed here as a whole airframe. It is to be found at Cardington, Beds. New exhibits here include the *JP* and Phantom, the long-promised Kittyhawk and the superb Westland Wallace II fuselage, built by Skysport — more details under Hatch, Beds. Correcting **W&R13**, MiG-15*bis* 01120 did not come here from South Lambeth, Gtr Lon, going directly to Cardington, Beds, for attention. It is due to come to Hendon in

September 1994. Unveiled on April 24, 1993 was the Spitfire Society's Spitfire prototype replica 'K5054'/BAPC.214, ex Thruxton, Hants. It was on temporary display, moving on by November 1993 to <u>Southampton</u>, Hants. Due during 1994 is the nose section of Victor K.2 XM717 from Marham, Norfolk, thereby completing the V-Bomber trio. On January 30, 1994 the Sabre arrived from restoration at Duxford, Cambs, in the hands of TFC, filling a major 'hole' in the post-war collection.

RAF Museum aircraft can also be found at the following locations : —

❑ Brooklands, Voisin replica. ❑ Cardington, Beds, Restoration and Storage Centre. ❑ Cosford, Salop, Aerospace Museum. ❑ Duxford, Cambs, Sabre with TFC. ❑ Midland Air Museum, Coventry, Warks — Meteor and T-33A. ❑ Museum of Science & Industry, Gtr Man. ❑ Newark Air Museum, Winthorpe, Notts — Harvard and Oxford. ❑ Rochester, Kent — Hurricane. ❑ St Athan, S Glam, Spitfire cache, MiG-21, Watkins Monoplane. ❑ Tangmere Military Aviation Museum, W Sussex — Meteor and Hunter (with Fury replica to come).

◆ On Graham Park Way, signposted from the end of the M1. Open 10am to 6pm all week, with the exception of Christmas and New Year. More details on the many activities going on can be had on receipt of an SAE, or via the 'hotline'. ✉ RAF Museum, Hendon, London, NW9 5LL. ☎ 081 205 2266. Event 'hotline' ☎ 081 205 9191.

❑	G-EBMB		Hawker Cygnet	ex Cardington, Henlow, Lympne No 14. CoA expired 30-11-61.	11-93
❑			*Nulli Secundus*	airship gondola, 1907.	11-93
❑	164	BAPC.106	Bleriot XI	ex Heathrow, Colerne, Hendon.	11-93
❑	'168'*	G-BFDE	Tabloid replica	ex Cardington, Hendon, Cardington. CoA expired 4-6-83. Arrived by 10-92.	11-93
❑	433	BAPC.107	Bleriot XXVII	ex Cardington, Nash collection.	11-93
❑	'687'	BAPC.181	BE.2b replica	ex Cardington.	11-93
❑	'2345'	G-ATVP	FB.5 Gunbus rep	ex Cardington, Hendon, Weybridge. CoA expired 6-5-69.	11-93
❑	'3066'		Caudron G.III	ex Henlow, Upavon, Heathrow, G-AETA, OO-ELA, O-BELA.	11-93
❑	A301		Morane BB	fuselage frame only.	11-93
❑	'E449'		Avro 504K	ex Henlow. Composite.	11-93
				[Includes parts from 504K G-EBJE and 548A G-EBKN.]	
❑	F938		SE.5A	ex Henlow, Heathrow, Colerne, 'B4563', Weybridge, G-EBIC. CoA exp 3-9-30.	11-93
❑	'A8226'	G-BIDW	1½ Strutter rep	ex Cardington, Land's End, '9382'. CoA expired 29-12-80.	11-93
❑	'C4994'	G-BLWM	Bristol M.1C rep	ex Cardington, 'C4912', Hucknall. CoA expired 12-8-87.	11-93
❑	'E2466'	BAPC.165	Bristol F.2b	ex Cardington, Weston-o-t-Green. Skeletal.	11-93
❑	F1010		DH.9A	ex Cardington, Krakow, Berlin, 110.	11-93
❑	F6314		Camel F.1	ex Heathrow, Colerne, Hendon, Tring, Waddon.	11-93
❑	'F8614'	G-AWAU	Vimy replica	ex 'H651', VAFA. CoA exp 4-8-69.	11-93
❑	'J9941'	G-ABMR	Hart	ex HSA, 'J9933'. CoA expired 11-6-57.	11-93
❑	K4232		Rota I	ex Cardington, SE-AZB, K4232, SAC.	11-93
❑	K6035*		Wallace II	ex Hatch, Henlow, Newark, Cranwell, 2361M, EWS, 502. Fuselage. Unveiled 24-3-93.	11-93
❑	K8042	8372M	Gladiator II	ex 61 OTU, 5 (P)AFU, A&AEE.	11-93
❑	K9942	8383M	Spitfire IA	ex 71 MU, 53 OTU, 57 OTU, 72. 'SD-V'. 501 Sqn c/s.	11-93
❑	L5343		Battle I	ex St Athan, Cardington, Leeming, Iceland, 98, 266. Crashed 13-9-40. 'VO-S'. 98 Sqn c/s.	11-93
				[Composite, parts from P2183.]	
❑	'L8756'	10001	Bolingbroke IVT	ex Boscombe Down, RCAF 10001. 'XD-E', 139 Sqn colours.	11-93
❑	N1671	8370M	Defiant I	ex Finningley, 285, 307. 'EW-D' 307 Sqn colours.	11-93
❑	'N5182'	G-APUP	Pup replica	ex Blackbushe, Old Warden. CoA expired 28-6-78.	11-93

☐ N5628		Gladiator II	ex 263. Lost in Norway 4-40. Forward fuse.	10-92
☐ N5912	8385M	Sopwith Triplane	ex Henlow, 49 MU, 5 MU, Cardington, SAF Redcar, SAF Marske.	11-93
☐ P2617	8373M	Hurricane I	ex 71 MU, 9 FTS, 9 SFTS, 1, 607, 615. 'AF-F', 607 Sqn colours.	11-93
☐ P3175		Hurricane I	ex 257. Shot down 31-8-40. Wreck.	11-93
☐ R5868	7325M	Lancaster I	ex Scampton, 467, 83. 'PO-S', 467 Sqn c/s.	11-93
☐ R9125	8377M	Lysander III	ex 161, 225. 'LX-L', 225 Sqn colours.	11-93
☐ T6296	8387M	Tiger Moth II	ex Yeovilton SF, BRNC, RNEC, Stretton, 7 EFTS, 1 EFTS.	11-93
☐ W1048	8465M	Halifax II	ex Henlow, Lake Hoklingen, Norway, 35, 102. Force-landed 27-4-42. 'TL-S'. 35 Sqn c/s.	11-93
☐ X4590	8384M	Spitfire I	ex Cosford, Finningley, 53 OTU, 303, 57 OTU, 66, 609. 'PR-F', 609 Sqn colours.	11-93
☐ Z7197	8380M	Proctor III	ex St Athan, Swinderby, Finningley, G-AKZN, AST, 18 EFTS, 1 RS, 2 SS. CoA expired 29-11-63.	11-93
☐ 'BE421'	BAPC.205	Hurricane replica	gate guard. 'XP-G', 174 Sqn c/s..	11-93
☐ 'DD931'	9131M	Beaufort VIII	ex Cardington, Chino, New Guinea. Composite. 'L', 42 Sqn colours.	11-93
☐ 'FX760'*	9150M	Kittyhawk IV	ex USA. Composite. 'GA-?', 112 Sqn c/s. First noted 7-92.	11-93
☐ KK995		Hoverfly I	ex Cranfield, 43 OTU, R-4B 43-46558. 'E'.	11-93
☐ MF628		Wellington T.10	ex Abingdon, St Athan, Biggin Hill, Heathrow, Hendon, Wisley, Vickers, 1 ANS.	11-93
☐ 'MH486'	BAPC.206	Spitfire replica	gate guard. 'FF-A', 132 Sqn colours.	11-93
☐ ML824		Sunderland V	ex Pembroke Dock, *Aéronavale*, 330, 201. 'NS-Z', 201 Sqn colours.	11-93
☐ MN235		Typhoon IB	ex Shawbury, Smithsonian, USAAF FE-491, 47 MU, 51 MU.	11-93
☐ PK724	7288M	Spitfire F.24	ex Finningley, Gaydon, Norton, Lyneham.	11-93
☐ 'PR536'		Tempest II	ex Duxford, Cardington, Chichester, Indian AF HA457, RAF. 'OQ-H', 5 Sqn colours.	11-93
☐ RD253	7931M	Beaufighter TF.10	ex St Athan, Portuguese AF BF-13.	11-93
☐ TJ138	7607M	Mosquito TT.35	ex St Athan, Swinderby, Finningley, Colerne, Bicester, Shawbury, 5 CAACU, 98. 'VO-L', 98 Sqn colours.	11-93
☐ VT812	7200M	Vampire F.3	ex Cosford, Shawbury, Colerne, Cardington, 602, 601, 614, 32. 'N'.	11-93
☐ WE139	8369M	Canberra PR.3	ex Henlow, 231 OCU, 39, 69, 540.	11-93
☐ WH301	7930M	Meteor F.8	ex Henlow, Kemble, 85, CAW, 609, DFLS-CFE.	11-93
☐ WK281	7712M	Swift FR.5	ex St Athan, Swinderby, Finningley, Colerne, Northolt, 79. 'S', 79 Sqn colours.	11-93
☐ WS843	7937M	Meteor NF.14	ex St Athan, Henlow, St Athan, Kemble, 1 ANS, MoA, 228 OCU. 'Y'.	11-93
☐ WZ791*	8944M	Grasshopper TX.1	ex Syerston, Halton, High Wycombe, Hove. In main entrance. First noted 7-92.	11-93
☐ XB812*		Sabre F.4	ex Duxford, Rome, Italian AF MM19666, XB812 93, 112, RCAF (no service) 19666. Arrived 30-1-94. See notes above.	01-94
☐ XD818	7894M	Valiant BK.1	ex Marham, 49 'A' Flt.	11-93
☐ XG154	8863M	Hunter FGA.9	ex St Athan, 1 TWU, 229 OCU, 54, 43, 54.	11-93
☐ XG474	8367M	Belvedere HC.1	ex 66, 26, 66. 'O', 66 Sqn colours.	11-93
☐ XL318	8733M	Vulcan B.2	ex Scampton, 617, 230 OCU, Wadd Wing, 617, 230 OCU, Scamp Wing, 617.	11-93
☐ XM463		Jet Provost T.3A	ex 1 FTS, RAFC. Fuselage. 'Hands-on' exhibit. '38'.	11-93

☐ XS925	8961M	Lightning F.6	ex Binbrook, 11, 5-11 pool. 'BA'.	11-93
☐ XV424*	9152M	Phantom FGR.2	ex St Athan, Wattisham, 56, 228 OCU, 29, 92, 228 OCU, 29, 228 OCU, 111, 29. 'I'. Arrived 13-11-92.	11-93
☐ XW323*	9166M	Jet Provost T.5A	ex 1 FTS, RAFC. '86'. Arrived late 1992.	11-93
☐ XZ997	9122M	Harrier GR.3	ex 233 OCU, 1453F, 4, 1, 4. 'V'.	11-93
☐ A2-4		Seagull V	ex Cardington, Wyton, VH-ALB, RAAF A2-4.	11-93
☐ A16-199	G-BEOX	Hudson IIIA	ex Strathallan, VH-AGJ, VH-SMM, A16-199, FH174, 41-36975. 'SF-R'.	11-93
☐ HD-75		Hanriot HD.1	ex Cardington, N75, G-AFDX, OO-APJ, Belgian AF.	11-93
☐ 920		Stranraer	ex CF-BXO Queen Charlotte Airlines, RCAF 920. 'QN'.	11-93
☐ 4101	8477M	Bf 109E-3	ex St Athan, Henlow, Biggin Hill, Fulbeck, Wroughton, Stanmore, DG200, 1426 (EA) Flt, A&AEE, DH, Hucknall, RAE. Force-landed 27-11-40. '12'.	11-93
☐ 120227	8472M	He 162A-2	ex St Athan, Colerne, Leconfield, VH513, AM.65, Farnborough, Leck, JG.1.	11-93
☐ 360043	8475M	Ju 88R-1	ex St Athan, Henlow, St Athan, Biggin Hill, Fulbeck, Wroughton, Stanmore, PJ876, 47 MU, CFE-EAF, 1426 (EA) Flt, RAE. Defected 9-5-43. 'D5+EV'.	11-93
☐ 494083	8474M	Ju 87D-3	ex St Athan, Henlow, St Athan, Fulbeck, Wroughton, Stanmore, Eggebek. 'RI+JK'.	11-93
☐ 584219	8470M	FW 190F-8-U1	ex St Athan, Gaydon, Henlow, Fulbeck, Wroughton, Stanmore, Wroughton, Brize Norton, AM.29, Farnborough, Karup. '38'.	11-93
☐ 701152	8471M	He 111H-23	ex St Athan, Henlow, Biggin Hill, Fulbeck, Stanmore Park, RAE, 56th FG USAAF, Boxted. 'NT+SL'.	11-93
☐ 730301	8479M	Bf 110G-4-R6	ex St Athan, Biggin Hill, Stanmore Park, 76 MU, RAE, AM.34, Karup, I-NJG.3. 'D5+RL'.	11-93
☐	BAPC.92	Fi 103 (V-1)	ex Cardington. (Identity confirmed.)	11-93
☐ MM5701	8468M	Fiat CR-42	ex St Athan, Biggin Hill, Fulbeck, Wroughton, Stanmore Park, AFDU, RAE, BT474, 95 SCT. Force-landed Orfordness 11-11-40. '13-95'.	11-93
☐ '34037'	8838M	TB-25N-20-NC	ex Blackbushe, N9115Z, *Hanover Street*, *Catch 22*, USAAF 44-29366.	11-93
☐ '413573'	9133M	P-51D-25-NA	ex Halton, N6526D, RCAF 9289, 44-73415. Composite. 'B6-K', 363rd FS, *Little Friend*.	11-93
☐ 44-83868		B-17G-95-DL	ex Stansted, N5237V, Andrews AFB, TBM Inc, Aero Union, USN PB-1W 77233. 'N'.	11-93
☐	BAPC.82	Afghan Hind	ex Kabul, Royal Afghan AF, RAF.	11-93
☐	BAPC.100	Clarke TWK	ex Cardington, Hayes. Science Museum loan.	11-93

HOUNSLOW
■ **Imperial War Museum** : By March 1991, Mosquito T.3 TV959 had moved into storage at Duxford, Cambs.

HOUNSLOW HEATH
■ **Metropolitan Police Training Centre** : Still use their Trident for training.

☐ G-AVFK		Trident 2E	ex Heathrow, BA, BEA. CoA exp 15-8-83.	12-92

KENLEY
■ **450 Squadron ATC** : The unit here uses a Cadet as a travelling airframe.

☐ 'VM791'	XA312	Cadet TX.3	also 8876M. Travelling airframe.

KEW
■ **Kew Trucking** : Now in USAAF colours, the truck-mounted Skytrain nose has been seen at several airshows and events.
☐ 42-93510 6W-SAE C-47A-25-DK ex Ottershaw, Kew, Cranfield, F-GEFY,
Le Bourget, Senegalese AF, French AF, CSA
OK-WAR, 42-93510. 'CM'. Nose. 09-93

KINGSTON-UPON-THAMES
■ **British Aerospace** : By December 1992 this historic site had been closed down and cleared out. Harrier GR.1 XV281 and the nose of Harrier T.2 XW272/8783M are unaccounted for.

LONDON
■ *The Cockpit* : The Avirex-run shop at 77 Oxford Street displayed a most convincing P-51D replica, coded '88' and named *Cowboys in the Sky*, until mid August 1993 when the shop was cleared out. The replica was acquired by OFMC at <u>Duxford</u>, Cambs, and moved there for storage.
■ *Planet Hollywood* : Another exotic location. Fight your way through the filmstars and the piles of grotty sweatshirts and 'flying' from the ceiling is *Little Nellie*, the famous Wallis autogyro from *You Only Live Twice*. This is *not* the original, but has been assembled by Ken Wallis (see under Reymerston Hall, Norfolk) so is doubtless based on one of his 'spares'.
☐ 'G-ARZB'* Wallis WA-116 ex Reymerston Hall. *Little Nellie*. See above. 08-93

LONDON AIRPORT (or Heathrow, on the A4 west of Hounslow)
In terms of **W&R** content, Heathrow is the domain of the Trident...
☐ G-AVFG Trident 2E ex BA, BEA. CoA expired 2- 7-85. Fire. 11-93
☐ G-AWZK Trident 3B-101 ex BA, BEA. CoA expired 14-10-86. Inst.
Sweet Charity - Spirit of Fleet Maintenance. 11-93

LONDON CITY AIRPORT (or Docklands, on the A117, south of Newham)
The fire crews still have their Whirlwind to play with.
☐ XN259 A2604 Whirlwind HAS.7 ex Foulness, Lee, Arbroath, 771, 829, 847,
848. Fire crews. 10-92

NORTHOLT AIRFIELD (on the A4180 north west of Northolt)
■ **RAF Northolt** : After a brief return from limbo, the hulk of Devon C.2/2 VP976 was beyond recognition on the dump by February 1993. Varsity T.1 WF408 came from Cosford, Salop, by road to act as the new burning aid.
☐ G-ASDO Baron A55 ex Jersey. CoA expired 16-4-83. Dark brown
camouflage. Dump. 11-93
☐ 'MH777' BAPC.221 Spitfire replica gate guardian. 'RF-N', 303 Sqn colours. 11-93
☐ WF408* 8395M Varsity T.1 ex Cosford, 2 SoTT, 6 SS, 2 ANS, 1 RS, 11
FTS, 201 AFS. Arrived 8-10-92. Dump. 11-93

ORPINGTON
Auster 3 G-AHLI was exported to New Zealand.

RAYNERS LANE (on the A4090 south of Pinner)
■ *Grosvenor Cine-Bar Experience* : An unmarked Cessna 150 'flies' from the ceiling.
☐ Cessna 150 see notes above.

RUISLIP
■ **The Vampire Collection** : Alan Allen loaned the nose section of Supermarine 544 WT859 to <u>Brooklands</u>, Surrey, on July 18, 1992. During March 1993, he donated the pod of Vampire NF.10 to the Mosquito Museum at <u>London Colney</u>, Herts, and it was due to move during April/May. This will provide MAM with the basis to make an NF.10 and complete their Vampire 'set'. Alan's T.11 pod is still here.
☐ WZ581 Vampire T.11 ex Bushey, Keevil, 3/4 CAACU, 229 OCU, 233
OCU, 25. '77'. Nose. 12-93

SIDCUP

■ **Colin Mears** : By April 1993, the nose section of the former WAM Vulcan B.1 had arrived in this area for restoration.

| ☐ XA903* | | Vulcan B.1 | ex Cardiff-Wales, Farnborough, RB.199 test-bed, Olympus test-bed, *Blue Steel* trials, Avro. Nose. Here by 4-93. | 04-93 |

SOUTH KENSINGTON

■ **Science Museum** (ScM) : On October 17, 1992, the newly refurbished and rethought aeronautical gallery was opened. Simply entitled *Flight*, it is a stunning array of airframes and artefacts with the engine 'stacks' being particularly impressive. Alongside it is the inter-active *FlightLab* which is aimed at kids, but is more than absorbing for those of greater years! The Cessna 150 serves in the 'flying training' role here. See also under Hendon and Hayes, Gtr Lon, and Wroughton, Wilts.

All of this has required a fair number of airframes to move on, as follows : — <u>Hayes</u>, Gtr Lon : G-ATTN Piccard HAB basket and burner; G-BBGN Cameron A-375 gondola; OO-BFH Piccard gas gondola; <u>Middle Wallop</u>, Hants : Avro 504K D7560; <u>Wroughton</u>, Wilts : G-ATDD Beagle 206-1 nose; G-9-185 Hunter F.6 nose; EE416 Meteor III nose; VX185 Canberra B.8 nose; XP505 Gnat T.1.

◆ Open daily 10am to 6pm and Sundays 2.30pm to 6pm. In Exhibition Road, off the Cromwell Road. Nearest tube is South Kensington. ✉ The Science Museum, South Kensington, London SW7 2DD. ☎ 071 938 8000, **Fax** 071 938 8112.

☐	G-EBIB		SE.5A	ex Hendon, Savage Skywriting, F939. CoA expired 6-6-35.	12-93
☐	G-AAAH		DH.60G Moth	CoA exp 23-12-30. *Jason*. Amy Johnson.	12-93
☐	G-ANAV		Comet 1A	ex CF-CUM. Nose section.	10-92
☐	G-ASSM*		HS.125-1-522	ex Wroughton, Chester, Southampton, 5N-AMK, G-ASSM. Installed 28-6-92.	12-93
☐	G-AWAW		Cessna F.150F	ex OY-DKJ. CoA expired 8-6-92.	12-93
☐	G-AZPH		Pitts S-1S	ex N11CB. *Neil Williams*. Cr 10-5-91.	12-93
☐	*		S-Hirth Cirrus	—	12-93
☐	304	BAPC.62	Cody Biplane	with the Museum since 1913.	12-93
☐	J8067		Pterodactyl 1	ex Yeovil, Farnborough.	12-93
☐	L1592		Hurricane I	ex 615, 56. 'KW-Z', 615 Sqn colours	12-93
☐	P9444		Spitfire IA	ex Sydenham, 53 OTU, 61 OTU, 58 OTU, 72. 'RN-D', 72 Sqn colours.	12-93
☐	S1595		Supermarine S.6B	ex RAFHSF. Schneider winner 1931.	12-93
☐	W4041/G		Gloster E.28/39	ex Farnborough.	12-93
☐	AP507		Cierva C.30A	ex Halton, Sydenham, 76 MU, 5 MU, 529, 1448 Flt, Duxford Calibration Flt, RAE, G-ACWP. 'KX-P', 529 Sqn colours.	12-93
☐	KN448		Dakota IV	ex Ottawa, RCAF, 436, 10, 44-76586. Nose.	12-93
☐	XN344	8018M	Skeeter AOP.12	ex Middle Wallop, 654, 652.	12-93
☐	XP831	8406M	P.1127	ex Hendon, RAE Bedford, Dunsfold. Installed 31-5-92.	12-93
☐			Short Bros Gas Airship No 17	balloon basket.	10-92
☐			*Beta II*. Gondola only.		12-93
☐	210/16	BAPC.56	Fokker E.III	captured 8-4-16. Stripped airframe.	12-93
☐	100509		Fa 330A-1	ex Farnborough. In store at the Museum.	
☐	191316		Me 163B-1a	ex Halton, 6 MU, Farnborough, Husum, II/JG.400.	12-93
☐	442795	BAPC.199	Fi 103 (V-1)	—	12-93
☐		BAPC.50	Roe Triplane	Roe's second, first flown 13-7-09.	12-93
☐		BAPC.51	Vickers Vimy IV	Alcock and Brown's machine, 1919.	12-93
☐		BAPC.53	Wright Flyer rep	Hatfield-built.	12-93
☐		BAPC.54	JAP-Harding	Bleriot-based.	12-93
☐		BAPC.55	Antoinette	1909 model.	12-93
☐		BAPC.57	Pilcher Hawk rep	—	10-92
☐		BAPC.124	Lilienthal replica	built by the Museum.	10-92

[See under Hayes, Gtr Lon.]

SOUTH LAMBETH

■ **Imperial War Museum** (IWM) : The Museum stages regular special exhibitions and events. Needless to say, see also Duxford, Cambs (!). Harrier GR.3 XZ133 moved to Duxford, Cambs, by mid-1993.

◆ Open 10am to 6pm daily. ✉ Imperial War Museum, Lambeth Road, London SE1 6HZ. ☎ 071 416 5000.

☐	2699		BE.2c	ex Duxford, South Lambeth, 192, 51, 50.	12-93
☐	N6812		Camel 2F1	ex 'F4043'. Culley's aircraft.	12-93
☐	R6915		Spitfire I	ex Cardiff, RNDU, 57 OTU, 61 OTU, 609.	12-93
☐	DV372		Lancaster I	ex 1651 CU, 467. SOC 4-1-45. *Old Fred*. Nose.	12-93
☐	PN323		Halifax A.VII	ex Duxford, South Lambeth, Duxford, Staverton, Radlett, HP. SOC 28-5-48. Nose.	12-93
☐	120235		He 162A-1	ex Duxford, South Lambeth, Cranwell, Brize Norton, Farnborough AM.68, JG.1, Leck.	12-93
☐	733682		FW 190A-8	ex Duxford, South Lambeth, Biggin Hill, Cranwell, Brize Norton, Farnborough AM.75.	12-93
☐	'472258'		P-51D-25-NA	ex Duxford, RCAF 9246, USAAF 44-73979. 'WZ-I', *Big, Beautiful Doll*, 78th FG c/s.	12-93
☐			A6M *Zero*	ex Duxford, South Lambeth. Cockpit.	12-93
☐		BAPC.198	Fi 103 (V-1)	—	12-93

SOUTHALL (on the A4020 south east of Uxbridge)

■ **Ealing Tertiary College** : (Once Southall Technical College.)   A change of syllabus/direction here made all of the airframes surplus to requirements in mid-1993. Well-known collector Barry Parkhouse acquired all of the airframes held and moved the lot (Aztec G-AREF, Cessna 175B G-BRMN, American Eagle G-MBTY, Chipmunk T.10 WB763/G-BBMR and Skeeter AOP.12 XL763) to his store at Ottershaw, Surrey, during a busy July 1993.

■ **Gray Tuplin** : The freighters and trans-shippers took delivery of a Hunter from Fleetlands, Hants, during June 1992, for a US collector. It has been stored here since.

☐	XL600*		Hunter T.7	ex Fleetlands, Scampton, 12, 4 FTS, Wattisham SF, 65. 'Y'. Arr 5-6-92. See notes above.	12-93

STAINES

The former Saudi Arabian Auster is *thought* still held in store here, but it could be heading for *LOST!*

☐	VP-KKO		J/5G Autocar	ex Saudi Arabia, AP-AHK, VP-KKO. Stored.	

STANMORE PARK (on the A4140 in north west London)

Still on the parade ground is the Javelin.

☐	XA553	7470M	Javelin FAW.1	ex Yatesbury, Gloster.	11-93

SUNBURY-ON-THAMES

■ **Sunbury Salvage Company** : The Adams-Wilson Hobbycopter is still on show here.

☐			Hobbycopter	displayed.	10-93

UXBRIDGE (on the A4020 south of the town)

■ **RAF Uxbridge** : Still displays its Spitfire-on-a-stick.

☐	'BR600'	BAPC.222	Spitfire replica	gate guardian. 'SH-V', 64 Sqn colours.	09-93

WELLING (on the A207 east of Bexley)

[The entire location having moved from Kent!]

■ **Edwards Aviation** : Work on the Auster AOP.9 continues locally.

☐	XN437	G-AXWA	Auster AOP.9	ex Biggin Hill, Luton area, Odiham, Maghull, Hoylake, St Athan, Kenya. Restoration.	

■ **385 Squadron ATC** : During 1993 Chippax WK626 moved to Salisbury, Wilts.

WEST DRAYTON (off the A4/M4 north of London Airport)

■ **London Area & Terminal Control Centre** : (Note change of name.) During September 1993 the magnificent Lightning F.2 XN769/8402M here was put up for tender as a prelude to the RAF element, including the School of Fighter Control, leaving 'Drayton. It was scrapped and removed over the weekend of January 15/16, 1994, going to <u>Stock</u>, Essex.

WIMBLEDON

■ **King's College** : Bought the Grasshopper TX.1 that was on 'detachment' to them. It *may* still be found here.

☐ XK822*   Grasshopper TX.1   acquired 29-6-88. See notes above.   06-88

WOOLWICH

■ **Museum of Artillery** : The Auster AOP.9 is still to be found among a wide range of weaponry.

◆ Open April to October 12am to 5pm Monday to Friday and 1pm to 5pm Weekends and November to March Monday to Friday only 12am to 4pm. Located within the Royal Artillery Institution at *The Rotunda*. ✉ The Old Royal Military Academy, Woolwich, London SE18 4JJ. ☎ 081 854 5533.

☐ XR271   Auster AOP.9   ex Larkhill, St Athan, Middle Wallop.   01-94

■ **Royal Arsenal (West)** : By August 1993, the Canberra here was up for disposal, as the MoD made yet another bid to pay for itself! The deal fell through and WH952 was put back up for tender during November 1993.

☐ WH952   Canberra B.6   ex RAE Bedford, BAe Warton, RAE.   01-94

Greater Manchester

ALTRINCHAM

Alan Ellis and his Vampire pod XD595 moved to <u>Glentham</u>, Lincs.

ASHTON-UNDER-LYNE

■ **247 Squadron ATC** : Headquartered in Darnton Road. The unit's Chipmunk T.10 fuselage WP927/8216M (NB not a PAX trainer) would appear to have moved back to its 'parent', RAF Woodvale, Merseyside and please refer there for further confusion!

BARTON AERODROME (on the A57 south of the M62/M63 junction at Eccles)

W&R-wise the population is dwindling, which thankfully is not the case for the light aircraft based at this delightful aerodrome. Like many aerodromes in the UK, there are black clouds on the horizon relating to Barton, but this is not the first time this has happened and it is hoped that it will weather the current short-sighted storm. The hulk of Cessna F.172F G-EWUD was in store here by December 1992, but had moved to <u>Wickenby</u>, Lincs, by February 1993. 'Long-termer' Cessna F.150K G-AXWE hulk had gone by August 1992.

☐ G-ARLW   Cessna 172B   ex N7999X. Cr 20-2-90. Spares.   01-94
☐ G-BJXB   Slingsby T.67A   CoA expired 6-11-88. Restoration.   01-94
☐ G-MIST*   Cessna T.210K   ex G-AYGM, N9438M. Crashed 10-7-92. First
                                           noted 10-92. Wreck.   10-92
☐ N33528   G-BRXP   SNCAN SV-4C   ex F-BGGU, Fr mil, F-BDNX ntu. Stored.   01-94

DUKINFIELD

Anson nose VP519/G-AVVR moved to <u>Chelford</u>, Cheshire, by late 1993.

LEVENSHULME (on the A6 south east of Manchester)

■ **1940 Squadron ATC** : In St Oswald's Road they keep a Tiger Moth fuselage. See under Hatch, Beds, for their Hunter cockpit.

☐ N6720   7014M   Tiger Moth   ex Kings Heath, West Bromwich, 9 AFTS, 2 GS,
                                           Lon UAS, Queens UAS, 11 RFS, 11 EFTS,
                                           4 CPF, 206. 'RUO-B'. Fuselage.   08-91

MANCHESTER

■ **Museum of Science and Industry Air & Space Gallery** : Work continues on the restoration of the Rapide. There are regular special events and presentations, both on the aviation side and across the whole sweep of science and industry as portrayed at this superb museum. There is an active Friends of the Museum and, of course, the Museum has a close relationship with The Aeroplane Collection (TAC — see under Warmingham, Ches) and displays several of their airframes — marked ¥. Fa 330A-1 100549 moved to <u>Lashenden</u>, Kent, on March 22, 1994.

◆ Open every day from 10am to 5pm, including Bank Holidays but excluding December 23-25. ✉ Museum of Science & Industry, Liverpool Road, Manchester M3 4JP. ☎ 061 832 1830 (NB change of number).

☐ G-EBZM		Avian IIIA	ex Higher Blagdon, Peel Green, Lymm, Liverpool, Huyton, Manchester Airport, Hesketh Park, Giro Aviation, Merseyside Aero Club. CoA expired 20-1-38. ¥.	12-93
☐ G-ABAA		Avro 504K	ex 'H2311', Henlow, Nash Collection. CoA expired 11-4-39.	12-93
☐ G-ADAH		Dragon Rapide	ex East Fortune, Peel Green, Booker, Allied Airways. CoA exp 9-6-47. Restn. ¥	12-93
☐ G-APUD		Bensen B.7M	ex Firbeck, Nostell Priory, Wigan, Biggin Hill. CoA expired 27-9-60. ¥	12-93
☐ G-AWZP		Trident 3B-101	ex Heathrow, BA, BEA. CoA expired 14-3-86. Nose section.	12-93
☐ 'T9707'	8378M	Magister I	ex Hendon, G-AKKR, 'T9967', T9708, 51 MU, 16 EFTS, 239. CoA expired 10-4-65.	12-93
☐ BL614	4354M	Spitfire Vb	ex St Athan, 'AB871', Colerne, Credenhill, 118, 64, 222, 242, 611. 222 Sqn c/s, 'ZD-F'.	12-93
☐ WB440		Firefly AS.6	ex Heaton Chapel, Newton-le-Willows, Salford, Failsworth, Anthorn, 812. Cockpit. On loan.	12-93
☐ WG763	7816M	EE P.1A	ex Henlow, RAE, A&AEE, EE.	12-93
☐ WP270	8598M	Eton TX.1	ex Henlow, Hendon, 27 MU, 61 GCF.	12-93
☐ WR960	8772M	Shackleton AEW.2	ex Cosford, 8, 205, A&AEE, 210, 42, 228.	12-93
☐ WT619	7525M	Hunter F.1	ex Henlow, St Athan, 233 OCU, 222, 43.	12-93
☐ WZ736	7868M	Avro 707A	ex Waddington, Cosford, Finningley, RAE Bedford, A&AEE, Avro.	12-93
☐ XG454	8366M	Belvedere HC.1	ex Henlow, Abingdon, A&AEE, Bristol, Old Sarum, Belvedere Trials Unit.	12-93
☐ XL824	8021M	Sycamore HR.14	ex Henlow, Wroughton, CFS, 1564 Flt, 103, 284.	12-93
☐ 997	8485M	Ohka 11	ex Henlow, Cottesmore, Cranwell. BAPC.98.	12-93
☐ J-1172	8487M	Vampire FB.6	ex Cosford, Colerne, Dubendorf, Swiss AF.	12-93
☐	BAPC.6	Roe Triplane rep	ex London, Southend, Irlam, Peel Green, Old Warden, Woodford. *Bullseye Avroplane.* ¥	12-93
☐	BAPC.89	Cayley replica	ex Hendon, Lasham.	12-93
☐	BAPC.175	Volmer VJ-23	ex Old Warden.	12-93
☐	BAPC.182	Wood Ornithopter	ex Hale. Stored.	12-93

MANCHESTER AIRPORT (or Ringway, junction 5, M56)

Local products, in the shape of the HS.748, continue to be the main **W&R** item here, with one example having so far escaped our gaze, arriving in 1991. Two of the former SATA machines gained 'new-style' B-Condition markings and then adopted conventional UK identities. They have shown no real signs of fleeing the nest. Series 225s G-ATMI and G-ATMJ were acquired by Janes Aviation and departed during July 1992. Another departure, this time of a much longer term nature, was AA-5 Traveler G-BCCJ which was flying again by 1991, having been out of action since 1976.

☐ G-ARMX		HS.748-1A/101	ex Dan-Air, VP-LVN, G-ARMX. CoA expired 18-3-84. Dump.	09-93
☐ G-ARPK		Trident 1C	ex BA, BEA. CoA exp 17-5-82. Dump	11-93

☐	G-BAWV		Aztec 250B	ex Woodvale, G-BAWU ntu, 9J-REL, N5255Y.	
				CoA expired 11-10-85. Dump.	11-92
☐	G-BICK		HS.748-2A	ex G-11-782, CS-TAP, SATA, G-11-3, N748AV,	
				G-BICK. Open store.	11-93
☐	G-BJTL		HS.748-2B	ex G-11-790, CS-TAQ, SATA, G-BJTL, G-11-6,	
				N749AV, G-BJTL. Open store.	11-93
☐	G-BLDX		BN-2B-27	ex Air Furness. Crashed 21-8-87. Hulk.	12-93
☐	CS-TAO		HS.748-2A	ex SATA, G-11-4. Arr 16-10-90. Stored.	11-93
☐	V2-LDK*		HS.748-2B	ex LIAT, D-AHSD, G-BKAL. Arr 19-2-9<u>1</u>.	09-93

MOSTON (on the B6393 north of Manchester)
■ **Manchester College of Arts & Technology** : Moston Centre, Ashley Lane. Cherokee 140
G-ATOO was returned to its owner by December 1992, said to be going to fly again. Two Rallyes
have replaced it. Of the two Rallyes, 100T G-BIRB is somewhat problematical, having previously
thought to have been serving a similar purpose at Stockton-on-Tees, Cleveland — which see.

☐	G-AYTA*	MS.880B Rallye	ex Wickenby. CoA exp 7-11-88. See notes.	12-92
☐	G-BIRB*	MS.880B Rallye	ex 'Stockton-on-Tees', Carlisle, F-BVAQ.	
			CoA expired 16-6-90. See notes.	12-92

■ **Others** : The Airbuggy is *thought* to still reside as a source of spares.

| ☐ | G-AXYX | Ekin Airbuggy | damaged 30-7-83. Spares for G-AXYZ. | |

ROYTON (on the A627 north of Oldham)
■ **1855 Squadron ATC** : In Park Lane, they have a Meteor and Vampire. 'Parent' is Sealand.

☐	WS726	7960M	Meteor NF.14	ex Kemble, 1 ANS, 2 ANS, 25. 'G'.	06-91
☐	XK637		Vampire T.11	ex Woodford, Chester, St Athan, 4 FTS,	
				7 FTS. '56'.	06-91

SALFORD
■ **University of Salford** : On November 3, 1993 the University took delivery of two former
Halton *JPs* — one of several centres of academia taking on the type. Also here is a man-powered
aircraft — any details?

☐	*		man-powered a/c	see above.	11-93
☐	XS176*	8514M	Jet Provost T.4	ex Halton, CATCS, 3 FTS, 2 FTS. 'N'.	
				Arrived 3-11-93.	11-93
☐	XS179*	'8237M'	Jet Provost T.4	ex Halton, Kemble, Shawbury, CAW, RAFC.	
				Really 8337M. '20'. Arrived 3-11-93.	11-93

STOCKPORT
■ **162 Squadron ATC** : Should still have John Mott's Jodel.

| ☐ | G-AXUY | SAN DR.100A | ex F-BIZI. Crashed 3-9-78. Stored. | |

TIMPERLEY (on the A560 east of Altrincham)
■ **145 Squadron ATC** : Keep their Chipmunk T.10 PAX here.

☐	WD318	8207M	Chipmunk T.10	ex Chorlton, Sealand, Wrexham, Shawbury,	
				Dur UAS, Queen's UAS, Acklington SF, Ouston	
				SF, 19 RFS. PAX trainer.	

TRAFFORD PARK
■ **Eccles Demolition** : The scrapyard in Tennex Road took on a Trislander by September 1992.

| ☐ | G-OCME* | Trislander | ex Liverpool, G-AYWI, G-51-262. Crashed | |
| | | | 9-2-87. First noted 9-92. | 01-93 |

■ **Kamikazee Ken's Kitchens** : Within the trading estate by May 1992 a former Sandown
resident, Rallye Minerva 220 G-BCAC, was to be found bedecked in olive drab and the logo *Ken Air*,
helping to attract people to this kitchen enhancement emporium. The wings carry the legend *Shot down
by PRICE* and the fuselage *Ken kracks the cost of rigid kitchens*!

| ☐ | G-BCAC* | Minerva 220 | ex Tattershall Thorpe, Sandown. Crashed | |
| | | | 6-5-90. First noted 5-92 - see notes. | 05-92 |

WIGAN

■ **The Aeroplane Collection** (TAC) : Maintain an airframe store here — for greater details of TAC see under Warmingham, Ches. Nigel Ponsford (NHP — see under Leeds, W Yorks) also has a cache of airframes here. BAC Drone II G-ADPJ and other parts all moved to <u>Breighton</u>, Humbs, for restoration on April 8, 1993. Cadet TX.1 RA854 which was held here by Ken Fern — see **W&R 12** — has also passed on to NHP, but is due to move to Breighton along with OH-7 Coupe G-ARIF before too long. Cadet TX.1 cockpit RA848 came here from Harrogate, W Yorks, and did not go to Leeds, W Yorks, correcting **W&R13**. Beware, currently *both* Chrislea Airguards are here!

☐	'G-AFIN' BAPC.203	Airguard rep	ex Warmingham, Stoke-on-Trent. Arr 1993	12-93
☐	G-AFIN*	Airguard	ex Stoke-on-Trent, Warmingham, Wigan, Finningley. Arrived 9-93. NHP.	09-93
☐	G-AFIU	LA.4 Minor	ex Peel Green, Pembroke.	10-90
☐	G-ARIF	OH-7 Coupe	Stored. NHP. See notes above.	12-93
☐	BGA.1559 CHQ	T.31B	ex XN247. Stored. NHP.	12-93
☐	RA848*	Cadet TX.1	ex Harrogate, Wigan, Handforth. Cockpit. See notes above.	12-93
☐	RA854	Cadet TX.1	ex RAFGSA, Woodvale, 41 GS. NHP. Stored. See notes above.	09-92
☐	* BAPC.15	Addyman STG	ex Warmingham, Wigan, Harrogate. Arrived 7-6-93. Stored. NHP.	12-93
☐	BAPC.17	Woodhams Sprite	ex Irlam, Wigan, Liverpool, Leamington Spa. Incomplete. Stored.	
☐	BAPC.60	Murray Helicopter	ex Salford.	

WOODFORD AIRFIELD

■ **Avro Aircraft Restoration Society / The '603 Club** : Restoration of the Avro XIX was put 'on ice' during early 1994, amid worries that the aircraft may be sold off as both commercial and recessional thoughts take a hold of the airfield. While the running and preservation of Vulcan XM603 is a separate concern, there is so much overlap of personnel and goodwill that the two operations can be listed together. XM603 thankfully continues to attract a goodly degree of external fund-raising and her long term looks more assured. During November 1993 the nose section of the unfortunate XM602 was acquired from St Athan, S Glam.

◆ By prior permission only. ✉ British Aerospace Avro Aircraft Restoration Society, BAe Woodford, Stockport, Cheshire, SK7 1QR.

☐	G-AHKX	Avro XIX Srs 2	ex Strathallan, Kemp's Aerial Surveys, Treffield Aviation, Meridian, Smiths. CoA exp 10-4-73. Restoration.	03-94
☐	XM602* 8771M	Vulcan B.2	ex St Athan, 101, Wadd Wing, 35, 230 OCU, Wadd W, Cott W, 12. Nose. Arr 11-93.	11-93
☐	XM603	Vulcan B.2	ex 44, 101, Wadd Wing, Scampton Wing, 9.	06-93

■ **Avro International Aerospace** : (Note name change, Alliott Verdun Roe must be spinning in his grave!) With the removal of the BAe ATP (or Jetstream 61 if you prefer) production line to Prestwick, it may be that the ATP-related airframes here will also migrate north. A 'new' HS.748/ATP rig was noted by December 1992, but this *may* be Set 290 in another incarnation. The Andover test shell is thought to have been scrapped.

☐	G-BPNW	HS.748/217	ex Exeter, G-11-4, RP-C1042, V2-LIP, VP-LIP. Structure tests.	04-91
☐	c/no 06402	Comet 4	ex Nimrod development. Fuselage. Dump.	
☐	c/no 1809	HS.748-2B	uncompleted airframe. (Set 290) See notes.	06-93
☐	XV148	Nimrod prototype	ex A&AEE, makers. Fuselage. Stored.	06-93
☐	*	HS.748	fuselage, first noted 12-92. Velocity Minimum Ground Control rig - ATP rudder experiments. See notes above.	12-92

BIRKDALE (on the A565 south west of Southport)
■ **281 Squadron ATC** : In Upper Aughton Road, the unit keep a *Chippax*.
☐ WG477 8362M Chipmunk T.10 ex Hamble G-ATDP, G-ATDI ntu, Marham SF,
MECS, 114, Bri UAS, Abn UAS, 11 RFS,
2 BFTS, 25 RFS, Liv UAS, 25 RFS. PAX.

BIRKENHEAD DOCKS
■ **Warship Preservation Trust**: HMS *Plymouth* arrived here in late 1991 and went on display to
the public. Wasp HAS.1 XS570 is nominally based with the ship, but also made a sortie to the Arcade
Shopping Centre at Ellesmere Port during late 1992-early 1993 as a promotional exercise. Also on
public view is the submarine HMS *Onyx*.
◆ Open daily from 10am. ✉ Warship Preservation Trust, Birkenhead, L41 1DJ. ☎ / **Fax** 051 650
1573. General enquiries to ✉ WPT, Lodge Hill, Liskeard, Devon, PL14 4EL. ☎ 0579 343663
Fax 0579 346747.
☐ XS570* A2699 Wasp HAS.1 ex Glasgow, Plymouth, Lee-on-Solent. '445'
See notes above. 01-93

LIVERPOOL
By mid-1993 a Canberra nose section was delivered from Stock, Essex, to an owner here — more
details appreciated.
☐ WJ676* 7796M Canberra B.2 ex Stock, Wroughton, Colerne, Melksham, 245,
35, 50. Nose. See notes above. 05-93

LIVERPOOL AIRPORT (or Speke, south of the A561)
The hulk of Trislander G-OCME moved to Trafford Park, Gtr Man, by September 1992. On April 27,
1993 a former Early Birds PT-17 arrived by road for restoration by Keenair, joining the unfortunate
Argus. Janes Aviation (now Emerald Airways) have retired a HS.748 and after spares recovery, it will
be given to the local firemen.
☐ G-BEKE* HS.748-105 ex Janes, LV-HHG, LV-PUP. Last flight
24-7-93. See notes above. 01-94
☐ N55557* G-BRUJ Boeing PT-17 ex Rendcombe, Gloucester-Cheltenham, 42-16136.
Arrived 27-4-93, for restoration. 01-94
☐ 314887* G-AJPI Argus II ex HB614, 43-14887. Damaged 16-5-92.
Stored. 01-94

MEOLS
No news as to the health, or otherwise of this Vampire.
☐ WZ514 Vampire T.11 ex Irby, Bidston, Woodford, Chester, Shawbury,
5, 98. See notes above.

WOODVALE AIRFIELD
■ **RAF Woodvale** : In a spectacular example of not adhering to the notion that a gate guard should
be *relevant* to the history or associations of a base, a Phantom arrived here during July 1992. The
highly relevant Meteor T.7 WA591/7917M was put up for tender and left for Yatesbury, Wilts, by
March 1993. Now to the thorny question of "Whose Chipmunk are you?" According to the MoD's
Directorate of Support Policy, the 'PAX' trainer with 10 AEF here is the fuselage of WP927, last to be
found with 247 Squadron ATC at Ashton-under-Lyne, Gtr Man. This fits in well with the description
of the machine here, for it is not a PAX. However, that leaves us with the fate of WG418/8209M to
determine, or is this to be found in Ashton?
☐ WP927* 8216M Chipmunk T.10 ex Ashton-under-Lyne, Crosby, Hamble G-ATJK,
MCS, Oxf UAS, Lon UAS, Detling SF, Lon UAS.
Fuselage. See notes.
☐ XV468* 9159M Phantom FGR.2 ex 56, 92, 29, 56, 92, 19, 2, 17. 'AB'. Arrived
28-8-92 for gate. 03-93

BERKSWELL (between the A452 and the A45 west of Coventry)
■ **Ken Woolley** : Still keeps the Dingbat and the Wicko Warferry.
☐ G-AFJA   Dingbat   ex Headcorn. Crashed 19-5-75. Stored.   03-92
☐ DR613   G-AFJB   GM.1 Wicko   ex COA, ATA, G-AFJB. CoA expired 12-7-63.
     Restoration.   03-92

BIRMINGHAM
■ **Barrows Lane TAVR Centre** : In Sheldon, **2030 Squadron ATC** gave up their Meteor TT.20 WD646 and by August 1993 it had moved to <u>North Weald</u>, Essex.
■ **Haslucks Green Barracks** : In Haslucks Green Road, Shirley, **492 Squadron ATC** keep their Canberra nose here. Going back to **W&R13**, Wessex HAS.1 XS886 can be found under <u>Evesham</u>, H&W.
☐ WT534   8549M   Canberra PR.7   ex Halton, St Athan, 17. Nose.
■ **Museum of Science and Industry** : The Spitfire and Hurricane remain the main source of interest at the Museum, although there are a large amount of ancillary aviation displays to see.
◆ Open Monday to Saturday 9.30am to 5pm and Sunday 2pm to 5pm. ✉ Museum of Science and Industry, Newhall Street, Birmingham B3 1RZ. ☎ 021 236 1022.
☐ 'P3395'   KX829   Hurricane IV   ex Loughborough, 631, 1606 Flt, 137. 'JX-B',
     1 Sqn colours.   02-94
☐ ML427   6457M   Spitfire IX   ex Castle Bromwich, St Athan, South Marston,
     Millfield, Hucknall, FLS, 3501 SU. 'IS-T'.   02-94

BIRMINGHAM AIRPORT (or Elmdon, on the A45 east of Birmingham)
The non-destructive Trident looks confident, while the Gulfstream hangs on to an increasingly insecure future. Both are used by the airport fire crews.
☐ G-AWZZ   Trident 3B-101   ex BA, BEA. CoA exp 21-5-84. Fire crews.   01-94
☐ G-BOBX   Gulfstream I   ex 9Q-CFK, N748M, N748MN, N73M, N706G,
     N777G. Fire dump. Poor state.   06-93

BRIERLEY HILL
■ **2156 Squadron ATC** : 'Parented' by Cosford, the unit have a Lightning nose.
☐   Lightning F.3   ex Cosford, 29. Nose.   04-91

COVENTRY
■ **Brian Barnes — Typhoon International** : Brian has taken on the restoration of the Typhoon cockpit section previously with Mike Cookman.
☐ 'JR505'   Typhoon IB   ex Leeds, Gloucester, Kemble. Cockpit.   12-93
■ **Maurice & Peter Bayliss** : The Hurricane, most likely ex Canadian, is underway locally. The brothers' Spitfire Tr IX G-BMSB made its first flight during 1993 — see Coventry Airport, Warks.
☐   Hurricane   Restoration. See notes above.   12-93
■ **Mark Hales** : Took delivery of a Grumman Widgeon in March 1992 for restoration to fly.
☐ G-BTKJ*   G.44 Widgeon   ex Brooklands, Leavesden, 5N-AMG, N67867,
     5N-AMD, BuNo 32963. Arr 19-3-92. Restn. 03-92
■ **Roy Nerou** : Work continues on the Chilton.
☐ G-AFSV   Chilton DW.1A   CoA expired 12-7-72. Restoration.
■ **Rolls-Royce Heritage Trust, Coventry Branch** : Within a part of the soon-to-be-closed Rolls-Royce plant at Parkside can be found an astounding collection of engines and artefacts relating to the days when Armstrong Siddeley and then Bristol Siddeley engines were built and overhauled within Coventry. There is a chance the collection will stay on the site when it is redeveloped or it will move to the nearby Rolls-Royce Ansty plant. Either way, this collection is well worth making time for!
◆ By prior arrangement only, also annual open day(s). ✉ W Westacott, Rolls-Royce plc, Parkside, Coventry, CV1 2LE.

HOCKLEY HEATH (south of Solihull, near the M42-M40 interchange)
From museum piece to tactical achievement! Midland Air Museum at Coventry Airport, Warks, disposed of Aztec 250 G-SHIP and **W&R12** quoted it as "sold off to an owner in the West Midlands during 1988". It was sold to become the centre-piece of a 'jungle airstrip' deep in the West Midlands. Suitably camouflaged, it is part of an extensive arena where jaded accountants from Halesowen can work out their pent-up angst by blasting hyped-up double glazing salesmen from Smethwick with paintballs!

☐ G-SHIP*	Aztec 250F	ex MAM Coventry, Coventry Airport, Birmingham, N62490. Crashed 4-12-83. Arrived early 1989. See notes above.	11-92

SMETHWICK
■ **Staravia** : It is now known that the yard here took Hunter GA.11 WV382 from Lee-on-Solent, Hants, in mid-1989. Does it survive here?

SUTTON COLDFIELD
■ **Bob Mitchell** : The well-known PT Flight lives at Cosford, Shrop — *qv*. Bob has two potential restoration projects, held in this general area.

☐ G-AEUJ	Whitney Straight	ex Marple, East Midlands, Bournemouth. CoA expired 4-6-70. Stored.	
☐ G-AFRZ	Monarch	ex Shipdham, G-AIDE, W6463, Kemble, 10 GCF, FTCCF, 13 EFTS, G-AFRZ. CoA exp 29-6-70. Stored.	

■ **St George's Barracks** : Are guarded by a Scout.

☐ 'XR777' XT625	Scout AH.1	ex *XR625*, Middle Wallop, TAD625.	

WOLVERHAMPTON
■ **Boulton Paul Society** (BPS) : Established for quite some time, aiming to research the history of BP and to unite former employees, BPS acquired its first hardware on May 16, 1993 with the arrival of the two former Pennine Balliol cockpit sections. A workshop facility, courtesy of Dowty Boulton Paul Ltd, has been established. General enquiries about the BPS can be made to :

✉ Boulton Paul Society, Alec Brew, 35 Blakeley Avenue, Wolverhampton, WV6 9HR.

☐ WN149*	Balliol T.2	ex Bacup, Salford, Failsworth, RAFC. Cockpit section. Arrived 16-5-93. Restoration.	05-93
☐ WN534*	Balliol T.2	ex Bacup, Salford, Failsworth, 22 MU, RAFC. Cockpit section. Arrived 16-5-93. Restn.	05-93

Norfolk

COLTISHALL AIRFIELD (east of the B1150, north of Coltishall)
■ **RAF Coltishall** : Wallace Cubitt succeeded in a personal ambition when Hunter T.7 XL595/G-BTYL made its first flight on December 17, 1992. The aircraft made its display debut at Fighter Meet, North Weald, the following May. On a positioning flight to the Blackpool Airshow on June 11, 1993, the Hunter tragically crashed in the Peak District, killing Wallace. **W&R13** speculated that Canberra PR.3 WE173/8740M moved to a scrappy when it left on February 18, 1992. This was indeed so, it moved to <u>Stock</u>, Essex. Apart from the addition of a former Halton Jaguar, the other airframes at the base show no change from **W&R13**.

☐ 'V7467'	BAPC.223	Hurricane replica	'LE-D', 242 Sqn colours. Gate.	03-94
☐ XG254	8881M	Hunter FGA.9	ex Weybourne, Coltishall, St Athan, 1 TWU, 2 TWU, TWU, 229 OCU, 54, HS, 54.	01-94
☐ XM172	8427M	Lightning F.1A	ex 226 OCU, 56. 'B'. Gate guardian .	03-94
☐ XP361	8731M	W'wind HAR.10	ex Valley, Boulmer, Chivenor, 202, 22, 103, 110, 225. Dump.	03-94
☐ XX109	8918M	Jaguar GR.1	ex Warton, A&AEE. WLT.	11-93

☐ XX736	9110M	Jaguar GR.1	ex Shawbury, Warton, G-27-327, Indian AF JI013, 6, 226 OCU, JOCU.	08-93
☐ XZ382*	8908M	Jaguar GR.1	ex Halton, Shawbury, 14, 17. Arr 13-10-92.	11-93
☐ ZE364	9085M	F-4J(UK)	ex 74, USN 155894. 'Z'. Dump.	03-94

EAST DEREHAM

A collector here has taken on the two former Ugandan Scout hulks.

☐ 5X-UUW*		Scout Srs 1	ex Blackpool, Panshanger, Uganda Police.	06-93
☐ 5X-UUX*	G-BKLJ	Scout Srs 1	ex Tattershall Thorpe, Heysham, Panshanger, Uganda Police Air Wing. Poor state.	06-93

EAST WINCH (on the A47 east of King's Lynn)

The wreckage of AgCat G-BDZF came here and was 'packaged' along with the AgCat stock from Tattershall Thorpe, Lincs, and exported to the USA. A Pawnee and a Sioux have arrived.

☐ G-BEXK*		Pawnee 235D	ex Oman, N82424 ntu. Crashed 3/4-10-92. Fuselage only, arrived 4-93.	04-93
☐ G-BFOI*		W-Bell 47G	ex Paglesham, XT811. Crashed 31-7-86. Wreck. Arrived by 8-93.	08-93

EAST WRETHAM (east of the A1075 north of Thetford)

During June 1993 a Scout was noted within the NBC compound of the Army camp here. It carried the legend 'Nimrod Airfield Survey' on the boom.

☐ *		Scout AH.1	see notes above.	03-94

FELTHORPE AERODROME (south of the B1149, north west of Norwich)

By March 1994, Auster G-AGYD had moved to Little Gransden, Cambs.

☐ G-ARBG		Nipper II	crashed 16-5-84. Restoration, off-site.	05-91

KING'S LYNN

■ **Gary Knowles :** Took delivery of a *JP* during August 1993.

☐ XM468*	8081M	Jet Provost T.3	ex Stock, St Athan, Halton, Shawbury, 6 FTS, RAFC. Arrived by 8-93.	08-93

■ **Phil Thacker :** By February 1994, had taken delivery of the nose of a Lightning.

☐ XR754*	8972M	Lightning F.6	ex Stock, Honington, Binbrook, 11, 5-11, 23, 5, A&AEE. Nose. Arrived by 2-94.	02-94

LITTLE SNORING AERODROME (north of the A148, north of the village)

■ **Tinden Aircraft :** By January 1993 had gained an unidentified Chipmunk T.10 PAX Trainer and an equally obscure Cherokee fuselage, the latter stored upstairs! The Nord nears airworthiness.

☐ G-BOSJ*		Nord 3400	ex Coventry, N9048P, La Ferte Alais, ALAT 124/F-MMOO. Restoration.	10-93
☐ *		Cherokee	fuselage. Stored. F/n 1-93 - see notes above.	01-93
☐ *		Chipmunk T.10	PAX trainer. Stored. F/n 1-93. See notes.	01-93

LUDHAM AERODROME (north east of the village, north of the A1062)

■ **Hull Aero :** Status of Spitfire PR.IV restoration project AB130 is unknown. Due here during 1994 is Spitfire IX TD314 from Canada for restoration.

MARHAM AIRFIELD (south of the A47 west of Swaffham)

■ **RAF Marham :** On October 15, 1993 55 Squadron stood down as a Victor unit and the Victor K.2 ceased to be an operational type with the RAF. Withdrawals to act as *Christmas trees* to the remainder of the fleet have become a familiar sight on the edge of the airfield. The dispersal of the few flying airframes was put into action immediately :— XH672 made the type's last ever flight on November 30, 1993 when it flew to Shawbury, Salop, bound then by road to Cosford, Salop; XL161 to Lyneham, Wilts, October 20, 1993; XL164 to Brize Norton, Oxon, on November 11, 1993; XL190 to St Mawgan, Cornwall, on October 19, 1993; XL231 to Elvington, N Yorks, on November 25, 1993;

XM715 to <u>Bruntingthorpe</u>, Leics, on November 19, 1993. XM717 was 'topped' and its nose will go to Hendon, Gtr Lon, sometime during 1994 to complete the V-Bomber trio at the RAF Museum, once it has been turned into a 'walk-though' exhibit. It moved to <u>Cardington</u>, Beds, on March 2, 1994 for preparation for 'stardom'. Correcting **W&R13**, Tornado P.03 XX947 did *not* go to the scrappy at Snailwell, Cambs, and is still in use for weapons loading training. The fire crash rescue *JP* has suffered somewhat and an enterprising so-and-so has cut out the bogus Tornado serial number it wore! On April 5, 1994 re-inforcements arrived in the form of two *Bricks*, ready to be torched.

During October 1993 the following withdrawn 55 Squadron Victor K.2s were offered for tender :— XH671, which was damaged beyond repair on March 15, 1993 when it failed a static pressure test; XH675 on the dump since June 1991; XL158 withdrawn during 1990; XL512 withdrawn during 1990 and the noseless XM717 (see above). This was won by Birds of Long Marston, Warks, and the hulks were carted away by late March 1994.

☐ XA917	7827M	Victor B.1	ex Wyton, 232 OCU, 15, 101, RAE, A&AEE.	
			Cockpit., escape trainer. Up for tender 2-94.	02-94
☐ XH673	8911M	Victor K.2	ex 57, Witt Wing, 139, MoA. Outside SHQ.	10-93
☐ XL160	8910M	Victor K.2	ex 57, 55, 57, 55, Witt, 100, MoA. BDR.	03-94
☐ XL192	9024M	Victor K.2	ex 55, 57, Witt Wing, 100. Crash rescue.	03-94
☐ XV332*		Buccaneer S.2B	ex 12, 237 OCU, 208, 12, 216, 15, 237 OCU,	
			12. Flew in 5-4-94.	04-94
☐ XV393*		Phantom FGR.2	ex 74, 228 OCU. 'Q'. Flew in 28-10-92.	03-94
☐ XX947	8797M	Tornado P.03	ex Warton. WLT. See notes above.	01-93
☐ XZ431*		Buccaneer S.2B	ex 12, 208, 12, 208. Flew in 5-4-94.	04-94
☐ XZ968*	9222M	Harrier GR.3	ex St Athan, 233 OCU, 1417F, 1, 4. '3G'.	
			Fuselage, dump. Arrived 25-11-93.	03-94
☐ 'ZD713'	XM381	Jet Provost T.3	ex Halton 8232M, Kemble, Shawbury, RAFC,	
			2 FTS. Crash rescue. See notes above.	03-94
			[ZD713 is a resident 14 Sqn Tornado GR.1.]	

NARBOROUGH (on the A47 north west of Swaffham)

■ **Wellesley Aviation** : Lightning T.5s XS420 and XS459 were auctioned by Sotheby's at Billingshurst on November 27, 1993 reaching £1,000 and £1,200 respectively. Neither sold on that occasion but moved to <u>Wisbech</u>, Cambs, during April 1994.

◆ Other than the occasional open day the collection is not available for public access. General enquiries to :— ✉ Wellesley Aviation, Church Farm, Narborough, King's Lynn, Norfolk, PE32 1TE.

☐ WR971	8119M	Shackleton MR.3-3	ex Cosford, 120, Kinloss Wing, 201, 120,	
			Kinloss Wing, CA. 'Q'.	02-89
☐ XK824		Grasshopper TX.1	ex 1 MGSP.	02-89
☐ XM402	8055AM	Jet Provost T.3	ex W Raynham, Halton, Newton, Shawbury,	
			6 FTS, 2 FTS. 'J'.	07-91
☐ XS933		Lightning F.6	ex Binbrook, 5, 11, BAC, 5, 56, 11. Nose,	
			under restoration off site.	12-93

NEATISHEAD

■ **RAF Neatishead** : The Meteor is still on guard and it is hoped it will become part of the planned Air Defence Battle Command and Control Museum to be established here, dedicated to the development and use of both airborne and ground-base radar in air battle management. All of this will be housed in the old *Happidrome* building. The museum hopes to be open to the public — via a series of open days — during 1994.

☐ WK654	8092M	Meteor F.8	ex Kemble, 85, CFE, AWFCS, 247. 'X'.	11-93

NORWICH

■ **Classic Warbirds** : Phil Earthey and friends have established a project here, with the ambitious aim of putting a Typhoon back into the air. Progress is being made at a steady rate, with many Typhoon related parts being assembled. Another airframe project is on the cards for 1994.

◆ Visits by prior arrangement. ✉ 21 Brunt House Road, Cantley, Norwich, Norfolk NR13 3RT.

☐		Typhoon	long term restoration project.	01-94

NORWICH AIRPORT (or Horsham St Faith, east of the A140, north of the city)

■ **Ambassador Hotel** : The hotel is still 'guarded' by its replica Spitfire..

☐ 'BR600' BAPC.224 Spitfire V replica 'JP-A'. (NB change of code.) Built by TDL. 03-94

■ **Airport** : Air UK Apprentices now have a *JP* to play with. F.27-400M VR-BLY arrived for storage by March 17, 1992, and was eventually sold to, and converted for, the Pakistan Navy. It left as 69/AR-NZW on December 6, 1993. VR-BLX is also bound for Pakistan.

☐ G-AVEZ		Herald 210	ex Museum, Air UK, BIA, BUA, PP-ASW, G-AVEZ, HB-AAH. CoA exp 5-1-81. Fire. 03-94
☐ G-BCDO		F.27-200	ex Air Anglia, PH-OGB, JA8621, PH-FEZ. Fuselage. Damaged 19-7-90. Stored. 08-92
☐ VR-BLX*		F.27-400	ex PH-SFJ, A2-AEC, F-BYAA, OO-SBP, PH-FLL. Arr 15-10-91. For the Pak Navy. 03-94
☐ XM473*	'G-TINY'	Jet Provost T.3A	ex Halton 8974M, 7 FTS, 1 FTS, 7 FTS,1 FTS, CFS, 3 FTS, 1 FTS. Composite. Arr 13-6-92. Air UK Apprentices and in their colours. 08-93

■ **City of Norwich Aviation Museum** : Restoration work on the Herald and Vulcan involves a complete repaint and other airframes are receiving attention. A cafeteria is planned to be ready for the 1994 season. Opening hours have been extended to include Wednesday afternoons.

◆ Access from the A140. Open on Sundays October to April 10am to dusk and May to September 10am to 5pm; Tuesday evenings 7.30pm to dusk during May, June, July and August; Wednesdays 2pm to 5pm; Thursday evenings during June, July and August from 7.30pm to dusk. Good Friday, Easter Sunday and Bank holidays 10am to 5pm. ⌧ City of Norwich Aviation Museum, Old Norwich Road, Horsham St Faith, Norwich, Norfolk. ☎ 0603 625309 — recorded message out-of-hours

☐ G-ASKK		Herald 211	ex Air UK, PP-ASU, G-ASKK, PI-C910, CF-MCK. CoA expired 19-5-85. 12-93
☐ TX228		Anson C.19	ex Duxford, Crawley, WCS, TCCF, Old Sarum SF, SLAW, FCCS, SLAW, Hucknall SF. Stored. 12-93
☐ XD375	7887M	Vampire T.11	ex Cleethorpes, Elsham Hall, Duxford, Winterbourne Gunner, St Athan, 4 FTS, 1 FTS, 3 CAACU, 73. '72'. 12-93
☐ XH767	7955M	Javelin FAW.9	ex Monkton Farleigh, Worcester, Shawbury, 228 OCU, 11, 25. 'A'. 12-93
☐ XM612		Vulcan B.2	ex 44, Wadd Wing, Scampton Wing, 9. 12-93
☐ XP355	G-BEBC	W'wind HAR.10	ex Faygate, 8463M, 38 GCF, 21, MinTech, CFS. 'A'. 12-93
☐ XP458		Grasshopper TX.1	ex Fakenham area. On loan. 02-92
☐ XP919	8163M	Sea Vixen FAW.2	ex Chertsey, Halton, 766, 899, A&AEE. '706-VL'. For disposal? 12-93
☐ 121		Mystere IVA	ex Sculthorpe, French AF. '8-MY'. 12-93
☐ 16718	51-6718	T-33A-5-LO	ex Sculthorpe, Turkish AF ntu, French AF, '314-UJ'. 12-93

OLD BUCKENHAM AERODROME (on the B1077 south east of Attleborough)

■ **Eastern Stearman** : By December 1993 the operation had moved to <u>Swanton Morley</u>, Norfolk, taking with it PT-17s N3922B and 40-1766. N3922B first flew from here on November 11, 1993, landing at the new base. In early 1993 PT-17 N5075A was flying and had been delivered to a Yorkshire-based owner.

■ **Sigma Services** : Restoration of the Dornier continues.

☐ G-BMFG	Do 27A-4	ex Wycombe Air Park, Martlesham Heath, Portuguese AF 3460, *Luftwaffe* AC+955. Restoration. 11-93

REYMERSTON HALL

■ **Wallis Autogiros** : The store of 'retired' Wallis's with the two Auster AOP.9s has increased in number. WA-116/F G-ATHL has been reduced to spares and should be discounted. Please refer to the obvious venue of *Planet Hollywood*, London, Gtr Lon, for a Wallis of unknown pedigree.

◆ Please note the Hall is *not* open to public inspection.

☐	G-ARRT		WA-116/McC	CoA expired 26-5-83. Stored.	01-93
☐	G-ASDY*		WA-116/F	CoA expired 30-4-90. Stored.	01-93
☐	G-AVJV*		WA-117	CoA expired 21-4-89. Stored.	01-93
☐	G-AVJW		WA-118/M	CoA expired 21-4-83. Stored.	01-93
☐	G-AYVO		WA-120 Srs 1	ex S Kensington. CoA exp 31-12-78. Stored.	01-93
☐	G-AZBU	XR246	Auster AOP.9	ex Shipdham, 7862M, Middle Wallop, Beagle, 651. Stored.	01-93
☐	G-BGKT	XN441	Auster AOP.9	ex Shipdham, Scarning, St Athan, Aden, Kenya. Stored.	01-93
☐	G-BLIK*		WA-116/F-S	CoA expired 4-9-91. Stored.	01-93
☐	G-BMJX*		WA-116/X	CoA expired 1-4-89. Stored.	01-93
☐	G-BNDG*		WA-201/R	CoA expired 3-3-88. Stored.	01-93
☐	G-SCAN*		WA-116-100	CoA expired 10-7-91. Stored.	01-93
☐	G-VIEW*		WA-116/L	CoA expired 6-10-85. Stored.	01-93
☐	G-VTEN*		WA-117	CoA expired 3-12-85. Stored.	01-93

SHIPDHAM AERODROME (off the A1075 south west of East Dereham)
VT-DPE was been registered as G-BUJY for Aero Vintage and moved to Paddock Wood, Kent, in late 1993. Otherwise, things here are much as before.

☐	G-AYAF	Twin Com 160C	ex N8842Y. CoA expired 8-5-77. Stored.	06-93
☐	VT-CZV	Tiger Moth	ex G-AISY, N6740, 7 EFTS, 11 EFTS, 18 ERFTS. Stored.	06-93
☐	VT-DOU	Tiger Moth	ex Indian AF HU483. Stored.	06-93
☐	VT-DOX	Tiger Moth	ex Madras, Indian AF HU492. Stored.	06-93
☐	VT-DOY	Tiger Moth	ex Madras, Indian AF HU498. Stored.	06-93
☐	VT-DOZ	Tiger Moth	ex Indian AF HU504. US Mail c/s. Stored.	06-93
☐	VT-DPA	Tiger Moth	ex Madras, Indian AF HU511. US Mail c/s. Stored.	06-93
☐	VT-DPB	Tiger Moth	ex Madras, Indian AF HU708. Stored.	06-93
☐	VT-DPC	Tiger Moth	ex Indian AF 'HU187'. Stored.	06-93
☐	VT-DPH	Tiger Moth	ex Indian AF HU887. Stored.	06-93

SWANTON MORLEY AIRFIELD (east of the B1110, north of East Dereham)
■ **Eastern Stearman** : By December 1993 Jim Avis's Stearmans-from-scratch workshop had moved here from Old Buckenham, Norfolk. 'Budget' kits, based upon a stage-by-stage restoration of a former 'duster' up to ready-to-go rebuilds are offered.

☐	*	40-1766	PT-17 Kaydet	ex Old Buckenham, USA. Restoration.	12-93
☐	*		PT-17 Kaydet	ex USA. Restoration, for Dutch client.	12-93

■ **RAF Swanton Morley - Central Servicing Development Establishment** (CSDE) : The base is due to close around July 1995 with CSDE moving to Wyton, Cambs. On October 13, 1992 CSDE received a Harrier GR.3 from St Athan, S Glam. This replaced the Canberra B.6RC WJ775. This was chopped up during April 1992 and used for a post-crash management exercise before going to St Athan, S Glam. Contrary to **W&R13**, the Wallbro Monoplane is still kept here.

☐	G-BFIP		Wallbro Mono rep	CoA expired 22-4-82. Stored.	11-93
☐	'P8448'	BAPC.225	Spitfire replica	gate guardian. 'UM-D'. 152 Sqn colours.	11-93
☐	XZ998*	9161M	Harrier GR.3	ex St Athan, 233 OCU, 1417 Flt, 233 OCU, 1417 Flt, 233 OCU, 1417 Flt, 233 OCU. Arrived 13-10-92. CSDE.	11-93

■ **Norfolk & Norwich Aero Club** : The club has moved into a T2 hangar previously used as a grain store, with access through Worthing village. The club have acquired a derelict Apache to act as a 'spares ship' for their airworthy G-ASMY.

☐	G-ATMU*	Apache 160G	ex Southend, N4478P. CoA expired 14-4-90. Arrived 19-9-92. Spares use.	11-93

THORPE ABBOTTS (north of the A143, east of Diss)
■ **100th Bomb Group Memorial Museum** : Contents of the tower museum here are exceptional, offering poignant insights into the life and times of the men and machines of the *Bloody Hundredth*. The cockpit of Carvair CF-EPV had gone by early 1993, thought scrapped.
◆ Open 10am to 5pm weekends. ✉ 100th BG Association, Common Road, Dickleburgh, Diss, Norfolk.

WATTON (on the A1075, south of East Dereham)
■ **RAF Watton** : Another station that has passed into history. By November 1992 Meteor NF.14 WS807 had been sold and had moved to Yatesbury, Wilts, in December 1992 for a new life with Meteor Flight. In the former guardroom an impressive museum showing all aspects of the history of the base has been established. It is open at weekends.

WEST RAYNHAM (west of the A1065, south west of Fakenham)
■ **RAF West Raynham** : The closure date given in **W&R13** was premature, it is now set as July 1, 1994. The Javelin (and a Bloodhound *squib*) still guard the gate.
☐ XH980   7867M   Javelin FAW.8   ex Stafford, Shawbury, 41. 'A'.   11-93

WEYBOURNE (on the A149 west of Cromer)
■ **Muckleburgh Collection** : This impressive collection of military vehicles also displays a Meteor NF.11 within the grounds.
◆ Open Easter to October 10am to 5pm daily and weekends only winter 10am to 5pm. ✉ Muckleburgh Collection, Weybourne Camp, Weybourne, Norfolk. ☎ 026 370 608.
☐ WD686   Meteor NF.11   ex Duxford, RAE Bedford, Wroughton, TRE
                                                    Defford.   02-93

WYMONDHAM
■ **Wymondham College Aircraft Restoration Group** : The College have carried out work for the Imperial War Museum at Duxford, Cambs, over a number of years, but during June 1993 it took on its first whole airframe in the form of the Sea Vampire. Work is being carried out in a Nissen hut previously part of the 231st Station Hospital USAAF, which used the hall during World War Two.
☐ XG743*   Sea Vampire T.22   ex Duxford, Brawdy SF, 736, 764. '597-LM',
                                                    736 Sqn c/s. IWM loan. Arr 6-93. Restn.   01-94

Northamptonshire

CROUGHTON (on the B4031 south west of Brackley)
■ **USAF Croughton** : The former airfield bristles with aerials and BSkyB dishes. In the topsy-turvy world of military cut-backs and rethinks, what *was* a satellite to Upper Heyford is now 'in command' of the former airfield as it plunges into Care & Maintenance status. Emphasising this new role, the base has taken over the former 'Heyford gate guard and the Prisoner of War/Missing in Action F-105 which serves as a 'dedicated' memorial to such aircrew.
☐ 24428*   F-105G-RE   ex Upper Heyford, Davis-Monthan 'FK095', 128
                                            TFS, Georgia ANG. *POW-MIA You Are Not
                                            Forgotten* Gate..   03-94
☐ '63000'* 42212   F-100D-11-NA   ex Upper Heyford, Sculthorpe, French AF.
                                                    'FW-000'. Gate.   03-94

HINTON-IN-THE-HEDGES (just west of Brackley)
Para-trainer Cessna F.172H G-BAKK had been reduced to components by June 1993. Rebuild of the Terrier is thought to continue.
☐ G-ASYG   Terrier 2   ex 'Herts', Banbury, East Midlands, VX927, 661.
                                        CoA expired 19-12-70. Restoration.   04-91

KETTERING

■ **Kestner Caravan Park** : No news from the park and its Whirlwind and a Spitfire replica.

☐ XP399	W'wind HAR.10	ex Glastonbury, Hadfield, Pryton Hill, 32, 1563F, 230.	12-91
☐	Spitfire replica	built by Air Image.	12-91

KINGS CLIFFE (south of the A47, west of Peterborough)

■ **John Tempest** : The Condor makes progress and has been joined by a cache of Cosmic Wind material from the Halfpenny Green area — the latter as yet insufficient to list formally.

☐ G-AVJH	D.62B Condor	ex Mona. Crashed 31-7-83. Restoration.	12-93

■ **Others**: Locally, the Algerian-built Stampe makes progress.

☐ G-BEUS	AIA SV-4C	ex Gransden, Long Marston, F-BKFK, F-DAFK, French military. Restoration.	12-93

NORTHAMPTON

Moth Minor G-AFPR is best described as a kit of small parts and therefore too small for consideration (at this stage) in **W&R**. The project is now thought to be in the Wantage, Oxon, area.

NORTHAMPTON AERODROME (or Sywell, north east of Northampton, off the A43)

Two of the 'vintage' helicopters previously at Blackpool Airport, Lancs, had gravitated here by mid-1992. The former Blackpool Whirlwind also came here, this time rotorborne and has made the odd sortie into the air. The hulk of Pup 100 G-AWRA has not been noted for a long time and is assumed to have been scrapped. Sloane Helicopters have rebuilt a damaged Robinson to static condition and have marked it up as 'G-BEAR' — for the *Children in Need* appeal. It is loaned out for a whole series of fund-raising drives. The throughput of 'bent' helicopters via the operators and engineering concerns here is such that 'long-terms' are quite difficult to pin down. During March 1994, two Robinson R-22 cabin pods were to be found dumped next to a derelict Austin Maxi in a lorry yard on the airfield site. The throughput of R-22 cabins, booms and other bits is such that they are too transitory — and really too small — to revel in a listing in **W&R**.

☐ G-AJDY*		J/1 Autocrat	ex Spanhoe, Cossall, Sherburn. CoA expired 9-7-71. First noted 6-91.	06-91
☐ G-ANLW*		Widgeon 2	ex Blackpool, 'MD497', Wellingborough, Little Staughton, Tattershall Thorpe, Southend. CoA expired 27-5-81. Stored. F/n 7-92.	03-94
☐ G-APKY*		Hiller UH-12B	ex Blackpool, Wellingborough, Sywell, PH-NFL. CoA expired 7-5-74. Stored.	03-94
☐ G-AYIA		Hughes 369HS	damaged 1-6-88. Spares.	02-93
☐ G-BBOR*		B.206B JetRanger	CoA expired 18-7-91. Stored, boomless.	11-93
☐ 'G-BEAR'*	G-HOVR	Robinson R-22	ex N2647M. Crashed 9-1-89. See notes.	05-91
☐ 'G-CARS'	BAPC.134	Pitts S.2A	ex Torbay, 'G-RKSF'. Travelling display airframe, based here.	02-90
☐ G-HEWS		Hughes 369D	damaged 5-12-87. Wreck. Dump.	03-91
☐ G-LOYD		Gazelle Srs 1	ex G-SFTC, N47298. Crashed 15-2-89. Original fuselage. Dump.	03-91
☐ G-ROMA*		Hughes 369HS	ex Blackpool, G-ROPI, G-ROMA, G-ONPP, OY-HCP, D-HGER. Stored, damaged. First noted 2-93.	11-93
☐ G-SHLL*		Hughes 269A	ex N269QD, 66-18342. CoA exp 1-6-92. First noted 11-90. Spares.	10-91
☐ *		Enstrom F-28A	cabin shell. Fire dump.	05-93
☐ NL985*	7015M	Tiger Moth	ex Cranfield, Leighton Buzzard, Bushey, Leamington Spa, Finningley. Frame.	02-90
☐ XK940*	G-AYXT	W'wind HAS.7 △	ex Blackpool, Heysham, Carnforth, Panshanger, Elstree, Luton, Fleetlands, 771, Culdrose SF, 705, 825, 824, 845. F/n 7-92.	07-92

SPANHOE LODGE AERODROME (south east of Harringworth)
■ **Windmill Aviation** : Carl Tyers and his team continue to work restorative magic with airframes here. Auster IV G-ANHS was flying again by 1991. J/1 Autocrat G-AJDY moved to <u>Northampton Aerodrome</u>, Northants, by June 1991. The mysterious disappearance of David Martin, owner of the Tempest project, brought all work on the aircraft to a halt and it was put into store. As it became clear that David Martin was a murder victim, his estate put the airframe up for disposal and it moved to <u>Audley End</u>, Essex, on October 25, 1993. The second airframe noted as being here in **W&R13** was only transitory, involving a rear end and centre section from TFC at Duxford, Cambs, for calibration and comparison purposes.

☐ G-ASEE*	J/1N Alpha	ex Tongham, I-AGRI. Cr 9-2-74. Stored.	04-90
☐ G-BNJJ	Cessna 152 II	ex Nayland, Cranfield. Dam 18-5-88. Hulk.	08-93

WELLINGBOROUGH
■ **Wellingborough School** : On June 27, 1988, the school bought the Grasshopper that was operated by its CCF, presumably so that they could continue to play with it. Is this still the case?

☐ XP454*	Grasshopper TX.1	see notes above.	06-88

Northumberland

BOULMER AIRFIELD
■ **RAF Boulmer** : .The Lightning on the gate, F.3 XP745/8453M, was replaced by the obligatory Phantom. The Lightning was noted 'road-running' anti-clockwise around the dreaded M25 during April 1993. It was in good hands, travelling care of Vanguard Haulage to <u>Greenford</u>, Gtr Lon.

☐ XV415*	9163M	Phantom FGR.2	ex 56, 23, 92, 56, 92, 228 OCU, 56, 31. 'E'. Gate, first noted 3-93.	02-94

FELTON (on the B6345 south of Alnwick)
■ **David Thompson** : Took delivery of a Vampire T.11 at a farm near here during October 1992.

☐ XH278*	8595M	Vampire T.11	ex Henlow, Upwood 7866M, 27 MU, RAFC. Arrived 10-92.	10-92

OTTERBURN RANGES (on the A696 north of Newcastle-on-Tyne)
No further claims to just what is left up on the ranges, but through research work both the *JP* and Sea Vixen mentioned in **W&R13** can be identified. Dates at which the airframes were allocated as being targets are given below, but again it is stressed that only four of those listed below have any form of 'last seen' date. For completeness, research has dug up the following allocation dates for previous targets (which, who knows, may still live on!) : —
<u>Canberra B.2</u> WH794 ex Abingdon 22-3-83; <u>Devon C.2/2</u> WB535 ex Kemble 23-3-78; <u>Whirlwind HAR.10</u> XK969 ex Benson 22-3-83; XP302/8443M ex Halton 15-4-81; XP331/8649M ex Halton 7-5-81 with XR457/8644M.

☐ XF386	8707M	Hunter F.6A	ex Coltishall, Kemble, Laarbruch SF, 229 OCU, 92, 65. Allocated 9-12-85.	
☐ XG264	8715M	Hunter FGA.9	ex Brawdy, 2 TWU, TWU, 229 OCU, 58, 45, 54. Rear fuselage of XF445. Allocated 9-12-85.	
☐ XJ604	8222M	Sea Vixen FAW.2	ex Cranfield, Halton, Sydenham, 890. '755-VL'. Allocated 4-11-87 ex tyre trials, but left Cranfield 15-4-88.	07-90
☐ XM458		Jet Provost T.3A	ex Scampton, CFS, 1 FTS, 3 FTS, 26, 3 FTS, BSE, RAFC. Allocated 20-2-90.	07-90
☐ XP515	8614M	Gnat T.1	ex Wattisham, Kemble, 4 FTS, CFS, 4 FTS, CFS, 4 FTS. Allocated 9-12-85.	
☐ XP694		Lightning F.3	ex Binbrook, 5-11 pool, LTF, 5-11 pool, LTF, 5, 56, 29, 11, 29, Wattisham TFF, 29, A&AEE, BAC. Allocated 15-4-88.	04-88

☐ XP702	Lightning F.3	ex Binbrook, 5, 56, 29, 56, 74. Allocated 15-4-88.	04-88
☐ XS594	Andover C.1	ex Kemble, 84, St Athan Apps, A&AEE. Allocated 22-2-82.	
☐ XS601	Andover C.1	ex Kemble, A&AEE, 46, Andover CU. Allocated 22-2-82.	

Nottinghamshire

BALDERTON (on the A1 south east of Newark-on-Trent)
■ **A1 Commercials** : The compound still displays a very decrepit Lightning.

| ☐ XN728 | 8546M | Lightning F.2A | ex Coningsby, 92. 'V'. | 02-94 |

HUCKNALL AERODROME (south of the town)
■ **1803 Squadron, ATC** : Received the fuselage of former Bruntingthorpe, Leics, Harrier GR.3 XV747 on loan during 1993.

| ☐ XV747* | 8979M | Harrier GR.3 | ex Bruntingthorpe, Coltishall, St Athan, Wittering, 233 OCU, 1, 4, 233 OCU. Fuse. See notes. | 10-93 |

LANGAR AERODROME
The para-club still has its exit-trainer.

| ☐ G-BATD | | Cessna U.206F | ex Isle of Man, Sibson, Shobdon, N60204. Crashed 5-4-80. Para-trainer. | |

MANSFIELD
■ **384 Squadron ATC** : *Should* have their Canberra nose, but confirmation would be appreciated.

| ☐ WT507 | 8548M | Canberra PR.7 | ex Halton 8131M, St Athan, 31, 17, 58, A&AEE, 58, 527, 58. Nose. | |

NEWARK-ON-TRENT
■ **Cliff Baker** : Cliff continues to be the fount of much knowledge on the Auster and to hold a huge stock of airframe parts. Of the airframes held here, it is thought that little has changed.
◆ The workshop and store are *not* open to the public and visits here are *strictly* by prior permission.

☐ G-AIGR		J/1N Alpha	ex Northampton Airport, fuselage frame.	08-90
☐ G-AIJI		J/1N Alpha	ex East Midlands, Elsham Hall, Goxhill, Kirmington. Damaged 12-1-75.	02-89
☐ G-AIKE		Auster 5	ex Portsmouth, NJ728, 661. Cr 1-9-65.	08-90
☐ G-AKOT		Auster 5	ex North Denes, TJ433, 657. Cr 9-9-62.	02-89
☐ G-AKWT		Auster 5	ex East Midlands, Elsham Hall, Goxhill, Stroxton Lodge, Tollerton, MT360, 26, 175, 121 Wing, 181, 80, 486, 56, 19. Crashed 7-8-48.	08-90
☐ G-ALNV		Auster 5	ex Nottingham, Leicester, RT578, 341, 329. CoA expired 4-7-50.	08-90
☐ G-AMUJ		J/5F Aiglet Tnr	ex East Midlands, Winthorpe. Crashed 8-6-60.	08-90
☐ G-ANHU EC-AXR		Auster 4	ex Shoreham, Spain, G-ANHU, MT255, 659.	08-90
☐ G-ANHW		Auster 5D	ex Shipdham, TJ320, 664. CoA exp 9-3-70.	08-90
☐ G-ANHX		Auster 5D	ex Leicester, TW519, 661, A&AEE. Cr 28-3-70.	08-90
☐ G-AOCP		Auster 5	ex TW462, 666. Damaged 4-70. Restn.	08-90
☐ G-ARGB		Auster 6A	ex Waddington, VF635, 662, 1901 Flt. CoA expired 21-6-74.	

☐ G-ARGI		Auster 6A	ex Chirk, Heathfield, VF530, 661. CoA expired 4-7-76. 08-90
☐ G-AROJ		Airedale	ex Leicester, Thorney, HB-EUC, G-AROJ. CoA expired 8-1-76.
☐ G-ARTM		Terrier 1	ex Chirk, WE536, 651, 657, Schwechat SF. Crashed 28-5-70.
☐ G-ASWF		Airedale	ex Leicester. CoA expired 27-4-83. 08-90
☐ F-BBSO		Auster 5	ex Taunton, G-AMJM, TW452, 62 GCF. Frame. 08-90
☐	c/no 3705	Auster D.6-180	ex White Waltham, Rearsby. Frame only. 08-90
☐	c/no 608	Terrier 2	ex White Waltham, Rearsby. Frame only. 08-90

[Note that G-ASAN is c/no B.608 and is still airworthy. That being the case, this must be the original fuselage.]

NEWTON AIRFIELD (on the A46 east of Nottingham)
■ **RAF Newton** : Is now the home of the former IWM, Duxford, Cambs, Comet C.2(R) — see under Duxford for major details of the move. The fuselage provides the RAF Police Dog School with a suitable training aid. Other than this, the **W&R** airframes here are unchanged.

☐ WT694	7510M	Hunter F.1	ex Debden, 229 OCU, DFLS, 54. Gate. 09-93
☐ XK695*	9164M	Comet C.2(R)	ex Duxford, Wyton, 51, 216, G-AMXH. Fuselage. Arrived 11-92. See above. 09-93
☐ XL623	8770M	Hunter T.7	ex Cosford, 1 TWU, 74, 19, 1, 43, 92, 208, 65. '90'. 09-93
☐ XN641	8865M	Jet Provost T.3	ex Shawbury, 1 FTS, RAFC, 3 FTS. '47'. Fire dump. 09-93

NOTTINGHAM AIRPORT (or Tollerton)
Sole entry here for several editions, Auster J/1N Alpha G-AGVJ is *thought* to have been sold in France *circa* 1990. Confirmation appreciated. Keeping the location 'alive', Seabee G-SEAB arrived here for restoration during October 1991.

☐ G-SEAB*		RC-3 Seabee	ex Glasgow, N6210K, NC6210K. Arrived 10-91. Restoration. 10-93

RETFORD AERODROME (or Gamston, off the B6387 south of East Retford)
During 1991, Harvard G-TSIX ferried in here from Tatenhill, Staffs. It has apparently remained dormant ever since.

☐ G-TSIX*		Harvard IIA	ex Tatenhill, East Midlands, Port AF 1535, SAAF 7183, EX289, 41-33262. 'G-T6'. CoA expired 28-1-92.. Flew in 1991. Stored. 10-93

■ **Locality** : Two former Southend Chipmunks have moved to this area for rebuild, possibly into one airworthy example.

☐ 5N-AAE* G-AOJS		Chipmunk 22A	ex Southend area, Shoreham, Nigeria, VR-NBI, G-AOJS, D-EHOF, G-AOJS, WB745, Stn UAS, 14 RFS, Stn UAS, 14 RFS.
☐ 5N-AGP* G-AOZU		Chipmunk 22A	ex Southend area, Shoreham, Nigeria, G-AOZU, EI-AHP, WD290, HCEU, 228, HCEU, HCCS, 1 RFS.

SOUTH SCARLE (in between the A46 and the A1133 south west of Lincoln)
Rallye G-AZEE's *original* fuselage is thought still stored in the rafters at the strip here.

☐ G-AZEE		MS.880B Rallye	ex Shipdham, F-BKKA. See notes above. Stored. 11-90

STAPLEFORD (on the A453 south west of Nottingham)
■ **1360 Squadron ATC** : By July 1993, the unit had been 'redeveloped' — where their hut and Vampire T.11 XD463/8023M stood in Cliff Hill Avenue had become a car park! News of unit, the Vampire and *even* the hut eagerly awaited!

SYERSTON AIRFIELD (off the A46 south west of Newark-on-Trent)
■ **RAF Syerston** : The Central Gliding School store of 'historic' types was depleted in mid-1992 when Grasshopper TX.1 WZ791/8944M moved to Hendon, Gtr Lon. and stardom.

☐	XE799	8943M	Cadet TX.3	ex CGS.	02-92
☐	XN185	8942M	Sedbergh TX.1	ex CGS, 643 VGS, 4 MGSP, 633 VGS, 635 VGS.	02-92

WINTHORPE SHOWGROUND (on the A46 north east of Newark-on-Trent)
■ **Newark Air Museum** (NAM) : Quickly the huge and ambitious aircraft display hall has paid major dividends for NAM. Now the museum is an 'all-weather' site and the gain in visitors has been noticeable — school parties etc having established a good relationship with the museum and workcards, etc, being available. The 'liberation' of the workshop so that it can be just that has also given great flexibility to the mixed full time curatorial and volunteer staff that work on the airframes and exhibits. The Dove is currently inside undergoing restoration that not that long ago would have to be done with the co-operation of Mother Nature. Within the display hall itself can be found the completed Anson C.19 VL348 and a wide variety of airframes and other displays — including an intriguing line-up of ejector seats. Obviously pleased with the situation, the RAF Museum has renewed the loan agreement on the Harvard and Oxford. Touching down at Scampton, Lincs, on February 24, 1994 was a Danish Air Force Draken, a gift to the Museum. As **W&R** closed for press, arrangements to road this lovely to Winthorpe were underway. Outside, the Vulcan has completed its repaint and not far away can be found Shackleton MR.3/3 WR977 which has been restored to a superb condition by a largely volunteer team — a shining example of what can be done! Work on the interior of the *Shack* continues. Occasionally, the interiors of some of the exhibits are open to visitors. Next major project for NAM is another building. The current entrance hall and display area will be replaced by an enlarged entrance hall and shop — renowned for its stock of plastic kits and accessories — and extra display areas which should include a lecture hall and other facilities. A major boost for the project came in the autumn of 1993 when NAM was awarded a grant of £48,000 by the Newark & Sherwood District Council. Work will start in the summer of 1994.

To 'tidy up' one of the aircraft references here, Proctor II G-AHMP is really only a centre section plus other parts and is therefore not in the bounds of **W&R** 'territory'. By April 1993 the two former Torbay Aircraft Museum World War One replicas (Fokker Dr I BAPC.133 and SE.5A BAPC.167) had moved on, destination unknown, but possibly Kent. See under Innsworth, Glos, for a prospective exhibit.
◆ Signposted from the A1, on Newark Showground, off the A46 Lincoln Road. Open every day throughout the year excluding December 24-26. April-October weekdays 10am to 5pm, weekends 10am to 6pm; November-March every day 10am to 4pm. All buildings are suitable for the disabled, including the toilets. ✉ NAM, The Airfield, Winthorpe, Newark, Notts, NG24 2NY. ☎ 0636 707170.

☐	G-AHRI		Dove 1	ex Long Marston, East Kirkby, Tattershall, Little Staughton, 4X-ARI, G-AHRI. Restoration.	12-93
☐	G-ANXB		Heron 1	ex Biggin Hill, Fairflight, BEA Scottish, G-5-14. CoA expired 25-3-79. BEA Scottish c/s. *Sir James Young Simpson.*	12-93
☐	VH-UTH		Monospar ST-12	ex Australia. Stored.	12-93
☐	FE905		Harvard IIB	ex Cardington, Royston, London Bridge, Southend, LN-BNM, Danish AF 31-329, RCAF, 41 SFTS, FE905, 42-12392. RAF Museum loan.	12-93
☐	KF532		Harvard IIB	ex 781, 799, 727, 799, 758. Cockpit section.	12-93
☐	MP425		Oxford I	ex Cardington, G-AITB, Shawbury, Perth, MP425, 7 FTS, 18 (P)AFU, 1536F. CoA expired 24-5-61. RAF Museum loan.	12-93
☐	TG517		Hastings T.5	ex 230 OCU, SCBS, BCBS, 202, 53, 47.	12-93
☐	VL348	G-AVVO	Anson C.19	ex Southend, Shawbury, 22 GCF, 24 GCF, Colerne SF, 62 GCF, HCMSU, RCCF.	12-93
☐	VR249	G-APIY	Prentice T.1	ex 1 ASS, RAFC. CoA expired 18-3-67. 'FA-EL', Cranwell colours.	12-93
☐	VZ608		Meteor FR.9	ex Hucknall, Shoreham, MoS, RR. RB.108 test-bed.	12-93

☐	VZ634	8657M	Meteor T.7	ex Wattisham, 5 MU, MoA, Leeming SF, Stradishall SF, 41, 141, 609, 247. 12-93
☐	WF369		Varsity T.1	ex 6 FTS, AE&AEOS, AES, 2 ANS, 201 AFS. 'F'. 12-93
☐	WH863*	8693M	Canberra T.17	ex Marham, 360, RAE, IAM. Nose only. 12-93 [Omitted from **W&R13** — arrived July 1990.]
☐	WH904		Canberra T.19	ex Cambridge, 7, 85, West Raynham TFF, 228 OCU, 35, 207. '04'. 12-93
☐	WK277	7719M	Swift FR.5	ex Cosford, Leconfield, 2. 'N', 2 Sqn c/s. 12-93
☐	WM913	8162M	Sea Hawk FB.3	ex Fleetwood, Sealand, Culdrose A2510, Abbotsinch, 736. '456-J'. 12-93
☐	WR977	8186M	Shackleton MR.3/3	ex Finningley, 203, 42, 206, 203, 42, 201, 206, 201, 220. 'B' Completing restoration. 12-93
☐	WS692	7605M	Meteor NF.12	ex Cranwell, Henlow, 72, 46, 38 MU, 33 MU. Restoration. 'C'. 12-93
☐	WS739	7961M	Meteor NF.14	ex Misson, Church Fenton, Kemble, 1 ANS, 2 ANS, 25. 12-93
☐	WT651	7532M	Hunter F.1	ex Lawford Heath, Halton, Credenhill, 229 OCU, 233 OCU, 229 OCU, 222. 'C'. 12-93
☐	WT933	7709M	Sycamore 3	ex Sutton-in-Ashfield, Strensall, Halton, G-ALSW ntu. For disposal. 12-93
☐	WV606	7622M	Provost T.1	ex Halton, 1 FTS. 'P-B'. 12-93
☐	WV787	8799M	Canberra B.2/8	ex Abingdon, A&AEE. 12-93
☐	WW217		S Venom FAW.21	ex Cardiff-Wales, Ottershaw, Culdrose, Yeovilton, ADS, 891, 890. '736'. 12-93
☐	WX905	7458M	Venom NF.3	ex Henlow, Hendon, Yatesbury, 27 MU, 23. 12-93
☐	XD515	7998M	Vampire T.11	ex Misson, Linton-on-Ouse, 3 FTS, 7 FTS, 1 FTS, 5 FTS, 206 AFS. 12-93
☐	XD593		Vampire T.11	ex Woodford, Chester, St Athan, 8 FTS, CFS, FWS, 5 FTS, 4 FTS. '50'. 12-93
☐	XE317		Sycamore HR.14	ex Portsmouth, CFS, G-AMWO ntu. 12-93
☐	XH992	7829M	Javelin FAW.8	ex Cosford, Shawbury, 85. 12-93
☐	XJ560	8142M	Sea Vixen FAW.2	ex RAE Bedford, Farnborough, Halton, 893, 899, 892, 890. '242'. 12-93
☐	XL149	7988M	Beverley C.1	ex Finningley, 84, 30, 84, 242 OCU. Cockpit . 12-93
☐	XL764	7940M	Skeeter AOP.12	ex Nostell Priory, Rotherham, Middle Wallop, Arborfield, MoA, Middle Wallop. 12-93
☐	XM594		Vulcan B.2	ex 44, Scampton Wing, 617, 27. 12-93
☐	XM685		Whirlwind HAS.7	ex Panshanger area, Elstree, Luton, G-AYZJ ntu, Fleetlands, Lee-on-Solent, 771, *Ark Royal* Ship's Flt, 847, 848. '513-PO'. 12-93
☐	XN573		Jet Provost T.3	ex Blackpool Airport, Kemble, 1 FTS, CFS. Nose. 12-93 [Identity confirmed, was previously thought to be XN511.]
☐	XN819	8205M	Argosy C.1	ex Finningley, Shawbury, Benson Wing, 105, MoA. Cockpit section. In small display hall. 12-93
☐	XN964		Buccaneer S.1	ex Bruntingthorpe, East Midlands, Brough, Pershore, 807. '613-LM'. 12-93
☐	XP226	A2667	Gannet AEW.3	ex Lee-on-Solent, Southwick, Lee-on-Solent, Lossiemouth, Ilchester, 849. '073-E'. 12-93
☐	XS417		Lightning T.5	ex Binbrook, LTF, 5, 11, 5, 11, LTF, 56, 23, 11, 23, 226 OCU. 12-93
☐	XT200		Sioux AH.1	ex Middle Wallop. 12-93
☐	AR-107*		S.35XD Draken	ex Scampton, *Esk* 729, RDanAF. See notes. due
☐	83		Mystere IVA	ex Sculthorpe, French AF. '8-MS'. 12-93
☐	56321	G-BKPY	Safir	ex Norwegian AF. 12-93
☐	'5547'	19036	T-33A-1-LO	ex Sculthorpe, French AF. 12-93

☐	42223		F-100D-16-NA	ex Sculthorpe, French AF.	12-93
☐		BAPC.20	Lee Richards rep	ex *Those Magnificent Men*. Stored.	12-93
☐	*	BAPC.43	HM.14 *Flea*	ex East Kirkby, Tattershall, Wellingore. Arrived 9-3-94.	03-94
☐	*	BAPC.101	HM.14 *Flea*	ex Tumby Woodside, East Kirkby, Tattershall, Sleaford. Fuselage. Arrived 9-3-94.	03-94
☐		BAPC.183	Zurowski ZP.1	ex Burton-on-Trent. Homebuilt helicopter, unflown. Polish colours.	12-93

■ **Newark Gliding Club** : Since arrival circa 1990, an SF-27MB has been under slow restoration in the hangar.

☐	G-BSUM*		Scheibe SF-27MB	ex D-KIBE. Restoration.	03-93

WORKSOP
The Gnat kept by a collector here was put up for sale in mid-1993 and it travelled to Ipswich, Suffolk, by January 1994..

Oxfordshire

ABINGDON AIRFIELD (north west of Abingdon)
■ **RAF Abingdon** : Is no more... By July 1992 the base had adopted an uncanny emptiness — with great respect to the Army who have taken over (it is now called Dalton Barracks) and thankfully have held a series of exercises here. Once a haven for many **W&R** airframes, this narrative constitutes a listing of what-went-where and doubtless **W&R15** will do a 'rounding-up' exercise. Last aircraft to leave was Hunter T.7 XL569 bound for East Midlands Airport during March 1993.

    The RAF Exhibition Flight and the Aircraft Salvage & Transportation Flight left the base by June 1992, moving to St Athan, S Glam. There, they were 'contractorised' as of December 1, 1992, and are now operated by SERCO, out of St Athan, S Glam, with the following known to have made the move :— Spitfire XVI 'X4277'/TB382 and 'X4474'/TE311; Lightning F.1 nose XM191; Buccaneer S.1 nose XN962; 'plastic' Hawk T.1s 'XX263'/BAPC.152 and 'XX297'/BAPC.171; Gazelle HT.3 XX396; 'plastic' Jaguar GR.1 'XX718'/BAPC.150 and 'XZ363'/BAPC.151; Jaguar GR.1 nose XX753/9087M; Harrier GR.3 nose XZ135; Tornado GR.1 'ZA446'/BAPC.155; 'ZD472'/BAPC.191 'plastic' Harrier GR.5 and the travelling 'Nimrod' G-ALYW. Hunter FGA.9 nose XE643 moved to Belfast, Northern Ireland, to join the 'detachment' there. Unaccounted for are the following :— Canberra T.4 nose WJ876; Canberra B.2 WK146; Hunter F.4 nose XE670; Jet Provost T.3 nose XN137; Jet Provost T.3 nose XN503; Phantom FG.1 nose XT595; Buccaneer S.2 XV338/8774M;

    Of the other myriad airframes here, disposals etc have been as follows. Please note that in many cases an exact fate cannot be tied down and in the absence of a 'forwarding address' or confirmed scrapping details the reader should *assume* scrapping. These are listed by type :—
Buccaneer : S.2A XT274/8856M dismantled during 1-90 and moved to Pendine, Dyfed, on 23-1-90; S.2A XT284/8855M to St Athan, S Glam, 8-92; S.2C XV337/8852M to St Athan, S Glam, early 8-92; S.2A XV357 nose, last noted 2-90.
Canberra : B.2 WH869/8515M scrapped 4-92; B.2 WJ678/8864M sectioned by early 11-89, forward fuselage removed on a low-loader 6-11-89 to Pendine, Dyfed, remainder thought scrapped; T.19 XA536/8605M last noted 3-92 when the hulk was scrapped.
Harrier : GR.3 XV740/8989M nose section removed (scrapped or left the base?) 5-92, remainder scrapped 7-92; GR.3 XV753 no details — was it *ever* here?; GR.3 XV784/8909M noseless hulk, last noted 9-90, certainly gone by 5-91 (nose at Boscombe Down, Wilts); GR.3 XV810/9038M to Kemble, Glos, by 5-92; GR.1 cockpit marked '4 Spare Ser 41H-769733' and the other, 'FL-R-41H-725624' to Stafford, Staffs, where they were tendered during November 1992. Both were acquired by the ever-active Hanningfield Metals of Stock, Essex. '4 Spare Ser 41H-769733' went to Market Drayton, Salop, by 5-93; the other went to Stock, Essex.
Hawk : T.1 XX344/8847M to Farnborough, Hants, 29-7-92.
Hunter : F.5 WP185/7583M up for tender 3-92, left 7-92 — where did this go to?; T.7 XL569/8833M up for tender 3-92 and to East Midlands Airport, Leics, 3-93.

Jaguar : GR.1 XX115/8821M grizzly remains on the dump until removed during 3-92; GR.1 XX977/9132M last noted, in dismantled form, 7-92. It moved to St Athan, S Glam, by 22-7-92.
Jet Provost : T.5 XW298/9013M scrapped 5-92 and moved to Stock, Essex.
MiG-21PF : 1304 exported to the USA 4-92.
Nimrod : AEW.3 XV259, gutted fuselage departed by road 15-10-91 — destination?; AEW.3 XV262/8986M scrapped 4-92; AEW.3 XZ280 scrapped 4-92; AEW.3 XZ281 scrapped 11-92; AEW.3 XZ283 scrapped 11-92; AEW.3 XZ285 scrapped 5-92; AEW.3 XZ287 to Stafford, Staffs, 7-5-92.
Phantom : FG.1 XT863 last noted whole 3-91, at least the nose to Cowes, IoW, by 10-92. **Note** : The yard at Cowes certainly handled all of the Nimrod scrap and may have been the 'beneficiary' of the entire scrap contract for the base.
Spitfire : Mk IX MK356/5690M to St Athan, S Glam, by 7-91, via transient store at Wroughton, Wilts.
Super VC-10 : ZD243 by road to Filton, Avon, as spares for the K.4 programme, 6-92.
Tornado : Not noted in **W&R13**, four cockpit sections and/or mock-ups where here. Two ADV noses, one 'covered', the other skeletal arrived at the BDRF site 4-91. Former removed by road late 3-92, latter scrapped 4-92. IDS nose (said to be ex *Luftwaffe*) arrived around 8-91, no other details. Sections of GR.1 ZD710 (which crashed on take-off from here 14-9-89) lingered until scrapped 5-92 — although the nose may have moved through to St Athan, S Glam.
Wessex : HU.5 XT773/9123M last noted 2-92, moved to St Athan, S Glam, by 6-92.
Whirlwind : HAS.7 XK943/8796M cleared from the dump 3-92..

ARNCOTT (south of the A41 south east of Bicester)
Restoration of the Auster is thought to continue in the area.

☐ G-ASEF	Auster 6A	ex Somerton, Bicester, RAFGSA, VW985, 664. CoA expired 19-12-66.

BENSON AIRFIELD (east of the A423, east of Wallingford)
■ **RAF Benson** : As the new Headquarters of 1 Group, (it was at Upavon, Wilts) Benson has received a *second* gate guardian, in the form of a Harrier. Contrary to **W&R13**, the very battered and sectioned hulk of Avro 748MF G-ARRV was still to be found on the dump as late as February/March 1993, when they were removed to a scrapyard in Portsmouth (said to be 'Wells', a new one?). This leaves in doubt just how much went to Egham, Surrey. Wessex HC.2 XR509/8752M was joined on the dump by HU.5 XS241 by July 1992 and both were carted away during December 1992. As an aside, a local resident objected to the raspberry ripple scheme on XS241 and it was repainted a dark brown! John Bradshaw's Fury ISS N36SF '361' flew in here from Wroughton, Wilts, August 1, 1992 and remains based.

☐ 'EN343'	BAPC.226	Spitfire replica	gate.	12-93
☐ XN126	8655M	W'wind HAR.10	ex Halton, 2 FTS, Queens Flt. 'N'. BDR.	12-93
☐ XS642	8785M	Andover C.1	ex Kemble, 84, SAR Flt, 84. Dump.	12-93
☐ XZ971*		Harrier GR.3	ex HOCU, 1417F, 233 OCU. 'U' Gate. Assembled 1-12-93.	12-93

BICESTER AERODROME (on the A421 north east of Bicester)
■ **RAF Gliding and Soaring Association** : The future of the airfield is somewhat uncertain as the USAF withdraws from Upper Heyford, which uses the site for storage. In recent issues Chipmunks have dominated the **W&R** airframes listed here. Now, gliders appear to be taking the more logical dominance. Chipmunk T.10s WB556 and WG300 (the former engine test-bed) have not been noted for some time and are thought to have been scrapped. **W&R** has overlooked a 'spares-ship' here, rectified below. The hulk of Aztec 250B G-ASRI (which donated its engines to the *Supermunk* programme) may have gone to Witney Technical College, Oxon, several years ago — confirmation appreciated.

☐ EVU*	BGA.2994	Doppelraab	frame. Stored. First noted 10-91.	06-93
☐ FCC*	BGA.3145	Cadet TX.3	ex XN243. Stored. First noted 10-91.	03-92
☐ *		Cadet TX.3	Stored. First noted 3-92.	03-92
☐ WB645*	8218M ntu	Chipmunk T.10	ex Cottesmore SF, Edn UAS, 8 FTS, 1 CAACU, 17 RFS, 1 RFS. Here since at least 3-82! (SOC 25-9-72) Spares.	12-92

☐ WG303	8208M	Chipmunk T.10	ex Shawbury, Kemble, Gatow SF, Wittering SF, Marham SF, Bir UAS, 5 RFS, 2 BFTS. RAFGSA engine test-bed.	08-93
☐ WZ829*		Grasshopper TX.1	ex Launceston. Stored. First noted 3-92.	06-93

BRIZE NORTON AIRFIELD (on the A4095 south west of Witney)

■ **RAF Brize Norton** : Making a 're-entry' in this edition is the former Gulf-Air VC-10 ZD493, which survives on the dump, albeit as an ever-stripped fuselage. Hunter F.1 WT684 has been incorporated into the FR.10 composite being put together at <u>Long Marston</u>, Warks. A Victor K.2 flew in to join the dump on November 11, 1993.

☐ XL164*	8819M	Victor K.2	ex 55, 57, 55, 57, MoA. Flew in 11-11-93.	11-93
☐ XS479	8819M	Wessex HU.5	ex Wroughton, 845. JATE.	
☐ XT486	8919M	Wessex HU.5	ex Wroughton, 845. JATE.	06-93
☐ XT677	8016M	Wessex HC.2	ex Lyneham, Thorney Island, 18. Crashed 25-4-68. Dump.	9-91
☐ (ZD232)	8699M	Super VC-10	ex Heathrow, G-ASGD, BA, BOAC. Fuselage. MoD(PE) trials.	06-93
☐ (ZD234)	8700M	Super VC-10	ex Heathrow, G-ASGF, BA, BOAC. Nose with 241 OCU as tanker simulator.	
☐ (ZD493)		VC-10 1101	ex Heathrow, G-ARVJ, Gulf-Air, BA, BOAC. Fuselage, dump. See notes above.	06-93

■ **Air Movements School** (AMS) : AMS have their eyes on one of the soon-to-be-retired Hercules C.1Ks, this would replace the Andover for loading and centre-of-gravity training. Sioux AH.1 XT141 was written out of **W&R13**, but is still to be found with AMS, albeit in poor state.

☐ XS598		Andover C.1	ex Andover CU, Andover SF, HS, A&AEE. Crashed 5-7-67. Fuselage.	10-93
☐ XT141	8509M	Sioux AH.1	ex Middle Wallop. See notes above.	10-93
☐ XV118*	9141M	Scout AH.1	ex Wroughton, 657, 658, 652, 651, 660. 'T'. Arrived 3-4-92.	04-93
☐ XX914	8777M	VC-10 1103	ex RAE Bedford, G-ATDJ, 9G-ABQ ntu, G-ATDJ Fuselage.	10-93
☐ XZ994*	9170M	Harrier GR.3	ex St Athan, 1417F, 233 OCU, 1417F, 233 OCU. 'O'. First noted 4-93.	04-93

CHALGROVE AIRFIELD (on the B480 north west of Watlington)

■ **Martin Baker** : WL419 *Asterix* continues to act as a flying test-bed for MB. T.7 WA662 was disposed of and moved to <u>Willington</u>, Derbyshire, by late 1992. The exact status of the remaining Meteor airframe cache held here in support of '419 is not confirmed.

☐ WA638		Meteor T.7(mod)	ex ETPS, RAE. Spares.	07-92
☐ WL405		Meteor T.7	ex Farnborough, BCCS, 1 GCF, 231 OCU, Wittering SF, JCU, Hemswell CF. Spares.	07-92
☐ WL419		Meteor T.7(mod) ▲	ex 85, 13 GCF, CFE, 233 OCU.	09-93

CULHAM (on the A415 south east of Abingdon)

■ **UKAEA, Lightning Studies Unit** : Still have their Hunter GA.11 airframe.

☐ WV381		Hunter GA.11	ex Kemble, FRADU, FRU, FWS, 222. '732-VL'. Fuselage.	01-94

ENSTONE AERODROME (on the B4030 east of Chipping Norton)

Considerable changes here. Both of the Pawnees listed in **W&R13** (G-AVPY and G-AXBD) are thought to have been scrapped. There is certainly no trace of them. The well-established Terrier and Blanik have been joined by a handful of light aircraft, all awaiting various fates. Most interesting arrival was the Fraser Aviation Anson C.21 WD413/G-BFIR which flew down from Strathallan, Tayside, via a spell at Tees-Side Airport, Cleveland, by December 1992 It fled to <u>Lee-on-Solent,</u> Hants, on October 21, 1993.. Blanik CAW/BGA.1397 which had been held here for spares, was last noted during August 1991.

☐ G-ASCH		Terrier 2	ex Fakenham, Hinton-in-the-Hedges, Enstone, VF565, 654, 12 ILF, 1912F, 652. CoA expired 20-7-81. Restoration.	06-90
☐ G-AVGJ*		SAN DR.1050	ex F-BJYJ. CoA expired 22-4-85. Stored in roof. First noted 10-92.	10-92
☐ G-BBRY*		Cessna 210	ex Cranfield, Blackbushe, Chessington, 5Y-KRZ, VP-KRZ, N7391E. Under long term rebuild. First noted 10-92.	07-93

FARINGDON

Noted in September 1993 at *Magpie's Emporium* here was the nose and cabin section of an early Piper Apache, marked as 'G-IRIS'. Further sightings and comments appreciated! (See under Hullavington, Wilts, for a possible candidate.)

KIDLINGTON (on the A423 north of Oxford)

■ **Julian Mitchell** & **Stephen Arnold** : The pair continue to work on their high quality restoration of a salvaged Spitfire, using as many original parts from others as possible. Stephen also took on the cockpit of a Hunter F.6 during 1993.

☐ BL370		Spitfire V	ex Humber Estuary, 53 OTU, 64, 118, 350, 610, 130, 124, 130. SOC 30-3-44. Restn.	
☐ XF383*	8706M	Hunter F.6	ex North Scarle, Wittering, Kemble, 12, 216, 237 OCU, 4 FTS, 229 OCU, 65, 111, 263. Nose. Arrived by mid-1993.	03-94

OXFORD

■ **C W Engineering** : The status of the Spitfire project here is unconfirmed.

☐ SM520		Spitfire IX	ex Snake Valley, Pretoria, SAAF. Restn.	04-90

OXFORD AIRPORT (or Kidlington)

■ **Oxford Air Training School** : The Ground Training School lost the fuselage of Cessna 421 G-SHOE in an interesting career move to <u>Southampton Airport,</u> Hants, by July 1993, to join the dump there. A Jet Provost T.3A, previously flogging the circuit at Linton, joined the 'fleet' by March 1993. Of the rotorcraft with the GTS, Brantly B.2A G-ASEW was noted as "dynamic parts only" and Enstrom F.28A G-BBVI as "rotorhead/mast/gearbox only" by September 1992 so can be deleted.

☐ G-ARJR		Apache 160G	ex N4447P. CoA expired 24-10-78.	07-93
☐ G-ARMA		Apache 160G	ex N4448P. CoA expired 22-7-77.	07-93
☐ G-AVBU		Cherokee Six	crashed 28-2-81. Fuselage.	
☐ G-BDBZ		W'wind HAR.10	ex Luton, XJ398, Culdrose, RAE Bedford, ETPS, Weston-super-Mare, DH Engines, A&AEE, XD768 ntu.	07-93
☐ G-BFSK		Apache 160	ex OO-NVC, OO-HVL, OO-PIP.	07-93
☐ XN500*		Jet Provost T.3A	ex 1 FTS, 7 FTS, RAFC, 3 FTS, RAFC. '48'. Arrived 26-1-93.	07-93
☐ XT175		Sioux AH.1	ex TAD175, Middle Wallop.	07-93

■ **Others** : The forlorn Cessna 411 EI-BCT was registered as G-BVGC during November 1993 and is thought to have left, probably with air under its wings.

SHOTTESWELL (off the A41 north of Banbury)

Long-termer Cessna 170B G-BCLS moved to the Tees-side area for overhaul by June 1991.

SHRIVENHAM (on the A420 north east of Swindon)

■ **Royal Military College of Science** : A somewhat surprising leap was made in technology here when a Harrier GR.3 arrived during April 1993, apparently for display. It is not known if the Scout is still present.

☐ XT621		Scout AH.1	ex Wroughton, 655, 656, 666, 664, 666.	
☐ XV744*	9167M	Harrier GR.3	ex St Athan, 233 OCU, 1, 233 OCU. Arrived 4-93. See notes above. '3K'.	04-93

UPPER HEYFORD AIRFIELD (north of the B4030, north of Oxford)

■ **USAF Upper Heyford** : Another base now a thing of the past... The F-111s have gone and the airfield is rapidly scaling down. The Mysteres here continued to provide amusement to the very end. A visit during February 1993 revealed all four as present, but now numbered as 'EA55', '014', '033' and one too shy for any form of identity! One was also sprouting a new modification — a carphone aerial! A scrapdealer in Crediton, Devon, successfully tendered for all four Mysteres (36, 46, 127 and 129) and F-4C 37449, all moving on by March 1994. Midland Air Museum moved the MiG-killer Phantom 37699 to Coventry Airport, Warks, by road on October 7, 1993. F-105 24428, PoW/MIA memorial, and the former gate guard F-100 '63000'/42212 both moved to Croughton, Northants by August 1993.

WITNEY

■ **Reynard Racing Cars Ltd** : Spitfire XVIII SM845/G-BUOS moved to Audley End, Essex, in early 1994. Airworthy Spitfire VIII MT719/G-VIII has been sold in the USA and flies there as N719MT.

■ **Witney Technical College** : See under Bicester, Oxon, for a possible inmate here.

Shropshire

BATTLEFIELD (on the A49 north of Shrewsbury)

■ **John Dowly** : The scrapyard here *may* still have hulk of Vampire T.11 XH274.

☐ XH274	Vampire T.11	ex Telford, Ternhill, Shawbury, CATCS, 8 FTS, 4 FTS, 8 FTS. Hulk.	04-91

BRIDGNORTH

■ **Derek Leek** : Has acquired a Canberra nose to go with his Vampire variety..

☐ WD935* 8440M	Canberra B.2	ex Ottershaw, Egham, St Athan, 360, 97, 151, CSE, EE, BCDU, RAAF A84-1 ntu. Nose. Arr 12-1-94.	01-94
☐ XH330	Vampire T.11	ex Bushey, London Colney, Chester, Woodford, Chester, Shawbury, RAFC. '76'. Wings from WZ576.	01-94

CHETWYND AERODROME

■ **Staffordshire Sports Skydiving Club** : Keep their para-trainer on the airfield.

☐ G-ATIE	Cessna 150F	ex Market Drayton, N6291R. Cr 28-7-79.	06-91

COSFORD AIRFIELD (south of Junction 3 of the M54)

■ **Aerospace Museum** : The already huge collection of airframes and artefacts here has continued to expand, particularly in the 'heavy metal' category. The latest, and most impressive, catalogue, defines the Museum as being "four-in-one":— the Research & Development Collection, the Transport Aircraft Collection, the Missile Collection and the Warplane Collection (and there's also an extensive engine collection). Adding to the British Airways collection was a BAC One-Eleven during December 1992. On November 30, 1993, Victor K.2 XH672 completed the type's last ever flight when it touched down at nearby Shawbury. It was due to arrive by road here in February 1994 — Cosford's 3,700ft runway 06/24 being too short with no over-runs available to safely take a Mk 2 Victor. The arrival of the K.2 means almost certainly that B.1A XH592 is doomed. Another last-ever flight, this time comfortably possible at Cosford, was of the former Farnborough Varsity, on July 27, 1992. It replaced WF408, which went by road to Northolt. The arrival of the *Flea* from St Athan, S Glam, brings almost to an end the migration from that base. Restoration programmes continue on the 'fleet', the most ambitious involving the Mitsubishi *Dinah* which included sponsorship from the present-day Mitsubishi. Work started in August 1992, with the fuselage being undertaken by the resident 2 SoTT (as then was, see below). Other work (including the painting) was carried out at Cardington and St

Athan and the wings were contracted to Trent Aero at East Midlands Airport, Leics. Continuing the RAF Museum's refreshing policy of loaning aircraft out to other museums, the T-33A has gone to Midland Air Museum at Coventry Airport and the record-breaking Hunter and Meteor to the Tangmere Military Aviation Museum. The latter will be receiving the Fury replica during 1994.

Aerospace Museum airframes can be found out on loan as follows :— ❏ Brooklands, Viking G-AGRU. ❏ Coventry, Meteor WS838, T-33A 51-7473. ❏ Manchester, Shackleton WR960. ❏ Tangmere, Meteor EE549, Fury replica 'K7271' (due to move),Hunter WB188.

Departures have been as follows :— Meteor IV special EE549/7008M to <u>Tangmere</u>, W Sussex, September 19, 1992; Hawker P.1067 WB188/7154M to <u>Tangmere</u>, W Sussex, on September 19, 1992; Varsity T.1 WF408/8395M left by road for <u>Northolt</u>, Gtr Lon, on October 8, 1992; Canberra B(I).8 WT346/8197M was put up for tender during March 1992 and was acquired by the RNZAF Museum, emigrating during February 1993; T-33A 17473 to <u>Coventry Airport</u>, Warks, on October 26, 1993.

◆ Open daily 10am to 5pm with the exception of Xmas and New Year, last admission 4pm. Annual airshow in which several Museum aircraft (and others from the SOTT) not normally outside, are given an 'airing'— for 1994 this will be on June 19. Near to Junction 3 of the M54 and well signposted. ✉ Aerospace Museum, Cosford, Shifnal, Shropshire. TF11 8UP. ☎ 0902 374112 or '374872. **Fax** 0902 374813.

❏ G-AEEH*		HM.14 *Flea*	ex St Athan, Colerne, Bath, Whitchurch. Arrived by 12-92.	12-93
❏ 'G-AFAP'	T2B-272	CASA 352L	ex Spanish AF T2B-272. British Airways (the original lot!) colours.	12-93
❏ G-AIZE		Argus II	ex Henlow, Hanwell, N9996F, 43-14601. CoA expired 6-8-66. Stored.	12-93
❏ 'G-AJOV'	WP495	Dragonfly HR.3	ex Biggin Hill, Banstead, Warnham, Wimbledon. BEA colours. On loan.	12-93
❏ G-AMOG		Viscount 701	ex Cardiff-Wales, BOAC, Cambrian, BEA *Robert Falcon Scott*, G-AMNZ ntu. BEA colours. CoA expired 14-6-77.	12-93
❏ G-AOVF		Britannia 312F	ex Southend, 9Q-CAZ, G-AOVF, Stansted, Donaldson, British Eagle, BOAC. BOAC c/s.	12-93
❏ G-APAS	8351M	Comet 1XB	ex Shawbury, XM823, G-APAS, Air France, F-BGNZ, G-5-23. BOAC colours.	12-93
❏ G-APFJ		Boeing 707-436	ex British Airtours. BOAC. CoA exp 16-2-82. Airtours colours.	12-93
❏ G-ARPH		Trident 1C	ex BA, BEA. CoA exp 8-9-82. BA colours.	12-93
❏ G-ARVM		VC-10 Srs 1101	ex BA, BOAC. CoA exp 5-8-80. BA c/s.	12-93
❏ G-AVMO*		BAC 111-510ED	ex Bournemouth, BA, BEA. Flew in 29-12-92. *Lothian Region*.	12-93
❏ K4972*	1764M	Hart Trainer	ex Cardington, Hendon, St Athan, Carlisle, 2 FTS	06-92
❏ 'K7271'	BAPC.148	Fury II replica	Stored by 1-93. See notes above.	12-93
❏ DG202/G	5758M	F.9/40 Meteor	ex Yatesbury, Locking, Moreton Valance. Prototype Meteor.	12-93
❏ HS503	BAPC.108	Swordfish IV	ex Henlow, Canada. Stored.	12-93
❏ 'KG374'	KN645	Dakota IV	8355M, ex Colerne, AFN CF, MinTech, AFN CF, MinTech, AFN HQ, SHAPE CF, Malta CF, BAFO CS, 2nd TAF CS, 44-77003. 'YS'.	12-93
❏ KN751		B-24L-20-FO	ex Colerne, Indian AF 6 Sqn HE807, RAF KN751, 99.	12-93
❏ MT847	6960M	Spitfire XIV	ex Weeton, Middleton St George, Freckleton, Warton, 226 OCU, A&AEE. 'AX-H'.	12-93
❏ RF398	8376M	Lincoln B.2	ex Henlow, Abingdon, CSE, BCBS.	12-93
❏ TA639	7806M	Mosquito TT.35	ex CFS, 3 CAACU, Aldergrove TT Flt.	12-93
❏ TG511	8554M	Hastings T.5	ex 230 OCU, SCBS, BCBS, 202, 47.	12-93
❏ TS798		York C.1	ex 'MW100', Shawbury, Brize Norton, Staverton, 'LV633', G-AGNV, Skyways, BOAC, TS798 ntu. CoA expired 6-3-65.	12-93

☐	TX214	7817M	Anson C.19	ex Henlow, HCCS, MCS, RCCF, Staff College CF, 1 FU, 16 FU. 12-93
☐	VP952	8820M	Devon C.2/2	ex St Athan, 207, 21, WCS, SCS, Upavon SF, TCCF, MCS, BCCS, HCCS, A&AEE, MCCF, AAFCE, TCCF, Hendon SF, HS. 12-93
☐	VX461	7646M	Vampire FB.5	ex Henlow, Hendon, 8 FTS, 16, 26. Stored. 12-93
☐	VX573	8389M	Valetta C.3	ex Henlow, Wildenrath CF, Buckeburg CF. *Lorelei*. Stored. 12-93
☐	WA634		Meteor T.7(mod)	ex St Athan, Martin Baker. 12-93
☐	WD931		Canberra B.2	ex Aldridge, Pershore, RRE, RAE. Nose. 12-93
☐	WE600	7602M	Auster C4	ex St Athan, Swinderby, Finningley, Trans-Antarctic Expedition, 663. 12-93
☐	WE982	8781M	Prefect TX.1	ex Cardington, Henlow, Syerston, Manston, ACCGS, CGS, 1 GC, 621 GS, 612 GS, 644 GS, 643 GS, 166 GS, 143 GS. 12-93
☐	WG760	7755M	EE P.1A	ex Binbrook, Henlow, Bicester, St Athan, Warton, A&AEE. 12-93
☐	WG768	8005M	Short SB.5	ex Topcliffe, Finningley, ETPS, RAE Bedford, RAE Farnborough, A&AEE, RAE-Bedford, A&AEE. 12-93
☐	WG777	7986M	Fairey FD-2	ex Topcliffe, Finningley, RAE Bedford. 12-93
☐	WK935	7869M	Meteor F.8(mod)	ex St Athan, Colerne, RAE. Prone-pilot . 12-93
☐	WL679*	9155M	Varsity T.1	ex Farnborough, RAE, BLEU. Flew in 27-7-92. 12-93
☐	WL732		Sea Balliol T.21	ex Henlow, A&AEE, Lossiemouth, Anthorn. 12-93
☐	WP912	8467M	Chipmunk T.10	ex Hendon, Kemble, Man UAS, RAFC, ITS, Cam UAS, CFS, 2 FTS, Lon UAS, FTCCS, HCCS, 8 FTS. 12-93
☐	WV562	7606M	Provost T.1	ex Cranwell, Henlow, 22 FTS. 'P-C'. Stored. 12-93
☐	WV746	8938M	Pembroke C.1	ex 60, 207, 21, WCS, TCCF, FTCCS, BCCS, HS, 2 TAF CF. 12-93
☐	WZ744	7932M	Avro 707C	ex Topcliffe, Finningley, RAE, Avros. 12-93
☐	XA564	7464M	Javelin FAW.1	ex 2 SoTT, Locking, Filton. 12-93
☐	XA893	8591M	Vulcan B.1	ex Abingdon, Bicester, A&AEE, Avro. Nose. 12-93
☐	XD145		SARO SR.53	ex Brize Norton, Henlow, Westcott, A&AEE. 12-93
☐	XD674	7570M	Jet Provost T.1	ex St Athan, Swinderby, Finningley, 71 MU, Percivals. 12-93
☐	XF785	7648M	Bristol 173 Srs 1	ex Henlow, G-ALBN. Stored. 12-93
☐	XF926	8368M	Bristol T.188	ex Foulness Island, RAE, A&AEE. 12-93
☐	XG337	8056M	Lightning F.1	ex 2 SoTT, Warton, A&AEE, Warton. 12-93
☐	XH171*	8746M	Canberra PR.9	ex 2 SoTT, 39, 13, 39 MoA, 58. 12-93
☐	XH592	8429M	Victor B.1A	ex 2 SoTT, St Athan, 232 OCU, TTF, 232 OCU, Honington Wing, 15. See notes above. 12-93
☐	XH672*		Victor K.2	ex Shawbury, 55, 57, 543, MoA. See notes. Due
☐	XJ389		Jet Gyrodyne	ex Southampton, G-AJJP, XD759, makers. Stored. 12-93
☐	XJ918	8190M	Sycamore HR.14	ex 2 SoTT, 32, MCS, Kemble, Wroughton, 110, Seletar, A&AEE, 275. 12-93
☐	XK724	7715M	Gnat F.1	ex Cranwell, Bicester, Henlow, Follands. 12-93
☐	XL703	8034M	Pioneer CC.1	ex Manchester, Henlow, 209, 230. 12-93
☐	XL993	8388M	Twin Pioneer CC.1	ex Henlow, Shawbury, 21, 78. 12-93
☐	XM555	8027M	Skeeter AOP.12	ex Shawbury, Ternhill, CFS, HQ BAOR, 654. Stored. 12-93
☐	XM598	8778M	Vulcan B.2	ex 44, Wadd Wing, Cott Wing, 12. 12-93
☐	XN714		Hunting 126	ex RAE Bedford, NASA Ames and Moffett, Holme-on-Spalding Moor, RAE. 12-93
☐	XP299	8726M	W'wind HAR.10	ex 22, 230, 1563F, Queen's Flt, 230, CFS, MoA. Queen's Flt c/s. 12-93

☐ XP411	8442M	Argosy C.1	ex 2 SoTT, 6 FTS, Kemble, 70.	12-93
☐ XR220	7933M	TSR-2 XO-2	ex Henlow, A&AEE. Never flown.	12-93
☐ XR371		Belfast C.1	ex Hucknall, Kemble, 53. *Enceladus*.	12-93
☐ XR977	8640M	Gnat T.1	ex 2 SoTT, Red Arrows, 4 FTS. *Reds* c/s.	12-93
☐ XW547*	9169M	Buccaneer S.2B	ex Shawbury, 9095M, Gulf Det, 12, 237 OCU, 208, 12, 216, 12, 237 OCU, 12. *Guinness Girl/ Pauline/The Macallan*. Pink c/s. Arr 20-1-93.	12-93
☐ 8469M		Fa 330A-1	ex Henlow, Farnborough.	12-93
☐ 8476M	BAPC.83	Ki 100-1b	ex St Athan, Cosford, Henlow, Biggin Hill, Fulbeck, Wroughton, Stanmore, Sealand.	12-93
☐ 8486M	BAPC.99	Ohka 11	ex St Athan, Cosford, Westcott.	12-93
☐ 8583M	BAPC.94	Fi 103 (V-1)	—	12-93
☐		P.1121	ex Henlow, Cranfield. Sections. Stored.	12-93
☐ A-515	ZD485	FMA Pucara	ex A&AEE, Yeovilton, Stanley Airport, Argentine AF A-515.	12-93
☐ L-866	8466M	PBY-6A	ex Colerne, Danish AF ESK.721, 82-866, BuNo 63993.	12-93
☐ 112372	8482M	Me 262A-2a	ex St Athan, Cosford, Finningley, Gaydon, Cranwell, Farn'gh, VK893/AM.51, I/KG.51.	12-93
☐ 191614	8481M	Me 163B-1a	ex Biggin Hill, Westcott, Brize Norton, Farnborough, Hussum, II/JG.400.	12-93
☐ 420430	8483M	Me 410A-1-U2	ex St Athan, Cosford, Fulbeck, Wroughton, Stanmore Park, Brize Norton, Farnborough, AM.72, Vaerlose. '3U+CC'.	12-93
☐ 475081	7362M	Fi 156C-7	ex St Athan, Coltishall, Bircham Newton, Finningley, Fulbeck, VP546, AM.101, Farnborough, 'RR+KE', 'GM+AK'.	12-93
☐ 5439	8484M	Ki 46 *Dinah*	BAPC.84, ex St Athan, Biggin Hill, Fulbeck, Wroughton, Stanmore Park, Sealand, Tebrau, ATAIU-SEA. Restoration started 8-92. See notes above.	12-93
☐ 204		SP-2H Neptune	ex Dutch Navy 320 Sqn, Valkenburg, 5 Sqn, 321 Sqn.	12-93
☐ 6130	AJ469	Ventura II	ex SAAF Museum, SAAF. Stored.	12-93
☐ J-1704		Venom FB.4	ex Greenham Common and Swiss Air Force.	12-93
☐ '6771'	FU-6	F-84F-51-RE	ex Rochester, Southend, Belgian AF, USAF 52-7133. Stored.	12-93

■ **1 School of Technical Training** (SoTT) - **Weapons School** (WS) : With the demise of Halton, Bucks, the No 1 'numberplate' has been bestowed on the School here. The main event in the airframe 'fleet' here has been the arrival of *JP* T.5s and the beginning of the end for the T.3s. The Canberras are no more, all having been disposed of as another major era comes to a close. Going back to **W&R13**, Canberra PR.7 WT532 did not gravitate to Bruntingthorpe. Instead, it turned up as spares at Bournemouth Airport, Dorset.

Disposals have been as follows :— Canberra PR.7 WH775/8868M had gone by April 1993, turning up at Bruntingthorpe, Leics; as a nose only, the rest scrapped on site;, B.2 WJ640/8722M was up for tender April 1991 and moved to Henfield, W Sussex; Canberra B.15 WH984/8101M was up for tender during October 1991 and gone by April 1993, again to Bruntingthorpe, Leics, as a nose only, the rest scrapped on site; Canberra PR.9 XH136/8782M was up for tender during October 1991. It was dismantled by January 1993 with the nose going to Bruntingthorpe, Leics, by April 1993; PR.9 XH171/8746M was transferred to the Aerospace Museum, see above; Victor B.1A XH593/8428M is an example of how tenacious an entry can be, this machine being scrapped during 1987!; Jet Provost T.3 XM367/8083M, XN594/8077M and T.3A XN636/9045M had all gone by April 1993; Whirlwind HAR.10 XP338/8647M had gone by April 1993, *possibly* to Pounds' at Portsmouth, Hants; Buccaneer S.2A XT277/8853M was in external store by April 1993 and the nose was spirited to Bruntingthorpe, Leics, by October 1993; Wessex HU.5 XT466/8921M had also left by April 1993. It is thought that 17 *JP*s from here have been acquired by Global Aviation — see under Binbrook, Lincs. *JP* XN586 is reported earmarked for Brooklands, Surrey. All this makes the current situation as follows :—

☐	XM349	9046M	Jet Provost T.3A	ex CFS, RAFC, CFS, 2 FTS, A&AEE. 'T'.	04-93
☐	XM351	8078M	Jet Provost T.3	ex Halton, Shawbury, 3 FTS, 7 FTS, 2 FTS. 'Y'. For disposal.	04-93
☐	XM403	9048M	Jet Provost T.3A	ex CFS, 1 FTS, 2 FTS. 'V'.	04-93
☐	XM455	8960M	Jet Provost T.3A	ex CFS, 3 FTS, CFS, 1 FTS, 3 FTS, RAFC. 'K'.	04-93
☐	XM471	8968M	Jet Provost T.3A	ex 7 FTS, 1 FTS, CFS, 3 FTS, 2 FTS, RAFC, 6 FTS, CFS. '93'.	04-93
☐	XN472	8959M	Jet Provost T.3A	ex 7 FTS, 1 FTS, 3 FTS, 7 FTS, CFS. '86'.	04-93
☐	XN492	8079M	Jet Provost T.3	ex Halton, 6 FTS, RAFC. Crated by 4-93.	04-93
☐	XN501	8958M	Jet Provost T.3A	ex CFS, 1 FTS. 'G'.	04-93
☐	XN577	8956M	Jet Provost T.3A	ex 7 FTS, 1 FTS, 7 FTS, RAFC. '83'.	04-93
☐	XN582	8957M	Jet Provost T.3A	ex 7 FTS, 1 FTS, 3 FTS, RAFC. '95'.	04-93
☐	XN586	9039M	Jet Provost T.3A	ex 7 FTS, 1 FTS, CFS, 2 FTS, RAFC. '91'. See notes above.	04-93
☐	XN593	8988M	Jet Provost T.3A	ex 7 FTS, 1 FTS, 2 FTS. '97'.	06-93
☐	XN640	9016M	Jet Provost T.3A	ex Church Fenton, 7 FTS, RAFC, 3 FTS, CFS, 6 FTS. '99'.	04-93
☐	XP547	8992M	Jet Provost T.4	ex 1 TWU, SoRF, CATCS, RAFC, A&AEE.	04-93
☐	XR679	8991M	Jet Provost T.4	ex 1 TWU, SoRF, CAW, 3 CAACU, CAW, RAFC. '04'.	04-93
☐	XS178	8994M	Jet Provost T.4	ex 1 TWU, CATCS, RAFC, 7 FTS, CFS. '05'.	06-93
☐	XS219	8993M	Jet Provost T.4	ex 1 TWU, CATCS, CAW. '06'.	04-93
☐	XS641*	9198M	Andover C.1(PR)	ex Shawbury, 60, 115, 46, 84, SAR Flt, 84. F/n 6-93..	06-93
☐	XS793*	9178M	Andover CC.2	ex Northolt, CinC RAFG, 60, 32, QF, 152, 21, MECCF, Abingdon CF. Arrived 2-93.	06-93
☐	XV752	9078M	Harrier GR.3	ex 4, 3, 1, 233 OCU, 1, 233 OCU. 'B'.	06-93
☐	XW290*	9199M	Jet Provost T.5A	ex Shawbury, 3 FTS, RAFC, CFS. '41'.	01-94
☐	XW304*	9172M	Jet Provost T.5	ex 6 FTS, CFS, 1 FTS. 'X'. F/n 4-93.	06-93
☐	XW309*	9179M	Jet Provost T.5	ex Shawbury, 6 FTS, 1 FTS. 'V'. F/n 4-93.	04-93
☐	XW311*	9180M	Jet Provost T.5	ex Shawbury 6 FTS. 'W'. First noted 6-93.	06-93
☐	XW321*	9154M	Jet Provost T.5A	ex Shawbury, 1 FTS, 7 FTS, RAFC, 3 FTS. '62'. First noted 4-93.	06-93
☐	XW328*	9177M	Jet Provost T.5A	ex 1 FTS, RAFC, CFS, RAFC. '76'. First noted 4-93.	06-93
☐	XW358*	9181M	Jet Provost T.5A	ex Shawbury, 1 FTS, RAFC. '59'. First noted 4-93.	04-93
☐	XW360*	9153M	Jet Provost T.5A	ex Shawbury, 1 FTS, RAFC, 7 FTS. '61'. Arrived 15-6-93.	06-93
☐	XW364*	9188M	Jet Provost T.5A	ex Shawbury, 3 FTS, RAFC, CFS, 1 FTS. '35'. Arrived by 6-93.	06-93
☐	XW405*	9187M	Jet Provost T.5A	ex Shawbury, 6 FTS, 1 FTS, 7 FTS, 6 FTS, 1 FTS, RAFC. 'J'. Arrived by 6-93.	06-93
☐	XW410*	9125M	Jet Provost T.5A	ex Shawbury, 1 FTS, RAFC, 3 FTS. '80'. First noted 4-93.	06-93
☐	XW418*	9173M	Jet Provost T.5A	ex Shawbury, 1 FTS, 7 FTS, CFS, 3 FTS, Leeming SF, 3 FTS. First noted 4-93.	04-93
☐	XW430*	9176M	Jet Provost T.5A	ex 1 FTS, CFS, 3 FTS, Leeming SF, 3 FTS. '77'. First noted 4-93.	04-93
☐	XW432*	9127M	Jet Provost T.5A	ex Shawbury, 1 FTS, Leeming SF, 3 FTS. '76'. First noted 4-93.	06-93
☐	XW544	8857M	Buccaneer S.2C	ex Shawbury, 16, 15. 'Y'.	06-93
☐	XX110	8955M	Jaguar GR.1	ex Shawbury, 6, A&AEE, BAC. 'EP'.	06-93
☐	XX140	9008M	Jaguar T.2	ex Shawbury, 226 OCU, 54, JOCU. 'D'.	04-93
☐	XX727	8951M	Jaguar GR.1	ex Shawbury, 6, 54, 6, JOCU. 'ER'.	06-93
☐	XX730	8952M	Jaguar GR.1	ex Shawbury, 6, JOCU. 'EC'.	04-93

☐ XX751	8937M	Jaguar GR.1	ex 226 OCU, 14. '10'.	04-93
☐ XX756	8899M	Jaguar GR.1	ex 14, 41, 14, 20, 226 OCU, 14. 'AM'.	06-93
☐ XX819	8923M	Jaguar GR.1	ex Shawbury, 20, 17. 'CE'.	06-93
☐ XX826	9021M	Jaguar GR.1	ex Shawbury, 2, 20, 14. '34'.	04-93
☐ XX844	9023M	Jaguar T.2	ex CIT Cranfield, 226 OCU, 17, 31. 'F'.	06-93
☐ XX948	8879M	Tornado P.06	ex WS, Warton. 'P'. 617 Sqn colours.	04-93
☐ XX958	9022M	Jaguar GR.1	ex Shawbury, 17, 14. 'BK'.	04-93
☐ XX959	8953M	Jaguar GR.1	ex Shawbury, 20, 14. 'CJ'.	06-93
☐ XX967	9006M	Jaguar GR.1	ex Shawbury, 14, 31. (Wings of XX837) 'AC'.	06-93
☐ XX968	9007M	Jaguar GR.1	ex Shawbury, 14, 31. 'AJ'	06-93
☐ XX969	8897M	Jaguar GR.1	ex 226 OCU, 3, 17, 31, 14, 31. '01'.	06-93
☐ XZ130	9079M	Harrier GR.3	ex 4, 3, 233 OCU, 3, 1453F, 1, 4, 20. 'A'.	06-93
☐ XZ368	8900M	Jaguar GR.1	ex Coltishall, 14, 41, 14, 6, 14. 'AG'.	06-93
☐ XZ370	9004M	Jaguar GR.1	ex Shawbury, 17. 'JB'.	06-93
☐ XZ371	8907M	Jaguar GR.1	ex WS, Shawbury, 14, 17. 'AP'.	04-93
☐ XZ374	9005M	Jaguar GR.1	ex Shawbury, 14, 20. 'JC'.	06-93
☐ XZ383	8901M	Jaguar GR.1	ex Coltishall, 14, 41, 54, 14, 226 OCU, 14, 17. 'AF'.	06-93
☐ XZ384	8954M	Jaguar GR.1	ex Shawbury, 17, 31, 20. 'BC'.	06-93
☐ XZ390	9003M	Jaguar GR.1	ex Shawbury, 2, 20, 31. '35'.	06-93

■ **PT Flight** : Care of the CO of RAF Cosford, bob Mitchell's PT Flight is based here. (See also Sutton Coldfield, W Mids.) They are not available for inspection as such, but are 'regulars' on the airshow circuit.

☐ N1344*	PT-22 Recruit ▲	ex 41-20877.	01-94
☐ N49272*	PT-23-HO ▲	ex USAAF. '23'.	01-94
☐ N56421*	PT-22 Recruit ▲	ex 41-15510. '855'.	01-94
☐ N58566*	BT-15 Valiant ▲	ex USAAF.	01-94

■ **Others** : The Hunter is still displayed on the parade ground. Meteor F.8 G-METE is under restoration for Adrian Gjertsen of Jet Heritage — see under Bournemouth Airport, Dorset. Most interesting is the wrecked fuselage of a T.31 in Air Cadet 'raspberry ripple' red and white hung as a 'trophy' inside the clubhouse of the Wrekin Gliding Club/RAFGSA.

☐ VZ467	G-METE	Meteor F.8	ex Scampton, Shawbury, 1 TWU, 229 OCU, 500, 54, A&AEE. Restoration to fly.	11-93
☐ XG225	8713M	Hunter F.6A	ex Weapons School, 2 SoTT, Kemble, 229 OCU, 92, 74, 20. 'S'. On parade ground.	06-93
☐ *		T-31 (?)	see notes above. First noted 8-91.	06-93

■ **Locally** : Dumped in a field near Junction 3 of the M54 motorway is a Vampire hulk, used as a 'set-piece' for a war-gaming group.

☐ XE993	8161M	Vampire T.11	ex Cosford, 8, 73. See notes above.	01-93

LUDLOW

In the area, the Comper Swift and Brochet Pipistrelle are still under restoration. Tiger Moth G-AHLT had moved to <u>Reading</u>, Berks, by August 1990.

☐ G-ABUS	Comper Swift	ex Heathfield. CoA exp 19-6-79. Restn.	
☐ G-BADV	MB.50 Pipistrelle	ex Dunkeswell, F-PBRJ. CoA expired 9-5-79. Restoration.	

MARKET DRAYTON

Under restoration here is the former Seighford, Staffs, Hunter FGA.9 nose. (See under that location for details of the nose's past.) Much work and effort has been put into the restoration, including gun pack, instrumentation etc. Also here and being restored as fully as possible — in this case including the ejector seat and HUD — is a Harrier nose (see under Abingdon, Oxon, for more details).

☐ XJ690*	G-9-451	Hunter FGA.9	ex Seighford, Macclesfield, Bittesswell, 20, 14. Nose, under restoration. See notes above.	05-93
☐ *		Harrier GR.1	ex Stafford, Abingdon, Hamble. Cockpit. '4 Spare Ser 41H-769733'. Restn. See notes.	05-93

OSWESTRY
■ **1165 Sqn, ATC** : By July 1993, the hulk of Cessna FA.150L G-AYOV could be found at Sleap, Shrop.
■ **D Higgins** : Continues to work on his Whirlwind cockpit here.
☐ XJ758   8464M   W'wind HAR.10   ex Shrewsbury, Shawbury, CFS, 230, CFS, 217,
                                        1360F, 22. Cockpit.

SHAWBURY AIRFIELD (on the B5063 north of Shawbury)
■ **Storage Site** : The storage site consists of six hangars, two on the main site and four blisters to the west. The two hangars on the main apron (east end of the airfield) act as 'reception' and/or 'departure lounge' and the other as a holding hangar ready to go to the four blisters. Jet Provosts continue to come and go. While it is true to say that many of the *JPs* listed are 'too new' in terms of delivery to store for **W&R**, they do represent the end of the line for the type and the book will doubtless be monitoring their fates for a long time to come. It is thought that some 41 *JPs* from here will go to Global Aviation— see under Binbrook, Lincs. Latest types to join the fold are Andovers and Phantoms. The Navy's Chipmunks have started to arrive, and the final examples were due in during March 1994 when the Navy paid off the type. They will likely go to auction. Departures from the site have been as follows : —
Andover C.1 : XS597 flew in 25-3-92 and XS637 arrived 2-4-92, both were entered in the London MoD auction of 8-7-93, netting £86,000 and £80,000 for their engines alone. They were ferried to Southend, Essex on 11-11-93 and 1-11-93 respectively. (See *Appendix* D.) XS641 flew in 18-6-92, but moved on to Cosford, Shrop, by 6-93.
Buccaneer S.2 : XV350 flew in from BAe Warton 28-4-93, but moved by road to East Midlands Airport, Leics, during 12-93; XW547/9169M by road to Cosford, Salop, 20-1-93. XT286, XV163 and XW534 were in the process of being scrapped during 8-93, and after a couple of satellite passes, left by road on 6-9-93. XN982, XV165 and XV869 were up for tender during 9-93 and were acquired by Hanningfield Metals, travelling to Stock, Essex during 2-94.
Chipmunk T.10 : WK511 was auctioned on July 8, 1993 (see *Appendix* D) and flew to Cranfield, Beds, for its new life with Kennet Aircraft as G-BVBT.
Hunter T.7 : XL573 was offered for tender during 9-93 and was acquired by Barry Pover, moving by road to Exeter Airport, Devon, by 12-93, becoming G-BVGH. T.7A XL613 also moved to Exeter Airport, Devon, by 12-93, but for another owner, soon also acquired by Barry. Also tendered at the same time were XL565, XL586, and XL591. All had gone by 12-93. **T.8C** : 'WT722' flew out to Bournemouth Airport and rejoined FRADU on March 4, 1993. Its departure allows mention of the fact that the aircraft is in the majority WT799! WT722 has served FRADU for some time as '878'. This 'WT722' is coded '879'. Photographic evidence shows the Hunter with the rear end of WT799, yet underwing serial is WT799 and the nose code '879'. (To add further to this one, it wore the camouflaged fin of a former RAF T.7 during much of its life at Shawbury!)
Jaguar : T.2A XX146 left by 1-92, returned to service; GR.1A XZ361 departed to St Athan and then on to Coltishall with 41 Squadron by 10-92; XZ103 to 41 Squadron as 'P' 12-6-92. GR.1A XZ366 left on 4-6-92 for 41 Squadron.
Jet Provost T.3A : The following all arrived some time during 1992 and left by road on 20-1-93 XM464, XN509, XN595, XN629, going to Colsterworth, Lincs. XN506 had arrived for storage by 6-92, but was sold in the USA 2-93. Note that Global Aviation have purchased most, if not all of the *JPs* here and they will be moving quickly — seen under Binbrook, Lincs.
Jet Provost T.5/A/B : XW290 and XW312 to Cosford, Shrop; XW332 sold in the USA early in 1993, becoming N332RC; XW334 sold in the USA early 1993; XW364 to Cosford, Shrop, by 6-93; XW405 to Cosford, Shrop, by 6-93; XW421 to Halton, Bucks; XW425 left by road 20-7-93, destination? The following had arrived on site by 2-93, only to move on to Cosford, Salop : XW309, XW311, XW321, XW358, XW410, XW418, XW432. The following were sold, all to International Air Parts, of Sydney, Australia : XW295≠, XW357, XW362≠, XW374, XW408 and XW435≠. (Those marked ≠ were not listed in **W&R13**.) The following were in store briefly, all going to the USA : XW316 as N316HC, XW332 as N332RC, XW334 as N334XW, XW373 as N373XW. During February 1994 the following were moved out of (very short term) store here to Immingham Docks for delivery to the USA, care of Global Aviation :— XW354, XW359, XW368, XW369 and XW415. XW310, XW326 and XW355 were entered into the MoD auction in London on 8-7-93 (see *Appendix* D) and are assumed to have sold — details? See under Binbrook, Lincs, for the Global Aviation mass purchase.

Lightning F.6 : XR724/G-BTSY flew to <u>Binbrook</u>, Lincs, on a special ferry flight 23-7-92.
Wessex HU.5 : XR519*, XS506 and XT451 were disposed of and all moved to the yard at <u>Stock</u>, Essex, by 3-93.

☐	LA226	7119M	Spitfire F.21	ex Abingdon, Biggin Hill, South Marston, London, South Marston, Little Rissington, 3 CAACU, 122. Stored for Bentley Priory, Gt Lon. 03-92
☐	WK574*		Chipmunk T.10	ex Yeovilton SF, BRNC, Waddington SF, Marham SF, 5 AEF, Cam UAS, Lon UAS, Cam UAS, Lon UAS, Oxf UAS, Cam UAS, Lon UAS, Hull UAS, Cam UAS, Birm UAS, Cam UAS, Bri UAS, Cam UAS, Acklington SF, Q UAS, Dur UAS, 11 FTS, 21 GCF, RAFC. Flew in 1-4-93. For tender 2-94. 02-94
☐	WK635*		Chipmunk T.10	ex Yeovilton SF, BRNC, Waddington SF, Nott UAS, Leeds UAS, Nott UAS, 16 RFS, 18 RFS. Flew in 1-4-93. 04-93
☐	WP776*		Chipmunk T.10	ex 771, Scampton SF, Lon UAS, 6 AEF, Lon UAS, Ox UAS, 1 RFS. '817-CU'. Flew in 9-7-93. 07-93
☐	WP803		Chipmunk T.10	ex 8, BRNC, Oxf UAS, 1 ANS, 6 FTS, Benson SF, Hull UAS, 15 RFS. 10-91
☐	WP809*		Chipmunk T.10	ex BRNC, 10 AEF, 61 GCF, 5 RFS, 24 RFS. First noted 2-93. '78'. 02-93
☐	WP906*		Chipmunk T.10	ex 771, Scampton SF, 6 AEF, Lon UAS, 6 AEF, Lon UAS, 22 RFS, 5 BFTS. '816-CU'. Flew in 19-3-93. 03-93
☐	WT799		Hunter T.8	ex Kemble, FRADU, FRU, 759, RAE Bedford, 4, 111. '879-VL'. 02-93
☐	WT806		Hunter GA.11	ex Abingdon, Chivenor, FRADU, CFS, 14. 02-93
☐	XF301*		Hunter GA.11	ex FRADU, 229 OCU, 43. Flew in 3-3-93. '873-VL'. 02-93
☐	XM374*		Jet Provost T.3A	ex 1 FTS, 7 FTS, RAFC, 3 FTS, CFS, 2 FTS. '18'. First noted 2-93. 02-93
☐	XM387*		Jet Provost T.3A	ex CFS, 3 FTS, 2 FTS. 'I'. F/n 3-92. 09-93
☐	XM459*		Jet Provost T.3A	ex CFS, 3 FTS, RAFC. 'F'. F/n 6-92. 02-93
☐	XN459*		Jet Provost T.3A	ex CFS, 1 FTS. 'N'. First noted 6-92. 02-93
☐	XN462*		Jet Provost T.3A	ex 1 FTS, 7 FTS, 3 FTS, CFS, 2 FTS, 1 FTS. '17'. First noted 2-93. 02-93
☐	XN502*		Jet Provost T.3A	ex CFS, 2 FTS, 1 FTS. 'D'. F/n 3-92. 02-93
☐	XN553*		Jet Provost T.3A	ex St Athan SF, 1 FTS, RAFC. Arr 23-9-92. 02-93
☐	XT896*		Phantom FGR.2	ex 74, 228 OCU, 29, 228 OCU, 19, 228 OCU. 'V'. Flew in 6-10-92. 10-93
☐	XT897*		Phantom FGR.2	ex 56, 228 OCU. 'Y'. Flew in 6-10-92. 02-93
☐	XT910*		Phantom FGR.2	ex 74, 228 OCU, 56, 228 OCU, 29, 228 OCU, 29, 2. 'O'. Flew in 6-10-92. 10-93
☐	XV433*		Phantom FGR.2	ex 74, 56, 29, 228 OCU, 29, 228 OCU, 29, 228 OCU, 41. 'E'. Arrived 6-10-92.. 02-93
☐	XV469*		Phantom FGR.2	ex 74, 56, 19, 2, 17. 'N'. Flew in 6-10-92. 02-93
☐	XV487*		Phantom FGR.2	ex 74, 19, 29, 23, 29, 56, 92, 29, 31. 'G'. Flew in 6-10-92. 10-93
☐	XW287*		Jet Provost T.5	ex 6 FTS, RAFC. 'P'. Arrived 21-9-93. 10-93
☐	XW289*		Jet Provost T.5A	ex 1 FTS, RAFC, CFS. '73'. Arr 30-9-93. 10-93
☐	XW291*		Jet Provost T.5	ex 6 FTS, RAFC, CFS. 'N'. Arr 13-4-93. 04-93
☐	XW293*		Jet Provost T.5	ex 6 FTS, CFS. 'Z'. Arr 22-6-93. 06-93
☐	XW296*		Jet Provost T.5	ex 6 FTS. 'Q'. Arrived 21-9-93. 10-93
☐	XW302*		Jet Provost T.5	ex 6 FTS, CFS, RAFC, 1 FTS. 'T'. Arrived 20-9-93. 10-93
☐	XW305		Jet Provost T.5A	ex 3 FTS, RAFC, 1 FTS. '42'. 02-93

☐	XW306*	Jet Provost T.5	ex 6 FTS, 1 FTS. 'O'. Arr 13-4-93.	04-93
☐	XW307*	Jet Provost T.5	ex 6 FTS, RAFC. 'S'. Arrived 21-9-93.	10-93
☐	XW309*	Jet Provost T.5	ex 6 FTS, 1 FTS. 'V'. Arr 5-5-93.	05-93
☐	XW311*	Jet Provost T.5	ex 6 FTS. 'W'. Arr 29-10-93.	10-93
☐	XW313*	Jet Provost T.5A	ex 1 FTS, RAFC, 1 FTS. '85'. F/n 10-93.	10-93
☐	XW317*	Jet Provost T.5A	ex 1 FTS, RAFC, CFS, RAFC, CFS, 3 FTS. '79'. First noted 6-92.	09-93
☐	XW319*	Jet Provost T.5A	ex 1 FTS, CFS, 3 FTS, Leeming SF, 3 FTS. '76'. First noted 10-93.	10-93
☐	XW322*	Jet Provost T.5B	ex 6 FTS, RAFC, MoD(PE), RAFC. 'D'. Arrived 23-6-93.	06-93
☐	XW324*	Jet Provost T.5	ex 6 FTS, 3 FTS. 'U'. Arr 21-7-93.	07-93
☐	XW325*	Jet Provost T.5B	ex 6 FTS, RAFC, 3 FTS. 'E'. Arr 3-2-93.	02-93
☐	XW336*	Jet Provost T.5A	ex 1 FTS, RAFC. '67'. Arrived 22-9-93.	10-93
☐	XW372	Jet Provost T.5A	ex 6 FTS, 7 FTS, CFS, 7 FTS, 1 FTS, RAFC. 'M'.	02-93
☐	XW412*	Jet Provost T.5A	ex 1 FTS, RAFC. '74'. Arrived 22-9-93.	10-93
☐	XW422	Jet Provost T.5A	ex 3 FTS, RAFC, 1 FTS, RAFC. '3'.	02-93
☐	XW423	Jet Provost T.5A	ex 3 FTS, RAFC, 1 FTS, Leeming SF, 3 FTS. '14'.	02-93
☐	XW429*	Jet Provost T.5B	ex 6 FTS, 1 FTS, RAFC, Leeming SF, 3 FTS. Blue colour scheme. Arrived 21-1-93.	10-93
☐	XW431*	Jet Provost T.5B	ex 6 FTS, CFS, 3 FTS, Leeming SF, 3 FTS. 'A'. Arrived 25-5-93.	05-93
☐	XW433*	Jet Provost T.5A	ex CFS, 7 FTS, 3 FTS, Leeming SF, 3 FTS. '63'. First noted 6-92.	02-93
☐	XW438*	Jet Provost T.5B	ex 6 FTS, RAFC. 'B'. Arr 13-5-93.	05-93
☐	XX112*	Jaguar GR.1A	ex 6, 54, A&AEE. 'EC'. First noted 6-92.	10-93
☐	XX304	Hawk T.1A	ex Red Arrows. Cat 4 24-6-88. Hulk.	10-93
☐	XX720*	Jaguar GR.1A	ex 6, ETPS, 54, SEPECAT. 'EN'. F/n 2-93.	10-93
☐	XX724	Jaguar GR.1A	ex 54, 14, 54, JOCU. 'GA'.	02-93
☐	XX729*	Jaguar GR.1A	ex 54, 226 OCU, 6, 54, 6, JOCU. 'FC'. First noted 2-93.	10-93
☐	XX737	Jaguar GR.1A	ex 54, Indian AF JI015, 6, 54, 226 OCU, 54, 226 OCU. 'GG'.	02-93
☐	XX738	Jaguar GR.1A	ex 54, Indian AF JI016, 54, 6, JOCU. 'GJ'.	10-93
☐	XX832	Jaguar T.2	ex 226 OCU, ETPS, 226 OCU. 'S'.	10-93
☐	XX836	Jaguar T.2A	ex 6, 17, 14, 226 OCU, 14.	02-93
☐	XX838	Jaguar T.2A	ex 226 OCU, 17, 226 OCU. 'X'.	02-93
☐	XX840	Jaguar T.2	ex 41, 2, 226 OCU, 17. 'X'.	02-93
☐	XX955	Jaguar GR.1A	ex 54, 14, 17, 14. 'GK'.	02-93
☐	XZ111*	Jaguar GR.1A	ex 6, 2. 'EL'. Arrived 7-9-93.	10-93
☐	XZ378	Jaguar GR.1A	ex 6, 41, 17, 41, 20. 'EP'.	02-93
☐	XZ392	Jaguar GR.1A	ex 54, 20, 31.	02-93
☐	XZ400*	Jaguar GR.1A	ex 6, 54. 'EG'. First noted 6-92.	10-93

■ **Others** : The dump and the gate have changed little. Wessex HU.5 XS506 arrived on February 19, 1991, for instructional purposes, but was moved on to the Storage Site (see above) by the following February. The nose of Canberra T.19 WH724 had gone from the dump by October 1991.

☐	XM927	8814M	Wessex HAS.3	ex Wroughton. Dump.	10-93
☐	XN549	'8235M'	Jet Provost T.3	8225M, ex Halton, Shawbury, 1 FTS, CFS. Dump.	10-93
☐	XP351	8672M	W'wind HAR.10	ex BDR, 2 FTS, SAR Wing, 22. 'Z'. Gate.	10-93

SLEAP AERODROME (south west of Wem)

By July 1993 the former 1165 Squadron ATC Cessna hulk had re-appeared here.

☐	G-AYOV*	FA.150L	ex Oswestry, Sleap. Crashed 11-2-79. Cockpit. First noted 7-93.	07-93

TILSTOCK AERODROME (on the A41 south of Whitchurch)
Another location struggling to keep going as a place to fly from. The para-trainer Cessna is located on the aerodrome.

☐ G-ASNN Cessna 182F ex N3612U. Crashed 5-1-85. Para-trainer. 06-93

Somerset

BURNHAM-ON-SEA
■ **Air Scouts** : The local Air Scouts seem to be well ahead of the times. They have the forward fuselage of a Pilatus PC-9 — almost certainly a mock-up — in RAF red and white scheme at their premises.

☐ * Pilatus PC-9 forward fuselage. See notes above. 06-93

HENSTRIDGE AERODROME (south of the A30, east of Henstridge Marsh)
Planning permission is awaited on a scheme to make an airfield with houses-and-hangars for those with well-hung bank balances. The store of aircraft has expanded. The Taylorcraft Plus D, stored off-site has not been *physically* reported for some time.

☐ G-AHSD	T'craft Plus D	ex Wincanton, LB323, 310, 48 GCS, 656, 652, 654. CoA expired 10-9-62. Stored, off-site. See notes above.	
☐ G-AISC	Tipsy B Srs 1	ex Yeovil area. CoA exp 23-5-79. Restn.	01-91
☐ G-ALYG	Auster 5D	ex Charlton Mackrell, London Airport, Irby-on-Humber, MS968, 661, 653. CoA expired 19-1-70. Stored.	10-93
☐ G-ANEW	Tiger Moth	ex NM138, Oxf UAS, 8 RFS, 29 EFTS. CoA expired 18-6-62. Stored.	10-93
☐ G-ARJD	Colt 108	crashed 17-11-71. Frame. Stored.	
☐ G-BBKF*	Cessna FRA.150L	CoA expired 13-6-91. Stored.	08-93
☐ G-BPCY*	Seneca 200T II	ex Compton Abbas, N381BB, N3059Y. Damaged 17-9-91. Wreck. First noted 8-93.	08-93
☐ NC2612*	Stinson Junior SR	restoration. First noted 4-90.	11-93

WELLS
■ **1955 Squadron ATC** : Still keep their incorrectly marked Chipmunk in Webbs Close.

☐ 'WD355' WD335 Chipmunk T.10 ex Dur UAS, Oxf UAS, G&S UAS, Not UAS, Lon UAS, G&S UAS, Abn UAS, StA UAS, G&S UAS, 11 RFS, 23 RFS.

YEOVIL AIRFIELD (to the west of Yeovil)
■ **Westland Aerospace** : The three WG.30s are thought still to be stored and have been joined by others, all variously outside or inside depending on space needs. It could be that still *more* WG.30s will materialise here in the future. The Wessex lost from Sherborne, Dorset, came here. Lynx AH.7 XZ671 arrived here from Wroughton, Wilts on March 2, 1989, for use as an AH.9 rig but left for Fleetlands, Hants, by April 1993 as a stripped out cabin. Overlooked for some time is Sikorsky YUH-60A Blackhawk N4050S used for apprentice training and installation trials. Planned for production of the type at Yeovil has still to materialise. Westland continue to support the excellent International Helicopter Museum at Weston-super-Mare, Avon. Arriving during October 1993 was Whirlwind HAS.7 XG596 for restoration — details under Weston.

☐ G-BIWY	WG.30-100	ex Sherborne. CoA exp 30-3-86. Stored.	06-91
☐ G-BKGD*	WG.30-100	ex Penzance, G-BKBJ ntu. CoA expired 6-7-93. First noted 3-93. Stored.	03-93
☐ G-BKKI	WG.30-100	CoA expired 28-6-85. Stored.	06-91
☐ G-ELEC	WG.30-200	ex G-BKNV. CoA exp 28-6-85. Stored.	
☐ G-KATE*	WG.30-100	ex Penzance, Beccles, Great Yarmouth, BIH. CoA expired16-9-88. F/n 5-93. Stored.	05-93

☐ G-OGAS*	WG.30-100	ex Penzance, Beccles, Great Yarmouth, BIH, G-17-1, G-OGAS, G-BKNW. CoA expired 19-5-88. First noted 5-93. Stored.	05-93
☐ N4050S*	YUH-60A	ex Sikorsky. See notes above.	03-93
☐ XR526* 8147M	Wessex HC.2	ex Sherborne, Farnborough, Odiham, 72. Damaged 27-5-70. See notes above.	

YEOVILTON AIRFIELD (on the B5131, south of the A303, north of Yeovil)
■ **Fleet Air Arm Museum** (FAAM) : This exceptional museum continues to grow and to expand the ways it tells the story of naval aviation. On July 27, 1993 the Korean War exhibition was opened, featuring the Lim-2 (repainted in North Korean markings), the MiG-killing Sea Fury, the Firefly and the Dragonfly. Due to open during 1994 is the awesome *Carrier* exhibition which will give visitors the 'feel' of being on a large aircraft carrier and will allow much of the 'heavy metal' previously in storage to be put on display again. For some time the FAAM have had use of an off-site store at Houndstone, but this MoD facility was flogged off during 1993 and the airframes held here moved to <u>Wroughton</u>, Wilts, as follows : — Benson G-AZAZ on December 17, 1993; an anonymous Super Eagle hang glider was in store at Houndstone by July 1993, it moved December 21, 1993. Fa 300A-1 100545 arrived from Higher Blagdon, Devon, on May 19, 1992, but moved on to Wroughton, Wilts, on August 25-1993. The arrival of Wessex HU.5 XS508 from Lee-on-Solent on June 28, 1993 was also a milestone in its own way, '508 having been the last operational Wessex in FAA service. Barracuda II DP872 returned from the workshops at Andover, Hants, by September 1992. Restoration has been suspended for now, for a variety of reasons, not least of which is cash. The forward fuselage has gone back on display as a fund raiser. The rear fuselage and other components can be found at Wroughton, Wilts. There is but one out-of-museum departure to record and that is by way of a 'tidy-up'. The MB.339A noted at <u>Filton</u>, Avon, is now confirmed as the FAAM's former Argentinian 0767 and is heavily involved in the *T-Bird* II JPATS programme. It is still technically on loan from the FAAM.

FAAM aircraft can be found at the following locations:
☐ Cardiff-Wales Airport, S Glam, Gannet XG883, Meteor WM292. ☐ Coventry Airport, Warks, Gannet XA508. ☐ Crawley, W Sussex, Meteor T.7 WS103, P.531 XN334. ☐ East Fortune, Lothian, Whirlwind XG594. ☐ Filton, Avon, MB.339A 0767. ☐ Fleetlands, Hants, Sea Vixen XJ481. ☐ Helston, Corn, Skyraider WV106, Wasp XT427. ☐ Lee-on-Solent, Hants, P.1052 VX272, S.510 VV106. ☐ Montrose Tayside, Sea Hawk XE340. ☐ Weston-super-Mare, Avon, Dragonfly VZ962. ☐ Wroughton, Wilts, still used as FAAM store; various airframes. And, a little further away, Scimitar F.1 XD220 on the USS *Intrepid* in New York!
◆ Open every day (other than Xmas) March to October 10am to 5.30pm and November to February 10am to 4.30pm. ✉ FAAM, RNAS Yeovilton, Ilchester, Somerset, BA22 8HT. ☎ 0935 840 565.
Fax 0935 840181

☐ 'G-ABUL' XL717	Tiger Moth	ex G-AOXG, T7291, 33 MU, 24 EFTS, 19 EFTS.	02-94
☐ G-BSST	Concorde 002	UK prototype, ff 9-4-69. CoA exp 30-10-74.	02-94
☐ 8359	Short 184	ex Duxford, South Lambeth. Forward fuselage. IWM loan.	02-94
☐ 'B6401' G-AWYY	Camel replica	ex Leisure Sport, N1917H, G-AWYY. CoA expired 1-9-85.	02-94
☐ L2301	Walrus I	ex Arbroath, Thame, G-AIZG, Aer Lingus EI-ACC, IAAC N18, L2301.	02-94
☐ L2940	Skua I	ex Lake Grotli, Norway, 800. Remains.	02-94
☐ N1854	Fulmar II	ex Lossiemouth, Fairey's *hack* G-AIBE, A&AEE. CoA expired 6-7-59.	02-94
☐ 'N2078'	Sopwith Baby	ex Nash Collection. Comp. of 8214 & 8215.	02-94
☐ 'N2276' N5903	Gladiator II	ex 'N5226', Old Warden, 61 OTU. Shuttleworth loan.	02-94
☐ 'N4389' N4172	Albacore	ex Land's End, Yeovilton. '4M'.	02-94
☐ 'N5492' BAPC.111	Sopwith Triplane	ex Chertsey. *Black Maria*. 10 (Naval) Sqn, 'B' Flight colours. Static replica.	02-94
☐ 'N6452' G-BIAU	Pup replica	ex Whitehall. CoA expired 13-9-89.	02-94
☐ 'P4139' HS618	Swordfish II	ex 'W5984', Manadon A2001, Donibristle.	02-94

☐	AL246		Martlet I	ex Loughborough, 768, 802.	02-94
☐	DP872*		Barracuda II	ex Andover area, Yeovilton, Northern Ireland. Forward fuse. Arr by 9-92. See notes.	02-94
☐	EX976		Harvard IIA	ex Portuguese AF 1657, EX976, 41-33959.	02-94
☐	KD431		Corsair IV	ex Cranfield, 716, 731. 'E2-M'.	02-94
☐	KE209		Hellcat II	ex Lossie, Stretton, Anthorn, BuNo 79779.	02-94
☐	LZ551/G		Sea Vampire I	ex CS(A), DH, A&AEE, RAE. ScM loan.	02-94
☐	SX137		Seafire F.17	ex Culdrose, 'W9132', Stretton, 759, 1831, Culham.	02-94
☐	VH127*		Firefly TT.4	ex Wroughton, Yeovilton, Culdrose, FRU, 700, 737, 812. Arrived 20-5-92, on display 7-93.	02-94
☐	VR137		Wyvern TF.1	ex Cranfield. Eagle-powered prototype, never flown. Stored by 2-94.	02-94
☐	WA473		Attacker	ex Abbotsinch, 736, 702, 800. '102-J'. Stored.	02-94
☐	WG774		BAC 221	ex East Fortune, RAE Bedford, Filton.	02-94
☐	WJ231*		Sea Fury FB.11	ex Wroughton, Yeovilton 'WE726', Yeovilton SF, FRU. '115-O'. Returned 30-7-91. Repainted and on display 7-93.	02-94
☐	WN493		Dragonfly HR.5	ex Culdrose, 705, 701, A&AEE.	02-94
☐	WT121		Skyraider AEW.1	ex Culdrose, 849, USN 124121. Stored.	02-94
☐	WV856		Sea Hawk FGA.6	ex RAE, 781, 806.	02-94
☐	WW138		Sea Ven FAW.22	ex AWS, 831, 809. '227-Z', Suez stripes.	02-94
☐	XA127		Sea Vampire T.22	ex CIFE, 736. Pod. Stored.	02-94
☐	XB446		Avenger AS.4	ex Culdrose SF, 831, 751, 820, USN 69502. Stored during 1993.	02-94
☐	XB480	A2577	Hiller HT.1	ex Manadon, 705. '537'. Stored 1994.	02-94
☐	XD317		Scimitar F.1	ex FRU, RAE, 800, 736, 807. '112'.	02-94
☐	XG574	A2575	Whirlwind HAR.3	ex Wroughton, Lee-on-Solent, 771.	02-94
☐	XG900		Short SC.1	ex Wroughton, Hayes, South Kensington, RAE Bedford. Science Museum loan.	02-94
☐	XJ314		R-R Thrust Rig	ex East Fortune, Strathallan, Hayes, South Kensington, RAE. Science Museum loan.	02-94
☐	XK488		Buccaneer S.1	ex BSE Filton and Blackburns.	02-94
☐	XL503		Gannet AEW.3	ex RRE, 849 'D', 'A' Flts, A&AEE, 849 HQ Flt, C(A), 849 'A' Flt. '070-E'.	02-94
☐	XN332*	A2579	SARO P.531	ex Wroughton, Yeovilton, Manadon, G-APNV. Arr 24-9-91 via Finningley (see under Wroughton, Wilts). Stored.	07-93
☐	XN957		Buccaneer S.1	ex 736, 809. '630-LM'. Stored from 1994.	02-94
☐	XP142		Wessex HAS.3	ex 737. *Humphrey*. Stored from 1994.	02-94
☐	XP841		HP.115	ex Cosford, Colerne, RAE Bedford.	02-94
☐	XP980	A2700	P.1127	ex Culdrose, Tarrant Rushton, RAE Bedford, Cranwell, A&AEE.	02-94
☐	XS508*		Wessex HU.5	ex Lee-on-Solent, Wroughton. Arr 28-6-93.	02-94
☐	XS527		Wasp HAS.1	ex Wroughton, *Endurance* Flt.	02-94
☐	XS590		Sea Vixen FAW.2	ex 899, 892.	02-94
☐	XT176		Sioux AH.1	ex Coypool, 3 CBAS. 'U'. Stored 1994.	02-94
☐	XT596		Phantom FG.1	ex BAe Scampton, Holme-on-S Moor, RAE Thurleigh, Holme, Filton, Hucknall, Patuxent River, Edwards. Dbr 11-10-74.	02-94
☐	XT769*		Wessex HU.5	ex Lee-on-Solent, Wroughton, Culdrose, 771, 846, 848. '823-CU'. Arrived 7-9-93.	09-93
☐	XV333*		Buccaneer S.2B	ex 208, 12, 15, 16, FAA, 237 OCU, 12. Flew in 23-3-94.	03-94
☐			Fairey IIIF	fuselage frame.	02-94
☐	*		Sea Vixen	cockpit section. Stored.	07-93

☐	*	Vampire	ex Tinwald Downs. Pod only. Single-seater. Arrived 1992. 11-93
☐	A-522 8768M	FMA Pucara	ex St Athan, Stanley, Argentine AF. Stored. 02-94
☐	AE-422	UH-1H Iroquois	ex Wroughton, Yeovilton, Stanley, Argentine Army, 74-22520. 07-93
☐	0729	T-34C-1	ex Stanley, Pebble Island, Argentine Navy. '411'. Stored from 1994. 02-94
☐	'S.3398' G-BFYO	SPAD XIII rep	ex Land's End, Chertsey, D-EOWM. CoA expired 21-6-82. 02-94
☐	'D.5397' G-BFXL	Albatros D.Va rep	ex Leisure Sport, Land's End, Chertsey, D-EGKO. CoA expired 5-11-91. 02-94
☐	'102 /17' BAPC.88	Fokker Dr I replica	scale replica, based on a Lawrence Parasol. 02-94
☐	15-1585 BAPC.58	Ohka 11	ex Hayes, South Kensington. ScM loan. 02-94
☐	01420 G-BMZF	MiG 15bis / Lim-2	ex North Weald, Gamston, Retford, Polish AF. North Korean colours. 02-94
☐	155848	F-4S-MC	ex VMFA-232, USMC. 'WT'. 02-94
☐	159233	AV-8A-MC	ex VMA-231, USMC. '33-CG'. 02-94
☐	BAPC.149	Short S.27 replica	ex Lee-on-Solent. Stored. 02-94

■ **Royal Navy Historic Flight** (RNHF) : Major news with the Flight is the arrival of the *second* flyable Swordfish, following hand-over at Brough, Humbs, on May 22, 1993. It has already been busy on the show circuit. Going back to **W&R13**, the wreckage of Sea Fury T.20S WG655 was sold in the USA, becoming N20MD. The former Boscombe Down Sea Fury T.20S has arrived and restoration work to bring it to flying condition continues. RNHF used BRNC Chipmunk T.10 WK608 '906' for conversion training at times during 1993. As with BBMF, RNHF has a *hack* Chipmunk T.10, this is listed for the first time.

◆ Not available for public inspection at Yeovilton, but are frequent attenders at airshows all over the country.

☐	W5856* G-BMGC	Swordfish II Δ	ex Brough, Strathallan, Alabama, RCN, Wroughton, Manston. 810 Sqn c/s 'A2A'. Handed over 22-5-93. 07-93
☐	LS326	Swordfish II Δ	ex Westlands, Fairey G-AJVH, Worthy Down, 836. 'L2'. 07-93
☐	VR930 8382M	Sea Fury FB.11	ex Boscombe Down, Lee-on-Solent, Wroughton, Yeovilton, Colerne, Dunsfold, FRU, Lossiemouth, Anthorn, 801, Anthorn, 802. Stored. 07-93
☐	VZ345*	Sea Fury T.20S	ex Boscombe Down, DLB D-CATA, D-FATA, ES.8503, G-9-30, Hawkers, Dunsfold, VZ345, 1832. Accident 19-4-85. Arrived 24-11-92. For restoration. 07-93
☐	WB271	Firefly AS.5 Δ	ex RAN Nowra, 723, 725, 816/817, 814. '204-R'. 07-93
☐	WK608*	Chipmunk T.10 Δ	ex BRNC, Bri UAS, 7 FTS, 3 FTS, Edin UAS, 11 RFS. RNHF *hack*. See notes above. 01-94
☐	WV908 8154M	Sea Hawk FGA.6	ex Culdrose SF, Halton, Sydenham A2660, 738, 806, 898, 807. '188-A'. Stored. 07-93

■ **Others** : Sea Heron XM296 was stored at Yeovilton following retirement on December 18, 1989 until July 27, 1993, when she upped and flew away to Gloucestershire Airport for onward transit to the USA. Sea Vixen FAW.2 XN692 has been usurped on the gate by a Harrier GR.3 suitably modded with a glass fibre nose to 'Sea' Harrier status. The Engineering Training School (ETS) has taken on a Sea King HAS.6. The dump continues to have quite an appetite for airframes, although it actually consumes very few, the bulk being long-termers. Latest type to join is a Scout AH.1 The nose of Canberra B.2 WJ677 moved to Culdrose, Cornwall, on December 15, 1992.

☐	WP309	Sea Prince T.1	ex 750, Arbroath SF. '570-CU'. Dump. 12-93
☐	XD219	Scimitar F.1	ex Foulness, Farnborough, West Freugh, Brawdy, FRU, 736, A&AEE. Fuselage. Dump. 12-93
☐	XE369 A2633	Sea Hawk FGA.6	ex Culdrose, Lee-on-Solent A2580, Halton 8158M, Arbroath. '5'. Fuselage. Dump, poor state. 12-93
☐	XM845 A2682	Wessex HAS.1	ex Lee-on-Solent, Wroughton. Dump, poor state.

☐ XN308	A2605	Whirlwind HAS.7	ex Corsham, Lee-on-Solent, Wroughton, Lee-on-Solent, Arbroath, 771, 847, 848, 846, 814. '510-PO'. Dump. 12-93
☐ XN692	A2624	Sea Vix FAW.2	ex Culdrose, 893. Removed from FONA gate 24-7-93 and placed into store. 12-93
☐ XP157*	A2680	Wessex HAS.1	ex Lee-on-Solent, Wroughton. 'AN'. Arrived 3-11-92. Dump. 12-93
☐ XS128	A2670	Wessex HAS.1	ex Lee-on-Solent, 737. '437'. BDR. 12-93
☐ XS881*	A2675	Wessex HAS.1	ex Wroughton, FAAM, Yeovilton, Culdrose. '046-CU'. Arrived by 7-93. 12-93
☐ XT453*		Wessex HU.5	ex Lee-on-Solent, 845. 'A'. Arr 13-9-93. 09-93
☐ XT637*		Scout AH.1	ex Wroughton, 657, Garrison Air Sqn, 657, 656, 659, 665, 653, 663. Pod only. Arrived 27-7-92. Fire dump. 12-92
☐ XV277		Harrier GR.1	ex Filton, HSA. ETS. 12-93
☐ XV280		Harrier GR.1	ex Foulness, Boscombe Down, A&AEE, HSA. Nose, done up Sea Harrier style. Fire section, non destructive. 12-93
☐ XV755		Harrier GR.3	ex 233 OCU, 3, 233 OCU, 3, 233 OCU, 1, 233 OCU, 1, 233 OCU. 'M'. Rescue trainer. 12-93
☐ XV760*		Harrier GR.3	ex Culdrose, St Athan, 3, 4, 233 OCU. 'K'. Arrived 30-9-92. Mods to nose to render it a 'Sea' Harrier. On gate by 11-92. 12-93
☐ XZ129		Harrier GR.3	ex Cranfield, 233 OCU, 1, 233 OCU, 1, 233 OCU. 'ETS'. ETS. 12-93
☐ ZD631*		Sea King HAS.6	ex Fleetlands, Lee-on-Solent, 814. Crashed 10-9-91. '266-N'. Arr by 1-93. ETS. 12-93

Staffordshire

BOBBINGTON (between the A458 and B4176, east of Bridgnorth)
Long term store for the 'forgotten' Kensinger KF G-ASSV and a whole host of Le Vier Cosmic Wind airframe spares and components. The Kensinger went to <u>Tonbridge</u>, Kent, by September 1992, the Cosmic Wind components — not large enough to constitute an airframe — to Kings Cliffe, Northants.

BURNTWOOD
Lightning F.1A XM144/8417M is reported to have been scrapped here during January 1994. Status of the Canberra and Vulcan nose is unknown.

☐ WT520	8184M	Canberra PR.7	ex Swinderby, 8094M, CAW, 31, 17, 31, 17, 31, 80. Nose. 11-91
☐ XM652		Vulcan B.2	ex Sheffield, Waddington, 50, 35, 44, 9. Nose.

CANNOCK
■ **Keith Jones** : Is working on installing *original* instrumentation, fittings etc into a glassfibre Spitfire IX fuselage. Work is coming along well and Keith intends to finish the project with wings, tail feathers etc. This is not to be confused with the one at North Weald, Essex.

☐ 'EN398'*		Spitfire IX replica	fuselage only. 'JE-J'. 05-93

ECCLESHALL
■ **Malcolm Goosey** : The Tiger Moth under restoration here has yet to have its identity established, but it is *not* G-ANFC!

☐ 'G-ANFC'		Tiger Moth	ex Hadfield, London Colney, Dunstable. See above.

HALFPENNY GREEN AERODROME (south of the B4176, east of Bridgnorth)
The hulk of Duchess G-BOJT had been removed by July 1992. This leaves the long-serving T.31 with the local Air Scouts.
☐ BYS   BGA.1346 T.31   ex Bickmarsh, RAFGSA.297. wfu 1-79.

LICHFIELD
■ **1206 Squadron ATC** : Keep a *Chippax* in Cherry Orchard Road, near the City railway station. 'Parent' is Stafford.
☐ WK576   8357M   Chipmunk T.10   ex AOTS, 3/4 CAACU, Cam UAS, Oxf UAS,
                                          Lon UAS, Cam UAS, Lon UAS, Cam UAS, Hull
                                          UAS, Cam UAS, Bir UAS, Cam UAS, 22 RFS.
                                          PAX trainer.
■ **Phil Cartwright** : Former Cranfield Auster AOP.9 XP283 continues its restoration.
☐ XP283   7859M   Auster AOP.9   ex Cranfield, Shoreham, Middle Wallop, 654.
                                          Frame.   04-90
■ **Others** : Confirming **W&R13**, the fuselage of Gannet AEW.3 XL471 was broken up at a scrapyard on the former airfield site. It was reduced to little more than a centre section by February 1988. The former Lutterworth, Leics, Bensen has moved to the area.
☐ G-AXCI*   Bensen B.8M   ex Lutterworth, East Midlands. Stored.   09-93

ROCESTER (on the B5030 north of Uttoxeter)
■ **J C Bamford Excavators Ltd** : During April 1993, JCB put their Dove 8 showpiece up for sale, noting it as having last flown in June 1973. In the absence of other details, it is still listed here.
☐ G-ARJB   Dove 8   ex East Midlands. CoA exp 10-12-73. See notes
                                          above.   04-93

SEIGHFORD (south of the B5405, west of Stafford)
■ **Staffordshire Aviation Heritage Collection** (SAHC) : Using part of the former airfield, now an industrial estate, SAHC established a presence here. Canberra T.4 WH840/8350M was complete in terms of having all arrived from Locking, Avon, but has yet to be fully assembled. This remains the principal project for SAHC. The Hunter that was here, as part of the moribund Staffordshire Aviation Museum, is confirmed as being a considerable *bitza*! Delivered here from Macclesfield, Cheshire, was the composite fuselage of FGA.9 XJ690 with the centre section (at least) of former Danish AF T.7 ET-271. At the same time, or around this time, the wings of former Danish AF F.51 E-424 were also here. The centre section was in a bad way and was scrapped on site. The nose of XJ690 went on to Market Drayton, Shropshire, late 1991. The wings of E-424 have since been reunited with the rest of that airframe, at Firbeck, S Yorks. (The remainder of XJ690 can be found at Bournemouth Airport, Dorset, but that's another headache...) For the record, the nose of Hunter XE650 is at Firbeck, S Yorks. To come back to the Canberra, with an apparent lack of response or interest, Universal Abrasives Ltd, upon whose site it was located, attempted to find a good home for it. This came to be in March 1994 when it was taken on by Ian Hancock who moved it to Flixton, Suffolk, and the care of the Norfolk & Suffolk Aviation Museum.

SHENSTONE (on the A5127 south of Lichfield)
The Pup continues its restoration locally.
☐ G-AVLM   Pup 160   ex Tatenhill, Nottingham Airport, Cippenham.
                                          CoA expired 24-4-69. Restoration.   04-91

STAFFORD
■ **RAF Stafford** (Beaconside): Harrier GR.3 XZ987 has supplanted the Javelin on display here. Javelin FAW.2 XA801/7739M was put up for tender during September 1993, it was removed during early February 1994, going to Stock, Essex. The Tactical Supply Wing (TSW) maintains a variety of airframes for trials and training relating to supply techniques. TSW took a second Harrier for refuelling trials and also the fuselage of a former Abingdon Nimrod AEW.3. The latter is used in various exercises staged within the base and simulates an airliner.
☐ XP359   8447M   W'wind HAR.10   ex Abingdon, RAFEF, Wroughton, 103, 110,
                                          103, 225. Fire and crash rescue training.   09-92

☐ XS491		Wessex HU.5	ex Wroughton, 845.	09-92
☐ XS572	8845M	Wasp HAS.1	ex Wroughton. Dump.	09-92
☐ XT469	8920M	Wessex HU.5	ex Wroughton. TSW, instructional.	12-92
☐ XZ287*	9140M	Nimrod AEW.3	ex Abingdon, Waddington, JTU, Woodford. Fuselage. Arr 7-5-92. TSW — see notes.	12-93
☐ XZ965*	9184M	Harrier GR.3	ex St Athan, 4, 3. 'L'. Arrived by 6-93. TSW. Refuelling trials.	06-93
☐ XZ987*		Harrier GR.3	ex St Athan, 1417 Flt, 3, 4. 'C'. Gate. Arrived by 6-93.	12-93

STOKE-ON-TRENT

■ **City Museum and Art Gallery** : The Spitfire remains the centre-piece of a display honouring local hero R J Mitchell.

◆ Open daily 10.30am to 5pm Monday to Saturday and Sundays 2pm to 5pm. ✉ City Museum and Art Gallery, Bethesda Street, Hanley, Stoke ST1 3DE. ☎ 0782 273173.

☐ RW388	6946M	Spitfire XVI	ex Kemble, 'AB917', 71 MU, 19 MU, 5 MU, Andover, Benson, FC&RS, 612, 667. 'U4-U', 667 Sqn colours.	

■ **Vintage & Rotary Wing Collection** (V&RWC) : The loss of V&RWC's main storage facility meant that a sudden re-appraisal of the collection had to be made and several airframes were disposed of. Grasshopper TX.1 XK819 at Warmingham, Ches, and Cadet TX.1 RA854 at Wigan, Gtr Man, both owned by Ken Fern, have been transferred to Nigel Ponsford — further details under each location. Nigel also took on the Chrislea Airguard G-AFIN and Grunau Baby III CBK/BGA.1410. The former moving to <u>Wigan</u>, Gtr Man, the latter to <u>Breighton</u>, Humb, by September 1993. Austin Whippet replica 'K-158' (BAPC.207) moved to NEAM at <u>Sunderland</u>, T&W, during September 1992. Skeeter AOP.12 XL811 moved to the IHM at <u>Weston-super-Mare</u>, Avon. However, as will be seen from the list below, there have been new acquisitions and new projects and the search for a more formalised museum site goes on. During October 1993, V&RWC took delivery of the former Tumby Woodside, Lincs, Aviatik C.1 replica 'C19/18' (BAPC.118) with a view to a possible rebuild. The airframe was found to have been both very poorly built and to be in bad condition. It was put out of its misery in a humane manner! Ken and team have started to build a 'proper' Albatros replica in its stead.

◆ Visits to the Stoke workshop are by prior arrangement only. ✉ V&RWC, 311 Congleton Road, Scholar Green, Stoke-on-Trent ST7 3JQ. ☎ : 0782 773140.

☐ 'G-EASQ'*	B'87	Babe III replica	ex Hemswell, Cleethorpes, Selby. Arrived -92. Under restoration. Loan from R Murphy.	12-93
☐ VP-KJL*		Messenger 4A	ex Coventry Airport, G-ALAR, RH371, BAFO CW, AEAF CS. Restn. Arrived 25-5-92.	12-93
☐ *		Knight Twister	ex Tumby Woodside, Loughborough. Fuselage frame. Stored.	01-94
☐ XA293*		Cadet TX.3	ex Long Marston, Redditch. Arrived by 5-93.	12-93
☐ XP494*		Grasshopper TX.1	ex Stamford, Syerston, Stamford, Cosford, Ratcliffe College, Syerston. Arr mid-1993.	12-93
☐ *	BAPC.130	Blackburn 1912	ex Helston, *Flambards*. Arrived 6-93.	12-93
☐	BAPC.211	HM.14 *Flea*	started 1991. Using original parts from Burns Garage, Congleton. Stored and available for loan.	12-93

STONNALL (on the A452 south east of Brownhills)

The sorry-looking Horizon should still be stored here.

☐ G-AYOL		Horizon 180	ex St John's, St Lawrence, N3788, F-BNQU. Damaged 1982.	

SWYNNERTON (east of the A519 south of Newcastle-under-Lyme)

■ **Staffordshire Regiment** : A Whirlwind is inside the large Army camp here.

☐ XK987	8393M	W'wind HAR.10	ex Stafford, Brize Norton, 103, 110, 228, 22, 217, 1360 Flt, 22. Poor shape.	06-92

TAMWORTH

By late 1993 a member of the Macclesfield Historical Aviation Society was working on the fuselage of Vampire NF.10 WP250 (on loan from the Friends of Biggin Hill) with the apparent intention to turn it into a Mosquito cockpit. It takes all kinds...

☐ WP250*   Vampire NF.10   ex Chelford, North Weald, Sevenoaks, Booker, Sandhurst, A&AEE. Pod. See notes above.   11-93

TATENHILL AERODROME (south of the B5234, west of Burton-on-Trent)

The number of **W&R**-type inmates has expanded. The former White Waltham Pembroke flew in during October 1992 and has got no further on its planned migration to the USA. Harvard IIA G-TSIX was ferried to Retford, Notts, by 1991.

☐ G-ARNN   GC-1B Swift   ex Leicester, VP-YMJ, VP-RDA, ZS-BMX, NC3279K. Crashed 1-9-73. Restoration.
☐ G-AZHE*   Slingsby T.61B   ex N61TB, G-AZHE. Dam 17-6-88. Restn.
☐ G-BFNM   GC-1B Swift   ex Nottingham Airport, N78205. Restoration.
☐ G-BUPJ*   Fournier RF-4D   ex N7752. Gutted fuselage.   05-92
☐ N4234C*   XL954   Pembroke C.1   ex White Waltham, 9042M, Northolt, 60, RAFG CS, 2 TAF CS. Flew in 21-10-92. Stored.   12-93

Suffolk

BECK ROW (on the A1101 north of Mildenhall)

By February 1993 the former DRA Bedford Hunter had arrived here and was slowly being re-assembled.

☐ XG210*   Hunter F.6   ex DRA Bedford, BAe Hatfield, CFE, 19, 14. With wings of XL572 (stb) and XL623 (port). First noted 2-93.   07-93

BENTWATERS AIRFIELD (east of Woodbridge)

■ **USAF Bentwaters** : The last of the 81st TFW A-10A *Warthogs* left the base during early 1993, leaving a huge void in the area. There are talks about locating 'Ipswich Airport' either here or at the 'twin' airfield of Woodbridge, Suffolk, but as yet nothing definite has come of this. See under Lakenheath for details of a transient resident. The Mystere is consequently listed somewhat tenuously.

☐ 104   Mystere IVA   ex Woodbridge, Sculthorpe, French AF. See above.

BURY ST EDMUNDS

■ **N Hamlin-Wright** : HM.14 Flea G-AEMY was acquired by Nigel Ponsford and moved to Leeds, W Yorks, during 1993.
■ **301 Squadron ATC** : Keep a *Chippax* at the TAVR Headquarters, in Northgate Street.

☐ WG471   8210M   Chipmunk T.10   ex Stowmarket, Leeming, Abn UAS, 1 FTS, 6 FTS, 220 OCU, Aston Down CF, MCCS, 4 SoTT, Nott UAS, Leeds UAS, 19 RFS, 24 RFS, 3 BFTS, 16 RFS, 4 BFTS. PAX.

CROWFIELD AERODROME (east of the A140, east of Stowmarket)

Harvard G-ELMH arrived during January 1994 from the locality, for completion of its rebuild.

☐ G-ELMH*   Harvard III   ex locality, Sudbury, Alverca, Sintra, Port AF 1662, EZ341, 784. Arrived 1-94. Restn.   01-94

FLIXTON (on the B1062 west of Bungay)

■ **Norfolk and Suffolk Aviation Museum** (N&SAM) / **Royal Observer Corps Museum** (ROCM) : This delightful museum continues to make great strides. All the hard work in putting up the hangar is having benefits, the largest of which must have been pre-production Lightning F.1 XG329 which arrived courtesy of N&SAM member Ian Hancock. Transportation and re-erection was courtesy of the ever-busy Lightning Flying Club of Plymouth, Devon, led by the indefatigable Barry Pover. Ian then went on to supply a whole Canberra and a Canberra nose. Also new is a scale replica Fokker D.VIII which is taxiable, being powered by a 'waterpump' engine behind its mock-up rotary. Here for a long time is the extreme nose section of a Felixstowe F.5 flying-boat. While too small for a formal mention in the listings of **W&R**, it is nevertheless a significant artefact. It was acquired from Felixstowe in 1989. The Royal Observer Corps Museum — two rooms of it — is now open to the public. A Nissen hut is dedicated to a display of material in honour of the 446th BG, with a memorial dedicated to the Bomb Group having been unveiled by the 446th BG Association in 1993. Fund raising for the Museum buildings continues.

◆ Open Easter to October, Sundays and Bank Holidays 10am to 5pm; July to August Tuesday, Wednesdays and Thursdays 10am to 5pm. ✉ N&SAM, Huby Fairhead, 48 Monks Cottages, Langley, Norwich, Norfolk, NR14 8DG.

☐ N99153		T-28C Trojan	ex East Ham, France, Zaire/Congo AF FG-289, USN VT-3, VT-5, NABTC 146289. Crashed 14-12-77. Fuselage. Zaire/USN colours.	11-93
☐ 'P8140'	BAPC.71	Spitfire replica	ex Chilham Castle, 'P9390' and 'N3317', *Battle of Britain*. *Nuflier*, Norwich Union presentation aircraft.	11-93
☐ VL349	N5054	Anson C.19	ex Norwich Airport, G-AWSA, SCS, NCS, North Coates SF, WSF, FCCS, HCCS, HCEU, 116, CSE, 1 FU.	11-93
☐ VX580		Valetta C.2	ex Norwich Airport, MCS, MEAFCS, 114, HS. On loan.	11-93
☐ WF128	8611M	Sea Prince T.1	ex Honington, Kemble, Sydenham SF, A&AEE, 750.	11-93
☐ WF643		Meteor F.8	ex Coltishall, Kemble, 29, Nicosia SF, 611, 1, 56. 'X'. Composite.	11-93
☐ WH840*	8350M	Canberra T.4	ex Seighford, Locking, St Athan, Geilenkirchen SF, A&AEE, 97, 151, 245, 88, 231 OCU, CFS. Ian Hancock. Arrived 3-94.	03-94
☐ WV605		Provost T.1	ex Henlow, Higher Blagdon, 6 FTS, 3 FTS, 22 FTS. 'T-B'.	11-93
☐ XG329*	8050M	Lightning F.1	ex Swinderby, Cranwell, A&AEE, Warton. Arrived by 10-93. Ian Hancock.	11-93
☐ XH892	7982M	Javelin FAW.9R	ex Duxford, Colerne, Shawbury, 29, 64, 23. 'J'.	11-93
☐ XJ482	A2598	Sea Vixen FAW.1	ex Wimborne Minster, 766, 700Y. '713-VL'.	11-93
☐ XK624		Vampire T.11	ex Lytham St Annes, Blackpool, CFS, 3 FTS, 7.FTS, 1 FTS, 23 GCF, CFS, 7 FTS. '32'.	11-93
☐ XM279*		Canberra B(I).8	ex Firbeck, Nostell Priory, Cambridge, 16, 3. Nose. Ian Hancock. Arrived 3-94.	03-94
☐ XN304		Whirlwind HAS.7	ex Bedford, Henlow, Wroughton, Shrivenham, Wroughton, 705, Old Sarum, 848. '64'.	11-93
☐ XR485		W'wind HAR.10	ex Wroughton, 2 FTS, CFS. 'Q'.	11-93
☐ 79		Mystere IVA	ex Sculthorpe, French AF, ET.2/8, 314 GE, EC.1/5. '8-NB'.	11-93
☐ 42196		F-100D-11-NA	ex Sculthorpe, French AF. EC.4/11, EC.2/11, USAF 48th FBW, 45th FS. *Skyblazers* c/s.	11-93
☐ 54433		T-33A-5-LO	ex Sculthorpe, French AF, 328 CIFAS, 338 CEVSV, USAF 803rd ABG. 20th FBG c/s.	11-93
☐	BAPC.147	Bensen B.7	ex Loddon, Marham, Coltishall.	11-93
☐ *	BAPC.239	Fokker D.VIII	⁵/₈th scale replica. First noted 11-91.	11-93

HONINGTON AIRFIELD (on the A1088 south east of Thetford)

■ **RAF Honington** : The base is now in the hands of the RAF Regiment after all the Tornado flew northwards. It is understood that the UK prototype Tornado, XX946 will be moved from here to the Aerospace Museum at Cosford, Shrop. Full marks! Lightning F.6 XR754 was put up for tender during October 1991 and gravitated to <u>Stock</u>, Essex. Ignore the reference **W&R13** to the nose of Buccaneer S.2 XV338, refer to Abingdon, Oxon.

☐ XK526	8648M	Buccaneer S.1	ex RAE Bedford, RRE. Gate guardian.	03-92
☐ XT900	9099M	Phantom FGR.2	ex Wattisham Pool/PTF, 228 OCU, 31, 14, 228 OCU. 'CK'. BDR.	06-92
☐ XX886		Buccaneer S.2B	ex 208, 16. WLT. See notes above.	06-92
☐ XX946	8883M	Tornado P.02	ex Laarbruch, Honington, Warton. WLT.	06-92
☐ ZE361	9057M	F-4J(UK)	ex 74, USN 155734. 'P'. Crash rescue.	03-92

IPSWICH

■ **188 Squadron ATC** : Keep their *Chippax* at the TAVR Centre on the A12.

☐ WG463	8363M	Chipmunk T.10	ex Hamble G-ATDX, Stn UAS, Not UAS, StA UAS, Cam UAS, Colerne SF, Oxf UAS, Abn UAS, Oxf UAS, 24 GCF, Cottesmore SF, 3 BFTS, 16 RFS. PAX trainer.	

■ **R J Everett** : Has established a blossoming private collection (dealership?) in the area. Note that the identity of XN634 is unconfirmed.

☐ XE656*	8678M	Hunter F.6	ex Halton, 1 TWU, 229 OCU, DFLS, 92, 65. Arrived 6-93.	06-93
☐ XG274*	8710M	Hunter F.6	ex Halton, 4 FTS, 229 OCU, 66, 14. '71'. Arrived 6-93.	06-93
☐ XK911*	A2603	Whirlwind HAS.7	ex Wroughton, Lee-on-Solent, Arbroath, 771, 829, *Ark Royal* Flt, 824, 820, 845. Arr 29-8-92.	08-92
☐ XN634*		Jet Provost T.3	ex Scampton, 1 FTS, 7 FTS, RAFC, 6 FTS. Fuselage. See notes above. Arrived 5-93.	05-93
☐ XP567*	8510M	Jet Provost T.4	ex Halton, CATCS, 6 FTS, RAFC. '23'. Arrived 4-93.	04-93
☐ XR701*	9025M	Jet Provost T.4	ex Halton, CATCS, SoRF, 27 MU *hack*, 1 FTS. 'K'. Arrived 4-93.	04-93
☐ XR704*	8506M	Jet Provost T.4	ex Halton, St Athan *hack*, CAW, CFS. '30'. Arrived 4-93.	04-93
☐ XT420*		Wasp HAS.1	ex Fleetlands, Wroughton. '606'. Arr 4-94.	04-94
☐ 'PF179'*	XR541	Gnat T.1	ex Worksop, St Athan, 8602M, CFS, 4 FTS. Arrived by 1-94.	01-94
			[The 'serial' worn on the nose derives from the Paint & Finishing course at St Athan that last dealt with it!]	
☐ J-1614*	G-BLIE	Venom FB.50	ex Glasgow Airport, Dubendorf, Swiss AF. Pod arrived 10-1-93, rest shortly thereafter.	01-93

■ **Ipswich School** : Another educational emporium to 'privatise' its Grasshopper, acquiring the thing from the MoD on June 16, 1988. Is it still here?

☐ XP490*	Grasshopper TX.1	see notes above.	06-88

IPSWICH AERODROME (north of the A45 south of the town)

Another story of encroaching housing estates... The aerodrome is very much under threat. There is a scheme for both aircraft and estate agents to exist side-by-side, but the general feeling is that ultimately Ipswich town will move south and swallow the site. Colt 108 G-ARKM, mentioned in **W&R13**, returned by May 1992 and undertook its first test flight on August 26, 1992. Widgeons N750M and N3103Q/G-DUCK were crated and departed for France on October 14, 1992. That only leaves: —

☐ N4565L	DC-3-201A	ex Dublin, LV-GYP, LV-PCV, N129H, N512, N51D, N80C, NC21744. Stored.	01-94

KESGRAVE (on the A12 east of Ipswich)

■ **Kesgrave High School** : In **W&R11**, a former Italian Super Cub was reported as making a move via Feltwell to the Boston, Lincs, area. This was not so. The aircraft resides behind a hedge in a very narrow lane, very much the worse for wear and forgotten — except by **W&R** sleuths!

☐ MM54-2372*	Piper L-21B	ex Embry-Riddle, Woodbridge, Italian Army, 'EI-184', I-EIXM, USAF 54-2372. Derelict. See notes above.	06-92

LAKENHEATH AIRFIELD (on the A1065 south of Brandon)

■ **USAF Lakenheath** : The Super Sabre arrival charted in **W&R13** is now confirmed as 42265. Last noted in **W&R11** under Wethersfield, Essex, the F-100 was lifted out on January 20, 1988 by an HH-53C. Destination then was unknown, but it has since been revealed as Bentwaters, Suffolk. It now serves on the dump here. During February 1993 the USAF issued a tender for ten Mystere IVAs, one T-33 and a C-130. The Mysteres were here and the *T-Bird* and *Herk* at Mildenhall. Going by the speed in which they were process, its would seem the contract went to Mayer-Perry of Snailwell, Cambs. (The Mysteres were Nos 16, 75, 99, 113, 126, 145, 241, 285, 300 & 309.) Two more F-15s have arrived for BDR training.

☐ 24434		F-105G-RE	ex Davis-Monthan, 562 TFS.	
☐ 37471		F-4C-18-MC	ex 163 TFS/122 TFW, Indiana ANG. BDR.	
☐ 37610		F-4C-20-MC	ex 171 FIS, Michigan ANG. BDR.	
☐ 40131		F-15A-12-MC	ex 122 TFS/Louisiana ANG.	03-94
☐ 40707		F-4C-22-MC	ex Mildenhall, 171 FIS, Michigan ANG.	09-90
☐ 60029*		F-15A-15-MC	arrived 2-93. BDR.	03-94
☐ 60124*		F-15B-15-MC	arrived 2-93. BDR.	03-94
☐ '63319'	42269	F-100D-16-NA	ex '54048', French AF. Gate guardian.	03-94
☐ 42265		F-100D-16-NA	ex Bentwaters, Wethersfield, FAF. 'FW-2265'. See notes above. Dump.	08-92

MILDENHALL AIRFIELD (on the A11 south west of Thetford)

■ **USAF Mildenhall** : By April 1993 both the much-patched T-33A 16769 and the much-trundled C-130A 70524 had been scrapped — see Lakenheath, Suffolk, above.

MONEWDEN (south of the A1120, north of Ipswich)

Contrary to **W&R13**, the hulk of Cessna T.210L G-BENF still lives on at the farm strip. Green mosses (or perhaps lichens) on its side is matching its colour scheme and helping it blend beautifully into the undergrowth!

☐ G-BENF	Cessna T.210L	ex Ipswich, N732AE, D-EIPY, N732AE. Crashed 29-5-81. Fuselage, see notes above.	12-92

NAYLAND (on the B1087 north west of Colchester)

Two Cessnas, in varying states of being, can be found at a farm strip locally.

☐ G-BGFX*	Cessna F.152 II	CoA expired 23-6-91. Stored. F/n 1-90.	02-93
☐ N47351*	Cessna 152 II	wreck. Stored. First noted 2-93.	02-93

PARHAM AERODROME (or Framlingham, on the B1116 north of Woodbridge)

■ **Aerodrome** : The former Lakenheath Aero Club Cessna has been joined by a Cherokee.

☐ G-BFPE*	Cherokee 140C	ex OH-PCY. Cr 9-6-82. Wreck. F/n 11-<u>84</u>.	04-92
☐ N11824	Cessna 150M	stored, dismantled.	10-91

■ **390th Bomb Group Memorial Air Museum** : From 1976 to 1981 the tower here was restored and now houses a superb museum dedicated to the 390th and Parham, USAAF Airfield 153. Within can be found a wide array of engines and many other artefacts.

◆ Open 11am to 6pm on Sundays and Bank Holidays March through to October. ✉ Colin Durrant, Museum Manager, 101 Avondale Road, Ipswich, Suffolk, IP3 9LA.

SUDBURY

■ **AJD Engineering** : Output of fine replica aircraft continues from Tony Ditheridge's workshop. The two former Portuguese Harvards have moved on :— Mk III 1662 was registered as G-ELMH during July 1992, turning up at <u>Crowfield</u>, Suffolk; Mk 4 1766 was registered as G-BUKY to an owner in Maidstone, Kent. Mew Gull G-AEXF is here for another rebuild. An unidentified PT-17 Kaydet moved from here to ARCO at <u>Duxford</u>, Cambs, for restoration during 1993.

☐ G-AEXF*	Mew Gull	ex Old Warden, ZS-AHM. Crashed 17-7-91. Wreck, for rebuild. First noted 8-92.	08-92
☐ G-AEZX	Bü 133C	ex N5A, PP-TDP. Crashed 21-6-88. Stored.	11-91

☐ G-AZYJ*		Wilga 35	ex Tattershall Thorpe, Studley, Bickmarsh, SP-WEA. CoA expired 5-3-76. For rebuild. Arrived by 10-92.	10-92
☐ S-AHAA	G-EASD	Avro 504L	ex Sweden, S-AAP, G-EASD. Restoration.	
☐		JN4 'Jenny'	ex USA, *Great Waldo Pepper*. HAC. Stored.	04-94
			[See under Paddock Wood, Kent.]	
☐ BW853	G-BRKE	Hurricane XIIA	ex Canada, composite, parts from BW853 and BW881. For restoration.	11-91

SWEFLING (on the B1119 east of Framlingham)

■ **Swefling Engineering** : (Also known as Austin's.). Richard Austin died *circa* 1990 and the yard was closed soon afterwards.

WALPOLE (on the B1117 south east of Halesworth)

■ **Blyth Valley Aviation Collection** : The collection continues to prosper and boasts a 40ft x 30ft building partially sunk into the ground, so as not to annoy neighbours. A three acre site is being developed. By May 1993 the collection had aspired to its first complete airframe and a well-equipped Canberra PR.9 nose. An interesting item in the collection of artefacts is an airborne lifeboat from an SB-29 Superfortress.

◆ Occasional open days, but essentially by prior permission only. ✉ Cliff Aldred, *Vulcan's End*, Mells Road, Walpole, Halesworth, Suffolk, IP19 0PL.

☐ WN907	7416M	Hunter F.5	ex Ascot, St Athan, Colerne, 257. Nose.	12-93
☐ WZ458		Vampire T.11	ex Swefling, Foulness, Southend, North Weald, 8 FTS, 10 FTS, 208 AFS. '31'. Pod.	12-93
☐ XH165*		Canberra PR.9	ex Stock, St Athan, 1 PRU, 39, 13, 58. Nose. Arrived by 5-93.	12-93
☐ XL388	8750M	Vulcan B.2	ex Honington, 50, Wadd Wing, Scamp Wing, 9. Nose.	12-93
☐ XL445	8811M	Vulcan K.2	ex Lyneham, 50, 44, 35, 230 OCU, Wadd Wing, Akrotiri Wing, Wadd Wing, 27. Nose.	12-93
☐ XN696		Sea Vixen FAW.2	ex Farnborough, Tarrant Rushton, ADS, 899. '751'. Nose.	12-93
☐ XR718*	8932M	Lightning F.3	ex Wattisham, BDR, LTF, 11, LTF, 11, 5, LTF, 5, 11, LTF, 5, LTF, 5, 226 OCU, 29, 56. 'DA'. Arrived by 5-93.	12-93

WATTISHAM

■ **RAF Wattisham / 3 Regiment, Army Air Corps**: Traumatic times for Wattisham. First they took away the Phantom, then they took away RAF Wattisham! The base closed in July 1993 and will partially become a twee housing estate and, thank you the Army Air Corps, a helicopter base. As the RAF moved out, 3 Regiment from Soest, Germany (see Part 6) moved in, but it is not yet clear if any of their instructional airframes came with them. Bidding for the removal and quick scrapping of the Phantom *phleet* were Mayer & Perry (East Anglia) Ltd of Snailwell, Cambs, an un-named company based at Bury St Edmunds, Suffolk, and Hanningfield Metals of Stock, Essex, with the former getting the larger chunk of the work. With the removal of the Phantoms, carefully monitored as part of SALT II arms limitation agreements, the aircraft were largely destined to be very visibly destroyed, so that they could never be Phantoms again but might see the light of day as ingots that turn themselves into Eurofighter 2000s in due course. (Then again...) Due to the speed of processing these airframes, they have not been 'forwarded' as such to Snailwell. Those going to Stock have lingered in the form of fuselages and noses — *qv*.

Mayer & Perry took the following in September 1991 : XT865, XT872, XT875, XT901, XV396, XV400, XV429, XV476, XV480, XV574, XV575, XV576, XV583, XV584, XV592. In the middle of February 1992 the Bury St Edmunds company took the following, but all were actually 'processed' by Mayer & Perry : XT902, XV430, XV432, XV439, XV464, XV492, XV498. Mayer & Perry struck again at the end of September 1992 and consumed the following : XT894, XT909, XV407, XV410, XV438, XV488 and XV570. Hanningfield Metals took the following, in April 1993 : XT874, XT892, XT906, XV398, XV404, XV419, XV490, XV494, XV496, XV570, XV587. XT874 body-swerved and missed the severity of the axe and moved to Phoenix Aviation at

Bruntingthorpe, Leics. The nose of XV490 also moved to Bruntingthorpe, Leics, this time for the PRG. Hanningfield hope to 'display' XV404 at Stock, Essex — so refer there for that one!
Phantom FG.1 XV581/9070M moved by road to Buchan, Grampian, on April 24, 1992 for the gate there. Lightning F.6 XS922 was also acquired by Hanningfield Metals and moved to Stock, Essex, by June 1993. The noseless hulk of Phantom FG.1 XT595'8550M had gone by late 1993 — perhaps part of the massed exodus noted above. The Lightning was put up for tender during February 1994. The gate will now be guarded by a former Soest Sioux.

☐ XM192	8413M	Lightning F.1A	ex Wattisham TFF, Binbrook TFF, 226 OCU, 111. 'K'. 111 Sqn colours. Up for tender 2-94.	02-94
☐ XT190*		Sioux AH.1	ex Soest, Middle Wallop, UNFICYP. Arrived 29-6-93. For the gate.	06-93
☐ XV420		Phantom FGR.2	ex 92, 23, 29, 23, 19, 56, 29. 'O'. See notes below.	03-93

■ **Station Museum** : Phantom XV420 has been moved onto the airfield proper and the future of the collection is now in doubt with the change of 'landlords'. Established in an original wartime Nissen-type building the museum charts in artefacts, documents and photographs the history of the base, from 2 Group in May 1939, to Station 377 USAAF, to the Phantom.
◆ Access to the Museum is *only* possible by *prior application*, to :- ✉ Army Air Corps, Wattisham, Ipswich, Suffolk, IP7 7RA.

WOODBRIDGE AIRFIELD

■ **USAF Woodbridge** : Ceased to be in most terms during August 1992 and is due to be handed back to the RAF, although they have no plans for it. All five of the decoy Mystere IVAs (Nos 9, 25, 50, 133 and 276) are *assumed* to have been scrapped in the time up to August 1992. See also notes under Bentwaters, Suffolk. Another end of an era....

Surrey

BROOKLANDS (or Weybridge, on the B374 south of Weybridge)
■ **Autokraft Ltd** : Work continues on the Hurricane and flight cannot be far off. Both Tempests are coming along. The Autokraft Pilatus P.2, G-BLKZ, is kept at Wycombe Air Park, Bucks.

☐ 'BE417'	G-HURR	Hurricane XII	ex Canada, RCAF 5589. 402 Sqn c/s 'AE-K'. Nearing first flight.	01-94
☐ HA586	G-TEMT	Tempest II	ex Chichester, India, IAF, RAF MW763. Restn.	01-94
☐ HA604	G-PEST	Tempest II	ex Chichester, India, IAF, RAF MW401. Restn.	01-94

■ **Brooklands Museum** : Consolidation of the site continues. The Wellington project comes on apace and the aircraft is now the centre-piece of *The Vickers Hangar*, dedicated to telling the tale of Vickers both at Weybridge and generally. A second Wellington rear fuselage has been acquired, and this will be turned into a walk-through exhibit. Restoration of other exhibits is gaining pace, with the Hunter, Varsity and Viscount receiving refurbishment. Work on the Barnes Wallis stratochamber has come on sufficiently to place the nose of Valiant XD816 inside it. A scan down the list below will reveal a whole series of new inmates. One that is not readily apparent is Tiger Moth F-BGEQ which arrived on November 28, 1992. The fuselage moved out to Chessington, Gtr Lon, in late 1993, for rebuild by Geoff Masterton to flyable condition as a student project. The rest of the airframe will likely be 'done' at Shoreham, West Sussex. An ambitious US-based project to recreate the first crossing of the Atlantic by Alcock and Brown and the first flight from the UK to Australia may well see the replica Vickers Vimy donated to the Museum when the flights are completed during 1994/1995. Airframes that are part of the Mike Beach collection are marked MB.
Departures have been as follows :— Britannia 308F fuselage G-ANCF moved to Banwell, Avon, on March 27, 1993; Beagle 206 G-ARRM to Banwell, Avon, on January 29, 1994; Pup 200 G-AVDF was acquired by David Collings and John Chillingworth of the Beagle Pup Club and moved to St Ives, Cambs, for restoration to flying condition on October 30, 1993; Widgeon G-BTKJ left by road

on March 19, 1992 for <u>Coventry</u>, West Mids; BE.2c replica BAPC.117 donated to the Friends of Biggin Hill and left for <u>Sevenoaks</u>, Kent, in July 1993.

◆ On the B374 south of Weybridge, access from Junctions 10 or 12 of the M25. Open Tuesday to Sunday 10am to 5pm (last entry 4pm), Easter to October. Winter months, 10am to 4pm, last entry is 3pm. Normally closed Xmas and New Year. Pre-arranged guided tours available Tuesdays to Fridays, by telephoning 0932 857381. ✉ Brooklands Museum, The Clubhouse, Brooklands Road, Weybridge, Surrey, KT13 OQN. ☎ 0932 859000. **Fax** 0932 855465.

☐	'G-EBED' BAPC.114	Viking replica	ex 'R4', Chertsey, *The Land Time Forgot*.	11-93
☐	'G-AACA' B'.177	Avro 504K rep	ex 'G1381', Henlow. Restoration.	11-93
☐	'G-ADRY' BAPC.29	HM.14 *Flea*	ex Aberdare, Swansea. Ex MB.	11-93
☐	G-AEKV DZQ	Kronfeld Drone	BGA.2510. CoA expired 6-10-60. MB.	11-93
☐	G-AGRU	Viking 1	ex Cosford, Soesterberg, Channel, Lasham, Kuwait Oil, BWIA, VP-TAX, G-AGRU, BEA *Vagrant*. CoA expired 9-1-64. On loan.	
☐	G-APIM	Viscount 806	ex Southend, BAF, BA, BEA. Damaged 11-1-88. *Viscount Stephen Piercey*. Restoration.	12-93
☐	G-BJHV	Voisin replica	ex Old Warden. On loan from RAFM.	11-93
☐	G-LOTI	Bleriot XI replica	CoA expired 19-7-82.	11-93
☐	G-MJPB	Ladybird	microlight, on loan from Bill Manuel estate.	11-93
☐	G-VTOL ZA250	Harrier T.52	ex Dunsfold. CoA exp 2-11-86. Loan BAe.	11-93
☐	BGA.162*	Willow Wren ∆	ex Bishop's Stortford. *Yellow Wren*. MB First noted 5-93.	11-93
☐	AAA* BGA.231	Scud II	ex G-ALOT, BGA.231. MB F/n 5-93.	11-93
☐	AHC* BGA 400	Kite 1	ex Eaton Bray, Bedford, Bishop's Stortford, VD165. First noted 5-93. Stored.	11-93
☐	ATH BGA.643	Slingsby Gull 3 ∆	(Hawkridge Kittiwake) MB	11-93
☐	FCZ* BGA.3166	Falcon I replica ∆	ex Bishops Stortford.	11-93
☐	FHQ BGA.3277	Hols der Teufel ∆	replica. MB	11-93
☐		Curtiss D Pusher	replica. PFA number 119-10717. MB	11-93
☐		VC-10	test shell, nose section. BOAC colours.	11-93
☐	*	Rogallo h/g	*Aerial*. On loan.	11-93
☐	'D-12-354' BGA.1711	Rheinland ∆	CPZ, ex RAFGGA.521. MB	11-93
☐	A40-AB	VC-10 1103	ex Sultan of Oman, G-ASIX.	11-93
☐	'B7270' G-BFCZ	Camel replica ∆	ex Lands End, Duxford, Thorpe Park.	11-93
☐	N2980	Wellington 1A	ex Loch Ness, 20 OTU, 37, 149. Ditched 31-12-40. Restoration.	11-93
☐	WF372	Varsity T.1	ex Sibson, 6 FTS, 1 ANS, RAFC, 201 AFS. 'A'. Repainted 1993.	12-93
☐	WT859* A2499	Supermarine 544	ex Ruislip, Foulness, Culdrose, Fleetlands, Culdrose, Lee-on-Solent, RAE Bedford. Nose. Arrived 18-7-92. Loan from Alan Allen.	12-93
☐	XA292 BGA.3350	Cadet TX.3 ∆	FLR. MB	11-93
☐	XD816	Valiant BK.1	ex Henlow, BAC, 214, 148. Loaned. Nose.	12-93
☐	*	Typhoon 1A	ex Sevenoaks. Cockpit section. Arrived 8-92. Loan from Peter Smith.	11-93
☐	*	Typhoon 1B	ex Sevenoaks, Innsworth, Leeds, Cheltenham, Kemble. Arrived 8-92. Loan, Peter Smith.	11-93
☐	*	TSR-2	ex Farnborough. Nose. Arrived 8-92.	11-93
☐	E-421	Hunter F.51	ex Brooklands Tech, Kingston-on-Thames, Dunsfold, G-9-443, Aalborg, *Esk*.724, Danish Air Force. BAe loan. RDAF colours.	12-93
☐	BAPC.187	Roe I Biplane	replica, displayed in replica of Roe's shed.	11-93
☐	BAPC.194	Demoiselle replica	ex Henlow, Gatow, *Those Magnificent Men*.	11-93

■ **Brooklands Technical College** : Vampire T.11 XJ772 moved to <u>London Colney</u>, Herts, on March 29, 1994. The College is expecting a *JP* from Cosford, Shrop, *possibly* XN586. The College has also had Twin Comanche G-ASSB — but for how long?

☐	G-ASSB*	Twin Comanche	ex Bournemouth. CoA exp 6-5-88. See notes above. 03-94

CAMBERLEY

■ **Hands on Aviation** : Keith Attfield and Paul Raymond obtained a Jet Provost nose section from Barry Parkhouse at his Ottershaw, Surrey, store during September 1993. It is under restoration and the pair hope to have it touring events during the summer of 1994.

☐ 'XN493'* XN137 Jet Provost T.3 ex Ottershaw, Camberley, Abingdon, 3 FTS, CFS, Huntings. Nose. Arrived 9-93. 09-93

■ **Barry Parkhouse** : Collector Barry Parkhouse has his main store at Ottershaw, Surrey — which see. The nose of Vulcan B.2MRR XH537/8749M moved to <u>Ottershaw</u> during 1992. The former Southall, Gtr Lon, Chipmunk came here after brief storage at Feltham, Gtr Lon.

☐ G-AYDW Terrier 2 ex Cranfield, Bushey, G-ARLM, TW568, LAS, AOPS, 227 OCU, 43 OTU. CoA expired 1-7-73. Restoration. 12-93

☐ WB763* G-BBMR Chipmunk T.10 ex Feltham, Southall, 2 FTS, 4 FTS, AOTS, 1 ITS, 1 AEF, Bri UAS, 3 AEF. AAC, 652, Odiham SF, 24 RFS, 14 RFS. Arr 10-93. 12-93

■ **Others** : Terrier 2 G-JETS reverted to G-ASOM and moved to a location in Scotland for restoration. The other Auster is still to be found in this area.

☐ G-AJUD J/1 Autocrat ex Tongham. CoA exp 18-5-74. Restn.

CATERHAM

■ **Nalson Aviation Ltd** : Is the name of the 'scrapyard' here. They are not truly a scrapyard, being in the insurance reclaim business — see under Tattershall Thorpe, Lincs, for a large explanation. Aircraft coming here are broken down and sent off far and wide as components very quickly and as such it is felt wrong to list them here as throughput is both large and fast. Accordingly, all of the aircraft listed tentatively in **W&R13** were correctly listed and for this issue will not be listed at all!

CHARLWOOD (west of Gatwick Airport)

■ **Park Aviation Supply** : A Jet Provost fuselage inbound and the fuselage of SD.360 G-ROOM to Bruntingthorpe, Leics, otherwise the yard at Little Glovers Farm is unchanged. (See also under Faygate, West Sussex.)

☐ XT788 G-BMIR Wasp HAS.1 ex Tattershall Thorpe, Wroughton. 03-93
☐ XX223 Hawk T.1 ex Henlow, 4 FTS. Cr 7-7-86. Fuselage. 03-93
☐ XX734 8816M Jaguar GR.1 ex Coltishall, Abingdon, Indian AF JI014, XX734, 6, JOCU. Fuselage. 03-93
☐ * Jet Provost fuselage. '23'. First noted 1-93. 01-93

■ **Vallance By-Ways / Peter Vallance Collection** : Despite much campaigning, Peter Vallance lost his appeal against a planning permission hearing during June 1993. The collection has twelve months to vacate the site.

✉ Vallance By-Ways, Lowfield Heath Industrial Estate, Westfield Road, Lowfield Heath, Charlwood, Surrey, RH6 0BT. ☎ 0293 862915.

☐ G-DACA WF118 Sea Prince T.1 ex Gloucester-Cheltenham, Kemble, 750, A&AEE, 727, A&AEE, RAE Farnborough. 01-94
☐ G-GACA WP308 Sea Prince T.1 ex Gloucester-Cheltenham, Kemble, 750. 01-94
☐ G-JETH Sea Hawk FB.5 ex Bournemouth, Southend, 'XE364', XE489, FRU, 899. Composite. 01-94
☐ N46EA XK885 Pembroke C.1 ex Gloucester-Cheltenham, St Athan, 8452M, 60, 21, WCS, Seletar SF, B&TTF, Seletar SF, S&TFF, 209, 267. 01-94
☐ VZ638 G-JETM Meteor T.7 ex North Weald, Bournemouth, Southampton, Southend, Kemble, CAW, RAFC, 237 OCU, 501, Biggin Hill SF, FCCS, 85, 54, 25, 500. 01-94
☐ WH773 8696M Canberra PR.7 ex Wyton, 13, 58, 80, 31, 82, 540. 01-94
☐ WH903 8584M Canberra B.2 ex Hull, Wroughton; Abingdon, Bicester, 100, 85, MoA, 85, West Raynham TFF, 228 OCU, 102, 617. Nose. 01-94
☐ WR974 8117M Shackleton MR.3/3 ex Cosford, Kinloss Wing, 203, 42, 203, ASWDU, MinTech, ASWDU, CA. 'K'. 01-94

☐ WR982	8106M	Shackleton MR.3/3	ex Cosford, 201, 206, MoA, 205, 203, 206. 'J'	01-94
☐ XL472*		Gannet AEW.3	ex Boscombe Down, 849 'B', HQ, 'A' Flts. '044/R'. (Omitted from **W&R13**.)	01-94
☐ XN923		Buccaneer S.1	ex Boscombe Down, West Freugh.	01-94
☐ XP398	8794M	W'wind HAR.10	ex Peckham Rye, Shawbury, 22, 1563F, 202, 103, 110, 225.	01-94
☐ XS587	G-VIXN	Sea Vixen FAW.2	ex Bournemouth, TT mod, FRL, RAE-F, 8828M, FRL, ADS, 899.	01-94
☐ E-430		Hunter F.51	ex Faygate, Chertsey, Dunsfold, G-9-448, Aalborg, Esk.724, Danish AF. FAA c/s, GA.11-style.	01-94
☐ J-1605	G-BLID	Venom FB.50	ex Duxford, Swiss AF.	01-94

COULSDON (south of Croydon on the A23. Previously listed under 'Greater London')
■ **Bernie King** : The garage acquired other priorities (a classic car!) during late 1994 and Edwards Gyrocopter G-ASDF moved to the Woking, Surrey, area on February 12, 1994.

DUNSFOLD AIRFIELD
■ **British Aerospace** : There is a great question mark over the future of the airfield and it seems it will go the way of its cousin, Hatfield. Both of the Sea Vixens are reported to have been sold, one to the expanding collection on Cyprus and the other going to Brooklands (but not the museum), Surrey.

☐ G-ARPZ		Trident 1C	ex Heathrow, BA, BEA. CoA expired 26-1-86. RFD trials.	09-92
☐ WT488		Canberra T.4	ex Samlesbury, CSF, 360, 98, 360, 231 OCU, 360, 98, 231 OCU, 360, 231 OCU, Wyton SF, 360, 98, 245, 527, CSE. Dump.	03-93
☐ WV395	G-9-428	Hunter F.4	ex Cosford, 8001M, MoS, 20. Dump.	03-93
☐ XJ571	8140M	Sea Vixen FAW.2	ex Southampton, Cosford, Halton, Sydenham, 893, 892, 899. '242-R'. See notes above.	03-94
☐ XJ607	8171M	Sea Vixen FAW.2	ex Southampton, Cosford, Cranwell, 890, 892, 766, 892. '701-VL'. See notes above.	03-94

EGHAM
■ **Coopers** : (From July 1993 Coopers of Swindon took over the famous Coley's firm.) During September 1992 a visit here produced the grizzly remains of Jaguar T.2 XX843 and Cessna 152 G-BMHI which collided fatally over Powys on August 29, 1991. A visit during 1993 found "only bits" here and another report states that the yard has closed. The nose of Canberra B.2 WD935/8440M went to Ottershaw, Surrey, on March 4, 1992. The yard took on the noseless hulk of Canberra B.2 WJ640/8722M during March 1993 — see also under Guildford, Surrey.
■ **Peter Neilson** : It is assumed the Auster AOP.9 continues to be rebuilt here.

| ☐ XN435 | G-BGBU | Auster AOP.9 | ex Amersham, Heston, St Athan, 6 Liaison Depot Flt, MoA. | |

FAIROAKS AERODROME
It is thought that the A.109 travelling demonstrator is still resident here.

| ☐ G-GBCA | | A.109 Mk II | crashed 7-6-85. Travelling exhibit. | |

GODALMING
■ **1254 Squadron ATC** : In Hallam Road at the TAVR Centre, keep a Hunter nose.

| ☐ WV332 | 7673M | Hunter F.4 | ex Dunsfold, G-9-406, Halton, 234, 112, 67. Nose. | 11-92 |

GUILDFORD
■ **Mike Grant** : Took on the nose of Canberra B.2 WJ640 from Henfield, W Sussex, during March 1993. The remainder of the aircraft went to Coley's at Egham, Surrey.

| ☐ WJ640* | 8722M | Canberra B.2 | ex Henfield, Cosford, 100, 85, 51, 192, 231 OCU. Nose. Arrived 3-93. | 03-93 |

HEADLEY (on the B2033 south east of Leatherhead)

■ **RAF Headley Court** : (Previously wrongly listed under 'Uckfield', East Sussex.) No 2530 Squadron ATC should still have the *JP* nose in the hospital grounds.

☐ XP677   8587M   Jet Provost T.4   ex Abingdon, RAFEF, 2 FTS. Nose.

HORLEY

Previously listed under 'Reigate' (Kent *and* Surrey!!), the Heath and Bensen of Desmond St Cyrien's estate are stored in this area.

☐ G-AFZE*	Heath Parasol	CoA expired 10-5-64. Stored.	11-93
☐ *	Bensen gyroplane	Stored.	11-93

OTTERSHAW

■ **Barry Parkhouse** : Collector Barry Parkhouse acquired the entire contents of Ealing Tertiary College's moribund instructional airframe stock during July 1993 and four airframes arrived here from Southall, Gtr Lon. Aztec 250 G-AREF was quickly disposed of, as a source of spares. Cessna 175B G-ARMN was acquired for rebuild and moved to the Reading, Berks, area. The nose of Canberra B.2 WD935/8440M arrived here from Egham, Surrey, on March 4, 1993 but moved to <u>Bridgnorth</u>, Shrop, on January 24, 1994. The nose Scimitar F.1 XD215 moved to <u>Cheltenham</u>, Glos, on February 19, 1994. The nose of Scimitar F.1 XD235 went to <u>Southampton</u>, Hants, during 1992. Vampire T.11 XD528/8159M moved to <u>Firbeck</u>, S Yorks, on September 27, 1993. The nose of Jet Provost T.3 'XN493' (really XN137, amending **W&R13**) moved to <u>Camberley</u>, Surrey, during September 1993. The cockpit of Harvard III EZ259/G-BMJW arrived here on March, 4, 1992, but moved to <u>Wakefield</u>, W Yorks, by September 1993. Barry has also taken on the former Booker Aircraft Museum, see under Wycombe Air Park, Bucks. See also Camberley, Surrey.

☐ G-MBTY*	American Eagle	ex Southall. Arrived 7-93.	01-94
☐ KF435*	Harvard IIB	ex Wycombe AP, Camberley, Sandhurst, 1 FTS, 2 FTS, 22 SFTS, 20 FTS, 11 (P)AFU. Composite. Arrived 4-93.	01-94
☐ XD244	Scimitar F.1	ex Foulness, Brawdy, 803, 736, 803, 807. Nose.	01-94
☐ XH537* 8749M	Vulcan B.2MRR	ex Camberley, Abingdon, 27, 230 OCU, MoA. Nose. Arrived 1992.	01-94
☐ XL763*	Skeeter AOP.12	ex Southall, Wroughton, 15/19 Hussars, HQ 1 Wing, 654. Arrived 7-93.	01-94
☐ XX888	Buccaneer S.2B	ex Shawbury, St Athan, 16, 15. Nose.	01-94

REDHILL

■ **East Surrey Technical College** : Located in Gatton Hill. The Sea Devon is under restoration. No news of the Musketeer.

☐ G-AWTU	Musketeer	ex Deanland, AP-AWT, G-AWTU, N2769B.	07-90
☐ G-KOOL VP967	Sea Devon C.2/2	ex Biggin Hill, Kemble, 781, 21, 207, SCCS, SCS, WCS, SCS, NCS, SCS, MCS, MoA, MCS, CCCF, 38 GCF, TTCCF, FCCS, 2 TAF CS, MCCS, RAFG CS, 2 TAF CS, Wahn SF, RCCF.	04-93

■ **Redhill Technical College** : The Hiller airframe is located here.

☐ G-ANOA	Hiller UH-12A	ex Redhill Airfield, F-BEEG, N8170H. CoA expired 12-6-70.	11-92

REDHILL AERODROME (south of South Nutfield, south east of Redhill)

The new owner of the one-off TSR-3 G-AWIV lives in Cornwall and it is thought that the aircraft has moved southwest. Whirlwind Srs 3 G-AYNP has been acquired by the International Helicopter Museum of Weston-super-Mare, Avon — *qv* — and will be moving to Germany as part of an exchange that will bring a Mil Mi-2 to the Museum. Two Cessnas have become part of the scenery.

☐ G-AYNP	Whirlwind Srs 3	ex Bristow, ZS-HCY, G-AYNP, XG576. CoA expired 27-10-85. See notes above.	12-93
☐ G-BGJA*	Cessna FA.152	Crashed 2-8-87. Cut up fuselage.	10-93
☐ G-BIVY*	Cessna 172N	ex N73973. CoA expired 25-10-87. Stored.	10-93

REIGATE

[For reasons best known to himself, the Compiler put the 'Restorations Unlimited' part of 'Reigate' under 'Kent' — this is now amended!!]

■ **Restorations Unlimited** :   Have a small workshop in the area and are presently working on the restoration of two former Wellington gun turrets.   The late Desmond St Cyrien's Heath Parasol G-AFZE and Bensen gyroplane (adding to **W&R13**) are to be found stored in <u>Horley</u>, Surrey.

◆ • Visits to the workshop by prior arrangement. ✉ 2 Blackstone Close, Redhill, Surrey, RH1 6BG.

■ **Surrey County Fire Brigade Headquarters** :   The black and gold painted Trident fuselage is still regularly employed by the firemen.   No news of the Fuji however.

☐ G-AWZI	Trident 3B-101	ex Heathrow, BA, BEA. CoA expired 5-8-85. Fuselage.	09-92
☐ G-BEUB	FA.200-180	ex Betchworth. Crashed 30-7-79. Fuselage. See notes above.	01-90

TONGHAM (on the A3014 south of Aldershot)

Both Austers have fled from here, G-AJAB to <u>Skegness</u>, Lincs, by early 1991 and G-ASEE to <u>Spanhoe Lodge</u>, Northants, by early 1990.

VIRGINIA WATER (on the A30 south west of Egham)

Cessna T.210L G-OILS was disposed of several years back.

WOKING

■ **Computair Consultants** : Jeremy Parkin took delivery of the Edwards Gyrocopter on February 2, 1994. It is stored in this area while a permanent home is found for it.   •

☐ G-ASDF*	Edwards Gyro	ex Coulsdon. Arrived 12-2-94. See notes.	02-94

East Sussex

BATTLE

■ **Steve Atkins / Chris Warrilow** : Steve supplied technical assistance and co-ordination on the Dutch Spitfire Group's restoration of Mk IX MK732 G-HVDM 'H-25'. The restoration, undertaken partially in the UK and partially in Holland, came to fruition at Lydd, Kent, on June 10, 1993 when Pete Kynsey made the first flight. Although UK registered, the *Spit* lives in the Netherlands. Spitfire IX TA805 moved to <u>Sandown</u>, IoW, in January 1992. Spitfire IX restoration project LZ842's status is unconfirmed. It is possible that all (or some) of it has moved to Australia. Status of Seafire III 157 is also unconfirmed, possibly stored.

☐ 157	Seafire III	ex Dublin Tech, Casement, IAAC, RX168. See notes above.	

HAILSHAM

■ **Grenville Helicopters** : The helipad at the Boship Manor Hotel should still have its 'guardian'.

☐ G-AYOE	Bell 47G	ex F-OCBF, F-BKQZ, D-HEBO. Crashed 16-7-77. Composite, including Sioux parts.	06-91

■ **Ripleys** : This scrapyard holds a much cut-about Canberra. It has clearly been resident for a long time. A few clues to its likely identity are being followed up.

☐ *	Canberra	sectioned. See notes above.	07-93

HASTINGS

■ **John Wakeford** : Continues the restoration of the Klemm Swallow for D G Ellis.

☐ G-ACXE	L-25 Swallow	CoA expired 7-4-40. Restoration.

■ **Bo-Peep Garage** : The garage is no more, having been demolished. Meteor T.7 WL345 can be found more precisely under the heading of <u>Hollington</u>, E Sussex.

HEATHFIELD
A scrapyard in this area held an unidentified 'Beagle' during July 1993. A large amount of Britannia parts held here had gone by this date.

HOLLINGTON (on the B2159 west of Hastings)
■ **St Leonard's Garage** : Is the home of the pole-mounted former Hastings Meteor.
☐ WL345* Meteor T.7 ex Hastings, Kemble, CAW, 8 FTS, 5 FTS, CFE, 229 OCU. See notes above. 12-93

HOVE
■ **176 Squadron ATC** : Keep a *Chippax* at their headquarters.
☐ WD370 Chipmunk T.10 ex 3 AEF, 2 SoTT, 1 AEF, Hull UAS, 2 BTFS. SOC 12-3-75. PAX trainer.

IVYCHURCH (north of the A259, east of New Romney)
(Previously listed under 'Rye'.) Restoration of Ian Addy's Norecrin continues in the locality. Also here is the fuselage of an unidentified Cessna 172.
☐ G-BAYL Norecrin VI ex Solihull, Bodmin, F-BEQV. Restoration. 08-93
☐ * Cessna 172 fuselage only. First noted 3-91. 08-93

LEWES
■ **Fun Airplane Company** : Paul Penn-Sayers works on a Linnet and has a Jodel in store.
☐ G-APNS Linnet ex Chessington. CoA expired 6-10-78. Restn.
☐ G-BKCZ Wassmer D.120 ex F-BKCZ. Stored.

NEWHAVEN
■ **ATC** : The unit here have a Jet Provost cockpit section. Details appreciated.
☐ * Jet Provost cockpit section. See notes above. 02-93
■ **Newhaven Fort**: Robertsbridge Aviation Society (see below) have established a collection of aviation relics here. As yet no airframes, but still a most interesting assemblage.
◆ Late March to early October, daily 10.30am to 6.30pm. Also weekends in remainder of March and October and School Half Terms. ✉ Newhaven Fort, Fort Road, Newhaven, East Sussex, BN9 9DL. ☎ 0273 517622.

ROBERTSBRIDGE (on the A21 north west of Hastings)
■ **Robertsbridge Aviation Society** (RAS) : Located at the Bush Barn — essentially a run of converted chicken sheds — can be found the outstanding collection of artefacts assembled by the RAS since 1973. Well presented and researched, items range from an impressive collection of aero engines to a wide range of artefacts from 'digs' and much more. The arrival of the Su-7 nose represents a piece of exotica. It is really beyond restoration, but will make an excellent 'crash' scene centrepiece. RAS have an excellent clubroom and a coffee bar, all available to visitors. An arrangement has been established with the military exhibition at Fort Newhaven at Newhaven, E Sussex — see above. RAS's Mystere IVA remains on loan with LAWM at Headcorn, Kent — which see. The section of Horsa II TL615 here is for disposal and, although interesting, is beyond the scope of **W&R** and has been deleted from this edition.
◆ Open by appointment. : ✉ Philip Baldock, Upper Crabbe Cottage, Five Ashes, Mayfield, East Sussex, TN20 6HJ.
☐ G-AIVW Tiger Moth ex Redhill, T5370, 20 AFU, SAN, 10 EFTS, 25 PEFTS, 1 PFTS. Wrecked 27-8-82. Remains. Complex composite, largely based on G-ANLR / N6856. Restoration. 12-93
☐ WA630 Meteor T.7 ex Oakington SF, 4 FTS, 205 AFS, RAFC. Nose. 12-93
☐ WZ822 Grasshopper TX.1 ex Syerston. For disposal. 12-93
☐ XN238* Cadet TX.3 forward fuselage. On loan from Mark Hillier. First noted 4-93. 12-93

☐	XN511	'XM426'	Jet Provost T.3	ex Lutterworth, Liversedge, Kemble, CFS, 1 FTS, CFS. Nose. Restoration. Identity confirmed. 12-93
☐	XP701	8924M	Lightning F.3	ex High Halden, Hawkinge, Binbrook, LTF, 5, 11, 56, 29, 111, 29, A&AEE. Nose section. 12-93
☐	7907*		Su-7 *Fitter*	ex Farnborough, Egyptian AF. Nose. Fire damaged. Arrived 3-94. See notes above. 03-94

ST LEONARDS-ON-SEA

■ **Aero Vintage** : Restoration of the Bristol F.2b continues in this general area. It has been joined by the remains of a Hawker Nimrod II. Aero Vintage aircraft can also be found listed under Paddock Wood, Kent, and Hatch, Beds.

| ☐ | 'D7889' | G-AANM | Bristol F.2b | BAPC.166, ex Old Warden. Restoration. 04-94 |
| ☐ | K3661* | G-BURZ | Nimrod II | ex 802 Sqn. Other history obscure. Project. 04-94 |

SEAFORD

■ **Riverside Metals** : Display a forlorn Aztec at their premises on the Cradle Hill Industrial Estate.

| ☐ | G-BHNG | | Aztec 250E | ex Shoreham, N54125. Cr 19-12-81. Fuselage. |

SEDLESCOMBE AERODROME (north of Hastings)

Another location under threat. Jodel D.9 G-AWFT was flying by January 1994. Otherwise, the **W&R** situation is thought unchanged, but could be about to...

| ☐ | G-AXPG | | Mignet HM.293 | ex Hazeleigh Grange, Southend. CoA exp 20-1-77. |
| ☐ | G-BUNS | | Cessna F.150K | ex F-BSIL. Restoration. 01-93 |

UCKFIELD

W&R13 listed RAF Headley Court under this imaginative heading. It can in fact be found under Headley, Surrey — ie about 40 miles away!

WANNOCK (east of the A22, north of Eastbourne)

■ **Foulkes-Halbard Collection** : At Filching Manor is a staggering collection of vintage cars, easily going into three figures. Also here are a man-powered aircraft and the Aldritt Monoplane from Eire. The owner/curator is looking for more period aircraft.

◆ Open daily April to October 10.30am to 4.30pm, November-March Thursdays to Sundays, 10.30am to 4.30pm. ✉ Filching Manor, Wannock, East Sussex. ☎ 0323 487838.

| ☐ | | BAPC.127 | Halton Jupiter | ex Old Warden, Cranwell, Halton. 10-92 |
| ☐ | | IAHC.2 | Aldritt Mono | ex Portlaoise. Stored. 10-92 |

West Sussex

APULDRAM (off the A286 south of Chichester)

■ **Museum of D-Day Aviation** : *Circa* late 1993 the museum closed down and moved to establish itself at Shoreham Aerodrome, W Sussex. Spitfire replica 'MT791'/BAPC.209 moved during February 1994 to Shoreham. The Horsa fuselage section is not substantial enough to list and can be discounted.

CHICHESTER

■ **Tangmere Flight** : Tempest II HA557 is thought to be the machine that went to Spanhoe Lodge, Northants. HA580 is thought to have been the machine that moved to Duxford, Cambs, during 1992. Either way the store here is now clear. Also here was the composite Tempest V centred around the fuselage of EJ693 'SA-J' previously held at Henlow, Beds. This was exchanged for the fuselage of Mk II HA547 which is now in the composite airframe at Hendon, Gtr Lon. EJ693, along with a set of former Indian Mk II wings, was acquired from here by collector Kermit Weeks during his 'shopping spree' of September 1992 and exported to Florida, USA, being registered as N7027E.

CRAWLEY

■ **Crawley Technical College** : First, to go back to **W&R13** P.531 XN334 is here on loan to the College from the Fleet Air Arm Museum and *not* the International Helicopter Museum. Also coming from the FAAM is the former Wroughton Meteor, arriving for the same treatment during April 1993.

☐ WS103*		Meteor T.7	ex Wroughton, Lee-on-Solent, FRU, Kemble, Yeovilton Standards Squadron, Anthorn. FAAM. Arrived 19-4-93 for restoration.	07-93
☐ XN334	A2525	SARO P.531	ex Weston-super-Mare, Yeovilton, Arbroath, Lee-on-Solent. Restoration for FAAM.	07-93

■ **Others** : South of the A264 between Crawley and Faygate can be found a 'wargames' zone in which people pay a lot of money to a) wear themselves out, b) humiliate one another and c) get covered in splashes of red paint. To add to the 'realism' a Canberra fuselage was purchased in 1990. It can be seen during the winter, but is hidden during the summer by the vegetation. Any ideas?

☐ *		Canberra	fuselage. See notes above.

DURRINGTON (north of Worthing)

■ **Prospector Flying Group** : The three Percival Prospectors held by the Museum of Army Flying at Middle Wallop, Hants, have come to a workshop here so that a 'static' and a 'flyer' can result.

☐ G-APWZ*	Prospector	ex Middle Wallop, Goodwood. Damaged 7/8-2-84. Arrived by 7-93. See notes above.	07-93
☐ G-APXW*	Prospector	ex Middle Wallop, Shoreham, Lympne. Crashed 30-9-73. Arrived by 7-93. See notes above.	07-93
☐ G-ARDG *	Prospector	ex Middle Wallop, Shoreham, Lympne. Arrived by 7-93. See notes above.	07-93

FAYGATE (on the A264 between Horsham and Crawley)

■ **Park Aviation Supply** : A visit to this somewhat run-down yard during October 1993 found it much depleted, with the P.1127, Hawk, Sea Harrier and a Jaguar GR.1 (either XX114 or XZ120) extant. That leaves the assumption that the following have passed on to another form of existence (probably as beer cans!) :— AA-5A Cheetah G-BFTD; Canberra E.15 cockpit WH911; Hunter F.6A forward fuselage XG226/8800M; Wessex HU.5 XT459; Phantom FG.1 XT866; Jaguar T.2 XX137; and the anonymous F-4D forward fuselage.

☐ XP976		Hawker P.1127	ex Wittering, Foulness Island, Farnborough, Sevenhampton, Aston Down, 71 MU, BLEU, Dunsfold.	10-93
☐ XX293		Hawk T.1	ex 4 FTS. Crashed 17-4-85. Hulk.	10-93
☐ XZ438		Sea Harrier FRS.1	ex BAe. Crashed 17-5-82. Hulk.	10-93
☐		Jaguar GR.1	see notes above.	10-93

GATWICK AIRPORT

■ **Airport** : The Comet and the Trident serve on as towing/push-back trainer (amending **W&R13** and previous editions) and fire trainer respectively.

☐ G-APMB	Comet 4B	ex Dan-Air, Channel, BEA. CoA expired 18-5-79. Minus outer wings. See notes.	12-93
☐ G-AWZX	Trident 3B-101	ex Heathrow, BA, BEA. CoA exp 30-4-84.	12-93

■ **Gatwick Hilton** : The Moth replica still 'flies' in the lobby.

☐ 'G-AAAH'	B'168	DH.60G Moth rep *Jason.*	07-92

HENFIELD

■ **Interair**: Took on former Cosford, Shrop, Canberra B.2 WJ640/8722M following tender in April 1991 for spares recovery. During March 1993 it went in two directions, the nose to <u>Guildford</u>, Surrey, and the balance to <u>Egham</u>, Surrey.

LANCING

■ **Bob Kent** : Took delivery of composite Beagle Pup G-AXTZ from Earls Colne, Essex, on March 6, 1993, for restoration to static display standards for the museum at Shoreham Aerodrome, W Sussex. It moved on to <u>Shoreham</u>, W Sussex, by December 1993.

■ **Lancing School** : Purchased its CCF's Grasshopper TX.1 on June 21, 1988 and it may well still be stored in the grounds.

☐ XK820*   Grasshopper TX.1   see notes above.   06-88

■ **Sussex Spraying Services** : Jim Pearce's workshop has become a major haven for former CIS airframes, with the emphasis on *Luftwaffe* hardware. In late 1992 another *two* Bf 110s arrived, in much better condition than the first one. These two were thought to have been sold in late 1993 and were due to move on. Also here were a series of Hurricane frames. Some serials have been quoted, but they do not constitute enough 'meat' yet for a full inclusion. All of these frames and components have moved on, mostly to Tim Wallis, in New Zealand. Likewise, the rear end of a Ju 87R-4 (w/nr 6234) was held here, but has moved on, also for Tim. There is the promise of a much more substantial *Stuka* to come! The Fw 189 and the *Stuka* rear end were entered in the Sotheby's auction of September 13, 1992, (see *Appendix* D) reaching £30,000 and £8,000 respectively. Neither sold. Two Bf 109s ('E-1 w/nr 3579 and 'F-4 w/nr 8147) were here during 1992/1993, moving to Colchester, Essex.

☐	G-BSSY		Po-2 *Mule*	ex YU-CLJ, Yugoslav AF. For sale. 12-93
☐	RR232	G-BRSF	Spitfire IX	ex Winchester, Nowra, Bankstown, Point Cook, Cape Town, Ysterplaat, SAAF 5632, RR232, 47 MU, ECFS. Tail = JF620, wings = RM873. 12-93
☐	2100		Fw 189A-1	ex CIS/USSR, *Luftwaffe*. 'V7+1H'. Crashed 4-5-43. Restoration. 12-93
☐	3235*		Bf 110C-4	ex CIS/USSR, *Luftwaffe* JG77 'LN+ER'. 12-93
☐	4502		Bf 110E-2	ex CIS/USSR, *Luftwaffe* JG76 'M8+ZE'. Crashed 11-3-42. Restoration — see notes. 12-93
☐	5052*		Bf 110F-2	ex CIS/USSR, *Luftwaffe* 13(Z)-JG5 'LN+xx'. Crashed 11-1-43. Arr 11-12-92. See notes. 12-93

PLAISTOW (east of the A283, north of Petworth)

■ **Sussex Fire Brigade** : By January 1992, a former occupant of the dump at Shoreham Airport had arrived to act as a training aid for the local area fire brigade. When first seen it was badly hacked about and may not be long for this world.

☐ G-BATM*   Cherokee Six   ex Shoreham, Biggin Hill, 5Y-AOV, N8693N. Crashed 5-8-91. See above. F/n 1-93.   01-93

PULBOROUGH

The Whirlwind is still to be found outside the burnt-down cafe to the north of the town on the A29.

☐ XJ393   A2538   Whirlwind HAR.3   ex Higher Blagdon, Lee-on-Solent, Arbroath, Pershore, CS(A), XD363 and XD763 ntu.   04-93

SHOREHAM AERODROME (west of the River Adur, south of the A27)

■ **Aerodrome** : John Pothecary's Air South reflew Tiger Moth EC-AIU on August 28, 1992. Arriving by road on July 8, 1992, was the first of two MiGs for Graham Hinkley. This was SBLim-2A 622047 which was then allocated the registration G-OMIG. It made its first taxi runs on July 9, 1993 and made its first flight under UK conditions on November 19, 1993 initially to Lydd, Kent, and then to North Weald, Essex. Comanche 250 G-ARBO had gone by 1992 — destination unknown. The hulk of Enstrom F.28A G-AVUK was last noted here during August 1992, but had expired/gone by late 1993. Cherokee Six G-BATM appeared on the dump by July 1992 but moved to Plaistow, W Sussex, by January 1993. The cabin and tail section of Enstrom F.28A G-BBHC was to be found here by August 192, but had also gone in the late 1993 clear out. Harvard IV 'kit' 1730/G-BSBE arrived from Thruxton, Hants, by July 1992. It had moved on by September 1993, becoming G-TVIJ with an owner in Kent. There has been a considerable influx of **W&R** material here : —

☐	G-AAOR*	DH.60 Moth	ex EC-AAO. '30-76'. *La Madrina*. Stored. CoA expired 2-7-91. First noted 5-93. 12-93
☐	G-AKUI {2}*	Silvaire 8E	ex N45937, NC45937. Crashed 26-3-89. Air South. Restoration First noted 11-92. See N71776 below. 11-92
☐	G-AOIS	Tiger Moth	ex R5172, West Malling SF, 22 SFTS, 15 EFTS, 9 EFTS. CoA expired 7-6-81. Restoration. 12-93
☐	G-ARNG*	Colt 108	ex locality. CoA expired 10-12-73. Restoration. First noted 11-92. 12-93

☐ G-BJAP   Tiger Moth   ex Slinfold. Composite, under construction.
Air South.   12-93

☐ G-BTYW*   Cessna 120   ex Rochester, N77283, NC77283. Damaged,
stored.   05-93

☐ G-OATD   Short 330-100   ex Sydenham, N332SB, G-BKSV, G-14-3096.
Damaged by a bomb 27-11-89. Wreck.   05-93

☐   Tiger Moth   fuselage frame with Air South.   04-93

☐ N71776*   Silvaire 8A   ex Salisbury, NC71776. Spares for G-AKUI.
First noted 11-92.   11-92

☐ 5N-ABC   Navajo 310   ex Nigeria, N9206Y. Fuselage, spares use.   05-93

☐ 5N-AVC   Navajo 350   ex Nigeria, Nig AF 1003, N74970. Dump.   05-93

☐ 09008*   SBLim-2   ex Polish AF. Arrived 12-10-92. Graham Hinkley.
Stored.   05-93

☐ 1681*   G-BSBD   T-6G Texan   ex Thruxton, Mozambique, Portuguese AF 1681,
51-15007. Arrived 10-7-92.   12-93

☐ 1736*   G-BSBF   Harvard IV   ex Thruxton, Moz, PAF 1736, WGAF BF+058,
AA+058, 52-8590. Arrived 10-7-92.   12-93

☐ 1788*   G-BSBB   Harvard IV   ex Thruxton, Mozambique, PAF 1788, WGAF
AA+689, 53-4636. Arrived 10-7-92.   12-93

■ **Museum of _D-Day_ Aviation** : Ken Rimmel's museum moved into a hangar here during early
1993 and was busy re-establishing the huge collection of artefacts ready for the _D-Day_ celebrations.
The Museum was previously based at Apuldram, W Sussex, but had outgrown the site. While _D-Day_
is its primary subject, the Museum intends to portray the rich history of Shoreham itself in due course.
The Museum also formed the Typhoon & Tempest Association and has amassed a large amount of
artefacts and hardware on these two types. An RAF Air Sea Rescue gallery is backed up by no less
than four ASR boats being restored at locations on the south coast, it is hoped to amalgamate these at
nearby Shoreham harbour.
♦ Open 10.30am to 5pm daily April to November. ✉ Museum of D-Day Aviation, Shoreham
Aerodrome, Shoreham-by-Sea, West Sussex, BN4 5FF. ☎ 0273 440838.

☐ 'MJ751'* BAPC.209 Spitfire replica   ex Apuldram, _Piece of Cake_. 'DU-V'. 321 Sqn
colours. First noted 2-94.   02-94

■ **Shoreham Aviation Heritage Centre**: Not to be confused with the SAHT below, the centre
has been established inside the lovely terminal building at Shoreham and features displays on its long
history. The centre has a viewing park so that activity on the aerodrome can be monitored and several
historic aircraft are to be "attached" to the collection.
♦ Open 10.30am to 5pm daily April to November. ✉ Shoreham Aviation Heritage Centre, Shoreham
Aerodrome, Shoreham-by-Sea, West Sussex, BN4 5FF. ☎ 0273 440838.

      Bob Kent is/was working on the restoration to static condition of Pup G-AXTZ, it arrived
from Lancing, W Sussex, by December 1993.

☐ G-AXTZ*   Pup 100   ex Lancing, Earls Colne, Andrewsfield, G-35-148.
Wings from G-AVZO. Damaged 30-7-75. Arrived
by 12-93. See notes above.   12-93
      [Fuselage of G-AVZO can be found at East Tilbury, Essex.]

■ **Shoreham Aviation Heritage Trust** : During 1993 this group was established on land on the
aerodrome with a view to establishing a museum. The former Southern Aero Club building was taken
over and a couple of airframes placed on occasional loan from resident owners, including Graham
Hinkley's MiG (see above) and his MiG procedure trainer. However, the Trust's tenure did not last
long and by December 1993 had moved off-site.

■ **Northbrook College** : Condor G-AXGU moved to Terry McRae's workshop in <u>Shoreham-by-
Sea</u>, W Sussex. An additional Queen Air has joined the College's fleet of instructional airframes.

☐ G-AMNN   Tiger Moth   ex Redhill. Composite.   05-93

☐ G-APNJ   Cessna 310   ex EI-AJY, N3635D. CoA expired 28-11-74.   05-93

☐ G-AWKX   Queen Air A65   CoA expired 25-10-89.   05-93

☐ G-AYKA   Baron 55A   ex Elstree, HB-GEW, G-AYKA, D-IKUN,
N8683M. Crashed 18-6-89.   05-93

☐ G-BNPU   XL929   Pembroke C.1   ex Sandown, Shawbury, 60, Kemble, 207, SCCS,
TCCS, FCCS, BCCS.   05-93

☐ G-KEAB*	Queen Air B80	ex Manston, G-BSSL, G-BFEP, F-BRNR, OO-VDE. Arrived 20-2-92.	05-93
☐ G-OBUS	Archer 181	ex G-BMTT, N3002K. Cr 18-4-89. Fuse.	12-92
☐ G-TOBY	Cessna 172B	ex Sandown, G-ARCM, N6952X. Damaged 15-10-83.	08-92
☐ VQ-SAC	BN-2A Islander	crashed 4-9-76. Forward fuselage, dumped.	12-92

SHOREHAM-BY-SEA

■ **Terry McRae** : During 1992 Terry took over the Auster Alpha previously with BCAR at Hedge End, Hants, and is restoring it to flying condition for himself. In return, he is working on the restoration to flying condition of BCAR's Cadet glider. Condor G-ASRB was flying again by 1993.

☐ G-AGXT*	J/1N Alpha	ex Hedge End area, Warmingham, East Kirkby, Sibson, Wigan, Handforth. Crashed 7-6-79. Arrived -92. For restoration.	10-92
☐ G-AXGU*	D.62B Condor	ex Shoreham Airport, Billingshurst. Crashed 31-3-75. Restoration	08-92
☐ G-BRRL*	Super Cub 95	ex Kingsclere, D-EMKE, RNethAF R-44, 52-2450. Thought composite with original fuselage of G-AYPO. Restoration. F/n 10-92.	10-92
☐ *	Cadet TX.2	under restoration for BCAR, see notes above.	10-92

■ **Others** : Locally, the Tiger Moth rebuild has been joined by a stored and gutted Rallye.

☐ G-ALVP	Tiger Moth	ex Shoreham Lighthouse, R4770, 4 RFS, 4 EFTS, 10 FIS, 7 EFTS, 11 EFTS. CoA exp 15-2-61.	
☐ G-BGZO*	MS.880B Rallye	ex F-BKZO. Crashed 10-5-89. Stored. First noted 12-92.	12-92

SLINFOLD

Aiglet G-AMKU is thought still stored here.

☐ G-AMKU	J/1B Aiglet	ex ST-ABD, SN-ABD, G-AMKU. CoA expired 21-9-84. Stored.

TANGMERE

■ **Tangmere Military Aviation Museum** : With the Museum's new and impressive display hall came other rewards. The RAF Museum has lent them the record-breaking Meteor and Hawker P.1067, previously housed at Cosford, Shrop. Other airframes are 'in the pipeline'. Also from Cosford will come the Hawker Fury replica 'K7271' (BAPC.148). It will be painted in 1 Squadron markings, as operated from Tangmere. Due early in 1994 was SE.5A replica 'D2700' (BAPC.208) from the shopping centre at Farnborough, Hants. Finally, due by April 1994 is a TDL Replicas built Spitfire V, donated by the brother of a Danish pilot of 234 Squadron, lost from Tangmere in 1942. It will be painted as 'BL924' 'AV-G'. The museum entered Meteor F.8 WA984 and Hunter E-412 into the Sotheby's auction of September 19, 1992. They reached £2,000 and £1,900 each and failed to sell. (See Appendix D.) Plans for these two now centre around refurbishment and their being pole mounted at the main entrance, the Hunter in 34 Squadron colours and the Meteor to be brought back to standard configuration and given 43 Squadron colours — both representative of the units' tenure at Tangmere. Going back to **W&R13**, Meteor WA984 was acquired by Tangmere and is not on loan. T-33 19252 was due to go to Bruntingthorpe, Leics, during December 1993, but had not left as these words were put together. Robs Lamplough's Bf 109E left for Hungerford, Berks, during December 1993.
◆ Signposted from the A27. Open daily 10am to 5.30pm from February 1 to November 30. Parties can be accommodated at other times by arrangement. ✉ Tangmere Airfield, Chichester, West Sussex PO20 6ES. ☎ 0243 775223.

☐ EE549*	7008M	Meteor IV Special	ex Cosford, St Athan, Abingdon, Hendon, St Athan, Innsworth, Fulbeck, Cranwell, CFE, FCCS, RAFHSF. Arrived 19-9-92.	11-93
☐ WA984		Meteor F.8	ex Southampton, Wimborne, Tarrant Rushton, 211 AFS, 19. Composite, parts from VZ530. See notes above.	11-93

☐	WB188*	7154M	Hawker P.1067	ex Cosford, St Athan, Colerne, Melksham, Halton, Hawkers. Hunter prototype. (Hunter F.3 for speed records.) Arrived 19-9-92.	11-93
☐	'XF314'	E-412	Hunter F.51	ex Dunsfold, G-9-439, Danish AF, Aalborg, Esk.724. 43 Sqn colours. See notes above.	11-93
☐	19252		T-33A-1-LO	ex Hailsham, Sculthorpe, French AF. See notes above.	11-93

WEST CHILTINGTON (on the B2139 south of Horsham)

■ **P A Brook** Has no less than four aircraft restorations underway in the area. The two Hawk Trainer IIIs/Magisters went 'missing' under the Benington, Herts, heading in **W&R11**.

☐	G-AGOY*	Messenger 3	ex Hatch, Southill, Castletown, EI-AGE, HB-EIP, G-AGOY, U-0247. Restn. F/n 4-92.	04-92
☐	G-AIUA*	Hawk Tnr III	ex Benington, Bushey, Old Warden, Duxford, Felthorpe, T9768, 10 AGS, 7 FIS, 15 EFTS, Wyton SF. CoA exp 13-7-67. See notes above. Restn. First noted 11-92.	11-92
☐	G-ANWO*	Hawk Tnr III	ex Benington, Cranfield, Old Warden, Duxford, Felthorpe, L8262, 21 (P)AFU, CFS, 17 SFTS, RAFC, 2 FIS, 6 FIS, Coltishall SF, 5 EFTS, 8 EFTS, 29 ERFTS. CoA expired 18-4-63. See notes. Spares for G-AIUA. F/n 11/92.	11-92
☐	G-AOBO	Tiger Moth	ex Redhill, Fareham, N6473, 10 RFS, 16 EFTS, 10 EFTS, 19 ERFTS. CoA expired 28-9-69. Restoration.	11-92

Tyne & Wear

GATESHEAD

On March 8, 1993 Viscount fuselage 'G-WHIZ' (G-AMOE) at Saltwell Park was broken up. At least the nose moved to a local scrapyard, but it did not last long there.

NEWCASTLE

■ **John Stelling** : Continues to work on the Auster composite when he isn't restoring or displaying military vehicles.

| ☐ | 'NJ719' | G-ANFU | Auster 5 | ex NEAM, Bristol, TW385, 663, 227 OCU, 13 OTU. Composite, forward fuselage of G-ANFU, with 'spare' AOP.6 rear half. Stb wing from G-AKPH, pt from AOP.6. Restoration. | 05-93 |

NEWCASTLE AIRPORT (or Woolsington, on the A696 north west of Newcastle)

A *Shoebox* is in use for spares. The Devon is still in external store.

| ☐ | G-ANDX | XG496 | Devon C.2 | ex RAE Farnborough, G-ANDX. CoA expired 3-4-86. Stored. | 05-90 |
| ☐ | G-BGNH* | | Short 330-200 | ex N331L, G-BGNH. CoA expired 22-9-79. Spares. | 09-92 |

SUNDERLAND (Usworth, west of Sunderland)

■ **North East Aircraft Museum** (NEAM) : 1993 was the year when NEAM finally proved the potential that many always believed it had. A 100ft display hangar stands as proud testament to the small team's efforts and a large number of aircraft can now bask in being in the warm and dry. This also means that the restoration hangar can now be just that and work is underway on a series of airframes. The next step is to further upgrade the display buildings and reception area. The Royal Observer Corps Northern Area Collection display officially opened on May 21, 1993. To 'celebrate' the new display hangar, NEAM took on no less than five airframes during 1993 : Dove, Pucara,

SD.330, Whirlwind and Widgeon. The SD.330, courtesy of Gill Aviation at Newcastle Airport, is a most welcome exhibit. It is described by those at NEAM, somewhat tongue-in-cheek, as "the first wide-bodied airliner to go on display in the UK"! Three airframes have moved on :— the nose of Canberra T.4 XH584 moved to Firbeck, S Yorks, during mid-1993; the nose of Jet Provost T.3 XN597/7984M to Firbeck, S Yorks by December 1993; Whirlwind HAR.10 XP360 moved to Upper Hill, H&W, in late 1992.

◆ North of the A123T, off the A1290 Washington Road, follow signs for the Nissan plant. Open every day 10am to 5pm (or dusk in winter). Group visits are welcome with prior notice. ✉ NEAM, Old Washington Road, Sunderland, Tyne & Wear, SR5 3HZ. ☎ 091 519 0662

☐	'K-158'*	BAPC.207	Austin Whippet rep	ex Stoke-on-Trent. Loan V&RWC. F/n 9-92. 12-93
☐	G-APTW*		Widgeon	ex Helston, Southend, Westlands. CoA expired 26-9-75. Arrived by 10-93. 12-93
☐	G-ARHX*		Dove 8	ex Wycombe AP, Southgate, Leavesden, Hunting Surveys. CoA exp 8-9-78. Arrived by 1-93. 12-93
☐	G-AWRS		Avro XIX-2	ex Strathallan, Kemps, Junex, Hewitts, TX213, WCS, 22 GCF, OCTU, 18 GCF, 2 TAF CS, 527, CSE, RCCF. CoA expired 10-8-73. Under restoration. 12-93
☐	G-BEEX		Comet 4C	ex East Kirkby, Tattershall, Woodford, Lasham, Dan-Air, SU-ALM. Nose. 12-93
☐	G-MBDL		Lone Ranger	microlight. Stored. 12-93
☐	G-OGIL*		SD.330-100	ex Gill Aviation, G-BITV, G-14-3068. Damaged 1-7-92. Arrived 4-93. 12-93
☐	G-SFTA	G-BAGJ	Gazelle 1	ex Carlisle, G-SFTA, HB-XIL, G-BAGJ, XW858 ntu. Crashed 7-3-84. Under restoration. 12-93
☐	RH746		Brigand TF.1	ex Failsworth, CS(A), ATDU Gosport, Bristols, ATDU, A&AEE, Bristols. Fuselage. Stored. 12-93
☐	VV217	7323M	Vampire FB.5	ex Barnham, Bury St E, 'VV271', Oakington, DH. Stored. 12-93
☐	VX577		Valetta C.2	ex Northern Parachute Centre, MCS, 70, Malta CF, 70, MECS, Gibraltar CF, Malta C&TTS, 2 TAF CS, 30. 12-93
☐	WA577	7718M	Sycamore 3	ex Kings Heath, Shirley, St Athan, A&AEE, G-ALST ntu. 12-93
☐	WB685		Chipmunk T.10	ex Leeds, Irlam, Edn UAS, Lyneham SF, 8 RFS, 1 RFS. Composite, rear fuselage of WP969/ G-ATHC. Loan, Nigel Ponsford. 12-93
☐	WD790	8743M	Meteor NF.11	ex Darlington, Leeming, RAE Llanbedr, RS&RE, RRE, TRE. Nose. 12-93
☐	WD889		Firefly AS.5	ex Failsworth. Cockpit section. 12-93 [Rear fuselage of VT409, stored.]
☐	WG724		Dragonfly HR.5	ex Chester-le-Street, Moor Monkton, Blackbushe, Lossiemouth SF, Ford SF. 12-93
☐	WJ639		Canberra TT.18	ex Samlesbury, 7, 57. 12-93
☐	WK198	7428M	Swift F.4	ex Failsworth, Kirkham, Aldergrove, MoS. Fuselage, under restoration. 12-93
☐	WL181		Meteor F.8	ex Chester-le-Street, Acklington, Kemble, CAW, Tangmere SF, 34. 'X'. 12-93
☐	WN516		Balliol T.2	ex Failsworth, RAFC. Cockpit, stored. 12-93
☐	WZ518		Vampire T.11	ex Chester-le-Street, Handforth, Pomona Dock, 5 FTS, Oldenburg SF, 2 TAF CF, 14. Wings of WZ608. 12-93
☐	WZ767		Grasshopper TX.1	ex Syerston. 12-93
☐	XG518	8009M	Sycamore HR.14	ex Balloch, Halton, Wroughton, CFS, Khormaksar SF, El Adem SF, Habbiniya SF, Amman SF. 'S-E'. 12-93
☐	XG523	7793M	Sycamore HR.14	ex Hayes, Middle Wallop, Ternhill, CFS, JEHU. Damaged 25-9-62. Nose section. Stored. 12-93

☐	XG680		Sea Ven FAW.22	ex Sydenham, ADS, 891. '735-VL'. 12-93
☐	XL319		Vulcan B.2	ex 44, Wadd Wing, 35, 230 OCU, 617, 230 OCU, Scampton Wing, 617. 12-93
☐	XM660		Whirlwind HAS.7	ex Almondbank, Fleetlands, Lee, Lossiemouth SAR Flt, 737, 700H, 824. '78'. 12-93
☐	XN258*		Whirlwind HAR.9	ex Helston, Culdrose SF, *Endurance* Flt, Culdrose SF, *Hermes* Flt. '589-CU'. Arrived by 10-93. 12-93
☐	XP627		Jet Provost T.4	ex London Colney, Hatfield, Shawbury, 6 FTS, 3 FTS, 1 FTS. 12-93
☐	XT236		Sioux AH.1	ex Middle Wallop, MoAF, Sek Kong. Stored. 12-93
☐	XW276		Gazelle 03	ex Wroughton, Southampton, Middle Wallop, Farnborough, Leatherhead, F-ZWRI. MoAF loan. 12-93
☐	ZF594		Lightning F.53	ex Warton, RSAF 53-696, 2 Sqn Tabuk, 13 Sqn Dhahran, 2 Sqn Tabuk, 6 Sqn Khamis Mushayt, LCU Dhahran, 2 Sqn Dhahran, G-27-66. 12-93
☐	A-528*	8769M	FMA Pucara	ex Middle Wallop, Cosford, Abingdon, Stanley, Argentine AF. Arrived by 10-93. 12-93
☐	E-419		Hunter F.51	ex Dunsfold, G-9-441, Aalborg, Dan AF *Esk*.724. 12-93
☐	146		Mystere IVA	ex Sculthorpe, French AF. '8-MC'. 12-93
☐	42157		F-100D-16-NA	ex Sculthorpe, French AF. 12-93
☐	54439		T-33A-1-LO	ex Sculthorpe, French AF. 12-93
☐	6171		F-86D-35-NA	ex Hellenikon, Greek AF, USAF 51-6171. Restoration. 12-93
☐	6541		F-84F-40-RE	ex Hellenikon, Greek AF, USAF 52-6541. 12-93
☐		BAPC.96	Brown Helicopter	ex Stanley. Stored. 12-93
☐		BAPC.97	LA-4 Minor (mod)	ex Sibson, Sunderland, Stanley. Stored. 12-93
☐		BAPC.119	Bensen B.7	ex Stanley. 12-93
☐		BAPC.228	Olympus	hang glider 12-93
☐	*		C-10A mock-up	ex Wycombe Air Park, Bushey, West Ruislip, Stanmore, St Albans, Radlett. Nose section, USAF colours. 12-93

■ **2214 Squadron ATC** : Still have their Vampire.

☐	XD622	8160M	Vampire T.11	ex Leeming, Barkston Ash, Shawbury, 118, RAFC. 12-93

■ **Others** : John Stelling's workshop is more precisely listed under Newcastle, T&W — *qv*.

Warwickshire

ATHERSTONE

E C Taylor is making good progress with the much-travelled Fleet Canuck here. Also present is at least the fuselage of the unconverted Tiger Moth G-APGL. It was last used as a source of spares for the reborn G-AJVE, but may itself be rebuilt in due course.

☐	G-APGL*	NM140	Tiger Moth	ex Fairoaks, LAS, AOPS, 14 RFS, 8 RFS, 8 EFTS, 3 EFTS, 22 EFTS, 3 EFTS, ORTU, Tarrant Rushton SF. Fuselage. See notes above.
☐	CS-ACQ*	G-FLCA	Canuck	ex Chilbolton, Coventry Airport, Rochester, Blackbushe, Portugal, CF-DQP. Restn. 01-94

BIDFORD AERODROME (north east of Evesham at Bidford-on-Avon)

■ **Avon Soaring Centre** : A frustrated Blanik rebuild is a well established part of the scenery here.

☐ EUG* BGA.2958 Blanik ex RAFGSA.R56, RAFGSA.426, BGA.1953. Composite, including parts from BGA.1917 and BGA.2028. First noted 10-92. 10-93

COVENTRY AIRPORT (or Baginton, at the A45/A423 junction, south of the city)
■ **Air Atlantique / Atlantic Aeroengineering** : Work continues on the Prentice and on C-47B G-APML when time permits. Moving in from the other side of the Airport has been the moribund restoration project C-47A G-BPMP. Mentioned in **W&R13**, Twin Pioneer G-BCWF has reverted to G-APRS and has joined the Atlantic Group proper, initially for survey work. Atlantic Aeroengineering are custodians of the two SPT *Shacks* and keep them on a 'care and maintenance' basis — see below.

☐ G-APJB Prentice 1 ex VR259, 1 ASS, 2 ASS, RAFC. CoA expired 4-9-77. Restn for the Percival Collection - see below. 06-93
☐ 'G-ARME' G-APML C-47B-1-DK ex Martin Baker, Transair, KJ836, Henlow SF, MoS Para Test Unit, RAE Farnborough, 43-48359. CoA exp 27-7-84. Restoration. 06-93
☐ G-BPMP C-47A-50-DL ex Liverpool, N54607, Blackbushe, N9842A ntu, 20669 / CNA-LM Moroccan AF, CN-CCL, F-BEFA, 42-24211. See notes. 06-93

■ **Midland Air Museum** (MAM) **and Aerospace Education Centre** : A view of the list below will reveal yet another busy time for MAM with the arrival of some 'heavy metal' airframes. Restoration of airframes on site continues and the erection of a new workshop in the form of an original Robin hangar is underway. The aerospace education initiative continues to forge good links with aerospace companies both locally and nationally and with local centres of education. One acquisition during 1993 is not apparent below. Long promised to MAM, the former Rolls-Royce Beagle 206 G-ASWJ at Halton, Bucks, moved on loan to Brunel College during May 1993 and can be found under Bristol, Avon. MAM is actively negotiating to bring a MiG-15 from storage at AMARC Davis-Monthan, Arizona, having previously been used by the Defense Test & Evaluation Support Agency. It is thought to be a Lim-2. Messenger 4A VP-KJL was acquired by Ken Fern and moved to Stoke-on-Trent, Staffs, on May 25, 1992. The pod of Vampire T.11 XE872 was scrapped during February 1994, the remainder being used for spares. Two previous MAM inmates can now be 'cleaned up' : — Aztec 250 G-SHIP moved to Hockley Heath, West Mids, during 1989 and Cessna 172 'G-ASOK' went to Cruden Bay, Grampian, during 1988.
◆ Well signed from the A45/A423 junction. April to October Monday to Saturday 10.30am to 5pm and Sundays 10.30am to 6pm. November to March, Sunday, Monday, Thursday and Saturday 10.30am to 4.30pm. ✉ Midland Air Museum, Baginton, Coventry CV8 3AZ. ☎ 0203 301033.

☐ G-EBJG Pixie III ex Coventry, Stratford-on-Avon. CoA expired 2-10-36. Stored. 12-93
☐ G-ABOI Wheeler Slymph ex Coventry, Old Warden. On loan. Stored. 12-93
☐ G-AEGV HM.14 *Flea* ex Coventry, Knowle, Northampton, Sywell. 12-93
☐ G-ALCU Dove 2 ex airfield, VT-CEH. CoA exp 16-3-73. 12-93
☐ G-APJJ Fairey Ultra Light ex Heaton Chapel, Coventry, Hayes. CoA expired 1-4-59. 12-93
☐ G-APRL Argosy 101 ex ABC/Elan, Sagittair, N890U, N602Z, N6507R, G-APRL. *Edna*. CoA expired 23-3-87. 12-93
☐ G-APWN Whirlwind Srs 3 ex Cranfield, Redhill, VR-BER, G-APWN, 5N-AGI, G-APWN. CoA exp 17-5-78. Restored, Bristows colours. 12-93
☐ G-ARYB* HS.125 Srs 1 ex Hatfield, Astwick Manor, Hatfield. CoA expired 22-1-68. Arrived 2-12-93. 12-93
☐ G-MJWH Vortex 120 hang glider, former microlight. 12-93
☐ BGA.804 VM589 Cadet TX.1 stored. 12-93
☐ 'A7317' BAPC.179 Pup replica ex Waltham Abbey, North Weald, *Wings*. 12-93
☐ 'H3426' BAPC.68 Hurricane replica ex Wembley, Newark, *Battle of Britain*. Loan. Restoration. 12-93
☐ EE531 7090M Meteor F.4 ex Bentham, Coventry Airport, Birmingham, Weston Park, Birmingham, RAE Lasham, A&AEE, makers. 12-93

☐	VF301	7060M	Vampire F.1	ex Stoneleigh, Debden, 208 AFS, 595, 226 OCU. 'RAL-G', 605 Sqn colours. 12-93
☐	VM325		Anson C.19	ex Halfpenny Green, WCS, NCS, WCS, TCCF, Upavon CF, 173, 4 FP. Stored. 12-93
☐	VS623	G-AOKZ	Prentice T.1	ex Shoreham, Redhill, Southend, VS623, CFS, 2 FTS, 22 FTS. Restoration pending. 12-93
☐	VT935		BP-111A	ex Cranfield, RAE Bedford. 12-93
☐	VZ477	7741M	Meteor F.8	ex Kimbolton, APS, 245. Nose. Arr 4-6-92. 12-93
☐	WF922		Canberra PR.3	ex Cambridge, 39, 69, 58, 82. 12-93
☐	WS838		Meteor NF.14	ex Cosford, Manchester, Cosford, Shawbury, Colerne, RAE Bedford, RRE, MoS, 64, 238 OCU. Aerospace Museum loan. 12-93
☐	WV797	A2637	Sea Hawk FGA.6	ex Perth, Culdrose, Halton 8155M, Sydenham, 738, 898, 899, Fleetlands, 787. 12-93
☐	XA508	A2472	Gannet T.2	ex Yeovilton, Manadon, 737. '627-GN', 737 Sqn c/s. FAAM loan. 12-93
☐	XA699	7809M	Javelin FAW.5	ex Cosford, Locking, Shawbury, Kemble, Shawbury, 5, 151. 12-93
☐	XD626		Vampire T.11	ex Bitteswell, Shawbury, CATCS, CNCS, 5 FTS, RAFC, CFS. 12-93
☐	XE855		Vampire T.11	ex Upton-by-Chester, Woodford, Chester, 27 MU, 22 MU, 10 MU, AWOCU. Pod, spares. 12-93
☐	XF382		Hunter F.6A	ex Brawdy, 1 TWU, TWU, 229 OCU, FCS, 65, 63, 92. '15'. 12-93
☐	XJ579*		Sea Vixen FAW.2	ex Farnborough, A&AEE, Llanbedr, 899, 766. Nose section. Arrived 18-8-92. 12-93
☐	XK741		Gnat F.1	ex Leamington Spa, Fordhouses, Dunsfold, Hamble, Boscombe Down, Dunsfold. Fuse. 12-93
☐	XK907		Whirlwind HAS.7	ex Bubbenhall, Panshanger, Elstree, Luton, ETPS, RRE, Alvis. Cockpit only by 12-93. 12-93
☐	XL360		Vulcan B.2	ex 44, 101, 35, 617, 230 OCU, Wadd Wing, 230 OCU, Scamp W, 617. *City of Coventry*. 12-93
☐	XN685*	8173M	Sea Vixen FAW.2	ex Chester, Cosford, Cranwell, 890, 766, 893, HSA Hatfield. Arrived 14-9-92. 12-93
☐	XR771		Lightning F.6	ex Binbrook, 5, 11, 5, 56, 74. On loan from Magnatec Ltd. 'BM'. 12-93
☐	ZF598		Lightning T.55	ex Warton, RSAF 55-713, G-27-72. 12-93
☐			Beaufighter	ex Birmingham, Coventry. Cockpit. *Possibly* T5298, in which case 4552M, ex TFU. 12-93
☐	E-425		Hunter F.51	ex Dunsfold, G-9-446, Aalborg, Danish AF Esk.724. 12-93
☐	R-756		F-104G	ex Aalborg, Danish AF. 12-93
☐	70		Mystere IVA	ex Sculthorpe, French AF. *Patrouille de France* colours. 12-93
☐	51-4419		T-33A-1-LO	ex Sculthorpe, French AF. 12-93
☐	17473*		T-33A-1-LO	ex Cosford, Sculthorpe, French AF. Arrived 26-10-93. Loan from Aerospace Museum. 12-93
☐	54-2174		F-100D-16-NA	ex Sculthorpe, French AF. 12-93
☐	28368		Fl 282V-20	ex Coventry, Cranfield, Brize Norton. Frame. 12-93
☐	29640		SAAB J29F	ex Southend, R Swedish AF. 12-93
☐	24535		HH-43B Huskie	ex Woodbridge, 40 ARRS, Det 2, Upper Heyford. Under restoration. 12-93
☐	37699*		F-4C-21-MC	ex Upper Heyford, Fairford, Illinois ANG, 557 TFS, 356 TFS, 480 TFS. Arr 7-10-93. 12-93
☐	56-0312		F-101B-80-MC	ex Alconbury, Davis-Monthan, Kentucky ANG. Arrived 8-3-92. 60th FIS colours. 12-93
☐	58-2062		U-6A Beaver	ex Mannheim, US Army. 12-93

☐	63-7414	F-4C-15-MC	ex Woodbridge, New York ANG.	12-93
☐	70270	F-101B-80-MC	ex Woodbridge, Davis-Monthan, Texas ANG. Fuselage, for conversion to cockpit only, 'hands-on' exhibit. Arrived 14-2-92.	12-93
☐	BAPC.9	Humber Monoplane	ex Birmingham Airport, Yeovilton, Wroughton, Yeovilton, Coventry.	12-93
☐	BAPC.32	Tom Thumb	ex Coventry, Bewdley, Coventry, Banbury. Unfinished. Stored.	12-93
☐	BAPC.126	Turbulent	ex Shoreham, Croydon. Static airframe.	12-93

■ **Percival Collection / Aircraft Radio Museum** : Air Atlantique continue to work upon the restoration of Prentice G-APJB — see above. The Radio Collection is an extensive array of airborne radio equipment which is housed in Baginton village.
◆ Available for inspection only with prior permission. ✉ Aircraft Radio Museum, Coventry Airport, Baginton, Coventry, CV8 3AP.

☐	G-AMLZ	Prince 6E	ex VR-TBN ntu, G-AMLZ. CoA expired 18-6-71. External store, poor shape.	01-94
☐	G-AOKO	Prentice 1	ex Southend, VS621, CFS, 2 FTS, 22 FTS. CoA expired 23-10-72. Spares.	06-93
☐	G-APIU	Prentice 1	ex VR200, 1 ASS, 2 ASS, CFS, 2 FTS. CoA expired 23-2-67. Spares.	06-93

■ **Shackleton Preservation Trust** (SPT) : — The CAA has decreed that the 'flyer' Shackleton will need a respar before a Permit to Fly is issued. Fund raising is underway for what is a gargantuan task. In the meantime, Atlantic Aeroengineering — see above — are looking after the airframes and keep them 'live'. A huge spares holding has been accrued, especially in terms of Griffon engines and props.

The nose section of *Zebedee*, the Shackleton T.4 scrapped at Strathallan in February 1990, was saved by Norman Thelwell. It is trailer-mounted and is used to promote the cause of the SPT at various shows. The owner spends much time away from the UK and although VP293 'lives' at several locations it has been decided to list it here.
◆ The aircraft are located within an active maintenance area and viewing is not possible. General enquiries about the SPT can be made to : — ✉ Shackleton Preservation Trust, D Liddell-Grainger, Ayton Castle, Ayton, Berwick, TD14 5RD.

☐	VP293*	Shackleton T.4	ex Strathallan, RAE, MOTU, 206, 46, 224. Trailer-mounted nose . See notes above.	10-92
☐	WL790	Shackleton AEW.2	ex Waddington, Lossie, 8, 205, 210, 269, 204, 240. Stored.	02-94
☐	WR963	Shackleton AEW.2	ex Waddington, Lossiemouth, 8, 205, 28, 210, 224. Stored.	02-94

■ **Others** : The project to restore C-47A G-BPMP foundered during 1993 and it moved into the care of Air Atlantique — see above. Luton LA-5 Major 'G-AWSH' (G-ASWH) has not been seen for some time and is thought to have moved on. Spitfire Tr IX G-BMSB made its first flight after restoration on November 8, 1993. B-25 '151632'/NL9494Z hulk was put up for sale by the Airport Authority in lieu of ramp payments. During February 1994 it started to move, section by section, to <u>Headcorn</u>, Kent. The pile of replicas and 'fancifuls' that also lay with the B-25 have been salvaged and gone in two different directions, see under <u>Macclesfield</u>, Ches, and <u>Sevenoaks</u>, Kent.

☐	G-AYKZ	SAI KZ-VIII	ex HB-EPB, OY-ACB. CoA expired 17-7-81. Stored.	
☐	G-BGTS*	Cherokee 140F	ex Liverpool, OY-BGD. Crashed 17-6-89. Stored. F/n 12-92.	12-92
☐	G-BHFL*	Cherokee 180	ex N15189. Cr 1-11-89. Wreck. F/n 12-92.	12-92
☐	G-BMIU	Enstrom F.28A	ex OO-BAM, F-BVRE ntu. Crashed 9-7-86. Cabin, stored.	01-94
☐	*	Enstrom F.28A	cabin, stored. First noted 3-93.	06-93

HATTON (on the A4177 near Warwick)
■ **Midland Warplane Museum** (MWM) : Until such time as the Bessoneau has been erected, along with planning permission, MWM's exhibits have been put into store and visits are not possible

for the time being. The wings and other parts that were stolen from the Sea Venom were recovered but badly damaged and were passed on to Alan Simpson of Stone, Staffs, who hopes to marry them up with a Sea Venom pod.
✉ M J Evans, 46 Arthur Street, Kenilworth, Warks, CV8 2HE.

☐ XG692	Sea Ven FAW.22	ex Alcester, Wellesbourne Mountford, Sydenham, Castlereagh, Sydenham, 750. Pod. Stored. 11-93
☐	Harvard	cockpit section. Stored, off site. 11-93

HENLEY-IN-ARDEN (on the A34 south of Solihull)
■ **Abrasive Development Ltd** : Still have an Aztec for trials. The company also have major premises at Seighford, Staffs.

☐ G-ASRE	Aztec 250C	ex Ipswich, Southend. CoA expired 12-4-81.

LAPWORTH (on the B4439 , south of Solihull)
■ **Willpower Garage** : The Vampire pod continues to rot outside this garage.

☐ XD435	Vampire T.11	ex Kenilworth, Studley, Harpurhey, Woodford, Hawarden, St Athan, 8 FTS, 5 FTS, 41. Pod. 09-93

LONG MARSTON AERODROME (south of the A439, south west of Stratford-upon-Avon)
■ **Jet Aviation Preservation Group** (JAPG) : Widening the terms of reference of the Vampire Preservation Group resulted in a change of name during 1993. Working quietly away here are Stewart and Tony Holder, who have managed to assemble a series of airframes. It needs to be said that JAPG are nothing to do with the demised SAC, and are unable to answer enquiries relating to the collapse of the latter. The Hunter composite is essentially a set of F.6 wings, an FGA.9 tailcone and will have an FR.10 nose cone with camera ports. This nose has given JAPG the notion of completing the restoration as an FR.10 and it will represent XJ714 'B' of 4 Squadron, 2nd TAF. The small group are working hard at preserving the types in their care. Alan Allen's Vampire T.11 XE849 arrived here during April 1994. It is offered for disposal to a good home.
◆ Visitors are welcome at weekends when the JAPG crew are at work on their airframes. ✉ JAPG, Stewart Holder, 62 Avon Street, Evesham, Worcs WR11 4LG.

☐ WE192*	Canberra T.4	ex Firbeck, Winsford, Samlesbury, St Athan, 231 OCU, 360, 231 OCU, 39, 231 OCU, 3, 231 OCU. Cockpit section. Arrived by 12-93. 02-94
☐ XD447	Vampire T.11	ex SAC, E Kirkby, Tattershall, Woodford, Chester, St Athan, 8 FTS, RAFC, 5 FTS. '50'. Restn. 02-94
☐ XE849* 7928M	Vampire T.11	ex Yatesbury, Monkton Farleigh, Conington, Ware, St Athan, CNCS, 5 FTS, 7 FTS, 1 FTS, 4 FTS. 'V3'. Arr 4-94. See notes above. 04-94
☐ XG737*	Sea Ven FAW.22	ex Cardiff-Wales, Yeovilton, FRU, Sydenham, 894, 893, 891. '220-Z'. Stored. Arr by 7-92. 02-94
☐ XP568	Jet Provost T.4	ex Faygate, Hatfield, Hatfield Tech, Shawbury, RAFC. Restoration. 02-94
☐	Hunter composite	nose ex RAF Stafford unused, middle section of XG226, ex Abingdon. (With parts from WT684 - Brize Norton, Oxon, -XF383 - North Scarle, Lincs, ET-272, Chelford, Ches.). See notes above. 02-94

■ **Stratford Aircraft Collection** (SAC) : Most of the airframes continue to rot in the aftermath of the collapse of the former collection. Disposals have been as follows :— *Flea* 'G-ADRY'/BAPC.77 to Cheltenham, Glos; Chipmunk T.10 WB624 moved to Firbeck, S Yorks, by October 1993; Venom NF.3 WX788 (previously at Cardiff-Wales, S Glam) moved to the Kenilworth, Warks, area having been acquired by the Midland Warplane Museum, but it moved on to Elvington, N Yorks, during 1993; Grasshopper TX.1 WZ779 moved to Old Sarum, Wilts, by March 1993; Cadet TX.3 XA293 moved to Stoke-on-Trent, Staffs, by May 1993; Lightning nose XG331 to Chelford, Ches; Auster AOP.9 XK421/8365M moved to Fownhope, H&W. Bensen B.7 BAPC.200 moved briefly to Cheltenham, Glos, before settling upon Leeds, W Yorks. Whirlwind HAS.7 XL840 has been acquired by Phil Cartwright, but will remain here for resale. Jet Provost T.4 XP568 and the Hunter components went to VPG (later JAPG), see above. Wessex HAS.3 XM833 *never* arrived, remaining at Lasham, Hants.

☐	WG718*	A2531	Dragonfly HR.3	ex Cardiff-Wales, Yeovilton, SAH Culdrose, Fleetlands. Poor state. Arr by early 1992.	02-94
☐	WL332		Meteor T.7	ex Cardiff-Wales, Croston, Moston, FRU, Lossiemouth SF, Ford SF. '888'.	02-94
☐	WM735	G-RACA	Sea Prince T.1	ex Staverton, Kemble, 750, BTU, A&AEE. '571-CU'.	02-94
☐	WR985	8103M	Shackleton MR.3/3	ex Cosford, 201, 120, 206, 203, 206, A&AEE, 206. 'H'.	02-94
☐	WT482		Canberra T.4	ex Charlwood, Hull, Wyton, '160 CSE', 231 OCU, 85, 231 OCU, Bruggen SF, 88, 17, Wahn SF, Wildenrath SF, Gutersloh SF, 103. SOC 6-1-76. Nose.	02-94
☐	WT483		Canberra T.4	ex Filton, Samlesbury, 231 OCU, 39, 231 OCU, 16, Laarbruch SF, 68, Laarbruch SF, 69.	02-94
☐	XE856		Vampire T.11	ex Lasham, Welwyn Garden City, Woodford, Chester, St Athan, 219, North Weald SF, 226 OCU.	02-94
☐	XG629		Sea Ven FAW.22	ex Fleetlands, Higher Blagdon, Culdrose, ADS, 831, 893. '668-LM'.	02-94
☐	XL840		W'wind HAS.7	ex Norwich, Sibson, Blackpool, Fleetwood, Wroughton, 705, Brawdy SF, Culdrose SF, 705, 820. Stored. See notes above.	02-94
☐	XP346	8793M	W'wind HAR.10	ex Tattershall Thorpe, Shawbury, Lee-on-Solent, Akrotiri, 84, 22, 225.	02-94
☐	XW315		Jet Provost T.5	ex 'Lincolnshire', CFS, 3 FTS, CFS. Nose.	02-94

■ **Others** : By late 1992 a Provost had arrived.

☐	WW388*	7616M	Provost T.1	ex Cardiff-Wales, Llanelli, Chinnor, Chertsey, Cuxwold, Chessington, Halton, 2 FTS. 'O-F'. Arrived late 1992. Stored, dismantled.	02-94

NUNEATON

■ **Ted Gautrey** : Continues to restore his Fox Moth.

☐	G-ACCB		Fox Moth	ex Coventry Airport, Redhill, Blackpool, Southport. Ditched 25-9-56. Restoration.	

WARWICK

■ **John Berkeley** : Continues to work on his Seafire in this area.

☐	SX300	A2054	Seafire F.17	ex Leamington Spa, Warrington, Bramcote A646.	

■ **Warwick School** : Another educational establishment that bought the Grasshopper that was allocated to it. Is it still here?

☐	XK789*		Grasshopper TX.1	acquired 20-6-88. See notes above.	06-88

■ **Paul Williams** : Restoration is underway on the Hutter with the Nyborg to follow.

☐			Hutter H.17a	ex Moreton-in-the-Marsh. Restoration.	01-92
☐		BAPC.25	Nyborg TGN.III	ex Moreton-in-the-Marsh, Stratford. Stored.	01-92

WELLESBOURNE MOUNTFORD AERODROME (south of the B4086, east of Stratford)

■ **Wellesbourne Wartime Museum** : Operated by the Wellesbourne Aviation Group, the Museum charts the history of the well-known airfield based around the restored Battle Headquarters. Work continues on their three airframes, the Sea Vixen and Provost following the high standards already set with the Vampire. The McBroom hang-glider is available for disposal.

◆ Open every Sunday 10am to 4pm and Bank Holidays, same times. ✉ Dell Paddock, 2 Longford Close, Bidford-on-Avon, Alcester, Warwickshire, B50 4EB.

☐	*		McBroom Argus	hang-glider, built 1974. For disposal.	01-94
☐	WV679	7615M	Provost T.1	ex Dunkeswell, Higher Blagdon, Halton, 2 FTS. 'O-J'. Restoration.	12-93
☐	XJ575	A2611	Sea Vixen FAW.2	ex Long Marston, Helston, Culdrose, 766. 'SAH-13'. Nose.	12-93

☐ XK590   Vampire T.11   ex Witney, Brize Norton, CATCS, 4 FTS, 7 FTS.
                                              'V'.   12-93

■ **Delta Engineering Association** : In July 1992 an out-of-court settlement sold Vulcan XM655 to the operators of the airfield, Radarmoor Ltd, for £1. Since then a refreshingly realistic approach to the preservation of this great delta lady has arisen and great strides are being made to keep her 'live', and dropping all of the notion of flying her. As with any project, Delta Engineering need help - particularly from former Vulcan people.

✉ Delta Engineering Association, c/o Warwick Aero Services Ltd, Aviation House, Wellesbourne Mountford Aerodrome, Warwick, Warwickshire, CV35 9EU. ☎ 0789 470181.

☐ XM655   G-VULC   Vulcan B.2   ex N655AV ntu, 44, 101, 50, 44, 9. See notes
                                    above.   03-94

■ **Others** : The Seneca III hulk on the dump, G-BJEO, was scrapped by December 1993.

Wiltshire

BOSCOMBE DOWN AIRFIELD (south of the A303 at Amesbury)

■ **Aircraft & Armament Evaluation Establishment** (A&AEE) : With the amalgamation of the former DRA Farnborough fleets and the new, widened, role for the A&AEE, so a change of name came about in May 1992. Flying in from Farnborough, Hants, on January 29, 1993 was Comet 4 XV814, to act as spares for the world's last flying Comet, XS235 *Canopus*. Going in the opposite direction, to Farnborough, Hants, by road during August 1991 was Sukhoi Su-22M-4 98+10 to join their exotic collection of Soviet-built hardware. Sea Fury T.20S VZ345 moved by road to Yeovilton, Som, on November 24, 1992 for completion with the Historic Flight. The nose of Hunter F.5 WN980 was 'discovered' here by BCAR members and it moved to Hedge End, Hants, September 12, 1992. Another 'anonymous' nose has been seen on the airfield, this time confirmed as a Sea Hawk — any ideas of its identity? **W&R13** noted Canberra B.29mod) WH876 as leaving, destination unknown, during January 1990. It turned up on the missile range at Aberporth, Dyfed. Fascinating development during October 1993 was the placing of Vampire T.55 U-1216/ZH563 up for sale by tender via a private company. Was this not a gift to the nation?

☐ G-ALRX   Britannia 101   ex WB473 ntu, VX447 ntu. Crashed 4-2-54.
                                                Nose. Aeromedical & Safety School.   12-93
☐ FS890   7554M   Harvard IIB   ex Little Rissington, Nott UAS, Man UAS, Nott
                                                UAS, Bir UAS, Nott UAS, 1 FTS, 2 FTS, 600,
                                                21 FTS. Spares for flyers FT375 and KF183.
☐ VP968   Devon C.2/2   ex Northolt, 207, 26, TCCS, NCS, SCS, FCCS.
                                                                                     12-93
☐ WT309   Canberra B(I).6   ex A&AEE, HS. Stored.   05-93
☐ XL629   Lightning T.4   ex ETPS, A&AEE. Gate guardian.   03-94
☐ XR650*   8459M   Jet Provost T.4   ex Halton, SoRF, CAW, CATCS, 3 FTS, CAW,
                                                7 FTS. '28'. Arrived by 5-93.   03-94
☐ XT597*   Phantom FG.1   ex A&AEE. Last flight 28-1-94. Stored. 01-94
☐ XV401*   Phantom FGR.2   ex Wattisham, 23, 29, 228 OCU, 56, 111, 41, 41.
                                                Spares use.   03-94
☐ XV784   8909M   Harrier GR.3   ex Wittering, 233 OCU, 4, 1, 4. Damaged 2-4-86.
                                                Nose.   06-92
                                                [Remainder was at Abingdon, Oxon.]
☐ XV814*   Comet 4   ex RAE Farnborough, BOAC, G-APDF. Flew in
                                                29-1-93. Spares for XS235.   12-93
☐ *   Sea Hawk   red and white nose. First noted 6-92. 03-94
☐ U-1216   ZH563   Vampire T.55   ex Swiss AF. Stored. For sale 10-93. 10-93

CHILMARK (south of the A303 between Wylye and Cricklade)

■ **RAF Chilmark** : The Wessex allocated here for fire crash rescue was offered up for tender during early 1993 and may well have moved on.

☐ XP140   8806M   Wessex HAS.3   ex Wroughton, 737. '653-PO'. See notes. 02-93

CHIPPENHAM

■ **Flowers** : The sectioned Sea Hawk is still be within the yard, which has a public footpath crossing through. The airframe is stencilled 'R/P/S4/VB7234' — which is an AWA Coventry process number — and, 'DIFIED', 'R178893''. Does this help at all?

□	Sea Hawk	see notes above.	11-93

CHISELDON (on the B4005 south of Swindon)

A farm in this locality holds the hulk of a Rallye, previously consigned to the limbo of *LOST!*.

□ G-AVZY*	MS.880B Rallye	ex *LOST!*, Chessington. CoA expired 21-4-79.	
		Damaged. F/n 12-92.	12-92

HULLAVINGTON AIRFIELD (north of Junction 17 of the M4, north of Chippenham)

■ **RAF Hullavington** : Making history as an MoD airfield with a preservation order on it, it also makes an entry into **W&R** with the appearance of dumped Apache 160 G-ARJW (ex Bristol Airport) by September 1992. It had gone by May 1993 and is a candidate for the nose at Faringdon, Oxon.

KEEVIL

By October 1993 the pod of Vampire T.11 XE921 had appeared at <u>Firbeck</u>, S Yorks. It is not known if the other example, WZ620, is still to be found here.

□ WZ620	Vampire T.11	ex Exeter, 3/4 CAACU. '68'. Stored.	

LYNEHAM AIRFIELD (west of the A3102, south west of Wooton Bassett)

■ **RAF Lyneham** : Hunter F.6A XJ676, acquired by OFMC as spares for their 'flyer' G-BUEZ did not make the move to <u>Duxford</u>, Cambs, until October 1993. On October 20, 1993 a Victor arrived for the dump.

□ XK699	7971M	Comet C.2	ex Henlow, Lyneham, 216. Gate guardian.	04-93
□ XL161		Victor K.2	ex 55, 57, 55, 543, MoA. Flew in 20-10-93.	10-93
□ XV261	8986M	Nimrod AEW.3	ex Abingdon, Waddington, Woodford, Kinloss Wing, St Mawgan Wing, 203. Fuse, dump.	07-91

MALMESBURY

■ **Avon Air Museum** (AAM) / **Meteor Flight** : Work to restore premises at the former RAF Yatesbury site as completed in 1992 allowing Meteor T.7 WF825 and Vampire T.11 XE849 to move to <u>Yatesbury</u>, Wilts, during the year.

MARLBOROUGH

■ **2293 Squadron ATC** : Keep their *Chippax* in London Road.

□ WP863	8360M	Chipmunk T.10	ex Chippenham, Shawbury, Hamble G-ATJI, RAFC, 664, RAFC. PAX trainer.
			04-89

NETHERAVON AIRFIELD

■ **7 Regiment, AAC / Army Parachute Association** : No less than *three* Whirlwind HAR.10s arrived from Halton, Bucks, by the middle of 1992, but XR458 moved on quickly to <u>Middle Wallop</u>, Hants. By July 1993, the Sioux on the gate had been joined by a Scout. Auster AOP.9 WZ706/7851M became G-BURR and moved to the Aldershot, Hants, area. Scout AH.1 XP907 arrived from Wroughton by January 1989, but moved on to Fleetlands, Hants, on August 11, 1992 for return to operational status. In addition to three Scouts inbound for use as instructional airframes, two former Wroughton, Wilts, examples briefly transited through here. XR602 and XT648 arrived June 26, 1992 and July 29, 1992 respectively. Both moved on to <u>Cyprus</u> by December 1992.

□ G-BBRP		BN-2A-9	crashed 20-2-82. Para-trainer, fuselage only.	
□ XD165*	8673M	W'wind HAR.10	ex Halton, SARTS, 202, 228, 22, 225, 155, Navy loan. 'B'. Dump. First noted 9-92.	08-93
□ XJ435*	8671M	W'wind HAR.10	ex Halton, 2 FTS, CFS, 1563 Flt, 22. 'V'. Dump. First noted 9-92.	08-93
□ XP902*		Scout AH.1	ex Wroughton, Garrison Air Sqn, 3 CBAS. BDR. Arrived 26-6-92.	08-93

☐ XT150	7883M	Sioux AH.1	ex Middle Wallop, composite, with 7884M. Gate.	05-93
☐ XT470		Wessex HU.5	ex Lyneham, Wroughton, 845. Dump. 'A'.	
☐ XV119*		Scout AH.1	ex Wroughton, 659, 660, 669. BDR. First noted 5-93.	08-93
☐ XV136*		Scout AH.1	ex Almondbank, Wroughton. Gate by 7-93.	07-93

OAKSEY PARK AERODROME (south of Cirencester, east of the A429)
By March 1993, the strip had accumulated no less than four aircraft in the **W&R** category.

☐ G-AZMN*		Airtourer T5	ex Bristol, Glasgow. Cr 23-6-87. Wreck.	07-93
☐ G-BBJD*		Cessna 172M	ex Badminton, Sywell, N20537. Crashed 30-6-78. Para-trainer. First noted 8-92.	07-93
☐ G-BFKD*		Commander 114	ex N5835N. CoA expired 26-4-90. Stored.	07-93
☐ G-OBED*		Seneca II	ex Bristol, N36579. Cr 23-6-89. Restn.	07-93

OLD SARUM AERODROME (north of Salisbury)
Going back to **W&R13**, Opticas G-BGMW and G-TRAK may or may not have moved to FLS Aerospace at Bournemouth Airport, but are too small to be considered for an entry. A former Bournemouth Cessna had arrived by May 1992 for rebuild. The Grasshopper is stored for BCAR — see under Hedge End, Hants.

☐ G-ASLH*		Cessna 182F	ex Bournemouth Airport, Ipswich, N3505U. Crashed 14-6-81. For rebuild. F/n 5-92.	05-92
☐ WZ779*		Grasshopper TX.1	ex Long Marston, Urmston, Cosford. Arrived by 3-93. See notes above. Stored.	07-93

SALISBURY

■ **Hampshire Light Planes Services** : Latest testament to Cliff Lovell's prowess, Percival Vega Gull G-AEZJ was flying by late 1991. Restoration of Moth Major EC-ADE for a Spanish client via John Pothecary's Air South continues and is now the only 'long-termer' at the workshop.

☐ EC-ADE		Moth Major	ex Spain. Fuselage, stored.	4-91

■ **Wiltshire Historic Aviation Group** (WHAG) : Tony Dyer and friends continue to centre their activities in and around the town. Tony's personal collection has been formalised under the banner, The Air Defence Collection (TADC) and is listed below. Another leading light in WHAG is Lynsey Pennell, but there are several 'names' working within this voluntary enterprise. We next must chart some entertaining comings and goings (the meat of **W&R**!)..An anonymous *JP* nose section was acquired from Firbeck, S Yorks, by March 1992. This moved to Milford Haven, Dyfed, in exchange for their Chipmunk fuselage, WD386. This however, was exchanged with VAT at Cranfield, Beds, for some Tiger Moth bits and moved directly there. Coming inbound have been two Chipmunk PAX trainers. A glass fibre Spitfire cockpit section made by TDL Replicas of Lowestoft, Suffolk, was with WHAG briefly, but was traded to BCAR at Hedge End, Hants, by March 1993.

☐ WK626*	8213M	Chipmunk T.10	ex Welling, White Waltham, Bicester, Odiham SF, Ox UAS, South Cerney SF, 1 FTS, Bicester SF, Odiham SF, FTCCS, Lon UAS, Cam UAS, Colerne SF, Leeds UAS, Nott UAS, 16 FRS, 18 RFS. SOC 31-10-72. PAX. Arrived 1993.	12-93
☐ WV843*		Sea Hawk FGA.4	ex Higher Blagdon, 738. Crashed 31-8-56. Nose. Arrived 3-94.	03-94
☐ *		Chipmunk T.10	ex Blackburn. PAX trainer, identity unknown. See notes above. Arrived 1993.	12-93

■ **The Air Defence Collection** (TADC) : As explained in the above, Tony Dyer's collection has been rationalised under this title. The restoration of the Hurricane cockpit remains a major focus and the work carried out on this restoration is to very high standards. The Gnat nose section from Southampton, Hants, has been acquired. The two-seat MiG-21 nose section represents a bit of a *coup*, but will require a lot of 'ferreting' to fit out.

☐ P3554		Hurricane I	ex Swanage, 607, 213, 56, 32. Shot down 5-10-40. Composite, centre section and cockpit.	03-94
☐ WT648	7530M	Hunter F.1	ex Kexborough, Stock, St Athan, DFLS. Cockpit. Under restoration.	03-94

☐ XF113	Swift F.7	ex Bath, Frome, Farnborough, ETPS, A&AEE, Handling Sqn. Nose.	03-94
☐ *	Gnat T.1	ex Southampton. *Possibly* ex Fareham and XM692. Nose. Arrived 1993.	03-94
☐ 0446*	MiG-21UM	ex Farnborough, Egyptian AF. Nose. Arrived 3-94. For restoration.	03-94

◆ Both WHAG and TADC airframes are stored in a variety of locations. Accordingly, viewing is strictly by prior permission only. ✉ Lynsey Pennell, Mill House, Shrewton, Wilts.

■ **Cockpit Collector's Club** (CCC) : Both groups have 'kick started' this organisation, designed to help those involved in the 'growth industry' of cockpit sections. Enquiries to the address above.

SWINDON
■ **1244 Sqn ATC** : Still have their Cherokee. Their hut, in Upham Road, is open Wednesday and Friday evenings.

☐ G-BPWF	Cherokee 140	ex Shrivenham, OY-BCN, N9978W. Damaged 25-1-90.	2-91

TROWBRIDGE
■ **E J Shanley & Sons** : SH-3D Sea King XV372 is still to be found in the yard, alongside an equally forlorn-looking coach.

☐ XV372	SH-3D Sea King	ex Yeovil, Lee-on-Solent, RAE, Westlands.	09-93

UPAVON
Stored not far from the airfield is an Auster.

☐ G-AIGF	J/1N Alpha	CoA expired 19-5-85. Stored.	04-91

WARMINSTER
Both of the Stampes continue their restoration at a strip in the area.

☐ G-AYDR	SNCAN SV-4C	ex Raveningham, F-BCLG. CoA expired 27-3-75. Restoration.	08-93
☐ G-BEPF	SNCAN SV-4A	ex Raveningham, F-BCVD. Restoration.	08-93

WINTERBOURNE GUNNER (east of the A338 north east of Salisbury)
■ **Defence Nuclear, Biological and Chemical Centre** : (Note change of name.) A case of all change here, the previous inmates (Buccaneer S.1 XK531, Whirlwind HAR.10s XR478 & XR482 and Wasp HAS.1 XT430) are all believed scrapped. They have been replaced by :—

☐ XV804*	Harrier GR.3	ex 4, 3, 1, 3, 4, 233 OCU, 1417F, 233 OCU. 'O'. First noted 12-91.	03-94
☐ XS862*	Wessex HAS.3	ex Lee-on-Solent, Wroughton, 737. '50'. Arrived 4-92.	03-94

WROUGHTON AIRFIELD (on the A4361 south of Swindon)
■ **Princess Alexandra Royal Air Force Hospital** : With the military out of the airfield proper by the end of 1992, only the Hospital provides links with the past. This was cemented still further during the summer of 1993 when a hardstanding went down for what turned out to be a former Halton, Bucks, *JP*. Canberra B.2 WJ676, reference **W&R13**, did not turn up at Bruntingthorpe, Leics. At least the nose section chose Stock, Essex, as its initial destination..

☐ XN512* 8435M	Jet Provost T.3	ex Halton, St Athan, Shawbury, CFS. Arrived by 7-93. Gate guardian.	07-93

■ **Royal Naval Aircraft Yard** (RNAY) - **Fleet Air Arm Museum Store** (FAAM) : The RNAY finally closed on September 3, 1992 and, with it, the military vacated the airfield. The RNAY is deserted, but it would appear that the FAAM have come to some arrangement to keep some of their airframes here, probably only as a short term move. Before dealing with the mass migration from here, back to **W&R13** where SARO P.531 XN332 was noted as going to Weston-super-Mare. This was not the case. It left the RNAY on September 18, 1991 to appear at the Battle of Britain Show at Finningley, S Yorks — as part of the ever-growing BAPC display there — and then travelled to Yeovilton, Somerset, September 24, 1991. So far evading the pages of **W&R** have been the frustrated

Qatari Lynx Mk 28s which were stored here from March 1990. They moved to <u>Almondbank</u>, Tayside, on June 7, 1992, via a night stop at Lee-on-Solent, Hants.

And so to listing the 'removals', many of which have been to the 'new' RNAY at Almondbank, Tayside. This is a good opportunity to note that much of the material stored at Wroughton was well beyond the scope of **W&R**, and only 'long-termers' are dealt with. Disposals — all by road unless noted — are listed by destination :-

Almondbank, Tayside : <u>all</u> Scout AH.1s : XP890 23-6-92; XR628 3-8-92; XR629 16-6-92; XR639 23-6-92; XT616 30-6-92; XT617 23-6-92; XT639 23-6-92; XT642 16-6-92; XT645 23-6-92; XV122 (omitted from **W&R13**) 16-6-92; XV136 (also omitted from **W&R13**) 2-6-92; XV138 30-6-92; XW284 30-6-92; XW795 2-6-92.

Arborfield, Berks : <u>all</u> Scout AH.1s : XP855 29-6-92; XT623 30-6-92; XT633 1-7-92.

Brize Norton, Oxon : Scout AH.1 XV118 3-4-92.

Chelsea, Gtr Lon : Scout XV127 3-3-92.

Crawley, W Sussex : Meteor T.7 WS103 left by 7-93.

Dishforth, N Yorks : Scout AH.1 XP850 7-7-92; Wessex HU.5 XS481 21-7-92; Wessex HU.5 XT471 21-7-92.

Firbeck, S Yorks : Scout AH.1 XP190 was actually offered for tender during 7-92 and snapped up by SYAPS, leaving by road 27-8-92.

Fleetlands, Hants : CH-47C AE-520 by 8-92; Sea King HAS.5 XV669 21-7-92; Wessex HU.5 XT759 2-9-92.

Ipswich, Suffolk : Whirlwind HAS.7 XK911 left by road 29-8-92.

Lee-on-Solent, Hants : Wessex HAS.1 XS888 7-7-92; Wessex HU.5 XT769 9-7-92.

Middle Wallop, Hants : <u>all</u> Scout AH.1s : XP893 29-7-92; XR627 19-6-92; XV124 19-6-92; XV131 3-7-92; XW796 3-7-92.

Netheravon, Wilts : <u>all</u> Scout AH.1s : XP902 by 5-92; XR602 26-6-92; XT648 29-7-92; XV119 by 5-93.

Yeovilton, Somerset : Firefly TT.4 VH127 on 20-5-92; Scout AH.1 XT637 27-7-92; Wessex HAS.1 XS881 was transferred from FAAM charge back to the FAA, moving out by 7-93. Additionally, omitted from **W&R13** was Sea Fury FB.11 WJ231, stored here. This moved by 9-92.

Others : XT626 to 666 Sqn 7-4-92; XW281 to 666 Sqn 29-7-92. Whirlwind HAS.7 XN385 was sold to Helimed — Savvas Constantinides' company — for export to Cyprus via Bournemouth Airport, Dorset, 3-93. The sighting of Scout AH.1 XR630 during 1-91 here is thought in error, it was last heard of on the dump at Middle Wallop, Hants, in July 1988. Wasp HAS.1 XT429 departed on 10-8-92 for spares use by the Malaysian Navy. Gazelle AH.1 XZ290 to 670 Sqn by 3-91; XZ324 to Fleetlands, Hants, 18-8-92 and returned to service by 4-93; XZ326 to Fleetlands, Hants, 26-6-92 for eventual return to service.

It would seem the FAA Museum still have a tenure here, with three 'new' airframes arriving in December 1993.

☐ G-AZAZ*	Bensen B.8M	ex Houndstone, Yeovilton, Manadon. Arrived 17-12-93. Stored.	12-93
☐ *	Super Eagle h/g	ex Houndstone, Yeovilton. Arrived 21-12-93. Stored.	12-93
☐ WP313	Sea Prince T.1	ex Kemble, 750, Sydenham SF, 750, Lossiemouth SF, 750. '568-CU'. FAAM.	07-93
☐ XA129	Sea Vampire T.22	ex Yeovilton, CIFE, 736. FAAM.	07-93
☐ XA466	Gannet COD.4	ex Yeovilton, Lee-on-Solent, Lossiemouth, 849. '777-LM'. FAAM.	07-93
☐ XA864	Whirlwind HAR.1	ex Yeovilton, RAE Bedford, A&AEE, RAE, CA, G-17-1. FAAM.	07-93
☐ XS120 8653M	Wessex HAS.1	ex Abingdon, Wroughton. Dump.	07-90
☐ 100545*	Fa 330A-1	ex Yeovilton, Higher Blagdon, Farnborough. Arrived 25-8-93. Stored.	08-93

■ **Science Museum Air Transport Collection and Storage Facility** (ScM) : The site has been consolidated considerably with a huge storage building for small artefacts having been erected on site. The number and tempo of ScM open days etc have shown no sign of growing — which is a considerable pity considering the importance of the airframes on site. The airfield also hosts the annual Great Warbirds Air Display. The store has gained some airframes from the reshuffle at 'headquarters'.

Going the other way on June 28, 1992 was HS.125 G-ASSM, to <u>South Kensington</u>, Gtr Lon. John Bradshaw's Fury ISS N36SF moved on during 1992, initially settling on Abingdon, Oxon.
◆ Occasional open days and special events, details from the numbers below. Otherwise, no access.
✉ The Science Museum, South Kensington, London SW7 2DD. ☎ 071 938 8000. Wroughton office ☎ 0793 814466.

☐ G-AACN		HP Gugnunc	ex Hayes and K1908.	09-93
☐ G-ACIT		DH.84 Dragon	ex Southend, Beagle, ANT Blackpool, BEA, Scottish, Highland. CoA exp 25-5-74.	09-93
☐ G-AEHM		HM.14 *Flea*	ex Hayes, Whitchurch, Bristol.	09-93
☐ G-ALXT		Dragon Rapide	ex Strathallan, Staverton, 4R-AAI, CY-AAI, G-ALXT, NF865, 5 MU, 18 MU, MCS.	09-93
☐ G-APWY		Piaggio P.166	ex Southend, Marconi. CoA exp 14-3-81.	09-93
☐ G-APYD		Comet 4B	ex Dan-Air, Olympic SX-DAL, G-APYD, BEA. CoA expired 3-8-79.	09-93
☐ G-ATDD*		Beagle 206-1	ex South Kensington, Leeds-Bradford. Nose section. Arrived by 10-92.	09-93
☐ G-AVZB		Z-37 Cmelak	ex Southend, OK-WKQ. CoA exp 5-4-84.	09-93
☐ G-AWZM		Trident 3B-101	ex Heathrow, BA, BEA. CoA exp 13-12-85.	09-93
☐ G-MMCB		Pathfinder II	microlight.	
☐ G-RBOS		Colt AS-105	hot air airship. CoA exp 6-3-87.	09-93
☐ G-9-185*		Hunter F.6	ex South Kensington, Kingston-upon-Thames, Dutch AF N-250. Nose. Arr by 10-92.	09-93
☐ EI-AYO		DC-3A-197	ex Shannon, N655GP, N65556, N225JB, N8695SE, N333H, NC16071. [Note amended registration history.]	09-93
☐ NC5171N	G-LIOA	Lockheed 10A	ex *Wings and Wheels*, Orlando, N5171N, NC243 Boston-Maine AW, NC14959 Eastern.	09-93
☐ N18E		Boeing 247	ex *Wings and Wheels*, Orlando, Sky Tours, NC18E, NC18, NC13340 CAA, United/National Air Transport.	09-93
☐ N7777G	G-CONI	L-749A-79	ex Dublin, Lanzair, KLM PH-LDT, PH-TET.	09-93
☐ EE416*		Meteor III	ex South Kensington, Martin Baker. Nose. Arrived by 10-92.	09-93
☐ VP975		Devon C.2/2	ex RAE Farnborough, A&AEE, CCCF, 19 GCF, CPE.	09-93
☐ VX185*	7631M	Canberra B.8	ex S Kensington, EE. Nose. Arr by 10-92.	09-93
☐ XP505*		Gnat T.1	ex South Kensington, RAE Bedford, MinTech, Dunsfold, CFS. Arrived by 10-92.	09-93
☐	BAPC.162	Manflier MPA	major parts.	09-93
☐	BAPC.172	Chargus Midas	hang glider.	09-93
☐	BAPC.173	Grasshopper	powered hang glider.	09-93
☐	BAPC.174	Bensen B.7	gyroglider.	09-93
☐	BAPC.188	Cobra 88	hang glider.	09-93

YATESBURY (north of the A4, east of Calne)
■ **Avon Air Museum** (AAM) / **Meteor Flight**: Having restored a building that was part of the camp of the former RAF Yatesbury, the two organisations have turned the location into a Meteor haven. Work has started on the restoration to flying condition of NF.14 WS807. Alan Allen's Vampire T.11 XE849 moved to <u>Long Marston</u>, Warks during April 1994
◆ Visits possible by prior arrangement. ✉ AAM, E Brown, 8 Hobbes Close, Malmesbury, Wilts, SN16 0DA. ✉ Meteor Flight , Mark Jones, 26 Springfield Road, Westbury, Wilts, BA13 3QQ.

☐ WA591*	7917M	Meteor T.7	ex Woodvale, St Athan CCAS, Kemble, CAW, 8 FTS, 5 FTS, CAW, 12 FTS, 215 AFS, 208 AFS, 203 AFS, 226 OCU, CFE. Arrived by 3-93.	02-94
☐ WF825*	8359M	Meteor T.7	ex Malmesbury, Monkton Farleigh, Lyneham, Kemble, CAW, 33, 603. 'A'. Stored.	02-94

| ☐ WH364* | 8169M | Meteor F.8 | ex Kemble, 601, Safi SF, Takali SF, Idris SF, Takali SF, Safi SF, 85. Arrived mid-1993. | 02-94 |
| ☐ WS807* | 7973M | Meteor NF.14 | ex Watton, Kemble, 1 ANS, 2 ANS. 'N'. Arrived 12-92. | 02-94 |

North Yorkshire

CHOP GATE (on the B1257 north of Helmsley)
■ **North Yorkshire Aircraft Recovery Centre** (NYARC) : Latest addition to Ken Ward's NYARC collection is Lightning F.3 XR749, although it faces a problematical future — see below. Ken's Valiant nose can be found at Bruntingthorpe, Leics.
◆ Visits by prior arrangement. ✉ NYARC, *Appletree Hurst*, Chop Gate, via Middlesbrough, TS9 7LN.

☐ WM145		Meteor NF.11	ex Rotherham, Finningley, 5, 29, 151, 219. Nose.	11-91
☐ WZ557		Vampire T.11	ex Huntingdon, Acaster Malbis, Woodford, Chester, St Athan, 5 FTS, 16.	11-91
☐ XM169	8422M	Lightning F.1A	ex Thirsk, Leuchars, Leuchars TFF, 23, Binbrook TFF, 111, A&AEE, MoA, EE. Nose.	11-91
☐ XN607		Jet Provost T.3	ex Leeds, 3 FTS. SOC 28-5-76. Nose. Identity confirmed.	11-91

■ *The Buck Inn* : The landlord of the inn took on the NYARC Lightning F.3 with the view of displaying it, but fell foul of planning permission and the North Yorks Moors National Park Authority, during early November 1993. The decision gave just 56 days to have the aircraft removed. Help was at hand and it moved to Tees-side Airport, Durham, for restoration and display.

CHURCH FENTON AIRFIELD (south of the B1223, south east of Tadcaster)
■ **RAF Church Fenton** : Spitfire replica 'L1096' (BAPC.229) moved to Digby, Lincs, with the closure of the base. The hulks of Jet Provost T.3As XM350/9036M and XN473/8862M on the dump are unaccounted for — they are assumed to have been cleared.

DISHFORTH AIRFIELD (on the A1, west of Ripon)
■ **9 Regiment, Army Air Corps** : As can be seen, the AAC have taken on a wide range of airframes to support their operations from here. Lynx 1-02 XW835 represents quite an 'arrival'. It was last noted in **W&R12**, under Middle Wallop, as leaving there by road on September 30, 1988.

☐ XJ727*	8661M	W'wind HAR.10	ex Halton, 2 FTS, CFS, 1310 Flt, 228, 22. 'L'. First noted 4-93. Boom painted as 'ZZ117'.	01-94
☐ XP850*		Scout AH.1	ex Wroughton, 660. Pod only, arr 7-7-92.	08-93
☐ XR627*		Scout AH.1	ex Middle Wallop, Wroughton, Garrison Air Sqn, 3 CBAS. First noted 4-93.	10-93
☐ XS481*		Wessex HU.5	ex Wroughton, Yeovilton, Culdrose, Yeovilton, 771, 707. Arrived 21-7-92.	01-94
☐ XT471*		Wessex HU.5	ex Wroughton, Yeovilton, 771, 707, 845, 847, 771, Fleetlands, 848. Arrived 21-7-92.	01-94
☐ XW835*	G-BEAD	Lynx 1-02	ex Middle Wallop, Yeovil. See notes above. Boomless. First noted 4-93.	08-93

ELVINGTON (off the A1079 south east of York)
■ **Yorkshire Air Museum** (YAM) : Many changes to record with YAM. The only blot on the landscape is the closure of the RAF base 'next door', thereby removing the 'aerial delivery' possibility. This was brought into sharp focus on November 25, 1993, when YAM's *second* Handley Page bomber was delivered, in the form of a Victor K.2. A major milestone was reached in the career of the Halifax recreation when it was 'rolled-out' on Friday August 13, 1993. (It was more accurately the

guests who were rolled-out of the hangar and into the sunlight to see the bomber on its undercarriage — but not capable of 'rolling' yet — for the first time!) Next major achievement for this project will be the erection of its own hangar, after the project will be able to move into indoors and *really* make headway. The hangar, a T2 thought last at Keevil, Glos, was acquired in March 1994 from the estate of the late Charles Church. A host of *JP* noses and a whole example have arrived. YAM is custodian of the extensive Barnes Wallis artefact collection (available by prior arrangement only).

◆ Signed from the A64 southern York ring road, at the A64/A166/A1079 junction. Open from March 31 to October 28 inclusive on Saturdays 2pm to 5pm, Sundays and Bank Holidays 11am to 5pm and Tuesdays, Wednesdays and Thursdays 11am to 4pm. Other times by arrangement. ✉ YAM, Elvington, York, YO4 5AT. ☎ 0904 608595.

■ **Night Fighter Preservation Team** (NFPT) : Tony Agar and team succeeded in gaining the *FlyPast* Twite trophy for 1991 and the project now has its own 'home' — the building previously used by the *Friday 13th* team. Superb progress is being made. Members of NFPT have also acquired the former Long Marston Venom for long term work and have an interest in the former Pennine Anson.

◆ Open as per YAM above. ✉ NFPT, Val Agar, 2 Upper St Paul's Terrace, Holgate Road, York, YO2 4BP.

☐ 'G-AFFI'	BAPC.76	HM.14 *Flea*	ex Hemswell, Cleethorpes, Nostell Priory, Rawdon. Off-site, early 1994.	11-93
☐ 'F943'	G-BKDT	SE.5A replica	ex Selby, Elvington, Selby.	11-93
☐ HJ711		Mosquito NF.II	ex Huntington. Complex composite. Restoration. NFPT. 'VI-C', 169 Sqn c/s. See notes.	11-93
☐ 'LV907'	HR792	Halifax II	ex Isle of Lewis. Complex composite. 'NP-F', *Friday the 13th*, 158 Sqn colours. Restoration. Unveiled 13-8-93.	11-93
☐ 'TJ704'	G-ASCD	Terrier 2	ex Holme-on Spalding Moor, Nympsfield, Blackbushe, PH-SFT, G-ASCD, VW993, 651, 663. CoA expired 26-9-71. Stored.	03-94
☐ VV901*		Anson T.21	ex Bacup, Burtonwood, Cosford, Irton Holme, Leconfield, CFCCU, Dur UAS, 1 RFS. Arrived 8-6-93. for restoration by NFPT.	03-94
☐ WH846		Canberra T.4	ex Samlesbury, St Athan, Laarbruch SF, 231 OCU.	03-94
☐ WS788	7967M	Meteor NF.14	ex Leeming 'WS844', Patrington, 1 ANS, 2 ANS, 152. 'JCF'.	03-94
☐ WX788 *		Venom NF.3	ex Kenilworth, Long Marston, Cardiff-Wales, Bledlow Ridge, Connah's Quay, DH. NFPT. Arrived late 5-92. Stored off-site.	11-93
☐ XD377	8203M	Vampire T.11	ex Cosford, Birmingham, Shawbury, Hawarden, 66. 'A'. Spares for XD453.	03-94
☐ XD453	7890M	Vampire T.11	ex Old Sarum, Salisbury, St Athan, 1 FTS, CNCS, Oldenburg SF, 26. On loan, under restn.	03-94
☐ XL231*		Victor K.2	ex 55, 232 OCU, 57, Witt Wing, Victor TF, Witt Wing, 139. *Lusty Linda*. Flew in 25-11-93.	03-94
☐ XN600*		Jet Provost T.3	ex 3 FTS. SOC 28-5-76. Nose.	08-93
☐ XN974		Buccaneer S.2	ex BAe Brough.	03-94
☐ XP640*	8501M	Jet Provost T.4	ex Halton, CATCS, 6 FTS, CAW, CFS, 3 FTS. 'D'. Arrived 10-93.	03-94
☐ XS903		Lightning F.6	ex Binbrook, 11, 5-11 pool.	11-93
☐ 21417*		CT-133	ex Sollingen, CAF Arrived 25-6-93.	03-94
☐ QA-10		Hunter FGA.78	ex Bournemouth Airport, Qatar AF, G-9-286, Dutch AF N-268. .	03-94
☐ *		Canberra	nose. First noted 10-92.	11-93
☐ *		Jet Provost T.3	ex Linton-on-Ouse. Procedure trainer. Arrived 10-92.	11-93
☐ *		Jet Provost T.3	Nose. First noted 8-93.	11-93

FELIX KIRK AERODROME (north east of Thirsk)

By April 1992, two aircraft hulks were noted at the airfield. The Cessna F.150L is readily identifiable, but the Cherokee/Archer/whatever is not!

☐ G-BAUV*	Cessna F.150L	ex LN-BEJ. Cockpit section, first noted 4-92.	04-92
☐ *	Cherokee	fuselage, first noted 4-92.	04-92

HARROGATE

A collector here took on the nose section of a former Rossington Lightning.

☐ XR726*	Lightning F.6	ex Rossington, Binbrook, LTF, 11, LTF, 11, 5. 'TVI726'. Nose section. First noted 3-93.	03-93

KIRKBYMOORSIDE AERODROME (south of the town)

■ **Slingsby** : Now actively exporting T-3As to the USAF. Four T-67Cs, (c/ns 2064, 2065, 2070 and 2071) produced *circa* late 1988, were never assembled and lay in storage at the factory until January 1992 when all four were removed to a location near Nottingham for further storage. The Skyship has been acquired by FOCAS and will journey eventually to Cardington, Beds.

☐ G-BECE	AD-500 Skyship	destroyed 9-3-79. Stored. See notes above.	
☐ (G-BIUZ) c/n 1998	T-67B	static test airframe. 1st allocation of reg.	05-92
☐ c/n 2006	T-67	static test airframe.	05-92
☐ ZE686	Viking TX.1	ex BGA.3099. Static test airframe.	05-92

LEEMING AIRFIELD (east of the A1, west of Bedale)

■ **RAF Leeming** : The Lightning here is certainly allocated for BDR work, but is neither on the dump, nor chopped about. It is lovingly looked after by XI Squadron and kept near their headquarters. A Buccaneer slewed off the runway and suffered a partial undercarriage collapse on September 10, 1993. With the proximity of the withdrawal of the mighty *Brick*, it was declared Category 5 and has been allowed to languish on the airfield, perhaps taking up the task that the Lightning was intended for!

☐ XA634	7641M	Javelin FAW.4	ex Shawbury, Colerne, Melksham, makers. 'L'. Gate guardian.	07-93
☐ XR753	8969M	Lightning F.6	ex Binbrook, 11, 5-11 pool, 23, FCTU. 'BP'. Displayed outside XI Sqn's headquarters, not as given in **W&R13**.	11-93
☐ XT914*		Phantom FGR.2	ex 74, 56, 228 OCU, 92, 228 OCU, 56, 228 OCU, 14. 'Z'. Arrived 5-10-92. Decoy.	10-93
☐ XV423*		Phantom FGR.2	ex 74, 56, 228 OCU, 23, 29, 56, 23, 29, 6. 'Y'. Flew in 5-10-92 for BDR.	12-93
☐ XV465*		Phantom FGR.2	ex 74, 19,92, 228 OCU, 29, 23, 31. 'S'. Flew in 5-10-92. Decoy.	07-93
☐ XV499*		Phantom FGR.2	ex 74, 92, 228 OCU, 29, 23, 19, 92, 41, 6. 'I'. Flew in 5-10-92. Decoy.	12-93
☐ XV867*		Buccaneer S.2	ex 208, 12, 208, 237 OCU, FAA. Landing accident 10-9-93. Withdrawn.	12-93
☐ XW764	8981M	Harrier GR.3	ex St Athan, 3. BDR. Fuselage, dump.	10-93

LINTON-ON-OUSE AIRFIELD (west of the A19, north west of York)

■ **RAF Linton-on-Ouse** : Gate guardian Provost T.1 XF545/7957M was auctioned in London on July 8, 1993 (see Appendix D). By November 1993 it had moved to <u>Thatcham</u>. Berks, but is thought bound for the USA in due course. It has been replaced on the gate by a *JP*. Also in that auction were Jet Provost T.3s XM479 and XN461. The former did not sell and has since made its way to <u>Binbrook</u>, Lincs. On October 28, 1992 two *JP* procedure trainers (ie *possibly* synthetic) were being readied for despatch by road, one reported bound for the Yorkshire Air Museum at Elvington, N Yorks (*qv* for a complex JP story there) and another to an ATC unit. Gnat T.1 XR569/8560M was put up for tender during October 1992 and moved to <u>Bruntingthorpe</u>, Leics.

☐ XN589*	9143M	Jet Provost T.3A	ex 1 FTS, RAFC. '46'. Gate.	01-94

■ **Memorial Room** : Within the base is a superb museum, known as the Memorial Room, largely the work of the late Sgt Bill Steel. It deals with all aspects of Linton's history via a wide array of photographs, archival material and small artefacts. ◆ Visits by prior appointment on 034 74 261.

MARKINGTON (west of the A61 south of Ripon)
SAN D.117A G-AZII was flying by 1992.

OLD MALTON
■ **Eden Camp** : (Previously listed as 'Malton') The former prisoner of war camp is now an award-winning museum. On April 5, 1993, the Spitfire was joined by a *doodlebug* replica and on July 7, 1993, by a Hurricane. All three have been built by TDL Replicas of Lowestoft.
◆ Open daily 10am to 5pm from February 14 to December 23. Located on the A64, north of Malton.
✉ Eden Camp, Malton, North Yorkshire, YO17 0SD. ☎ 0653 697777.

☐	'P2793'*	BAPC.236 Hurricane replica	'SD-M', 501 Sqn colours. Erected 7-7-93.	07-93
☐	'AA908'	BAPC.230 Spitfire replica	'UM-W', 152 Sqn colours.	07-93
☐	*	BAPC.235 Fi 103 replica	arrived 5-4-93.	07-93

RUFFORTH AERODROME (south of the A1237, west of York)
■ **MacLean's Sailplanes** : Have built a large hangar for their long-established craft of bringing gliders back to life. This has meant that a lot of flotsam and jetsam previously stored in myriad sheds has been consolidated into one place, making the situation much clearer here. As well as an abundance of former Air Cadet gliders, the long-out-of-use Sperling is stored here.

☐	G-BCHX*	SF-23A Sperling	ex Netherthorpe, D-EGIZ. Damaged 7-8-82. First noted 10-89. Frame.	08-93
☐	WB922*	Sedbergh TX.1	ex Syerston 615 VGS, CGS. Fuselage, stored. First noted 6-93.	06-93
☐	WZ769*	Grasshopper TX.1	ex Locking, Oxford. Stored.* F/n 6-93.	06-93
☐	XA286*	Cadet TX.3	ex Eaglescott, Syerston, 615 VGS. Fuselage. Stored. First noted 6-93.	06-93
☐	XA290*	Cadet TX.3	ex Syerston, Dishforth, 661 VGS, 643 VGS. Fuselage, stored. First noted 6-93.	06-93
☐	*	Sedbergh TX.1	stored. First noted 6-93.	06-93
☐	*	Grasshopper TX.1	stored. First noted 6-93.	06-93
☐	*	Grasshopper TX.1	stored. First noted 6-93.	06-93
☐	*	Grasshopper TX.1	stored. First noted 6-93.	06-93

THIRSK
■ **Calvert's Scrapyard** : A visit here during April 1992 found no aircraft. When asked, an employee said they had been "scrapped about three years ago." This accounts for Scimitars XD228 and XD231 and Lightning T.4 XM997. The nose section of Lightning F.1A XM169 moved to <u>Chop Gate</u>, N Yorks.

South Yorkshire

ARMTHORPE (on the A630 north of Doncaster)
■ **1053 Squadron ATC** : Should still have its *Chippax*. Note that this is 'parented' by Finningley and officially 'owned' by 9 AEF.

☐	WG419	8206M	Chipmunk T.10	ex Finningley, MoA, Laarbruch SF, Gutersloh SF, Ahlhorn SF, Oldenburg SF, CFS, Abn UAS, Bir UAS, 15 RFS, 4 BFTS, 6 RFS. PAX.	09-93

BAWTRY
■ **216 Squadron ATC** : Thanks to a Chipmunk sleuth, we can add an identity to this *Chippax*.

☐	WK584	7556M	Chipmunk T.10	ex Church Fenton, Linton-on-Ouse, Edzell SF, Ox UAS, Glas UAS, 11 RFS. PAX trainer.	09-92

DONCASTER AERODROME (on the A638 east of Doncaster)
Sadly, this looks set to be the last time that **W&R** can call this location an 'aerodrome'. During the death throes of the site, Doncaster made a re-entry into the realms of **W&R**, although we have to journey back to **W&R9** for its last piece of limelight! By June 1992 a Bell 47 was decidedly withdrawn from use here.

☐ G-WYTE*   Bell 47G-2A   ex TF-MUN, 64-15426. Stored. F/n 6-92.   06-92

FINNINGLEY AIRFIELD (on the A614 north of Bawtry)
■ **RAF Finningley** : This very active base continues to hold a large number of **W&R** airframes. By a process of elimination, the Wessex HU.5 that went to Stoney Stanton, Leics — see **W&R13** — was XT768. **W&R13** made mention of time-expired Dominie T.1 XS732 leaving by road on March 27, 1991 for Fort Halstead. The latter is in Kent and the home of the Royal Armament Research & Development Establishment. XS732 was allocated to RARDE (now part of the DRA combine) on June 11, 1991 but has not been seen since. Whirlwind HAR.10 XJ729/8732M was up for disposal during March 1993 and had moved to Colsterworth, Lincs, by August 1993. See under Armthorpe, S Yorks, for a note on Chipmunk T.10 PAX Trainer WG419. That leaves the situation as follows :—

☐ G-ATXH		Jetstream 1	ex Filton. Cockpit trainer METS. 10-89
☐ WL168	7750M	Meteor F.8	ex 'WH456', St Athan, Swinderby, Finningley, APS Sylt, 604, 111. Gate. 09-93
☐ XM480*	8080M	Jet Provost T.3	ex Halton, 6 FTS, 1 FTS. '02'. Arr 9-2-94. 02-94
☐ XN302	9037M	Whirlwind HAS.7	ex A2654, Corsham, Lee-on-Solent, AES, S'ton, Culdrose, 771, *Lossie* SF, 847, 848. Dump. 09-93
☐ XN495*	8786M	Jet Provost T.3A	ex Halton, 7 FTS, RAFC, 1 FTS, 2 FTS, 7 FTS, RAFC. Damaged 30-3-83. Dump. F/n 6-92. 09-92
☐ XR662*	8410M	Jet Provost T.4	ex Halton, SoRF, CAW, CATCS, RAFC, CAW, 6 FTS, 7 FTS. '25'. Arrived 9-2-94. 02-94
☐ XS216		Jet Provost T.4	ex 6 FTS, CAW. Fuselage. SAREW. 09-93
☐ XS484		Wessex HU.5	ex Wroughton, 771, 845, BHC, A&AEE, Westlands, RAE, Westlands. '821-CU'. SAREW. 09-93
☐ XV263	8967M	Nimrod AEW.3	ex Waddington, JTU, Woodford, St M Wing, 203. AES. 09-93
☐ XX297	8933M	Hawk T.1A	ex Red Arrows. Crashed 30-11-86. Dump. 09-93
☐ XX477	8462M	Jetstream T.1	ex Little Rissington, CFS, G-AXXS. Crashed 1-11-74. Cockpit. Dominie escape trainer.
☐ ZE351	9058M	F-4J(UK)	ex 74, USN 153773. 'I'. Crash rescue. 09-93

FIRBECK (west of the A60 north of Worksop)
■ **South Yorkshire Aviation Museum** (SYAM) : SYAM's 'fleet' of airframes have changed little. Departing have been :— *Flea* 'G-AEKR'/BAPC.121 moved to the centre of *Flea*-dom, Breighton, Humbs, by mid-1993; Cessna F.150H G-AWFH moved to Winsford, Cheshire; Whirlwind HAR.21 WV198/G-BJWY moved to Carlisle, Cumbria, on November 13, 1992; Meteor F.4 VT260/8813M returned to Duxford, Cambs, in December 1993; Aviatik C.1 replica (note change of type) 'C19/18' BAPC.118 moved to storage at Tumby Woodside, Lincs, by May 1992; the 'smaller' CASA 2-111D nose section moved to East Kirkby, Lincs, by May 1992. NYARC's Valiant XD875 nose was restored courtesy of the RAF, at Finningley and Waddington, and used as a centre-piece at the infamous 75th anniversary of the RAF 'celebration' at soggy Marham, Norfolk, on April 1, 1993 and beyond that settled upon Bruntingthorpe, Leics. Fleetingly here was Canberra T.4 nose WE192 from Chelford, Cheshire, but this settled upon Long Marston, Warks, by December 1993. (This was exchanged for the Cessna that went to Winsford — see above.) Another exchange was arranged care of Ian Hancock. In return for a set of unused Lightning wings acquired by Ian from the moribund collection at Seighford, Staffs, Ian took the nose of Canberra B(I).8 XM279, moving it to Flixton, Suffolk, in March 1994. Several airframes are on loan from Bill Fern and are marked § accordingly.
◆ Open every Sunday 10am to 5pm and at other times by arrangement at Home Farm, Firbeck, near Worksop, Notts. ✉ Ian Kingsnorth, South Yorkshire Aviation Society, 21 Broom Grove, Rotherham, South Yorkshire S60 2TE.

☐ G-ALYB		Auster 5	ex Bristol, White Waltham, RT520. CoA expired 26-5-63. Restoration. 12-93
☐ 'A4850'	BAPC.176	SE.5A scale replica	ex Pontefract. Based on a Currie Wot. 12-93

☐ WB624*		Chipmunk T.10	ex Long Marston, Warmingham, East Midlands, Wigan, Dur UAS, Abn UAS, Henlow, St Athan, 22 GCF, Debden, Jurby SF, 8 FTS, 18 RFS. Loan from TAC. Arrived by 10-93.	10-93
☐ WJ880	8491M	Canberra T.4	ex North Weald, Halton, 7, 85, 100, 56, Laarbruch SF, RAE, 16, Laarbruch SF, Gutersloh SF, 104. Nose. On loan.	12-93
☐ WM267		Meteor NF.11	ex Hemswell, Misson, 151, 256, 11. Nose.	12-93
☐ WP255		Vampire NF.10	ex Ecclesfield, Bingley, Church Fenton, 27 MU hack, CNCS, 1 ANS, CNCS, 23. Pod. Loan Paul Flynn.	12-93
☐ XD528*	8159M	Vampire T.11	ex Ottershaw, Stafford, Penkridge, Wolverhampton, Stafford, Shawbury, FECS, RAFC, 9 FTS, 10 FTS. Pod only. Arrived 27-9-93. §	12-93
☐ XE650*		Hunter FGA.9	ex Kexborough, Macclesfield, Bitteswell, G-9-449, 8, 208, 1, 263. Nose. Loan Gary Martin. [See notes under Kexborough, S Yorks.]	10-93
☐ XE921*		Vampire T.11	ex Keevil, Exeter, 3/4 CAACU, 1 FTS, CFS. '64'. Pod. On loan. First noted 10-93.	10-93
☐ XE935		Vampire T.11	ex Sibson, Hitchin, Woodford, Chester, St Athan, 8 FTS. '30'.	12-93
☐ XH584*		Canberra T.4	ex Sunderland, Marham, 231 OCU. Nose. Arrived by 10-93. §	12-93
☐ XM561*	7980M	Skeeter AOP.12	ex East Kirkby, Tattershall, Moston, Middle Wallop, Arborfield, Wroughton, HQ 1 Wing, HQ 2 Wing, 651. Arrived early 1993.	04-93
☐ XN597*	7984M	Jet Provost T.3	ex Sunderland, Stoke-on-Trent, Bournemouth, Faygate, 2 FTS. Damaged 28-6-67. Nose. Arrived by 12-93. §	12-93
☐ XP190*		Scout AH.1	ex Wroughton, Arborfield. Arr 27-8-92. §	12-93
☐ XP557*	8494M	Jet Provost T.4	ex Bruntingthorpe, Halton, 6 FTS, RAFC. Arrived 29-1-94.	01-94
☐ XS897*		Lightning F.6	ex Rossington, Binbrook, 5, 11, 5, 11, 56, 74. 'TVI897'. Arrived by 10-93.	12-93
☐		Vampire FB.5	ex Malmesbury, 229 OCU. Pod. Loan Paul Flynn.	12-93
☐ E-424	G-9-445	Hunter F.51	ex East Kirkby, Tattershall, Cosford, Dunsfold, Aalborg, Danish AF, Esk-724.	12-93
☐ ET-272*		Hunter T.53	ex Chelford, Macclesfield, Bournemouth, Leavesden, Elstree, Hatfield, Aalborg, Danish AF Esk.722. Nose. Arrived by 12-93. §	12-93
☐		CASA 2-111	ex Eccleston, Henlow, *Battle of Britain.*	12-93

KEXBOROUGH (close to the M1 north of Cawthorne, west of Barnsley)
■ **Gary Martin** : The identity of Gary's Hunter nose is now confirmed — those wishing a good plot start reading at Seighford, Staffs, and radiate out from there! It moved to Firbeck, S Yorks, by October 1993.

NETHERTHORPE AERODROME (north of the A619, west of Worksop)
Rebuild of the Musketeer continues. It has been joined by a SAN-built Jodel and the ever-determined (and temporarily *LOST!*) Auster Kingsland..

☐ G-AJIT*	J/1 Autocrat (mod)	ex Shobdon and area. CoA expired 29-7-66. Restoration.	10-93
☐ G-ASBB	Musketeer 23	CoA expired 30-3-86. Restoration.	10-93
☐ G-AXXW*	SAN D.117	ex Sherburn, F-BIBN. CoA expired 20-2-86. Restoration. First noted 6-92.	06-92

ROSSINGTON (on the A638 north of Bawtry)

■ **Central Bottling Company / Tanks & Vessels Industries** : A combination of the recession and a smaller than envisaged 'market' for Lightnings saw the last of the Rossington examples come under the torch during July 1993. Those escaping were as follows :— nose of F.6 XR726 to Harrogate, N Yorks; nose of F.6 XR747 to Plymouth, Devon, on June 5, 1992; nose of F.6 XR759 to Haxey, Humb; all of T.5 XS416 to New Waltham, Humbs, December 12, 1992; and all of F.6 XS897 to Firbeck, S Yorks. All of the remainder, ie F.6 XR757 (noseless — see under New Waltham, Humbs); F.6 XR759; T.5 XS419; the noseless hulk of F.6 XS932 (nose with Hugh Trevor at Bruntingthorpe, Leics) and F.6 XS935 were scrapped.

SHEFFIELD

■ **Brimpex Metal Treatments** : Continue to restore their *Flea*.

☐   BAPC.13   HM.14 *Flea*   ex Derby, Wigan, Peel Green, Styal. Restn.   03-94

West Yorkshire

BATLEY

■ **Staravia** : The yard in Church Lane was cleared by mid-1993. Stored T.7 N-315 turned up at Hucclecote, Glos, on September 8, 1993.

DEWSBURY

■ **Northern Aeroplane Workshops** (NAW) : Work continues on the Bristol Monoplane for the Shuttleworth Collection of Old Warden, Beds.
◆ Visits to the workshop are on a prior permission only basis. ✉ Northern Aeroplane Workshops, 359 Layburn Road, Crolcar, Huddersfield, W Yorks, HD7 4QQ.

☐   c/n NAW.2 Bristol M.1D   (also PFA 112-10678). Under construction.   12-93

ELLAND (on the A6026 between Halifax and Huddersfield)

■ **Michael Runciman** : Has an extensive avionics collection, including a Comet nose.
☐ XK659   Comet C.2R   ex Northenden, Pomona Dock, Manchester Airport;
                                       51, 192, G-AMXC. Nose.

LEEDS

■ **Mike Cookman** : Passed on his Typhoon cockpit project to Brian Barnes of Coventry, Warks.
■ **Corn Exchange** : The former Eccleston Wright Flyer replica 'flies' inside the Exchange!
☐   BAPC.28 Flyer replica   ex Eccleston, Cardington, Finningley.   12-93
■ **Anne Lindsay** and **Nigel Ponsford** : 'Active' hub of Nigel and Anne's pioneering work on preserving historic light aircraft is now with the Real Aeroplane Club at Breighton, Humb. To this end, *Flea* G-AEFG/BAPC.75 moved to Breighton, Humbs, on August 15, 1993. The storage here has taken on yet another *Flea* and a 'historic' microlight. The store at Wigan, Gtr Man, is slowly being wound down — *qv*. Note that Cadet TX.1 RA848 did not come here, going to Wigan after Harrogate, W Yorks. See also under Sunderland, T&W, for the *Ponsford Air Force* Chipmunk.

☐ G-AEMY*		HM.14 *Flea*	ex Bury St Edmunds, Stowmarket. Substantial parts. Arrived 18-6-93. Stored.	12-93
☐ G-MBWI*		Lafayette 1	ex Leigh. Arrived 18-7-93. Stored.	12-93
☐ ALX	BGA.491	Dagling	ex Great Hucklow. Stored.	12-93
☐		Hutter H.17a	ex Accrington. Stored.	12-93
☐		Dickson Primary	ex Harrogate. Restoration.	12-93
☐	BAPC.14	Addyman STG	ex Harrogate, Wigan. Stored.	12-93
☐	BAPC.16	Addyman UL	ex Harrogate, Wigan. Stored.	12-93
☐	BAPC.18	Killick Gyro	ex Harrogate, Irlam. Stored.	12-93
☐	BAPC.39	Addyman Zephyr	ex Harrogate. Substantial parts, stored.	12-93

■ **Others** : A private owner took on Bensen BAPC.200 during 1993.
☐ *   BAPC.200 Bensen B.7   ex Cheltenham, Long Marston, Stoke.   11-93

LEEDS-BRADFORD AIRPORT (or Yeadon)

Yorkshire Light Aircraft (YLA) have had a small clear-out, F.172H G-AXZJ having gone by July 1992. Otherwise, the **W&R** scene is much as ever.

□ G-ACGT	Avian IIIA	ex Linthwaite, EI-AAB. CoA exp 21-7-39. Restoration, off site.	10-93
□ G-ATND	Cessna F.150F	crashed 9-12-72. Forward fuselage, engine test-rig. YLA.	10-93
□ G-AVGG	Cherokee 140	crashed 10-8-70. Spares.	10-93
□ G-AWES	Cessna 150H	ex Blackpool, Glenrothes, N22933. Damaged 2-10-81. Restoration.	10-93

PONTEFRACT

An AA-1B Trainer may still be in the area for spares use.

□ G-BBWZ	AA-1B Trainer	ex Verwood, Breighton. Spares.	04-90

SIDDAL (on the A646 south of Halifax)

A visit to the yard here during May 1992 found the fuselage of Whirlwind HAS.7 XG597 extant and upside-down. Whirlwind HAS.7s XL868, XM663 and Wessex HU.5 XT774 are all thought to have perished or have been buried in the huge scrap piles here.

□ XG597	W'wind HAS.7	ex Warton SAR Flt, CA, makers.	05-92

WAKEFIELD

■ **Bob Fenton** : Took delivery of a Harvard cockpit section by September 1993.

□ EZ259*	G-BMJW	Harvard III	ex Ottershaw, Bracknell, Tattershall, Oxford, Sandhurst, 766, 42-84182. Cockpit. Arrived by 9-93.	09-93

SCOTLAND

Shetland Isles

Orkney Isles

Western Isles

Highlands

Grampian

Tayside

Central   Fife

Lothian

Strathclyde

Borders

Dumfries &
Galloway

England

Borders

KIRK YELTHOLM (on the B6401 south of Coldstream)
Safir G-ANOK came here for storage during 1989.
☐ G-ANOK   SAAB Safir   ex Strathallan, East Fortune, SE-CAH ntu.
                                       CoA expired 5-2-73. Stored.   04-89

Central Region

ABERFOYLE (on the A81 west of Stirling)
■ **Scotland West Aircraft Investigation Group** (SWAIG) : The pod of Vampire T.11 XD547 moved to Tinwald Downs, D&G.

CAUSEWAYHEAD (north of Stirling)
■ **William Kerr** : By May 1992, there was no sign of Sycamore HR.14 XG504, it having been reduced to neat-looking "packets" of metal.

THORNHILL AERODROME
■ **Stirling Parachute Centre** : Took on the former Glenrothes para-trainer.
☐ G-ATES*   Cherokee Six 260   ex Glenrothes, Ipswich. Crashed 8-2-81.
                                       Para-trainer.   09-92

Dumfries & Galloway

BORGUE (on the B727 west of Kirkcudbright)
■ **Brighouse Bay Caravan Park** : Displayed inside the camp is the former Carlisle Meteor.
☐ WS792   7965M   Meteor NF.14   ex Carlisle, Cosford, Kemble, 1 ANS, 2 ANS.
                                       'K'.   05-93

FALGUNZEON
■ **Dumfries & Galloway Gliding Club** : A T.45 wreck and a Grasshopper were noted stored here during June 1992. The anonymous T.21B may or may not still be here.
☐ DHP*   BGA.2130 T.45   Composite of BGA.1032 & '1041. Wreck.   06-92
☐   T.21B   possibly BGA.1315 'BXJ'. Stored.   04-90
☐ WZ792*   Grasshopper TX.1   Stored.   06-92

TINWALD DOWNS (off the A701 north west of Dumfries on the former airfield)
■ **Dumfries and Galloway Aviation Museum** (DGAM) : Run by the Dumfries and Galloway Aviation Group, DGAM — the only private aviation museum in Scotland — continues to thrive. The accent here has become decidedly Spitfire. Restoration of the Loch Doon Mk IIA has progressed impressively. The airframe is currently off-site undergoing a guided restoration by a 'captive' workforce at a prison so, for obvious reasons, is not available for inspection at present! This work will greatly reduce the timescale of getting the completed project on show at DGAM. One Spitfire may have left the site, but another has arrived! This is Mk V AD540 *Blue Peter* and it will undergo restoration in due course. The wreck was salvaged with help from 819 Squadron at Prestwick, whose Sea King HAS.6 ZG816 provided the muscle. *Blue Peter* was salvaged *exactly* 51 years after it had crashed! From a completely different era, but similar circumstances, DGAM also have a salvaged Chipmunk within the collection. The former SWAIG Vampire T.11 pod has been acquired and moved from Aberfoyle, Central, and has replaced the pod of XD425 — see below. The single-seat Vampire pod has gone to Yeovilton, Som.

◆ DGAM is open Saturdays and Sundays 10am to 5pm or by prior arrangement. Located within the Heathhall Industrial Estate, on the former airfield. ✉ DGAG, David Reid, Chairman, 11 Ninian Court, Lochside, Dumfries. ☎ 0387 65745 (evenings only)

☐ P7540		Spitfire IIA	ex Loch Doon, 312, 266, 609, 66. Crashed 6-7-41. Restoration, off site. See notes.	11-93
☐ AD540*		Spitfire V	ex Carsphairn, 242, 122. Crashed 23-5-1942. Salvaged 23-5-93 — see notes above.	11-93
☐ WA576	7900M	Sycamore 3	ex East Fortune, Strathallan, Halton, RAE, A&AEE, G-ALSS ntu.	11-93
☐ WD377*		Chipmunk T.10	ex 12 AEF, Glas UAS, HCEU, 11 RFS, 2 BFTS. Cr 29-7-66. Stored. See notes.	11-93
☐ WJ903		Varsity T.1	ex Glasgow Airport, 6 FTS, AE&AEOS, 1 ANS, 2 ANS, 3 ANS. Nose.	11-93
☐ WL375		Meteor T.7(mod)	ex West Freugh, RAE.	11-93
☐ XD425		Vampire T.11	ex Stranraer, Woodford, Chester, St Athan, 8 FTS, 5 FTS, 7 FTS, 202 AFS. '16'. Wings etc to XD547. See below. Pod stored.	11-93
☐ XD547*		Vampire T.11	ex Aberfoyle, Strathallan, Milngavie, Glasgow, CATCS, 8 FTS, 1 RS, 263. 'Z'. Pod, fitted with wings etc from XD425 above.	11-93
☐		Venom	ex Silloth. Pod only, single-seater. [Possibly WK394]	11-93
☐ FT-36		T-33A-1-LO	ex Sculthorpe, Belgian AF, USAF 55-3047.	11-93
☐ 318		Mystere IVA	ex Sculthorpe, French Air Force. '8-NY'.	11-93
☐ 42163		F-100D-11-NA	ex Sculthorpe, French Air Force. '11-YG'.	11-93
☐ 68-0060*		F-111E	ex 20 TFW. Escape pod.	11-93

WEST FREUGH AIRFIELD (on the A715 south east of Stranraer)
■ **Test & Evaluation Establishment** (TEE) : [Note change of ownership and/or title here!] Devon C.2/2 VP977 gave up the ghost on the dump by October 1992. The Argosy and Phantom live on. A *Brick* arrived on April 27, 1993 for spares use and may well end up on the dump.

☐ XN817	Argosy C.1	ex A&AEE, MinTech, 115, MoA. Dump.	07-92
☐ XT852	Phantom FG.1	ex BAe Scampton, A&AEE. Dump.	07-92
☐ *	Buccaneer S.2B	ex Boscombe Down. Flew in 27-4-93. Spares.	04-93

Fife

CUPAR
The Cadet in store has been joined by a damaged Mascaret.

☐ G-BFEB*	SAN D.150	ex F-BMJR, OO-LDY, F-BLDX. Crashed 14-4-91. Restn.	05-91
☐ XE802	Cadet TX.3	ex 624 VGS. Stored.	03-91

GLENROTHES AERODROME (on the B9097 south west of Glenrothes)
Para-trainer Cherokee Six G-ATES moved to Thornhill, Central, by November 1991.

LEUCHARS AIRFIELD (on the A919, north west of St Andrews)
■ **RAF Leuchars** : Another base that has been hit badly by peace breaking out... Clearly most of the news from here relates to the nationwide Phantom cull, but there are some disposals from another generation to note first. Vampire T.11 'XE897'/XD403 returned to Errol, Tayside, by November 1991. Lightning F.3 XR749/8934M was dismantled by September 1991 and eventually made the move to Chop Gate, N Yorks, for a run-in with the planning authorities. By April 1992 the following Phantom FG.1s had moved to Glasgow, Strath, to meet the dreaded 'fragmentiser' :— XT859/8999M 'BK', XT870 'BS', XT873 'BA', XV567 'AI', XV568 'AT', XV571 'AA', XV572 'BG' less nose,

XV573 'BD', XV576 'BK' (omitted from **W&R13**), XV579 'AR' and XV590 'AX'. The nose of XV572 is reported to have gone for fire training somewhere. Two machines are unaccounted for at present, XV585 and the noseless XV588 — both of these disappeared at about the same time.

☐	XR713	8935M	Lightning F.3	ex LTF, 5, 11, 5, LTF, 11, LTF, 5, 111, Wattisham TFF, 111. Displayed outside the 111 Sqn shelters. Officially BDR. 'C'.	09-93
☐	XT857	8913M	Phantom FG.1	ex 111, PTF, 767, A&AEE, RAE, A&AEE. Damaged 7-85. 'MP'. ASF.	09-91
☐	XT864	8998M	Phantom FG.1	ex 111, 892, 767. 'BJ'. Gate.	05-93
☐	XT867	9064M	Phantom FG.1	ex 111, 892, 767, 700P. BDR. 'BH'.	04-93
☐	XT903*		Phantom FG.1	ex 56, 92, 228 OCU, 23, 228 OCU. 'X'. Decoy. First noted 10-92.	09-93
☐	XV482	9107M	Phantom FGR.2	ex BDR, 92, 29. 'T'. Flew in 16-2-92.	09-93
☐	XV577	9065M	Phantom FG.1	ex 43. 'AM'. BDR.	09-93
☐	XV582	9066M	Phantom FG.1	ex WLT, 43. 'M'. *Black Mike*. All black c/s. Displayed within the base. Officially WLT.	09-93
☐	XV586	9067M	Phantom FG.1	ex 43. Displayed 43 Sqn HAS area, officially BDR. 'AJ'.	09-93

Grampian

ABERDEEN
■ **Aberdeen Technical College** : Cadet WT905 departed for Bridge of Don, Grampian.

ABERDEEN AIRPORT (or Dyce, off the A96 north west of Aberdeen))
The wreck of Bonanza A35 N150JC left for "the south" on July 16, 1993 — White Waltham, Berks, being a possibility. Former Aberdeen Airways Gulfstream I G-BNCE was used as a source of spares to get sister-ship G-BMPA ready to spend a year in Air Provence during early 1993 and looks set to join the Trident on the dump.

☐	G-ARPN	Trident 1	ex Heathrow, BA, BEA. Fire service.	12-93
☐	G-BNCE*	Gulfstream I	ex Aberdeen Airways, N436M, N436, N436M, N43M, N709G. CoA exp 9-4-92. Spares.	01-94
☐	G-TIGH*	AS.332L S' Puma	ex Bristow, F-WXFL. *City of Edinburgh*. Crashed 14-3-92. Fuselage, escape trials.	12-93

ABOYNE
Restoration work on the Stampe continues close to the airfield.

☐	G-BALK	SNCAN SV-4C	ex 'Cheshire', Liverpool, Littleborough, F-BBAN, French military. Restoration.	09-93

BANCHORY (on the A93 west of Aberdeen)
■ **Donald Milne** : Keeps the nose section of a Vulcan here.

☐	XH563	8744M	Vulcan B.2MRR	ex Rotherham, Scampton, 27, 230 OCU, MoA, 230 OCU, Wadd W, 230 OCU, 12, 83. Nose.	04-90

BRIDGE OF DON (north of Aberdeen)
The former Aberdeen Tech Cadet has moved here for restoration.

☐	WT905*	Cadet TX.3	ex Aberdeen, Syerston, Dishforth, 645 VGS.	04-93

BUCHAN (east of the A952 at Boddam, south of Peterhead)
■ **RAF Buchan Radar** : On April 24, 1992, the base received a former Wattisham Phantom FG.1 for gate guardian duties. The type is most fitting, having been 'trade' for the base for a long time!

☐	XV581*	9070M	Phantom FG.1	ex Wattisham, 43. 'AE'. Arrived 24-4-92. On gate by 7-92.	07-92

CRUDEN BAY (on the A975 south of Peterhead)
■ **Hobson Home for Distressed Aeroplanes** : Malcolm Hobson has taken another airframe on for the recuperative process.

☐ G-AVKM	D.62B Condor	ex Edderton. Damaged 3-3-82.	09-92
☐ G-AXBU*	FR.172F	ex Bearsden, Kirknewton, Inverkeithing. Crashed 13-10-74. Wreck. Arrived 28-9-92.	09-92
☐ G-BCIL	AA-1B Trainer	ex Auchnagatt, N6168A. Crashed 14-6-86.	09-92

■ **Others** : Noted in a garden in the locality during October 1992 was the former Midland Air Museum Cessna F.172F 'G-ASOK' (D-ECDU) which was noted in **W&R12** as going to "a gent in Scotland". This was Mr M Dunn. The machine had gone again by December 1993.

ELGIN
■ **George F Williamson** : The demise of the mighty *Brick* has seen a considerable upsurge of activity at the Moycroft Industrial Estate site. From May 1992 several 'waves' of Buccaneers arrived at the yard which has also handled heavier metal from Kinloss. Noted in October 1992 was the nose section of Shackleton T.4 WB847, previously thought to have perished. Along with this was another *Shack* nose. There are several candidates possible for this. By November 1992 the chunks of Canberra E.15 WH972 had become too small for consideration. Unlike other yards, airframes tend to stay quite a while in a recognisable state and so they are given a more 'formal' listing. This is not so with the former Kinloss Nimrods, which were processed with great speed, possibly due to treaty requirements, or just because of their size or the metal 'cocktail' they represent :— MR.2Ps XV238 and XV253/9118M plus AEW.3 XZ282/9000M were first noted here during October 1992 but were unrecognisable by April 1993.

☐ WB847*	8020M	Shackleton T.4	ex Lossiemouth, MOTU, 236 OCU. Nose. See notes above. 'First' noted 10-92.	04-93
☐ WL798	8114M	Shack MR.2C	ex Lossie', Cosford, 204, 205, 38. Nose. [Rest at Quarrywood, Grampian.]	04-93
☐ XL609*	8866M	Hunter T.7	ex Lossiemouth, 12, 216, 237 OCU, 4 FTS, 56. Arrived 2-94.	02-94
☐ XN929	8051M	Buccaneer S.1	ex Lossiemouth, Honington. Nose.	04-93
☐ XT271*		Buccaneer S.2B	ex Lossiemouth, 237 OCU, 16, 15, 237 OCU, 208, 237 OCU. First noted early 1992.	04-93
☐ XT279*		Buccaneer S.2B	ex Lossie', 15, 16, 237 OCU, 12. F/n 4-93.	04-93
☐ XT281*	8705M	Buccaneer S.2B	ex Lossiemouth, 12. First noted early 1992.	04-93
☐ XT283*		Buccaneer S.2	ex Lossiemouth, 237 OCU, A&AEE, 208. First noted 10-92.	04-93
☐ XT287*		Buccaneer S.2B	ex Lossiemouth, 208, 237 OCU, 16, 15, 237 OCU. First noted 4-93.	04-93
☐ XV154*	8854M	Buccaneer S.2A	ex Lossiemouth, St Athan, 12, 237 OCU. First noted 10-92.	04-93
☐ XV342*		Buccaneer S.2B	ex Lossie', 16, 208, 237 OCU, 12. F/n 4-93.	04-93
☐ XV355*		Buccaneer S.2B	ex Lossie', 237 OCU, 208. First noted 4-93.	04-93
☐ XV868*		Buccaneer S.2B	ex Lossiemouth, 208, 12. First noted 4-93.	04-93
☐ XW529*		Buccaneer S.2B	ex Lossiemouth, BAe Scampton, A&AEE. First noted 10-92.	04-93
☐ XW533*		Buccaneer S.2B	ex Lossiemouth, 208, 237 OCU, 208, 15, 16, 237 OCU, 12, 237 OCU, 12, 216, 16, 12. First noted early 1992.	10-92
☐ XW546*		Buccaneer S.2B	ex Lossie', 237 OCU, 16,15. F/n 4-93.	04-93
☐ XZ432*		Buccaneer S.2B	ex Lossiemouth, 12, 237 OCU, 12, 237 OCU, 208, 216, 15. First noted 10-92.	10-92
☐ *		Shackleton	nose section. see notes above.	10-92

INSCH AERODROME (west of the B992 at Auchleven)
Received Airedale G-ASAI from Dundee during mid-1991.

☐ G-ASAI*	Airedale	ex Dundee, Dundee Airport, Islay. CoA expired 20-5-77. Restoration. Arrived mid-1991.	11-91

KINLOSS AIRFIELD (on the B9011 north of Forres)

■ **RAF Kinloss** : Is now the home of the Nimrod, the St Mawgan Wing moving in during September 1992. Four Nimrods have been mothballed in a manner that would please any Egyptian crypt-keeper. Three Nimrods moved to the yard at Elgin, Grampian, during October 1992 : — MR.2Ps XV238 and XV253/9118M and AEW.3 XZ282/9000M. That makes the situation as follows : —

☐ XL188	9100M	Victor K.2	ex 55, 57, 55, MinTech, Witt Wing, 232 OCU.	
			Dump.	10-93
☐ XV234*		Nimrod MR.2P	ex St Mawgan Wing, Kin Wing, St M Wing.	
			External store by 9-92.	10-93
☐ XV242*		Nimrod MR.2P	ex St Mawgan Wing, Kin Wing, St M Wing, Kin	
			Wing, St. M, 203, Kin Wing Stored by 9-92	10-93
☐ XV247*		Nimrod MR.2P	ex St Mawgan Wing, Kin Wing, St M Wing,	
			203, Kin Wing. External store by 9-92.	10-93
☐ XV249*		Nimrod MR.2P	ex St Mawgan Wing, Kin Wing, BAe, StM Wing,	
			Kin Wing. External store by 9-92.	10-93
☐ XW549	8860M	Buccaneer S.2B	ex St Athan, 12, 16. BDR. Sections.	04-93
☐ 8882M	G-BDIU	Comet 4C	ex Woodford, Bitteswell, Dan-Air, XR396,	
			214. BDR. Centre section.	04-93

LOSSIEMOUTH AIRFIELD (south of the B4090, west of Lossiemouth)

■ **RAF Lossiemouth** : The story here is the same with other bases, the withdrawal *en masse* of aircraft and their scrapping or other disposal. In *Lossie's* case, the aircraft involved is the superb Buccaneer — hero of the Gulf anti-airfield work. Buccaneer S.2B XV863 guards the gate in Gulf scheme. Its route to the gate is worth expanding upon. It was initially allocated as 9115M for the gate here, but was then 'slotted' for Abingdon for BDR use as 9139M. This was then allocated as 9145M — doubtless because someone had woken up to the fact that Abingdon was on its way out! — again for the gate! *Bricks* of course qualify for the SALT II talks and therefore have been appearing with blue crosses and their scrappings have been high profile affairs so that the pull back of capability could be made into good propaganda. S.1 XK532/8867M was put up for tender during March 1992 and removed from the gate on June 30. It was bought by Ken Charleton (see New Byth, Grampian) for the Fresson Trust and it moved to Inverness, Highland, on September 23, 1992. S.2B XT281/8705M moved to Elgin, Grampian, early in 1992. S.2A XV154/8854M also moved to Elgin, Grampian, in October 1992. The following were scrapped on May 12, 1992 : — XT279, XT287, XV355, XV868, all going to Elgin, Grampian; by October 1992 the following had gone : XT271, XT283, XV342, XW529, XW533, XW546, XZ432 again to Elgin, Grampian; and by April 1993 the following were axed : XT279, XT287, XV355, XV868, all also Elgin-bound. A batch of another seven was offered for tender during February 1994 : — XN981, XT280, XT288, XV161, XW530, XX892 and XX893 all of which had to be removed from base by March 30, 1994 — a scrapyard being the *only* destination for these machines. The former 8 Squadron procedure trainer Shackleton MR.2C cockpit WR967/8398M was exported to Cyprus via Liverpool Docks during August 1992. Hunter T.7 XL609/8866M was put up for tender during June 1993 and acquired by Ed Stead of Manchester, New Hampshire, USA, for some spare parts for his project. The remainder went for scrap, travelling to Elgin, Grampian, in early February 1994. S.2Bs XV353 and XW542 were retried by November 1993 and left by road on February 1, 1994 for Dalkeith, Lothian.

☐ XV863*	9145M	Buccaneer S.2B	ex 9115M, 9139M, 12, 208, 237 OCU, 12, 16,	
			809. Pink c/s. 'D'. Gate by 7-92. See notes.	10-93
☐ XX885*		Buccaneer S.2B	ex 12, 208, 12, 208, 216, 16. Stored by 11-93.	
				11-93

NETHERLEY (On the B979 north of Stonehaven)

With the death of the owner, the aerodrome is for sale and faces an uncertain future, having become a decidedly Auster oriented place. Spares ship Terrier G-ASBU has been joined by the aircraft benefiting from its 'off-cuts'. Airedale G-ARXD is also a long term retiree.

☐ G-ARXD*	Airedale	CoA expired 13-6-86. Stored. F/n 12-91.	05-93
☐ G-ASAX*	Terrier 2	CoA expired 7-9-91. Stored. F/n 5-93.	05-93
☐ G-ASBU	Terrier 2	ex WE570, LAS, CFS, 2 FTS, CFS. Crashed	
		12-8-80. Spares.	05-93

NEW BYTH (on the B9027 south of the A98 Fraserburgh-Macduff road)
■ **Ken Charleton** : At the Old Schoolhouse, Ken's collection expanded up to 1992. During late 1993, Ken moved back to Yorkshire. Ken acquired Buccaneer XK532 from Lossiemouth, Grampian, for the Fresson Trust and this is to be found under Inverness, Highland. Whirlwind HAR.9 XL898/8654M and the still to be identified *JP* (XN581, ex Scampton?) moved during late 1992 to a local scrapman. Hunter F.1 WT660/7421M arrived from Carlisle, Cumb, on July 9, 1992 but had been sold "to a local farmer" by late 1993. The Sycamore and Vampire are reported to be moving to Manchester.

☐ XE874	8582M	Vampire T.11	ex Valley, Woodford, Chester, Shawbury, 1 FTS, 4 FTS, 8 FTS, 4 FTS, 1 FTS, 4 FTS, 7 FTS. '61'.	02-94
☐ XJ380	8628M	Sycamore HR.14	ex Drighlington, Finningley, Catterick, CFS, MoA, HS, 275.	02-94

QUARRYWOOD (on the B9012 north west of Elgin)
■ **George F Williamson** : The two large heaps of Shackleton are still here along with small, but recognisable bits of a Firefly, Gannets, Sea Hawks and Sea Venoms. This yard is now dormant in favour of the one at Elgin, Grampian.

☐ WL738	8567M	Shack MR.2C	ex Lossiemouth, 8, 204, 210, A&AEE, 210, 37, 204, 240.	02-94
☐ WL798	8114M	Shack MR.2C	ex Lossiemouth, Cosford, 204, 205, 38. Minus nose - see under Elgin, Grampian.	02-94

STONEHAVEN
■ **Pete Morris** : Is working on the former Perth Prentice.

☐ VS356	G-AOLU	Prentice T.1	ex Perth, Strathallan, Biggin Hill, EI-ASP, G-AOLU, VS356, CFS, 2 FTS. CoA exp 8-5-76. Restoration.	11-93

Highlands

EDDERTON (on the A9 north west of Tain)
Condor G-ASEU moved to Inverness Airport on July 31, 1992 and was flying very soon afterwards.

FEARN (on the B9166 east of Tain)
By November 1992, the former Ely Hospital Meteor had arrived here.

☐ WS774*	7959M	Meteor NF.14	ex Ely, Upwood, Kemble, 1 ANS, 2 ANS. Arrived by 11-92.	11-92

INVERNESS
■ **Others** : Skeeter AOP.12 XN351/G-BKSC is under restoration in the general area.

☐ XN351*	G-BKSC	Skeeter AOP.12	ex Inverness Airport, Shobdon, Cardiff-Wales, Higher Blagdon, Old Warden, Wroughton, 3 RTR, 652, 651. CoA exp 8-11-84. Arr 10-6-92. Restoration.	06-92

INVERNESS AIRPORT (or Dalcross, off the A96 north east of Inverness)
■ **Airport** : Cessna 188-230 G-AZZG moved to <u>Lairg</u>, Highlands, by May 1992. Skeeter AOP.12 XN351/G-BKSC left by road on June 10, 1992 for a location within <u>Inverness</u>, Highlands, itself.
■ **Fresson Trust** : Work is in hand to establish an aviation museum in honour of the Scottish airline pioneer. The Buccaneer from Lossiemouth, Grampian, arrived on September 23, 1992 for storage.
◆ Visits are not yet possible. General enquiries can be made to : ✉ H M Lawson, Secretary, The Fresson Trust, Head Office, Highlands & Islands Airports Ltd, Inverness Airport, Inverness, Fife, IV1 2JU.

☐ XK532* 8867M   Buccaneer S.1   ex Lossiemouth, Manadon, A2581, Lossie, 736. Ken Charleton, loan Fresson Trust. '632/LM'. Arrived 23-9-92. Stored.   12-93

LAIRG (on the A836 north west of Tain)
By May 1992, the former Inverness Agwagon 230 had arrived here for rebuild.
☐ G-AZZG*   Cessna 188-230   ex Inverness, Southend, OY-AHT, N8029V. CoA expired 1-5-81. Restn. First noted 5-92. 05-92

TAIN
Aerial reconnaissance during June 1993 of the range area where Sea Venom FAW.22 XG731 used to lie revealed a blank space. It can be reasonably assumed that the hulk has passed on.

The Islands

BENBECULA AIRPORT (Outer Hebrides)
The RAF enclave here gained its first aircraft on August 6, 1992, when an obligatory Phantom touched down to be prepared for what constitutes the gate.
☐ XV467* 9158M   Phantom FGR.2   ex 56, 92, 19, 2. 'F'. Arr 6-8-92. 'Gate'.   08-92

ORPHIR (near Kirkwall, Orkney)
A ditched Jodel is still stored on a farm-strip.
☐ G-ASRP   SAN DR.1050   ex F-BITI. Ditched 17-3-86. Stored.

ROTHESAY (Isle of Bute)
During early 1992 two Tiger Moths arrived for restoration. One, G-ALWS, stayed only until October 1993 hen it moved to <u>Bromsgrove</u>, H&W.
☐ N6037* G-ANNB   Tiger Moth   ex Cumbernauld, Glasgow Airport, US N6037, D-EGYN, G-ANNB, T6037, 1 RFS, 12 RFS, 23 RFS, 5 RFS, 29 EFTS. Restoration.   04-92

STORNOWAY AIRPORT (Isle of Lewis)
Another to benefit from the RAF's *Now-where-shall-we-put-a-Phantom?* campaign. XV422 was put on display alongside the RAF enclave at the Airport on November 7, 1992.
☐ XV422* 9157M   Phantom FGR.2   ex 56, 19, 92, 23. 'T'. Arrived 6-8-92. Placed on display 7-11-92.   06-93

SUMBURGH AIRPORT (Shetland, on the A970 south of Lerwick)
The Potez 840 continues to serve the firemen and to provide a home for a family of foxes!
☐ F-BMCY   Potez 840   wheels-up landing 29-3-81. Fire dump.   12-93

Lothian

DALKIETH (on the A68 south of Edinburgh)
■ **Dalkieth Demolition** : On February 1, 1994, this yard took two *Lossie* Buccaneers.
☐ XV353*   Buccaneer S.2B   ex Lossiemouth, 208, 12, 237 OCU, 12, 237 OCU, 12. Arrived 1-2-94.   02-94
☐ XW542*   Buccaneer S.2B   ex Lossiemouth, 208, 12, 237 OCU, 16. Arrived 1-2-94.   02-94

EAST FORTUNE (north of the A1, west of East Linton)

■ **Aircraft Preservation Society of Scotland** (APSS) : Restoration of the Monarch G-AFJU has made good progress and it is scheduled to go on show in Hangar IV on April 1, 1994. Accordingly, it has been moved into the appropriate place within the Museum of Flight listing below. Work is also well underway on the Museum of Flight's Puss Moth VH-UQB. Target date for public display of the completed restoration is the 1995 season.

✉ c/o Museum of Flight, see below.

■ **National Museums of Scotland — Museum of Flight** (MoF) : Consolidation of the airfield site continues, with much of the architecture having gained 'listed' status. Greatest news from this quarter is that National Museums of Scotland now own the whole site and a ten year development plan is underway. The original Pilcher glider is now here, underlining the major status of this Museum. A MiG-15 and the cockpit section of a 'UTI have been acquired from Czechoslovakia.

◆ Open 10.30am to 4.30pm seven days a week April 1 to September 30. Parties at other times by appointment. ✉ Museum of Flight, East Fortune Airfield, North Berwick, Lothian, EH39 5LF. ☎ 062 088 308.

☐ G-ACYK		Spartan Cruiser	ex Hill of Stake, Largs. Crashed 14-1-38. Fuselage section.	04-93
☐ G-AFJU		Miles Monarch	ex York, Strathallan, Lasham, Staverton, X9306, G-AFJU. CoA exp 18-5-64. APSS. Restn.	12-93
☐ G-AGBN		GAL Cygnet II	ex Strathallan, Biggin Hill, ES915, MCCS, 52 OTU, 51 OTU, 23, G-AGBN. CoA expired 28-11-80.	04-93
☐ G-AHKY		Miles M.18-2	ex Perth, Strathallan, Blackbushe, HM545, U-0224, U-8. CoA expired 20-9-89.	04-93
☐ G-ANOV		Dove 6	ex CAFU Stansted, G-5-16. CoA expired 31-5-75.	04-93
☐ G-AOEL		Tiger Moth	ex Strathallan, Dunstable, N9510, 7 FTS, 2 GU, 11 RFS, 1 RFS, 7 RFS, 7 EFTS. CoA expired 18-7-72.	04-93
☐ G-ARCX		Meteor Mk 14	ex Ferranti, WM261. CoA expired 20-2-69.	04-93
☐ G-ARTJ		Bensen B.8M	ex APSS, Currie, Cupar. APSS loan.	04-93
☐ G-ASUG		Beech D.18S	ex Loganair, N575C, N555CB, N24R. CoA expired 23-7-75.	04-93
☐ G-ATFG		Brantly B.2B	ex APSS, Newport Pagnell. CoA expired 25-3-85. APSS loan.	04-93
☐ G-ATOY		Comanche 260B	ex Elstree, N8893P. Crashed 6-3-79. *Mythtoo*, Sheila Scott's aircraft.	04-93
☐ G-AXEH		Bulldog Srs 1	ex Prestwick, Shoreham. Prototype. CoA expired 15-1-77.	04-93
☐ G-BBVF		Twin Pioneer 2	ex Shobdon, XM961/7978M, SRCU, Odiham SF, 230, 21. Damaged 11-3-82.	04-93
☐ G-BDFU		Dragonfly MPA	ex Blackpool Airport, Warton, Prestwick.	04-93
☐ G-BDIX		Comet 4C	ex Lasham, Dan-Air, XR399, 216. CoA expired 11-10-81.	04-93
☐ BCB	BGA.852	T.8 Tutor	ex Portmoak, TS291.	04-93
☐ BED	BGA.902	Gull I	ex Newbattle, 'G-ALPHA'. *Possibly* ex VW912.	04-93
☐ BJV	BGA.1014	T.21B	ex Feshie Bridge, SE-SHK.	04-93
☐ W-2	BAPC.85	Weir W-2	ex Glasgow, East Fortune, Hayes, Cathcart.	04-93
☐ VH-SNB		Dragon I	ex Strathallan, VH-ASK, RAAF A34-13.	04-93
☐ VH-UQB		Puss Moth	ex Strathallan, Marshall Airways, Bankstown, G-ABDW. Restn by APSS — see notes.	12-93
☐ TE462	7243M	Spitfire XVI	ex Ouston, 101 FRS, Finningley SF.	04-93
☐ 'TJ398'	BAPC.70	Auster AOP.6	ex APSS, Inverkeithing, Perth. APSS loan.	04-93
☐ VM360	G-APHV	Anson C.19	ex Strathallan, Kemps, BKS, TRE, A&AEE.	04-93
☐ WF259	A2483	Sea Hawk F.2	ex Lossiemouth SF, 736. '171-A'.	04-93
☐ WV493	G-BDYG	Provost T.1	ex Strathallan, Halton 7696M, 6 FTS. CoA expired 28-11-80. '29'.	04-93

☐ WW145		Sea Ven FAW.22	ex Lossiemouth, 750, 891. '680-LM'.	04-93
☐ XA109		Sea Vampire T.22	ex Lossiemouth, 831, JOAC. Restoration started 8-92.	04-93
☐ XG594		Whirlwind HAS.7	ex Strathallan, Wroughton, 71, A&AEE, 705, 846, 737, 701, RAE Bedford, 700. FAAM loan. '517-PO'.	07-93
☐ XL762	8017M	Skeeter AOP.12	ex Middle Wallop, 2 RTR, 9 Flt, 651.	04-93
☐ XM597		Vulcan B.2	ex Waddington, 50, 35, 101, 9, 50, 35, Wadd Wing, 12.	04-93
☐ XN776		Lightning F.2A	ex Leuchars, 92. 'C'.	04-93
☐ 9940		Bolingbroke IVT	ex Strathallan, RCAF 5 B&GS. Restoration.	04-93
☐ 3309*		MiG-15	ex Czech AF. Arrived 12-93.	01-94
☐ *		MiG-15UTI	ex Czech AF. Cockpit section. Arr 12-93.	01-94
☐ 591		Rhonlerche II	ex D-0359.	04-93
☐ 'FI+S'	G-BIRW	MS.505 Criquet	ex Duxford, OO-FIS, F-BDQS. CoA expired 3-6-83. *Luftwaffe* colours.	04-93
☐ 191659		Me 163B-1a	ex Cambridge, Cranfield, Brize Norton, II/JG400. '15'.	04-93
☐		WACO CG-4A	ex Aberlady. Nose section.	04-93
☐	BAPC.12	HM.14 *Flea*	ex Chester-le-Street, Newcastle, Wigan.	04-93
☐ *	BAPC.49	Pilcher Hawk	ex Edinburgh. First flown at Eynsham 1896, crashed at Stanford Hall, Leics, 30-9-1899, killing Pilcher. See notes above.	07-93
☐	BAPC.160	Chargus 18/50	hang glider.	04-93
☐	BAPC.195	Moonraker 77	hang glider.	04-93
☐	BAPC.196	Sigma IIM	hang glider.	04-93
☐	BAPC.197	Cirrus 3	hang glider.	04-93

EDINBURGH

■ **Ferranti** : The factory is still guarded by a dramatically-posed Lightning.

☐ ZF584		Lightning F.53	ex Edinburgh Airport, Warton, RSAF 53-682, G-27-52. Gate.	06-90

■ **Royal Museum of Scotland** : Pilcher Hawk BAPC.49 on show moved to <u>East Fortune</u>, Lothian, during early 1993 for restoration and then display.

EDINBURGH AIRPORT (or Turnhouse, on the A8 east of Edinburgh)

■ **Airport** : The Trident is still in use with the firecrews. A Cessna is used for spares.

☐ G-ARPL		Trident 1C	ex BA, BEA. CoA expired 13-8-84. Dump.	09-93
☐ G-LEAN*		Cessna FR.182	ex Cumbernauld, G-BGAP. Arr by 2-93.	08-93

■ **RAF Turnhouse** : Is guarded by a plastic Spitfire.

☐ 'L1070'	BAPC.227	Spitfire replica	gate guardian. 'XT-A', 603 Sqn colours.	05-93

Strathclyde

BEARSDEN (north of Glasgow)

Cessna FR.172F G-AXBU moved to <u>Cruden Bay</u>, Grampian, on February 28, 1992.

CUMBERNAULD AERODROME (north of the A80, north of Cumbernauld)

■ **Computaplane** : Receiving a brief dash of nationwide television coverage in the autumn of 1993 was the cache of former Soviet L 29 Delfins (NATO — *Maya*) that arrived here with the hoped-for view of sales as 'cooking' warbirds to owners in Europe or the USA. The company says that a Mil Mi-2, an An-2 and a Po-2 are due to arrive. By December 1993, two of the Delfins had moved on, reportedly to 'Chester' — these being 491273 '51' which arrived during September 1993 and 591771 '18' which arrived on July 14, 1993. Bearing in mind that the Liverpool Docks cache of former Soviet hardware is also thought to be settling upon 'Chester', it may well be that the two operations are related. As a prelude to the Delfins, a Yak-18 and Yak-52 811202 '19' arrived during November 1992, but moved on to <u>Strathallan</u>, Tayside, on May 9, 1993.

☐ *	491273	L 29 Delfin	ex CIS, USSR. '51'. Arr 9-93.	11-93
☐ *	591771	L 29 Delfin	ex CIS, USSR. '18'. Arr 14-7-93. Dism.	11-93
☐ *	491119	L 29 Delfin	ex CIS, USSR. '37'. Arr 9-93.	12-93
☐ *	491165	L 29 Delfin	ex CIS, USSR. '40'. Arr 14-7-93.	12-93
☐ *	591378	L 29 Delfin	ex CIS, USSR. '09'. Arr 9-93.	12-93
☐ *	591636	L 29 Delfin	ex CIS, USSR. '06'. Arr 8-93.	12-93

■ **Cormack Aircraft Services** : Tiger Moth N6037/G-ANNB moved to <u>Rothesay</u>, Islands, early in 1992. On December 7, 1993 a Trislander arrived by road from Glasgow Airport, Strath, for storage, while it acts as a source of spares for its sister, still at Glasgow.

☐ ZK-SFF*	G-BDOT	Trislander	ex Glasgow, N900TA, N903GD, N3850K, VH-BPB, G-BDOT. Damaged. Arrived 7-12-93. See notes above.	12-93

DUNOON

■ **2296 Squadron ATC** : The unit keep their *Chippax*-plus-engine here.

☐ WZ866	8217M	Chipmunk T.10	ex Carluke, Cumbernauld, CoAT G-ATEB, Leeds UAS, Abn UAS, Bir, Abn, Oxf UAS's, Detling SF, Colerne SF.	11-93

GLASGOW

■ **Museum of Transport** : The Kay Gyroplane is on show, while the Pilcher replica remains stored. The Museum holds a wide variety of transport items.
◆ Open weekdays 10am to 5pm and Sunday 2pm to 5pm.
✉ Museum of Transport, Kelvin Hall, 1 Bunhouse Road, Glasgow, G3 8DP. ☎ 041 357 3929.

☐ G-ACVA		Kay Gyroplane	ex Strathallan, Perth, Glasgow, Perth.	12-93
☐	BAPC.48	Pilcher Hawk rep	built by 2175 Squadron ATC. Stored.	07-90

■ **John L Adams & Sons Ltd**, Meadowside Quay, Whitinch. By April 1992 the yard had taken a cache of Phantoms from Leuchars, Fife : — XT859/8999M 'BK', XT870 'BS', XT873 'BA', XV567 'AI', XV568 'AT', XV571 'AA', XV572 'BG' less nose, XV573 'BD', XV576 'BK', XV579 'AR' and XV590 'AX'. All had substantially gone by June 1992, doubtless as part of the arms limitation agreement that oversaw the departure of the type. They were mashed up in the company's 'fragmentiser' with just one cockpit section surviving until March 1993.
■ **William Tracey Ltd**, Carlibar Rd, Barrhead, Glasgow. *Some* Phantoms, and possibly *Bricks* from Lossiemouth, *may* also have been bought by this yard.
■ **Others** : By March 1993 the former Strathallan Pilcher Hawk replica BAPC.170 had returned to <u>Strathallan</u>, Tayside, for sale.

GLASGOW AIRPORT (or Abbotsinch, north of the M8 west of Renfrew)

Aztec 250D G-BIUU, noted in **W&R13** as departing to Eaglesham Moor for use in a film, actually relieved the tedium in an episode of *Taggart* as 'G-BNPD' and was scrapped by mid-1992. Also going back to **W&R13**, Seabee G-SEAB moved to <u>Nottingham Airport</u>, Notts. Cessna 310Q G-BMDZ, which was here as a spares source, has not been noted for a long time and is best deleted. Tomahawk 112 N9467T was last noted here in April 1988. It was roaded "south" in February 1990 — can we be more specific? Venom FB.50 J-1614/G-BLIE moved in stages to <u>Ipswich</u>, Suffolk, the pod leaving on January 10, 1993, with the wings following three days later. Two Trislanders arrived on April 22, 1993, ZK-SFG/G-BEDP was put into the air again on January 31, 1994. The other, ZK-SFF/G-BDOT, was used for spares and moved on to <u>Cumbernauld</u>, Strath, for storage on December 7, 1993.. A Nipper, under rebuild locally, has arrived for completion.

☐ G-ARPP		Trident 1C	ex Heathrow, BA, BEA. Fire crews. CoA expired 16-2-86.	12-93
☐ G-ATJC		Airtourer 100	CoA expired 30-9-87. Restoration.	11-93
☐ G-AWJF*		Nipper T.66	ex local area. CoA exp 7-6-88. F/n 11-93.	12-93
☐ G-AZHT		Airtourer T3	ex local area. Cr 29-4-88. Spares for 'TJC.	11-93

KILKERRAN
■ **Tom Pate** : Continues slowly to rebuild his Tiger Moth here. Tom also has small parts from G-ANNN, too small for listing in **W&R** and stored away from the location.

| ☐ | G-AREH | | Tiger Moth | ex G-APYV ntu, 6746M, DE241, 22 RFS, 22 EFTS. CoA expired 19-4-66. Stored. | 05-91 |

KILMARNOCK
■ **327 Squadron ATC** : 'Parented' by RAF Turnhouse, Lothian, they keep their *Chippax* and Canberra nose in Aird Avenue, off Dundonald Road.

| ☐ | WB584 | 7706M | Chipmunk T.10 | ex Edinburgh Airport, Bri UAS, 12 RFS, 22 RFS. PAX. | |
| ☐ | WJ872 | 8492M | Canberra T.4 | ex Halton, Wyton SF, 360, 13, Akrotiri SF, 231 OCU. | |

LOCHWINNOCH (on the A760 west of Paisley)
■ **Neil Geddes** : The Anson remains in store while restoration work should continue on the Auster.

| ☐ | G-AIGU | | J/1N Alpha | ex Kilkerran. CoA expired 5-9-74. Restn. | |
| ☐ | G-AYWA | | Avro XIX Srs 2 | ex Strathallan, Thruxton, OO-VIT, OO-DFA. Stored. | 04-90 |

MACHRIHANISH AIRFIELD (west of Cambletown)
■ **RAF Machrihanish** : The airfield is to be reduced to a Care & Maintenance basis — presumably so that ever fewer people will note the *Auroras* slipping in and out!. The Varsity serves to train dogs of the RAF Police Provost Training School and the Vulcan likewise for the firecrews.

| ☐ | WL635 | | Varsity T.1 | ex RAE Farnborough, Kemble, 5 FTS, 4 FTS, 1439F, Weston Zoyland SF. | 11-93 |
| ☐ | XL427 | 8756M | Vulcan B.2 | ex 44, Wadd Wing, Scampton Wing, 83. Dump. | 11-93 |

PRESTWICK
■ **Heathfield Retail Park** : Is guarded by a full-size TDL Replicas-built Spitfire.

| ☐ | * | | Spitfire replica | 'ZT-E'. First noted 12-93. Pole-mounted. | 12-93 |

PRESTWICK AIRPORT (east of the A79 north of Ayr)
■ **British Aerospace / Jetstream Aircraft** : The ATP (or Jetstream 61 if you will) is now in the process of being built here, after the move from Woodford, Gtr Man. Several unflown airframes are in store but as yet it would be unfair to consider them as **W&R** fodder. It is thought that the wreck of Bulldog T.1 XX660 had been scrapped by December 1993, it had certainly gone from its usual resting place. See also under Hatfield, Herts, and Woodford, Gtr Man, for prospective residents.

☐	G-ASAL	Bulldog 124	ex G-BBHF ntu, G-31-17. CoA expired 30-11-89. Stored.	01-94
☐	G-AZHJ	Twin Pioneer 3	ex Staverton, Flight One, Prestwick, G-31-16, XP295, Odiham SF, MoA, 1310F, Odiham SF, 230. CoA expired 23-8-90. Stored.	01-94
☐	N7RJ	Jetstream 1	ex USA, N10DG, G-AXLO. Nose.	02-92
☐	XX660	Bulldog T.1	ex Oxf UAS. Crashed 25-3-85. Forward fuselage and a wing dumped outside by 10-92.	10-92
☐		Jetstream 41EFT	fatigue rig.	02-92
☐		Jetstream 41	static rig.	02-92
☐		Jetstream 200	ex Radlett. Fuselage in static tank.	02-92
☐		Bulldog	static test.	02-92

■ **HMS** *Gannet* : The gate is still guarded by a singularly appropriate aircraft.

| ☐ | XL497 | Gannet AEW.3 | ex Lossiemouth, 849. '041-R'. | 06-92 |

■ **Others** : Work started on long term resident Noralpha G-ATDB during June 1992 and on August 26, 1993, it was roaded out to Skelmorlie, Strath, for restoration. The Trident serves on.

| ☐ | G-AWZJ | Trident 3B-101 | ex Heathrow, BA, BEA. CoA expired 12-9-85. Firecrews. | 12-93 |

SKELMORLIE (on the A78 north of Largs)
The former Prestwick Noralpha arrived here on August 26, 1993 for restoration.

| ☐ G-ATDB* | Noralpha | ex Prestwick, F-OTAN-6, French mil. CoA expired 22-11-78. Arrived 26-8-93. Restn. | 08-93 |

Tayside

ALMONDBANK (on the A85 west of Perth)
■ **Royal Naval Aircraft Yard** : Last mentioned in **W&R10** when it was giving up a lone Whirlwind, the location has decidedly re-entered the realms of **W&R** with the arrival of three former Qatar Police Lynx for instructional use and some of the 'deep store' Scouts from Wroughton, Wilts, on June 8, 1992. The Lynx were not to stay for long, with QP30 moving on to <u>Fleetlands</u>, Hants, by March 1993 for conversion to a procedures trainer, with QP31 moving likewise by December 1993. Scout AH.1 XV136 arrived by road from Wroughton, Wilts, on June 2, 1992, but moved to <u>Netheravon,</u> Wilts, by July 1993. Current situation here is as follows : —

☐ XP890*	Scout AH.1	ex Wroughton, ARWF. 'G'. Arr 23-6-92.	08-93
☐ XR628*	Scout AH.1	ex Wroughton, 656, 657, 666. Crashed 8-6-82. Arrived by 3-8-92.	08-93
☐ XR629*	Scout AH.1	ex Wroughton, Garrison Air Sqn. Arrived 16-6-92.	08-93
☐ XR639*	Scout AH.1	ex Wroughton, 658, 656, 658, 8 Flt, 663, 665, 663, 655. Arrived 23-6-92.	03-93
☐ XT616*	Scout AH.1	ex Wroughton, Middle Wallop, 658, 660, 656, 664. Arrived 30-6-92.	03-93
☐ XT617*	Scout AH.1	ex Wroughton, 653, 660. Arrived 23-6-92.	08-93
☐ XT639*	Scout AH.1	ex Wroughton, 658, 663, 664. Arr 23-6-92.	03-93
☐ XT642*	Scout AH.1	ex Wroughton, 656, 654, 663. Arr 23-6-92.	03-93
☐ XT645*	Scout AH.1	ex Wroughton, 656, 663, 653. Arr 23-6-92.	08-93
☐ XV122*	Scout AH.1	ex Wroughton. 'D'. Arrived 16-6-92.	08-93
☐ XV138 *	Scout AH.1	ex Wroughton, 658. Arrived 30-6-92.	08-93
☐ XW284*	Scout AH.1	ex Wroughton, ARWF. 'A'. Arr 30-6-92.	08-93
☐ XW795*	Scout AH.1	ex Wroughton, 659, 655, 669. Arr 2-6-92.	08-93
☐ QP32*	Lynx Mk 28	ex Wroughton, Qatar Police. Arrived 8-6-92. See notes above.	03-93

ARBROATH
Work continues on the restoration to flying condition of the Fraser brothers' Anson C.19 in this general area. See also under Strathallan, Tayside, for the movements of their other *Annie*.

| ☐ TX183 | G-BSMF | Anson C.19 | ex Duxford, Old Warden, A&AEE, HS, CNCS, 1 ANS, Abingdon SF. Under restoration. | 12-93 |

DUNDEE
Airedale G-ASAI moved from here during 1991 to continue restoration at <u>Insch,</u> Grampian.

DUNDEE AIRPORT (or Riverside)
AA-5 Traveler G-BDCK had moved "south" by 1992. Cessna F.172M N738<u>SB</u> (corrects **W&R13**) became G-BSNG and was flying again by 1992. A Tipsy Belfair has arrived for restoration.

| ☐ G-APOD* | Tipsy Belfair | ex Perth area, OO-TIF ntu. CoA expired 23-8-88. Arrived 6-12-92. Restoration. | 12-92 |

EDZELL (On the B966 north of Brechin)
■ **RAF Edzell** : At the former home of 44 MU, US Navy/National Security Agency aerials abound as the base goes about whatever it goes about.

| ☐ XD542 | 7604M | Vampire T.11 | ex Cranwell, 'XD429', Colerne, Melksham, FWS, CGS. '28'. Camouflaged. | 11-92 |

ERROL

Vampire T.11 'XE897' went to Leuchars only for a brief loan to 43 Squadron. It had returned to the site here on the former airfield by November 1991.

☐ 'XE897'* XD403	Vampire T.11	ex Leuchars, Errol, Strathallan, Woodford, Chester, 4 FTS, 1 FTS, 7 FTS, 8 FTS, 5 FTS, 4 FTS. Returned by 11-91.	07-92
☐ XG882 8754M	Gannet T.5	ex Lossiemouth, 845. Composite, including bits from XA463, XG889. '771-LM'.	07-92

MONTROSE

■ **Montrose Air Station Museum** (MASM) : Founded in 1983, the Montrose Aerodrome Museum Society initially set about protecting the flying sheds at Broomfield (Montrose) aerodrome — arguably the oldest buildings designed for military flying extant in the UK. These buildings have been 'listed' and are now within the industrial estate that was once the aerodrome. The Society has since gone on to form MASM and has acquired the use of the former station headquarters. During late 1993, the local Whirlwind was moved on site, followed by the Strathallan Sea Hawk.
◆ By prior arrangement at present. ✉ 96, Market Street, Brechin, Angus, Scotland D9 6BD.

☐ XE340*	Sea Hawk FGA.6	ex Strathallan, Wroughton, Staverton, Brawdy, 801, 898, 897, 800. '131-Z'. Arr by 12-93.. Loan from FAAM.	12-93
☐ XJ723*	Whirlwind HAR10	ex 2288 Sqn, OPITB, Wroughton, 202, 228, 155. Arrived late 1993.	12-93

■ **Offshore Petroleum Industry Training Board** : Still have their Bolkow for training.

☐ G-BATC	MBB Bo 105D	ex Bourn, D-HDAW. Original pod.	10-90

[G-BATC, with a new pod, flies with Bond from Inverness.]

■ **2288 Squadron ATC** : During late 1993, the Whirlwind was moved to the MASM — see above.

PERTH AIRPORT (or Scone)

■ **Air Service Training** (AST) : The fleet of instructional airframes has altered little. An inspection in March 1993 found an inmate missing :— the hulk of Cessna FRA.150L G-BBCF — *assumed* scrapped. Travelling all the way back to **W&R9**, the frame of Auster V TJ707 was written out as thought scrapped. No so, it can still be found suspended from the roof in the engine hall — it pays to look *up*!

☐ G-ARBC	Cessna 310D	ex N6934T. CoA expired 25-6-77. Dump	10-93
☐ G-ARPX	Trident 1C	ex Heathrow, BA, BEA. CoA exp 21-12-85.	10-93
☐ G-ARTX	Cessna 150B	ex N7377X. Crashed 14-9-72. Fuselage.	03-93
☐ G-ARTY	Cessna 150B	ex N7382X. CoA expired 6-10-68.	10-93
☐ G-ATNJ	Cessna F.150F	crashed 24-9-74.	03-93
☐ G-ATOF	Cessna F.150F	crashed 25-11-71. To dump by 3-93.	10-93
☐ G-ATOG	Cessna F.150F	crashed 27-1-81.	03-93
☐ G-AVDB	Cessna 310L	ex N2279F. CoA expired 8-7-79.	10-93
☐ G-AYBW	Cessna FA.150K	crashed 8-10-72.	10-93
☐ G-AYGB	Cessna 310Q	ex N7611Q. CoA expired 23-10-87.	10-93
☐ G-BEWP	Cessna F.150M	crashed 4-10-83.	10-93
☐ F-BGNR	Viscount 708	ex Air Inter. Arrived 8-10-73.	03-93
☐ 5N-AHN	B.206B JetRanger	ex Redhill, G-AWFV. Pod.	05-93
☐ TJ707	Auster V	ex A&AEE. Fuselage frame. See notes.	11-93
☐ XL875	Whirlwind HAR.9	ex Wroughton, Lee SAR Flt, CU SAR Flt, 847, 848, 815.	11-93
☐ XT140	Sioux AH.1	ex Middle Wallop.	11-93
☐ XX467	Hunter T.73	ex 1 TWU, Jordan AF 836, Saudi AF 70-617, G-9-214, XL605, 66, 92.	11-93
☐	Chipmunk T.10	ex 'G-ASTD', G-AOJZ, WB732, Not UAS, 16 RFS, 11 RFS, Abn UAS, 11 RFS. Crashed 31-5-66.	03-93

■ **Others** : Restoration of the Auster continues.

☐ G-AOFJ	Auster 5	CoA expired 20-9-79. Restoration.	05-93

PORTMOAK AERODROME

By July 1992, the hulk of a K-8 was strung up in the rafters, following a fire.

☐ DFQ* BGA.2083 Schleicher K-8B ex D-5077. '7'. See notes above. 07-92

STRATHALLAN AERODROME (west of the B8062, north of Auchterarder)

A story of much change here. The Roberts collection continues to wind down, although the Lysander was active during 1993 with a genuine attempt to 'market' it for airshow appearances. Of the aircraft listed in **W&R13**, it is largely a case of departures :— Tiger Moth G-ALWS moved to Rothesay, Islands, during 1992; Anson T.21 WD413/G-BFIR *flew* to Tees-side, Durham, in February 1992 as part of its migration south; Provost T.1 WW453 moved to Thatcham, Berks, on March 13, 1992; Sea Hawk FGA.6 XE340 moved to Montrose, Tayside, by November 1993. The nose section of Shackleton T.4 VP293 was saved by Norman Thelwell and it is listed under Coventry Airport, Warks. The two Fokker replicas are still to be found in store here. Coming inbound have been a Pilcher Hawk for storage and no less than five Yaks, all hoping to find UK customers.

☐	R1914	G-AHUJ	Magister I	ex Aboyne, Balado, Kemble, 137, 604, Middle Wallop SF, 604. CoA exp 8-5-87. Stored. 03-93
☐	'V9441'	G-AZWT	Lysander III ▲	ex RCAF 2355. 'AR-A', 309 Sqn c/s. 03-93
☐	YL-YAK*		Yak-50	ex CIS. '05'. c/n 832507. Arr 5-12-92. 12-93
☐	*	790404	Yak-52	ex CIS. '20'. Arrived 12-5-92. 12-93
☐	*	811202	Yak-52	ex Cumbernauld, CIS. '19'. Arr 9-5-93. 12-93
☐	*	811504	Yak-52	ex CIS. '56'. Arrived 5-12-92. 03-93
☐	*		Yak-18	ex Cumbernauld, CIS. Arrived 9-5-93. 05-93
☐	*	BAPC.170	Pilcher Hawk rep	ex Glasgow, Strathallan. For sale. F/n 3-93. 03-93
☐			Fokker Dr I replica.	Note type amended from **W&R13**. Stored. 03-93
☐			Fokker D.VII rep	Stored. 03-93

CHESTER AIRPORT (or Hawarden or Broughton, on the B5129 west of Chester)
■ **British Aerospace** : With the HS.125 production line destined — probably — for the USA, the production of whole aircraft is to become a thing of the past at the plant. The fuselage of a BAC 1-11 arrived on December 6, 1993 for use by the firemen. The Sports Club's Tiger Moth is currently stored. Sea Vixen FAW.2 XN685/8173M left by road on September 14, 1992 for the Midland Air Museum at <u>Coventry Airport</u>, Warks.

☐	G-ANTE*	Tiger Moth	ex T6562, Leeming SF, 228 OCU, 7 FTS, 3 EFTS. CoA expired 10-6-89. Stored.	04-92
☐	G-ARYA	HS.125-1	ex Connah's Quay, Chester, Hatfield. Nose. Apprentices.	
☐	*	BAC 1-11	fuselage. Arrived 6-12-93. Fire dump.	12-93
☐	RR299 G-ASKH	Mosquito T.3 ∆	ex *Mosquito Squadron*, 3-4 CAACU, FCCS, HCEU,	

■ **Others** : Causing considerable sensation at Seaforth Docks, Merseyside, on October 27, 1993 was the MV *Kreylis* which disgorged a varied collection of former-Soviet hardware that had been acquired in Latvia. They stayed a while within the confines of the Freeport, but by December 1993 had also settled here. The aim, of course, is to sell them to individuals and museums. This operation would appear to be linked with that at Cumbernauld, Strathclyde and it may well be that some (if not all) of the L 29 Delfins have, or will, gravitate here. While this Latvian cache is very new to the site, it is felt worthy of inclusion at this stage.

☐	CCCP-07268*		An-2 *Colt*	ex Seaforth, Latvia, USSR. Arr by 12-93	12-93
☐	CCCP-17939*		An-2 *Colt*	ex Seaforth, Latvia, USSR. Arr by 12-93	12-93
☐	CCCP-19731*		An-2 *Colt*	ex Seaforth, Latvia, USSR. Arr by 12-93	12-93
☐	CCCP-19733*		An-2 *Colt*	ex Seaforth, Latvia, USSR. Arr by 12-93	12-93
☐	CCCP-20320*		Mil-2 *Hoplite*	ex Seaforth, Latvia, USSR. Arr by 12-93	12-93
☐	CCCP-20619*		Mil-2 *Hoplite*	ex Seaforth, Latvia, USSR. Arr by 12-93	12-93
☐	CCCP-70748*		An-2 *Colt*	ex Seaforth, Latvia, USSR. Arr by 12-93	12-93
☐	CCCP-40749*		An-2 *Colt*	ex Seaforth, Latvia, USSR. Arr by 12-93	12-93
☐	CCCP-40783*		An-2 *Colt*	ex Seaforth, Latvia, USSR. Arr by 12-93	12-93
☐	CCCP-40784*		An-2 *Colt*	ex Seaforth, Latvia, USSR. Arr by 12-93	12-93
☐	CCCP-54949*		An-2 *Colt*	ex Seaforth, Latvia, USSR. Arr by 12-93	12-93
☐	CCCP-56471*		An-2 *Colt*	ex Seaforth, Latvia, USSR. Arr by 12-93	12-93
☐	23*		MiG-27 *Flogger*	ex Seaforth, Latvia, USSR. Arr by 12-93	12-93
☐	23*		MiG-27 *Flogger*	ex Seaforth, Latvia, USSR. Arr by 12-93	12-93
☐	03*	'715415	Mil-24 *Hind-D*	ex Seaforth, Latvia, USSR. Arr by 12-93	12-93
☐	06*	'505029	Mil-24 *Hind-D*	ex Seaforth, Latvia, USSR. Arr by 12-93	12-93
☐	23*	'15040	MiG-27M *Flogger*	ex Seaforth, Latvia, USSR. Arr by 12-93	12-93
☐	35*	25102	Su-17 *Fitter*	ex Seaforth, Latvia, USSR. Arr by 12-93	12-93
☐	50*	64800	MiG-23ML	ex Seaforth, Latvia, USSR. Arr by 12-93	12-93
☐	54*	69004	Su-17 *Fitter*	ex Seaforth, Latvia, USSR. Arr by 12-93	12-93
☐	71*	65982	MiG-27 *Flogger-D*	ex Seaforth, Latvia, USSR. Arr by 12-93	12-93
☐	*	3607	MiG-23ML	ex Seaforth, Latvia, USSR. Arr by 12-93	12-93
☐	*	'810853	Mil-24 *Hind*	ex Seaforth, Latvia, USSR. Arr by 12-93	12-93

CHIRK (on the A5 north of Oswestry)
■ **Dragon Aviation** : The store of Dragon Rapides and lone Norecrin remains undisturbed.

☐	G-AIUL	Dragon Rapide	ex Southend, British Westpoint, NR749, Kemble, 2 RS. CoA exp 29-9-67. Stored.	05-93
☐	G-AJBJ	Dragon Rapide	ex Coventry, Blackpool, NF894, 18 MU, HQ TCCF. CoA expired 14-9-61. Stored.	05-93
☐	G-AKOE	Dragon Rapide	ex British Airways, Booker, X7484, PTS. CoA expired 25-2-82. Stored.	05-93
☐	G-BEDB	Norecrin	ex Liverpool, Chirk, F-BEOB. CoA expired 11-6-80. Stored.	05-93

CONNAH'S QUAY (on the A548 west of Chester)
■ **North East Wales Institute** : The instructional fleet is unchanged. (Note also that there is a branch of the NEWI to be found at Wrexham — see below.)

☐ G-APMY		Apache 160	ex Halfpenny Green, EI-AJT. CoA expired 1-11-81. 06-93
☐ G-AZMX		Cherokee 140	ex Chester Airport, Halfpenny Green, SE-FLL, LN-LMK. CoA expired 9-1-82. 06-93
☐ XA460		Gannet AS.4	ex Brawdy, 849. '768-BY'. 05-91
☐ XR658	8192M	Jet Provost T.4	ex Bournemouth, Wroughton, Abingdon RAFEF, 6 FTS, CAW, 7 FTS. 05-91

HAWARDEN (on the A55 south west of Chester)
■ **2247 Squadron ATC** : 'Parented' by Sealand, 2247 keep their Vampire in Manor Lane.

☐ XE852	Vampire T.11	ex Chester Airport, Woodford, Chester, Shawbury, 1 FTS, 4 FTS. 'H'. 04-92

SEALAND (on the A550 south west of Ellesmere Port)
■ **RAF Sealand** : The former Danish Hunter is still 'on guard'. The Station 'parents' a series of ATC airframes (eg Birkdale, Hawarden, Royton). Two of its 'offspring' cannot be applied to a location and are listed here accordingly. The *JP* is fascinating in that 1005 Squadron, showing it off at the Woodford display in June 1993 claimed it to be XN466 and a look at its fuselage plate — PAC/W/10145 — confirmed this. The MoD however have the aircraft down as XM472/9051M. Bear in mind that XA231 represents an administrative listing from MoD and not a *physical* sighting.

☐ 'WT720'	8565M	Hunter F.51	ex Cranwell 'XF979', Brawdy, Dunsfold, G-9-436, Aalborg, Esk-724, Danish AF E-408. Gate. 11-93
☐ XA231*	8888M	Grasshopper TX.1	allocated to HQ East Cheshire/South Manchester Wing ATC. See notes above.
☐ XN466*		Jet Provost T.3A	ex 1 FTS, 7 FTS, 1 FTS. Nose. 1005 Sqn ATC. See notes above. 06-93

■ **Vampire Support Team** : This group took delivery of the former Scampton Vampire T.11 XE920 during October 1992. Restoration work is being carried out to airworthy standards.

☐ XE920*	8196M	Vampire T.11	ex Scampton, Henlow, Shawbury, CATCS, 8 FTS, 5 FTS, 1 FTS. 'D'. Arr 10-92. Restn.. 09-93

WREXHAM
■ **North East Wales Institute** : Located next to the football ground, the college took delivery of a former Halton JP on October 27, 1993. (See under Connah's Quay for another NEWI site.)

☐ XP585*	8407M	Jet Provost T.4	ex Halton, St Athan, RAFC, 6 FTS, RAFC. '24'. Arrived 27-10-93. 10-93

Dyfed

ABERPORTH AIRFIELD (north of the A487, east of Cardigan)
■ **Test & Evaluation Establishment** (TEE) : Note *another* change of name! The Hunter is still kept at the range control station on behalf of 1429 Sqn ATC. It is 'parented' by Brawdy. During January 1990 a Canberra arrived from Boscombe Down and was placed on the missile test site.

☐ WH876*		Canberra B.2(mod)	ex Boscombe Down, A&AEE, 73, 207, 115. Arrived 1-90. 03-94
☐ WT680	7533M	Hunter F.1	ex Weeton, DFLS, West Raynham SF. 'Z'. 11-92

BRAWDY AIRFIELD (north of the A487 east of St David's)
■ **RAF Brawdy** : A *JP* has been allocated for BDR work here. Hunter FGA.9 XF435/8880M was allocated to P&EE Pendine, Dyfed, on March 21, 1989. As it has not been reported since, it has been

transferred to the Pendine heading, but please read the preamble there. Jet Provost T.3A XN606/9121M arrived here for BDR training, only to have a brief life. It was offered for tender during November 1992 and sold in the USA, becoming N606RA. The future of the base is still uncertain, it *may* go to the Army.

☐ XE624	8875M	Hunter FGA.9	ex store, 1 TWU, 2 TWU, TWU, 229 OCU, West Raynham SF, 1. Gate.	
☐ XL728		Wessex HAS.1	ex Pendine, Farnborough. Dump.	
☐		Hunter F.6	cockpit, see notes in **W&R13**.	09-91

DALE (on the B4327 south west of Haverfordwest)

■ **John Webber** : Moved the Auster AOP.9 from Haverfordwest Aerodrome to a farm here by August 1991 (see **W&R13**). Its identity is still not solved.

| ☐ 'XK378'* | | Auster AOP.9 | ex Haverfordwest. Possibly XS238. Arrived by 8-91. Restoration. | 10-92 |

HAVERFORDWEST AERODROME (or Withybush, on the A40 north of Haverfordwest)
See Dale, above, for details of the whereabouts of Auster AOP.9 'XK378'.

LLANELLI

■ **Jeremy Hassell** : During September 1992, Jeremy offered his Proctor restoration project for sale or exchange.

| ☐ G-AHTE | | Proctor V | ex Cardiff-Wales, Swansea, Llanelli. CoA expired 10-8-61. See notes above. | 09-92 |

MILFORD HAVEN

■ **1284 Squadron ATC** : (See under Tenby, Dyfed.) An anonymous *JP* nose arrived here, in exchange for Chipmunk T.10 WD386, which moved to <u>Cranfield</u>, Beds. The move was part of a complex exchange, see under Salisbury, Wilts.

| ☐ * | | Jet Provost | ex Salisbury, Firbeck, Coventry. Bicester, Kemble. Nose. c/n PAC/W/10169. See notes above. | 06-93 |

PENDINE RANGES (on the A4066 east of Tenby)

■ **Proof & Experimental Establishment** : During August 1992 a tender was put out for a series of airframes here, namely : — Buccaneers XK536, XN926, XN933, XV333 and XW545; two Canberra cockpits and a noseless fuselage; Hunter XF435; Lightning XM139 and Victor 'XA953' (likely XA938). It is reported that the response to the tender was *very* leisurely as the airframes need 24 months from bid date to be rendered safe (de-radiation treatment?). A visit during March 1994 found the aircraft noted below, plus the following : — four anonymous Buccaneers, a Hunter nose, two anonymous Hunters, Hunter 'XG177', Hunter with 1 TWU badge, a single seat Lightning, Phantom '1272', Wessex 'Z' camouflaged, Wessex 'C' camouflaged and another camouflaged Wessex. Obviously, some (or all) of these will relate to the list below. Scimitars XD241 and XD243 are assumed to have been scrapped/destroyed. The former was last noted during July 1991 while the rear fuselage of the latter was noted during March 1994. Whirlwind HAR.10 XJ411, also last noted July 1991, also assumed to have been scrapped/destroyed. The two F-4J(UK) were not for P&EE but the Royal Armament Research & Development Establishment (RARDE) — headquartered at Fort Halstead, Kent, and now a part of DRA.

☐ WH703	8490M	Canberra B.2	ex Abingdon, Marham, 100, 85, 231 OCU. Allocated 18-1-90. See notes above.	07-91
☐ WJ678*	8864M	Canberra B.2	ex Abingdon, Wyton, 100, 85, C(A). Overstressed 19-10-83. 'CF'. Forward fuselage. Arrived 6-11-89.	03-94
☐ WH844		Canberra T.4	ex Farnborough, RAE, 231 OCU. Cockpit.	03-94
☐ XA938		Victor K.1	ex Foulness, St Athan, RAE, 214, 15, 10. Sectioned. See notes above.	07-91
☐ XF435*	8880M	Hunter FGA.9	ex Brawdy, St Athan, 1 TWU, TWU, 229 OCU, 208, 8, 8-43 pool, 8, 43, 247. Allocated 21-3-89. See notes above.	

☐	XF439	8712M	Hunter F.6A	ex Abingdon, 5 MU, 1 TWU, 229 OCU, 1, 54, 19, 43, 247. See notes above.
☐	XG158	8686M	Hunter F.6A	ex Farnborough, 5 MU, 4 FTS, TWU, 229 OCU, 4 FTS, 229 OCU, 65, DFLS. See notes. 07-91
☐	XK536		Buccaneer S.1	ex Foulness, Boscombe Down. See notes. 07-91
☐	XM139	8411M	Lightning F.1	ex Wattisham, Wattisham TFF, Leuchars TFF, 226 OCU, 74. Allocated 23-1-86. See notes. 07-91
☐	XM147	8412M	Lightning F.1	ex Wattisham, Wattisham TFF, 226 OCU, 74. Allocated 23-1-86. See notes above. 07-91
☐	XM299		Wessex HAS.1	ex Farnborough. See notes above. 07-91
☐	XM926		Wessex HAS.1	ex Farnborough, Bedford. See notes above. 03-94
☐	XN926		Buccaneer S.1	ex Foulness, Chatham, Honington, Lossiemouth, 736. See notes above. 07-91
☐	XN933		Buccaneer S.1	ex Foulness, Lossiemouth, 736. See notes. 07-91
☐	XN965		Buccaneer S.1	ex Farnborough, RAE, Lossiemouth, 736. See notes above.
☐	XP708		Lightning F.3	ex Foulness Island, Wattisham, 29, 23. 03-94
☐	XP735		Lightning F.3	ex Leconfield, 29, Wattisham TFF, 23. See notes above. 07-91
☐	XP748	8446M	Lightning F.3	ex Wembury, Binbrook, 11, 111, 56. 03-94
☐	XR479		W'wind HAR.10	ex Farnborough, Wroughton, RAE, 103, 110, 103. 07-91
☐	XS895		Lightning F.6	ex Binbrook, 5, 11, LTF, 5-11 pool, 23, 111, 23, 5, 74. 03-94
☐	XT274*	8856M	Buccaneer S.2A	ex Abingdon, St Athan, 237 OCU, 12, 237 OCU, 208, 237 OCU, 12. Arrived 23-1-90. 03-94
☐	XV338		Buccaneer S.2	ex St Athan, 237 OCU, 12. Minus cockpit. See notes above. 07-91 [Remainder *was* at Abingdon, Oxon, as 8774M.]
☐	XV340	8659M	Buccaneer S.2	ex Foulness, Honington, Brough, 15. See notes above. 07-91
☐	XV759*		Harrier GR.3	ex St Athan, 233 OCU, 1417F, 233 OCU, 1, 233 OCU, 1, 233 OCU. 'O'. 03-94
☐	XW545*	8859M	Buccaneer S.2B	ex St Athan, BAe, 15. BDR. 03-94
☐	ZE355*		F-4J(UK)	ex St Athan, 74, USN 153803. 'S'. 03-94
☐	ZE362*		F-4J(UK)	ex St Athan, 74, USN 155755. 'V'. Allocated 31-1-91. See notes above.

ROSEMARKET (north east of Milford Haven)
A Cub has been stored at a farm near here since 1989. Update appreciated.

☐	G-AYCN	J3C-65 Cub	ex F-BCPO. CoA expired 27-1-89. Stored. 06-90

TENBY
■ **1284 Squadron ATC** : By 1992 the unit was to be found at Mildford Haven, Dyfed, or possibly was always there — *qv*.

Mid Glamorgan

BRIDGEND (on the A473 west of Cardiff)
■ **1092 Squadron ATC** : By November 1993, the squadron (located at the TAVR Centre) put its Viscount nose up for disposal, via its 'parent', St Athan.

☐	G-AOHR	Viscount 802	ex Cardiff-Wales, BA, BEA. wfu 26-8-75. Nose. See notes above. 11-93

■ **Glynn Jones** : Acquired one of the St Albans college Vampires and has moved it here.
☐ WZ584*   Vampire T.11   ex St Albans, Hatfield, CATCS, 1 FTS, 2 CAACU,
                                         32. 'K'. Arrived by late 1992.   01-93

KENFIG HILL (north of the B4281 east of Pyle)
■ **2117 Squadron ATC** : Off Main Street, in the School grounds, is the unit's Hunter F.1. It is 'parented' by St Athan.
☐ WT569   7491M   Hunter F.1   ex St Athan, A&AEE, Hawkers trials.   03-93

South Glamorgan

CARDIFF
■ **Welsh Industrial & Maritime Museum** : Located in Cardiff Docks, this museum takes in the full spread of industrial and maritime history and accordingly includes a Wessex.
◆ Open every day except Monday (Bank Holidays excepted) Tuesday to Saturday 10am to 5pm and Sundays 2.30pm to 5pm. ✉ Welsh Industrial and Maritime Museum, Bute Street, Cardiff, CF1 6AN. ☎ 0222 481919.
☐ XM300   Wessex HAS.1   ex Cardiff-Wales, Farnborough, RAE, Westlands.
                                                        04-91

CARDIFF-WALES AIRPORT (or Rhoose, on the A4226 west of Barry)
■ **Airport** : While the scenery changes dramatically at the Airport, little has changed in the way of **W&R** 'fodder'. The Viscount serves on and the Tomahawk is *thought* extant. Dave Thomas moved three of his airframes from the WAM site (see below) to adjacent the fire service compound. Two of these were very much interlinked Canberras, which have always caused the Compiler (and many others!) headaches. One was the nose of PR.7 WH798 with the rear fuselage of WJ581 and anonymous wings. The other constituted the fuselage and wings of WJ581 with the rear fuselage of WT518. *One* of these was scrapped several years ago. The other was scrapped during 1992 with the nose going to Brenzett, Kent by October 1992. At present, the nose that went to Kent is *thought* to be from WJ581. Dave's third airframe is Pembroke C.1 WV753. This is currently for disposal and if it does not find a buyer, will be scrapped.
☐ G-ANRS   Viscount 732   ex WAM, 'G-ARBY', 'G-WHIZ', British Eagle,
                                           Misrair SU-AKY, Hunting G-ANRS, MEA
                                           OD-ACH, Hunting G-ANRS. CoA exp 5-5-69.
                                           Fuselage. Fire crews.   02-93
☐ G-AVGH*   Cherokee 140   CoA expired 5-12-91. Fuselage. F/n 10-93. 10-93
☐ G-BGSS   Tomahawk 112   dbr 14-12-81. Cabin section, Cambrian F/C.
☐ WV753* 8113M   Pembroke C.1   ex WAM, St Athan, 207, SCS, FCCS, BCCS,
                                           MoA, FECS, 81. Fire service area by 8-92. 01-93

■ **Wales Aircraft Museum** (WAM) : Consolidation of the 'new' site continues. Since **W&R13**, there has been a mixture of disposals and new arrivals. A change of legal status now has the holding title of WAM as Aircraft Museum (Wales) Ltd. WAM's penchant for painting their exhibits in 'original' schemes continues, prize going to the Varsity which now wears RNZAF markings — the type *never* having been operated by the *Kiwis*! Tidying up **W&R13**, Whirlwind HAR.10 XJ409 moved to Grangetown, S Glam, by August 1991. Disposals have been as follows : — Dragonfly HR.3 WG718/A2531 to Long Marston, Warks by early 1992; Venom FB.4 WR539/8399M to Fownhope, H&W, 1992; Provost T.1 WW388/7616M to Long Marston, Warks, by late 1992; Pembroke C.1 WV753/8113M and Canberra PR.7 WH798/8130, both owned by Dave Thomas, moved to the local fire service by August 1992 — see above, Dave also owns the nose of WP515, see below; Venom NF.3 WX788 to Long Marston, Warks, *circa* 1991; Vampire T.11 WZ425 to Birlingham, H&W, by March 1993; Valiant BK.1 nose 'WZ826'/XD826 to Rayleigh, Essex during 1992; Vulcan B.1 nose XA903 to Sidcup, Gtr Lon, by April 1993; Sea Venom FAW.22 XG737 to Long Marston, Warks, by July 1992; the nose of Canberra PR.9 moved to Stock, Essex, on February 1, 1994. Additionally,

Rallye Club G-BFTZ made an unusual, and brief, appearance here by August 1992, by late 1993 it had moved to Fownhope, H&W.

◆ Open 12am to 6pm every day May to September and weekends 12am to 4pm the remainder of the year. ✉ D R Sims, 19 Castle Road, Rhoose, near Barry, South Glamorgan, CF6 9EU.

☐	G-AOJC		Viscount 802	ex BA, BEA. BEA colours. CoA expired 20-1-77. 12-93
☐	WB491		Ashton 2	ex Dunsfold, Farnborough, RAE. Nose. BOAC colours by 2-93!! 12-93
☐	WJ576		Canberra T.17	ex St Athan, 360, MoA, *Swifter* Flight, 231 OCU. 12-93
☐	WM292		Meteor TT.20	ex Yeovilton, FRU, Kemble, 527. '841'. FAAM loan. 09-93
☐	WP515*		Canberra B.2	ex St Athan, 100, 85, CAW, RAFC, 231 OCU, 109, 12. 'CD'. Nose, first noted 2-93. 09-93
☐	WV826	A2532	Sea Hawk FGA.6	ex Swansea, Culdrose SAH-2, Lossiemouth, 738. '147-Z'. 09-93
☐	'XF383'	E-409	Hunter F.51	ex 'WV309', 'XF383', Dunsfold, G-9-437, Aalborg store, Danish AF Esk-724. *Black Arrows* colours. 09-93
☐	XG883		Gannet T.5	ex Yeovilton, 849. '773'. FAAM loan. 09-93
☐	XL449		Gannet AEW.3	ex Lossiemouth, 849. 09-93
☐	XM569		Vulcan B.2	ex 44, Waddington Wing, 27, Cottesmore Wing, 27. 09-93
☐	XN458*	'8234M'	Jet Provost T.3	ex St Athan, Halton, Shawbury, 1 FTS. '19'. Really 8334M. First noted 2-93. 09-93
☐	XN650	A2639	Sea Vixen FAW.2	ex A2620/A2612, Culdrose SAH-12, RAE Bedford, 892. 09-93
☐	XN928	8179M	Buccaneer S.1	ex St Athan. '353'. 09-93
☐	XT911*		Phantom FGR.2	ex St Athan, 92, 19, 228 OCU. 'T'. Nose section. Arrived by 4-93. 09-93
				[Remainder to Stock, Essex.]
☐	ZF578		Lightning F.53	ex Warton, RSAF 53-670, G-27-40. 09-93
☐	59		Mystere IVA	ex Sculthorpe, French Air Force. '2-SF'. 09-93
☐	'NZ233'	WJ944	Varsity T.1	ex 6 FTS, 1 ANS, 5 FTS, 1 ANS, 2 ANS, CNCS. '04'. RNZAF colours! 09-93
☐	29963		T-33A-1-LO	ex Sculthorpe, French Air Force. 09-93
☐	'63000'	42160	F-100D-16-NA	ex Sculthorpe, French Air Force. 'FW-000' 09-93

GRANGETOWN (south of Cardiff)

Pump House Restaurant : Former Wales Aircraft Museum Whirlwind HAR.10 XJ409 is displayed alongside the eatery here.

☐	XJ409*	W'wind HAR.10	ex Cardiff-Wales, Wroughton, Warton SAR Flt, 1310F, 228, 155, XD779 ntu. F/n 3-92. 03-92

ST ATHAN AIRFIELD (on the B4265 west of Barry)

■ **RAF St Athan** : Continued expansion here, as outlined in **W&R13**, after the closure of Abingdon, Oxon, and the base taking on sundry other duties. The base has gained a gate guardian in the form of a Phantom FGR.2 — see below.

■ **Historic Aircraft** : The clear-out of RAF Museum 'display' aircraft (as opposed to the Spitfires in the exchange 'pool') produced a *fourth* V-1 *Doodlebug* for the RAF Museum. It moved to Cardington, Beds, during 1992. *Flying Flea* G-AEEH made the move to Cosford, Salop, by December 1992. Within the Spitfire 'pool' the arrival of Mk IX MK356 is not indicative of its availability for exchange. It has moved here for continued restoration to flying condition on behalf of the Battle of Britain Memorial Flight at Coningsby, Lincs. There have been two departures : — Mk V EP120/8070M going to The Fighter Collection at Duxford, Cambs, in return for a former RAF Sabre and Mk XVI SL542/8390M going to Jeet Mahal in return for the Hampden. SL542 was offered for sale and has been exported, believed to the USA. Restoration of the gondola of the airship K88 continues for FOCAS — see under Cardington, Beds. Vulcan B.2 XM602/8771M was cut up and dismantled by October 1992, with the pieces due to go into store, but this scheme fell through. The nose section was put up for tender during October 1993 and it was acquired by the '603 Club at Woodford, Gtr Man, leaving during November 1993. Going back to **W&R13**, Swallow TX.1 XS650/8801M became HBX/BGA.3823 and is flying again.

☐ '6232'	BAPC 41	BE.2c replica	ex Halton. Travelling exhibit.	
☐ 'D3419'	BAPC.59	Camel replica	ex St Mawgan, 'F1921', St Athan, Colerne.	06-91
☐ 'H1968'	BAPC.42	Avro 504K rep	ex Halton. Travelling exhibit.	06-91
☐ LA198	7118M	Spitfire F.21	ex Leuchars, Locking, Worcester, 3 CAACU, 602, 1. 'RAI-G'.	11-93
☐ MK356*	5690M	Spitfire IX	ex Abingdon, St Athan, Henlow, Bicester, Hawkinge, Halton, 84 GSU, 443. Restoration. First noted 7-92. See notes above.	11-93
☐ PK624	8072M	Spitfire F.24	ex Abingdon, Northolt, Uxbridge, North Weald, 'WP916', 9 MU, 614. 'RAU-T'. Stored.	11-93
☐ PK664	7759M	Spitfire F.22	ex Binbrook, Waterbeach, 615. 'V6-B'. Stored.	11-93
☐ PM651	7758M	Spitfire PR.XIX	ex Hendon, Benson, Bicester, Andover, Hucknall, Leconfield, Church Fenton, C&RS, 3 CAACU, 604. 'X'. Stored.	11-93
☐ RW393	7293M	Spitfire XVI	ex Edinburgh Airport-Turnhouse, 602, 3 CAACU, 31, FCCS, 203 AFS. 'XT-A'. Stored.	11-93
☐ SL674	8392M	Spitfire XVI	ex Biggin Hill, Little Rissington, 501, 17 OTU. 'RAS-H'. Stored.	11-93
☐ XV500*	9113M	Phantom FGR.2	ex 56, 29, 23, 56, 111, 43, 54. 23 Sqn colours. Gate from 26-6-92.	11-93
☐		K88 Airship	ex Pensacola, Florida swamp, USN. Gondola, restoration for FOCAS, Cardington.	11-93
☐ 501		MiG-21PF	ex Farnborough, Hungarian AF.	11-93
☐	BAPC.47	Watkins CHW	ex Cardiff. Stored.	06-91

■ **RAF Exhibition, Production & Transportation Unit** (EP&TU) : With the demise of Abingdon, Oxon, what was the RAF Exhibition Flight (RAFEF) moved here, bringing its much-travelled airframes with it. As of December 1, 1992, the unit came 'on stream' operated in a 'contractorised' manner by SERCO. EP&TU has subsumed not only the RAFEF, but the former Aircraft Recovery and Transportation Flight that had come here from Abingdon and the Exhibition Production Flight from Henlow, Beds. At least the 'exhibition' side of EP&TU comes under the gaze of the Directorate of Recruiting and Selection, previously the Inspectorate of Recruiting. From 1993, EP&TU started a ten year programme to update its airframes and will be acquiring still more full-size 'plastic' airframes, including at least one Eurofighter 2000. Two Harrier GR.3 and one Jaguar GR.1 nose sections are now in use and it is expected that the Buccaneer and Lightning noses will be disposed of. A new addition to the fleet for 1994 is a full-blown Bulldog T.1.

☐ 'X4277'*	TB382	Spitfire XVI	7244M ex Abingdon, Henlow, Ely, Middleton St George, 602. 'XT-M', 603 Sqn colours.	06-93
☐ 'X4474'*	TE311	Spitfire XVI	7241M ex Abingdon, Henlow, Wattisham, 2/3 CAACU, 103 FRS, 102 FRS, 83 GSU, 421. 'QV-I', 19 Squadron colours.	06-93
☐ XM191*	8590M	Lightning F.1	ex Abingdon, 7854M, Wattisham, 111. Crashed 9-6-64. Nose. See notes above.	06-93
☐ XN962*	8183M	Buccaneer S.1	ex Abingdon. Nose. See notes above.	06-93
☐ 'XX263'*	B'152	Hawk T.1 replica	ex Abingdon, 'XX162'.	
☐ 'XX297'*	B'171	Hawk T.1 replica	ex Abingdon/Henlow, 2 FTS. Crashed 30-6-81.	
☐ XX396*	8718M	Gazelle HT.3	ex Abingdon/Henlow, 2 FTS. Crashed 30-6-81. 'N'. See notes above.	06-93
☐ XX637*	9197M	Bulldog T.1	ex Northumbria UAS. 'U'. See notes.	06-93
☐ 'XX718'*	B'150	Jaguar GR.1 rep	ex Abingdon, 'XX732'. 'GA'.	
☐ XX753*	9087M	Jaguar GR.1	ex Abingdon, Shawbury, 226 OCU, 6. Nose.	06-93
☐ XZ131*	9174M	Harrier GR.3	ex 1417 Flt, 233 OCU, 4, 1, 4. Nose section. First noted 9-92.	06-93

☐	XZ135* 8848M	Harrier GR.3	ex Abingdon, 4. Nose, truck mounted.	06-93
☐	'XZ363'* BAPC.151	Jaguar GR.1 rep	ex Abingdon, 'XX824'. 'A'.	
☐	'ZA446'* BAPC.155	Tornado GR.1 rep	ex Abingdon, 'ZA600', 'ZA322'. 'F'. *MacRobert's Reply.*	
☐	'ZD472'* B'191	Harrier GR.5 rep	ex Abingdon. '01'.	06-93
☐		'Nimrod MR.1'	ex Abingdon, G-ALYW, Farnborough, Heathrow, BOAC. Comet fuselage suitably converted and fitted out.	

■ **Maintenance Unit — Picketston Site** : The wide-sweeping wind-down of the RAF has been well reflected here. Canberra TT.18s WJ614, WK126 and WK142 were offered in the MoD auction of July 8, 1993 (see *Appendix* D) but apparently failed to sell. WJ614 and WK142 have since been placed on the US register, implying some sort of move. **W&R13** noted that it is "a sign you are getting old when they start scrapping Nimrods". Well, now they are reducing Tornados (albeit F.2s) to components and GR.1s are going into what is described as "deep store". Also on the Tornado front are two F.3s (possibly more) which are grounded following reported "maintenance damage" and are subject to doubtless a long dispute. *Another* reminder of one's mortality is the placing of the immortal Dominie into store. Disposals/fates have been as follows :—

Buccaneer S.2B XW545/8859M was *allocated* to the ranges at Pendine, Dyfed, on 30-3-90. S.2B XW550 was scrapped here during 1992, going to Stock, Essex.

Canberra T.22 WH780 had its nose removed by 2-93 and it at least travelled to Stock, Essex, the remainder lingered here until about 11-93; **T.22** WH797 to Stock, Essex, by 8-92; **TT.18** WJ717/9052M had its nose removed 1-4-92 and it moved to the SoTT (see below), the remainder was out on the dump by 9-92 and was later taken on by Hanningfield Metals of Stock, Essex; **T.4** WJ861 on the dump moved by road to Stock, Essex, 1-2-94; **B.2** WP515 was offered for tender during 10-91, its nose moving to Cardiff-Wales Airport, S Glam, by 2-93; **PR.9** XH133 moved from storage to the dump by 6-92 and by 6-93 the nose had moved to Stock, Essex; **PR.9** XH165 was out on the dump by 6-92 and was last noted there 1-93 moving on to Stock, Essex; PR.9 XH175 moved to Stock, Essex, 11-91. Additionally, **W&R13** charted the removal of TT.18 WE122 to Stock, Essex. This was only the nose section, the remainder lingered on the dump until at least 11-93.

Harrier GR.3 XV744 ex 233 OCU was here by 9-92, but moved to Shrivenham, Oxon, 4-93; XV759 to the ranges at Pendine, Dyfed, on 30-3-90; XV778 moved to Valley, Gwynedd; XW763 appeared here as a fuselage by 1-93, but had moved (as a nose section) to Duxford, Cambs, by 10-93; XZ968 moved to Marham, Norfolk, on 25-11-93; XZ998 moved to Swanton Morley, Norfolk, arriving 13-10-92.

Hunter F.6 XF526/8679M was acquired by a Mr Martin Kelly during late 1991 and moved out. It is possible Mr Kelly is from the Bristol area; **T.7** XL578 moved to Cranfield, Beds, 3-4-92.

Phantom FGR.2s were on the dump here by 7-92 but had moved on to Stock, Essex, by 4-93 : XT898, XT911, XV399, XV402, XV486, XV489 (with the cockpit going to Bruntingthorpe, Leics), XV490, XV495, XV591.

Tornado F.2 ZD935 moved to Coningsby, Lincs, by 10-93; Tornado F.2 ZD939 moved to the Saudi Support Unit at Warton, Lancs, by 10-91.

That leaves the following :—

☐	WH849*	Canberra T.4	ex 231 OCU, 7, 231 OCU, 100, 85. 'BE' Arrived 3-2-92. Stored.	11-93
☐	WJ614* N76765	Canberra TT.18	ex FRADU, 100, 85, FAA, 98, RAFC, 6, 35. '846'. See notes above.	11-93
☐	WJ775* 8581M	Canberra B.6RC	ex Swanton Morley, 51, 192. Dismantled. Arrived by late 1992.	11-93
☐	WK126*	Canberra TT.18	ex FRADU, 100, 9. '843'. Stored. See notes above.	11-93
☐	WK142* N76764	Canberra TT.18	ex FRADU, 90, 207, 115. Stored. '848'. See notes. Reported bound for the USA.	11-93
☐	XH174*	Canberra PR.9	ex DRA Bedford (?), Wyton, St Athan, 1 PRU, 39, 13, 39, MinTech, 39, 58. Nose section. Dump. First noted 9-92.	11-93
☐	XP558* 8627M	Jet Provost T.4	ex 4 SoTT, SAH Culdrose A2628, CAW, 3 CAACU, RAFC. '20'. Dump by 7-92.	12-93
☐	XP680* 8460M	Jet Provost T.4	ex 4 SoTT, CAW, 6 FTS. Dump by 10-92.	12-93

☐ XS180*	'8238M'	Jet Provost T.4	ex Halton, Kemble, CAW, 6 FTS. Really 8338M. '21'. Dismantled. First noted 4-93.	11-93
☐ XS711*		Dominie T.1	ex Finningley, 6 FTS, 1 ANS. 'L'. Stored by 9-93.	09-93
☐ XS712*		Dominie T.1	ex Finningley, 6 FTS, 1 ANS. 'A'. Stored by 3-93.	03-93
☐ XS730*		Dominie T.1	ex Finningley, 6 FTS, 1 ANS. 'H'. Stored by 9-92.	03-93
☐ XS734*		Dominie T.1	ex Finningley, 6 FTS, CAW. 'N'. Stored by 3-93.	03-93
☐ XS739*		Dominie T.1	ex Finningley, 6 FTS, 1 ANS. 'F'. Stored by 9-92.	09-92
☐ XT284*	8855M	Buccaneer S.2A	ex Abingdon, St Athan, 237 OCU, 15, 208. 'T'. BDRT by 4-93.	11-93
☐ XT773*	9123M	Wessex HU.5	ex Abingdon, Wroughton. Arrived by 9-93.	11-93
☐ XV337*	8852M	Buccaneer S.2C	ex Abingdon, A&AEE, 208, A&AEE. BDRT by 4-93.	11-93
☐ XX977*	9132M	Jaguar GR.1	ex Abingdon, Shawbury, 31. BDRT. Arrived by 9-93.	11-93
☐ XZ970*		Harrier GR.3	ex 4, 3. 'H'. Stored by 9-92.	09-93
☐ XZ991*	9162M	Harrier GR.3	ex 233 OCU, 4, 1417F, 233 OCU, 1, R-R, 1, 3, 1. '3A'. BDRT by 4-93.	11-93
☐ XZ993*		Harrier GR.3	ex 4, 1, 1453F, 3. 'M'. Arrived by 9-93.	11-93
☐ ZA412*		Tornado GR.1T	ex 16, 20, 16, 15. 'FX'. Arrived by 9-93.	11-93
☐ ZA547*		Tornado GR.1	ex 27, 617, TWCU. 'JC'. Arrived by 9-92.	11-93
☐ ZA553*		Tornado GR.1	ex 27, 617, 27, TWCU. 'JE'. Arr by 11-92.	11-93
☐ ZA557*		Tornado GR.1	ex 15, TWCU, 27, 617, 27, TWCU. 'TB'. Arrived by 10-92. Stored.	11-93
☐ ZA588*		Tornado GR.1	ex TTTE, 17 TWCU, 9. 'B-52'. Arr by 9-92.	11-93
☐ ZA590*		Tornado GR.1	ex 15, TWCU, 9. 'TF'. Arrived 6-10-92.	11-93
☐ ZA591*		Tornado GR.1	ex 27, 16, 617, TWCU, 9. 'JH'. Arr by 4-92.	11-93
☐ ZA592*		Tornado GR.1	ex 617, 19. 'B'. Arrived 6-7-92. Stored.	11-93
☐ ZA598*		Tornado GR.1T	ex 617, TWCU, 9. 'S'. Arrived 14-9-93.	11-93
☐ ZA606*		Tornado GR.1	ex TWCU, 27, 617. Arr by 6-92. Stored.	11-93
☐ ZD901		Tornado F.2	ex 229 OCU. 'AA'. Spares recovery.	11-93
☐ ZD903		Tornado F.2	ex 229 OCU. 'AB'. Spares recovery.	11-93
☐ ZD904		Tornado F.2	ex 229 OCU. 'AE'. Spares recovery.	11-93
☐ ZD905		Tornado F.2	ex 229 OCU. 'AV'. Spares recovery.	11-93
☐ ZD906		Tornado F.2	ex 229 OCU. 'AN'. Spares recovery.	11-93
☐ ZD932		Tornado F.2	ex 229 OCU. 'AM'. Spares recovery.	11-93
☐ ZD933		Tornado F.2	ex 229 OCU. 'AO'. Spares recovery.	11-93
☐ ZD934		Tornado F.2	ex 229 OCU. 'AD'. Spares recovery.	11-93
☐ ZD936		Tornado F.2	ex 229 OCU. 'AP'. Spares recovery.	11-93
☐ ZD937		Tornado F.2	ex 229 OCU. 'AQ'. To BDRT by 9-93.	11-93
☐ ZD938		Tornado F.2	ex 229 OCU. 'AR'. Spares recovery.	11-93
☐ ZD940		Tornado F.2	ex 229 OCU. ('AT') Spares recovery.	11-93
☐ ZD941		Tornado F.2	ex 229 OCU. 'AU'. Spares recovery.	11-93
☐ ZD992*		Harrier T.4	ex Gutersloh SF, 4 233 OCU. 'Y'. Arrived 8-4-92. Stored.	11-93
☐ ZE258*		Tornado F.3	ex 56, 43, 23, 5, 29. Arrived 4-93. Grounded — see notes above.	11-93
☐ ZE728*		Tornado F.3	ex 56, 229 OCU, 29, 11, A&AEE. Arrived by 6-93. Grounded — see notes above.	11-93
☐ ZG754*		Tornado GR.1	ex 9. 'AW'. Collision 23-6-93. Arrived 23-11-93 for storage.	11-93

■ **4 School of Technical Training** (4 SoTT) / **Civilian Technical Training School** (CTTS) : Contrary to **W&R13**, Jet Provost T.3 XN458 was not scrapped, but moved to <u>Cardiff-Wales Airport</u>, S Glam. Contrary to **W&R13**, Canberra TT.18 WJ717/9052M was never on the charge of the SoTT/CTTS as a whole airframe, only the nose came here, on April 1, 1992, the remainder being as detailed above; Jet Provost T.3 XM468/8081M moved to <u>Stock</u>, Essex, by June 1993; likewise, *JP* T.4s XP558/8627M and XP680/8460M moved to the dump by July 1992 — see above. The cockpit section and rear fuselage of Canberra PR.7 WT518/8691M (rear fuselage in part of the complex duo listed under Cardiff-Wales Airport, S Glam — *qv*) remained with CTTS until August 1993 when they were removed to <u>Stock</u>, Essex. That makes the current fleet : —

☐ WJ717	9052M	Canberra TT.18	ex FRADU, 61, 15. '841'. Nose only. See notes above.	09-92
☐ XA243	8886M	Grasshopper TX.1	ex Bournemouth. Glider Ground School.	09-90
☐ XE793	8666M	Cadet TX.3	Glider Ground School.	
☐ XM386*	8076M	Jet Provost T.3	ex Halton, Shawbury, 2 FTS, CFS, Huntings. '08'. Arrived by 9-93.	11-93
☐ XM419	8990M	Jet Provost T.3A	ex 7 FTS, 3 FTS, CFS, RAFC, CFS, 3 FTS, RAFC, 6 FTS, RAFC, 2 FTS. '102'.	11-93
☐ XN551	8984M	Jet Provost T.3A	ex 7 FTS, RAFC, 1 FTS, 3 FTS, 6 FTS, RAFC. '100'.	11-93
☐ XP502	8576M	Gnat T.1	ex 4 FTS. '02'.	11-93
☐ XP542	8575M	Gnat T.1	ex 4 FTS. '42'.	09-90
☐ XW404	9049M	Jet Provost T.5A	ex 1 FTS. '77'.	11-93
☐ XW409	9047M	Jet Provost T.5A	ex 7 FTS, 1 FTS. '123'.	11-93
☐ XX635	8767M	Bulldog T.1	ex Ems UAS. 'S'.	11-93
☐ XX763	9009M	Jaguar GR.1	ex Shawbury, 226 OCU. '24'.	11-93
☐ XX764	9010M	Jaguar GR.1	ex Shawbury, 226 OCU, 14. '13'.	11-93

West Glamorgan

SWANSEA AIRPORT (or Fairwood Common, on the A4118 west of Swansea)
A new maintenance operation, Air Engineering Services, has been established here and has started to restore to flying condition a Harvard, previously located vaguely in the 'Exeter' area. The Pup 100 continues to gather dust . The glider mentioned in **W&R13** has gone.

☐ G-AWKM		Pup 100	CoA expired 29-6-84. Stored.	06-92
☐ 'FT323'*	EX884	Harvard II	ex 'Exeter', Cranfield, Bushey, East Ham, Port AF 1513, SAAF 7426, EX884, 41-33857. Restoration. First noted 6-92.	06-92

Gwent

CAERLEON (on the A4236 north east of Newport)
■ **1367 Squadron ATC** : Still have their *Chippax*.

☐ WD293	7645M	Chipmunk T.10	ex Cwmbran, QuB UAS, StA UAS, G&S UAS, StA UAS, Chatham Flt, SMR, 1 BFTS. On loan.	

TREDEGAR
No news on the Cherokee hulk at the strip.

☐ G-AXTM		Cherokee 140B	crashed 21-2-81. Wreck.

CAERNARFON AERODROME (or Llandwrog)

■ **Caernarfon Air World** : (Note change of name.) With the airfield, the Museum and the pleasure flying now in the hands of Air Atlantique, a steady expansion of operations has been noticed. All of this means that G-AIDL will be 'touring' more during 1994 and beyond, but otherwise the exhibits remain as before. After closer inspection the Varsity nose is a 'synthetic' procedure trainer and has been dropped from the list. A Canberra is due to join the exhibits, likely from St Athan, S Glam.
◆ Open March 1 to November 30, 9.30am to 5.30pm. Groups at other times can be arranged. ✉ Snowdon Mountain Aviation, Caernarfon Airport, Llandwrog, Caernarfon, Gwynedd, LL54 5TP. ☎ 0286 830800.

☐ G-AIDL		Dragon Rapide 6 ▲	ex Biggin Hill, Allied Airways, TX310. See notes above.	01-94
☐ G-ALFT		Dove 6	ex Higher Blagdon, Stansted, CAFU. CoA expired 13-6-73.	11-93
☐ TX235		Anson C.19/2	ex Higher Blagdon, Andover, Shawbury, SCS, FCCS, CTFU, OCTU, 64 GCS, 2 GCS. Restoration.	11-93
☐ WM961	A2517	Sea Hawk FB.5	ex Higher Blagdon, Culdrose SAH-6, FRU, 802, 811. 'J'.	11-93
☐ WN499		Dragonfly HR.3	ex Higher Blagdon, Blackbushe, Culdrose SF. 'Y'. Plaything.	11-93
☐ WV781	7839M	Sycamore HR.12	ex Finningley, Odiham, Digby, HDU, CFS, ASWDU, G-ALTD ntu.	11-93
☐ XA282		Cadet TX.3	ex Syerston.	11-93
☐ XD599		Vampire T.11	ex Bournemouth, Blackbushe, Staverton, Stroud, CATCS, RAFC, 1. 'A'. Gate.	11-93
☐ XH837	8032M	Javelin FAW.7	ex Northolt, Ruislip, 33. Forward fuselage.	11-93
☐ XJ726		W'wind HAR.10	ex Sibson, Wroughton, 2 FTS, CFS, ME SAR Flt, 22. 'F'.	11-93
☐ XK623		Vampire T.11	ex Bournemouth 'G-VAMP', Moston, Woodford, Chester, St Athan, 5 FTS. '56'.	11-93
☐	BAPC.201	HM.14 *Flea*	ex Kidlington. Fuselage & tail. Modified u/c.	11-93

■ **Others** : Seneca N42CL came to grief on landing on June 28, 1992 and was stored. It was last noted in May 1993 — flying again?

LLANBEDR

■ **Maes Artro Craft Village** : Restoration of the Anson continues in a large building — part of the former domestic site for the airfield — devoted to a history of Llanbedr airfield and its surroundings.
◆ Open daily Easter to October 10am to 5.30pm. ✉ Artro Enterprises, Reception Building, Maes Artro, Llanbedr, Gwynedd. ☎ 0341 23 467.

☐ 'MW467'	BAPC.202	Spitfire V replica	ex *Piece of Cake*.	03-93
☐ VS562	8012M	Anson T.21	ex Portsmouth, Llanbedr, A&AEE, AST Hamble, CS(A). Restoration.	03-93
☐ A92-664		Jindivik 4A	ex airfield.	06-92

LLANBEDR AIRFIELD (west of Llanbedr and the A496 on the road to Shell Island)

■ **Test & Evaluation Establishment** (TEE) : Note *another* change of name! The long-suffering Canberra on the dump has a high-tech replacement, although it has yet to be put to the torch. Two Canberra TT.18s have arrived for storage, although one has since gone up for the dreaded tender.

☐ WH453		Meteor D.16	ex 5 CAACU, 72, 222. Stored. 'L'.	11-93
☐ WH887*		Canberra TT.18	ex St Athan, FRADU, Upwood Sf, 21, 542, 1323F. '847'. Arrived by 12-92. Stored.	01-94
☐ WJ574*		Canberra TT.18	ex FRADU, 57, 540. '844'. Arrived 3-12-92. Up for tender 9-93.	09-93
☐ WK143		Canberra B(TT).2	ex FRL. Dump, poor state. Serial amended from **W&R13**.	10-93

☐	XN657	Sea Vixen D.3	ex RAE, FRL, RAE, ADS, 899, 893. Sectioned, dump.	10-93
☐	XS577	Sea Vixen D.3	ex FRL, RAE Farnborough, 899. Stored.	11-93
☐	XV435*	Phantom FGR.2	ex 92, 228 OCU, 92, 228 OCU, 23, 228 OCU, 14. For dump, first noted 6-92. 'R'.	10-93
☐	A92-480	Jindivik 4A	gate guard.	08-91

VALLEY AIRFIELD (south of the A5, south east of Holyhead)
■ **RAF Valley** : By March 1993 the hulk of Vulcan XL392 on the dump had been offered up for disposal, having been replaced by a Phantom. It was cut up and removed by August 1993.

☐	XR534	8578M	Gnat T.1	ex 4 FTS, CFS. '65'. Gate guardian.	11-93
☐	XS177	9044M	Jet Provost T.4	ex Shawbury, CATCS, 3 FTS, 2 FTS, RAFC. 'N'. Fire crews.	11-93
☐	XT772	8805M	Wessex HU.5	ex Wroughton. SARTU inst.	11-93
☐	XT895*	9171M	Phantom FGR.2	ex 74, 56, 228 OCU, 92, 228 OCU, 11, 228 OCU. 'Q'. Damaged 10-92 by missile misfire. On dump by 2-93.	11-93
☐	XV778*		Harrier GR.3	ex St Athan, 1, 1453F, 1, 1417F, 1. Sectioned. Dump. First noted 4-93.	11-93

Powys

WELSHPOOL
■ **Sue & Roy Jerman** : Powys makes a re-entry into **W&R**. During late November the couple took delivery of two nose sections from Bruntingthorpe, Leics. Both are very complete and kept undercover. It is hoped that they will form the basis of a small collection.

☐	WK102*	8780M	Canberra T.17	ex Bruntingthorpe, Cosford, 360, 45, RNZAF, 207. Nose. Arrived 11-93.	11-93
☐	XT277*	8853M	Buccaneer S.2A	ex Bruntingthorpe, Cosford, Shawbury, 237 OCU, 12. Nose. Arrived 11-93.	11-93

CHANNEL ISLES

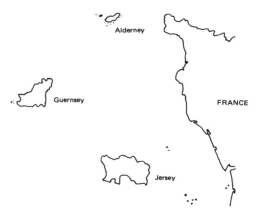

Alderney

Guernsey

FRANCE

Jersey

ALDERNEY AIRPORT

Tipsy Junior G-AMVP was flying (from Sandown) by November 1992. The Aztec serves on with the fire crews, near the 08 threshold.

☐ G-ASHV   Aztec 250B   ex Guernsey, (N5281Y). CoA expired 22-7-85.
Dump.   01-92

GUERNSEY

No news on the three long-term inmates on the Island.

☐ G-ASTH   Mooney M.20   ex France, N6906U. Crashed 16-11-66. Stored
at Sausmarez Park.
☐ G-ATEP   EAA Biplane   CoA exp 18-6-73. Stored at Sausmarez Park. 01-92
☐ G-ATHN   Noralpha   ex F-BFUZ, French military. CoA expired 27-6-75.
Stored in St Peter Port. Crated by 1-90.   01-92

GUERNSEY AIRPORT

On the dump, Sea Prince WJ350 gave in to the inevitable and had perished by September 1992. A replacement arrived on April 19, 1993 when Chinook HC.1 ZA682 air-lifted in Wessex HAS.1 XS888 from Lee-on-Solent. During December 1993, the Herald and the Wessex got up and moved from their location near the fire station and the aero club to a new location to the north of 09/27. The Trislander has not been reported for a while.

☐ G-BAZJ   Herald 209   ex Air UK, Alia 4X-AHR, G-8-1. Fire.   12-93
☐ G-BCYC   Trislander   ex Glasgow, Loganair, EL-AIB, G-BCYC.
Crashed 15-5-79. Fuselage, fire section.   09-92
☐ WL131   7751M   Meteor F.8   ex APS Sylt, 601, 111. Nose, Air Scouts.
☐ XS888*   Wessex HAS.1   ex Lee-on-Solent, Wroughton, Fleetlands. Arr
19-4-93 via Chinook. Fire dump.   12-93

JERSEY

Is the Herald nose still in use as a plaything at Longueville?

☐ G-APWG   Herald 201   ex Airport, Air UK, BIA, BUA. Nose.

JERSEY AIRPORT

The contents of the dump have not changed.

☐ G-AOJD   Viscount 802   ex BA, BEA. CoA expired 13-6-77. Fire.   01-92
☐ G-AVHJ   Super Baladou   CoA expired 9-4-87. Fire crews.   01-92
☐ G-BBXJ   Herald 203   ex BIA, I-TIVI. Cr 24-12-74. Fire service.   01-92

Part 8

IRELAND

Northern Ireland

Antrim	Down	Londonderry
Armagh	Fermanagh	

Ireland

Carlow	Kilkenny	Offaly
Cavan	Laois	Roscommon
Clare	Leitrim	Sligo
Cork	Limerick	Tipperary
Donegal	Longford	Waterford
Dublin	Louth	Wexford
Galway	Mayo	Wicklow
Kerry	Meath	
Kildare	West Meath	

BALLYMONEY (County Down)
A strip here holds a Super Cub and a Champion, both licking their wounds.

☐	G-BPJH*	Super Cub 95	ex MM52-2380, I-EICA, MM52-2380, 52-2380. Damaged 1-9-92. Restoration.	10-93
☐	G-BRFI*	7DC Champion	ex N1058E, NC1058E. Damaged 1990.	10-93

BANNFOOT (County Armagh)
A private strip here holds the former Cork Aircoupe.

☐	EI-AUT*	F.1A Aircoupe	ex Cork, G-ARXS, D-EBSA, N3037G. CoA expired 30-7-76. Restoration.	10-93

BELFAST (County Antrim)
■ **Campbell College** : The CCF still have their Vampire pod, it is 'parented' by Aldergrove.

☐	XD525	7882M	Vampire T.11	ex Aldergrove, 1 FTS, 4 FTS, 5 FTS, 7 FTS. Pod. 10-93

■ **1137 Squadron ATC** : Should still have their Devon nose.

☐	VP957	8822M	Devon C.2/2	ex Bishop's Court, Belfast Airport, Northolt, 207, 21, WCS, SCS, NCS, SCS, WCS, SCS, Andover SF, 38 GCF, AAFCE, 2 TAF CS, BAFO CS. Nose. 01-92

BELFAST CITY AIRPORT (or Sydenham, County Down, north of the city centre)
[Note change of name, changed from Belfast Harbour in September 1991.]
■ **Shorts** : The Belfast test shell spoken of in **W&R13** was a piece of optimism. There *was* such a thing, but it was broken up æons ago! The two Tucano test rigs are thought to survive within the plant. A swap over of Shorts 330 airframes for the Ulster Aviation Society took place during April 1993. Prototype G-BSBH has been allocated to the firemen to play with. Pre-production G-BDBS, retired from *hack* duties in 1992 was donated to UAS and was 'delivered' to Langford Lodge care of an RAF Chinook on April 7, 1993. Static test Tucano T.1 S45-T42 turned up at a farm near Waverton, Cheshire, during mid-1993.

☐	G-BSBH	Short SD.330	CoA exp 13-4-81. Fire. See notes above.	10-93
☐	1317	T-27 Tucano	ex EMBRAER, Brazil AF. Engine rig.	11-92

BELFAST INTERNATIONAL AIRPORT (or Aldergrove, County Antrim, west of the city)
■ **Airport** : The Trident continues to serve the firemen. Woodgate Aviation have had an Aztec long out of use here and withdrew another, for spares use, during 1993.

☐	G-AVFE	Trident 2E	ex BA, BEA. CoA exp 6-5-85. Fire crews.	10-93
☐	G-AZRG*	Aztec 250D	ex N6536Y. Withdrawn for spares use 1993.	10-93
☐	G-BCJS*	Aztec 250C	ex N6479Y. CoA exp 25-11-87. Stored.	10-93

■ **RAF Aldergrove** : By October 1993 the hulk of Wessex HC.2 XT669/8894M had perished. Joining the JP nose with the Exhibition, Production & Transportation Unit (note change of name) 'detachment' here has been a former Abingdon Hunter nose.

☐	WT486	8102M	Canberra T.4	ex Wildenrath, 14, 17, 88, Wildenrath SF. Dump. 10-93
☐	XE643*	8586M	Hunter FGA.9	ex Abingdon, 208, 56, 63, 66, 92. Nose. 10-93
☐	XR700	8589M	Jet Provost T.4	ex Abingdon, Shawbury, CATCS, 3 FTS, 1 FTS. Nose. 01-92
☐	XT456		Wessex HU.5	ex Wroughton. BDR. 10-93

ENNISKILLEN AERODROME (County Fermanagh, or St Angelo, north of Enniskillen)
There are now two Irish registered aircraft in store here.

☐	EI-AWW*	Cessna 414	ex OY-AKI, N8233Q ntu. CoA expired 2-6-90. Stored.	10-93
☐	EI-BAG*	Cessna 172A	ex Abbeyshrule, G-ARAV, N9771T. CoA expired 26-6-79. For rebuild. Arrived by mid-1991.	

HOLYWOOD (County Down, north of Belfast)

■ **Ulster Folk and Transport Museum** : With much of general interest, the Museum continues to display Ferguson Monoplane IAHC-1, the Short SC.1 and both McCandless gyroplanes. The other aircraft remain in store awaiting more space.

◆ Open July-August Monday to Saturday 10.30am to 6pm, Sunday 12am to 6pm; April, May, June and September Monday-Friday 9.30am to 5pm, Saturday 10.20am to 6pm, Sunday 12am to 6pm; October to March Monday to Friday 9.30am to 4pm and Saturday-Sunday 12.30am to 4.30pm. ✉ Cultra Manor, Holywood, Northern Ireland BT18 0EU. ☎ : 0232 428428. **Fax** 0232 428728.

☐	G-AJOC	Messenger 2A	ex East Fortune, Strathallan, Dunottar. CoA exp 18-5-72. Stored.	10-93
☐	G-AKEL	Gemini 1A	ex Kilbrittain Castle. CoA exp 29-4-72. For rebuild into one with G-AKGE. Stored.	10-93
☐	G-AKGE	Gemini 3C	ex Kilbrittain Castle, EI-ALM, G-AKGE. CoA expired 7-6-74. Stored. See G-AKEL.	10-93
☐	G-AKLW	Sealand	ex Bradley Air Museum, Windsor Locks, Connecticut, Jeddah, RSaudiAF, SU-AHY, G-AKLW. Stored.	10-93
☐	G-AOUR	Tiger Moth	ex Belfast, NL898, 15 EFTS. Crashed 6-6-65. Stored.	10-93
☐	G-ARTZ (No 1)	McCandless M-2	ex Killough. Displayed.	10-93
☐	G-ATXX	McCandless M-4	ex Killough. wfu 9-9-70. Displayed.	10-93
☐	ALA BGA 470	Nimbus I	ex Bishop's Stortford, Duxford. Stored.	10-93
☐	VH-UUP	Scion I	ex East Fortune, Strathallan, G-ACUX, VH-UUP, G-ACUX. Stored.	10-93
☐	XG905	Short SC.1	ex Shorts, Sydenham, Thurleigh, RAE.	10-93
☐	IAHC.6	Ferguson Mono	ex Dublin. Displayed.	10-93
☐	IAHC.9	Ferguson Mono	ex Belfast Airport, Holywood. Stored.	10-93

LANGFORD LODGE (County Antrim, on the shores of Lough Neagh, west of Belfast)

■ **Ulster Aviation Society** (UAS) : The collection continues to go from strength to strength. Permission has been granted to restore the control tower and work started in October 1993. The Wildcat has arrived from Newtownards and its restoration continues. A dramatic arrival was the 'production prototype' Short SD.330 G-BDBS, care of an RAF Chinook. UAS would like to hear from anyone who may have items relating to aviation in Northern Ireland.

◆ Opening is by prior arrangement only, but the UAS are working towards regular Saturday openings. ✉ Raymond Burrows, 15 Arnold Grove, Lower Ballinderry, Lisburn, County Antrim, Northern Ireland, BT28 2JL.

☐	G-BDBS*	Short SD.330	ex Belfast City, Shorts, G-14-3001. CoA expired 2-9-92. Flew in by Chinook 7-4-93.	12-93
☐	JV482*	Wildcat V	ex Newtownards, Castlereagh, Lough Beg, 882. Crashed 24-12-44. Arrived 30-1-93. Restn.	12-93
☐	WN108	Sea Hawk FB.3	ex Newtownards, Belfast City, Bournemouth, FRU, 806, 895, 897, 800. '033'.	12-93
☐	WZ549 8118M	Vampire T.11	ex N'ards, Coningsby, Tattershall, Coningsby, CATCS, 1 FTS, 8 FTS, FTU, C(A). 'F'.	12-93

LONDONDERRY

■ **John McGonagal** : Works on his Traveler in this area.

☐	G-ARAP*	7EC Traveler	ex Eglinton. Crashed 22-9-81. Restoration.	12-92

LOUGH FOYLE (Londonderry)

Just off shore can be seen the hulk of Corsair II JT693:R, ex 1837 Squadron.

MOVENIS AERODROME (near Garvagh, County Londonderry)

This blossoming airfield still holds the Cessna hulk.

☐	G-AWJA	Cessna 182L	ex N1658C. Crashed 12-9-84. Fuselage.	10-93

MULLAGHMORE (Londonderry)
The Rallye hulk has not been noted for some time.

☐ G-AWSZ Minerva 220 ex F-BPSO. Crashed 20-10-78. Wreck. 07-91

NEWTOWNARDS AERODROME (County Down, south of the town)
■ **Airfield** : The '150 fuselage still lives on. The '175B is thought long gone and is a virtual certainty to be a *LOST!* candidate.

☐ G-ARFM Cessna 175B ex N8176T. CoA expired 23-10-79. Stored.
☐ G-BBTT Cessna F.150L crashed 9-3-75. Fuselage. 10-93

■ **Ulster Aviation Society** : The move to Langford Lodge, Antrim, is now complete. Wildcat V JV482 moved there on January 30, 1993. As related in **W&R13**, Sea Venom FAW.22 XG736 was disposed of.

UPPER BALLINDERRY (near Crumlin, Antrim)
Restoration work continues slowly on the Whitney Straight here.

☐ G-AERV Whitney St ex Newtownards, EM999, Kemble, Abingdon SF,
  Halton SF, G-AERV. CoA exp 9-4-66. 10-93

Ireland

ABBEYSHRULE AERODROME (Westmeagh, north west of Mullignar)
The airfield continues to hold a large stock of dead and dying airframes, plus a few that are being restored. Determining just exactly what is stored here has taken on new meaning of late. A visit in September 19939 by a correspondent was concluded with : "There are some more fuselages behind the lock-up hangars but these are under plastic sheeting which has odd bits of manure etc dumped on top! There are limits as to how far I will go..." The following list is therefore even more full of the usual **W&R** pitfalls! Moving on since **W&R14** have been the following :— Champion 7AC EI-AVB was flying again by 1991; Cessna F.172M EI-AYK was flying again by 1991; Cessna 172A EI-BAG moved to Enniskillen, N Ireland; Rallye 150ST EI-BBI was flying again by 1991; Stampe EI-BAJ had gone by September 1993 and is thought to have gone north of the border; Rallye Club EI-BDB has been noted only as a rear fuselage in the last couple of years and is therefore best deleted; Rallye Clubs EI-BDH and EI-BGN are *thought* to have been scrapped; Musketeer EI-CCA (ex G-AWTR) was flying again by 1992. Cessna 182L G-FALL succeeded in becoming EI-CDP and is airworthy. With several additions, Abbeyshrule remains the largest single entry for the Republic.

☐ EI-AMF* Taylorcraft Plus D ex G-ARRK, G-AHUM, LB286, Coltishall SF,
  309, 70 GCF, 84 GCF, 22 EFTS, 43 OTU, 653.
  Restoration. First noted 4-92. 04-92
  [Registration was cancelled 3-4-70 as scrapped!]
☐ EI-ANN Tiger Moth ex Dublin, Kilcock, G-ANEE, T5418, 63 GCF,
  24 EFTS, 19 EFTS, 12 EFTS. Crashed 18-10-64.
  Spares for EI-AOP. 11-93
☐ EI-AOP Tiger Moth ex Dublin, G-AIBN, T7967, 18 EFTS, 1667 CU,
  1 GCF, 16 PFTS. Crashed 5-5-74. Restn. 11-93
☐ EI-ARW SAN DR.1050 ex F-BJJH. Crashed 28-7-86. Wreck. 11-93
☐ EI-ATK Cherokee 140 ex G-AVUP. Crashed 14-2-87. Wreck. 11-93
☐ EI-ATL Champion 7AC ex 'local', Abbeyshrule, Clondalkin, N1119E.
  Damaged 26-11-75. Spares for EI-AVB.
☐ EI-AUP Rallye Club ex Coonagh, G-AVVK. Cr 1-9-83. Wreck. 11-93
☐ EI-AYA Rallye Club ex G-BAON. CoA expired 10-9-89. Stored. 09-93
☐ EI-AYL Airedale ex G-ARRO, (EI-AVP), G-ARRO. CoA expired
  1-2-86. Stored. 11-93
☐ EI-AYT Rallye Minerva ex G-AXIU. Crashed 12-11-89. Stored. 11-93
☐ EI-BAL Airedale ex G-ARZS. Dismantled. 11-93
☐ EI-BBK Airedale ex G-ARXB, (EI-ATE), G-ARXB. CoA exp
  11-11-83. 11-93

☐ EI-BCW*	Rallye Club	ex G-AYKE. First noted 9-93.	09-93
☐ EI-BEP	Rallye C'dore	ex F-BTJT. CoA exp 28-4-90. Dismantled.	06-91
☐ EI-BFI	Rallye 100ST	ex F-BXDK. Crashed 14-12-85. Spares.	11-93
☐ EI-BGB*	Rallye Club	ex G-AZKB. CoA exp 18-5-91. F/n 9-93.	09-93
☐ EI-BGS	Rallye 180GT	ex F-BXTY. Crashed 20-7-90. Spares.	11-93
☐ EI-BKE	Super Rallye	ex F-BKUN, F-WKUN. Cr 5-4-81. Wreck.	06-91
☐ EI-BMV*	AA-5 Traveler	ex G-BAEJ. First noted 9-93.	09-93
☐ EI-BNR	AA-5 Traveler	ex N9992Q, CS-AHM. Crashed 21-2-88.	04-92
☐ EI-BOP	Rallye C'dore	ex Coonagh, G-BKGS, F-BSXS. Crashed 29-3-86.	11-93
☐ EI-BUJ*	Rallye C'dore	ex G-FOAM, G-AVPL. First noted 9-93.	09-93
☐ G-SKYH*	Cessna 172N	ex A6-GRM, N76034. Damaged 9-91. Stored, first noted 9-93	09-93

BALLYJAMESDUFF (Cavan)
■ N Reilly : Restoration continues on the Taylorcraft Plus D (with EI-ALH airworthy from here) while a migratory Cadet glider has settled here.

☐ EI-ANA	Taylorcraft Plus D	ex G-AHCG, LB347, 657, 655. Restn.	04-92
☐ XE808*	Cadet TX.1	Stored. First noted 4-92.	04-92

CARBURY (Kildare)
Thought still stored here is Dick Robinson's 1937 *Flea*.

☐	IAHC 3	HM.14 *Flea*	stored, engineless. Never flew.

CASEMENT AIRFIELD (or Baldonnel, west of Dublin, County Dublin)
■ Irish Army Air Corps (IAAC) : Budgetary changes within the IAAC threaten to withdraw from use all of the Fouga Magisters. As a type they will attract the jet warbird merchants so may well not enter into a long period of storage. The Cessna 172 avionics rig gets about a bit. It is used for charity events and the like, it has been pushed from Dublin to Cork. Chipmunk T.20 164 may well have been at Gormanston, Co Dublin, during the early months of 1992, but was to be found stored here again by August 1993. Two hulks are thought to have perished on the dump, certainly by July 1993, Provost T.51 189A and the pod of Vampire T.55 193. Whirlwind HAR.9 XN309 is thought not to have stayed long at Casement. It is thought to have been used for submergence testing/training and *may* have gone to the navy dockyard at Haulbowline, Cork.

☐ 164	Chipmunk T.20	stored. See notes above.	08-93
☐ 198	Vampire T.11	ex 'gate', XE977, 8 FTS. Unflown by IAAC. Under restoration by 8-93.	08-93
☐ 207*	Cessna FR.172H	Apprentice School, first noted 10-92.	10-92
☐ 221	CM-170-2	ex French Air Force No 79 '3-KE', inst.	08-93
☐ 233*	SF-260MC	ex I-SYAS. Fuselage. *Still* present 10-92.	10-92
☐ (G-ARLU)	Cessna 172B	ex Southend, N8002X. Damaged 30-10-77. Avionics rig. See notes above.	08-93
☐	c/no 1012 Alouette III	instructional, non-flying, rig.	08-93

CASTLEBRIDGE (north of Wexford, County Wexford)
Once home to Avro Cadet EI-ALP (which is at Weston), the strip now only hosts a Slingsby version.

☐ VM659	Cadet TX.2	Stored.	

CELBRIDGE (Kildare)
■ Phil Bedford : Restoration of the Proctor is *thought* to continue here.

☐ G-AHWO	Proctor V	ex Whitehall, Dublin Airport, (EI-ALY). Crashed 5-5-59. Restoration.	12-93

CORK AIRPORT (County Cork)
A clear out here. Aircoupe EI-AUT moved to Bannfoot, Northern Ireland for a rebuild; Leopard Moth G-ACMA was flying by 1992 and the Geronimo N4422P is thought long gone.

CURRAGH (County Kildare)

■ **Irish Army** : The famous army base has within it the fuselage of a former Shannon Airport Boeing 707. It is use for security force training. It is thought mostly likely to be the former 4R-ALB — see **W&R13**, but more details welcomed.

| ☐ | * | Boeing 707 | fuselage. See notes above. | 09-93 |

DUBLIN

■ **Irish Aviation Museum** (IAM) : Storage of the artefacts and airframes for the hoped-for IAM continues at Castlemoate House. Please note that inspection by the public is not possible.

☐	EI-AOH	Viscount 808	ex Dublin Airport, Aer Lingus. Nose section.	07-93
☐	G-ANPC	Tiger Moth	ex Edinburgh (?), Strathallan, Portmoak, R4950, 2 GS, Kirton-in-Lindsey SF, Hemswell SF, Oakington SF, 28 EFTS, 25 PEFTS, 17 EFTS, Benson SF. Crashed 2-1-67.	
☐	G-AOGA	Aries 1	ex Kilbrittain Castle, EI-ANB, G-AOGA. Damaged 8-8-69. Stored off site.	07-93
☐	34	Magister	ex Casement, N5392.	07-93
☐	141	Anson XIX	ex Casement.	07-93
☐	183	Provost T.51	ex Casement.	07-93
☐	191	Vampire T.55	ex Casement.	07-93

■ **Institute of Technology** : Located in Bolton Street and last mentioned in **W&R12**, this location has regained a whole airframe in the shape of a long-withdrawn Cessna 337 from Weston.

| ☐ | EI-BHM* | Cessna F.337E | ex Farranfore, Weston, OO-PDC, OO-PDG. CoA expired 9-7-82. First noted 4-92. | 04-92 |

DUBLIN AIRPORT (or Collinstown, County Dublin, north of the City)
Two landmarks from the Iona hangar have moved on. Cadet EI-ALU and J/1 Autocrat EI-AMK had moved to <u>Newcastle</u>, Co Wicklow, by September 1993. The Ryanair HS.748 was to have moved to the museum at Waterford, but this now seems to have fallen through. The early series Aer Lingus Boeing 737s have entered storage — some in sophisticated cocoons and look set for a long stay.

☐	EI-ABI*	DH.84 Dragon △	ex EI-AFK, G-AECZ, AV982, EE, 7 AACU, 110 Wing, G-AECZ. *Iolar*. Aer Lingus 'Historic Flight'.	12-93
☐	EI-ARY	Cessna F.150H	crashed 14-6-70. Wreck.	07-90
☐	EI-ASD*	Boeing 737-248C	ex ALT. *St Ide*. Stored. CoA exp 23-10-92	09-93
☐	EI-ASE*	Boeing 737-248C	ex ALT. *St Fachtna*. Stored. CoA exp 25-11-91.	09-93
☐	EI-ASG*	Boeing 737-248	ex ALT, HR-SHD, EI-ASG, N7360F, EI-ASG, SU-AYT, EI-ASG. *St Cormac*. Stored. CoA expired 29-5-91.	09-93
☐	EI-ASH*	Boeing 737-248	ex ALT, HR-TNS, EI-ASH, C-GTAR, EI-ASH, N80AF, EI-ASH, N361F, EI-ASH, C-GTAR, EI-ASH, C-GTAR, EI-ASH, CF-TAR, EI-ASH. St Eugene. Stored. CoA expired 26-3-91.	09-93
☐	EI-AUH	Cessna F.172H	cr 25-2-72. Fuselage, wings on EI-AVA.	04-92
☐	EI-AYJ	Cessna 182P	ex N52229. Crashed 19-9-76. Wreck.	03-90
☐	EI-BCR*	Boeing 737-281	ex ALT, 9Q-CNL, JA8403. *St Oliver Plunkett*. Stored. CoA Expired 3-3-91.	09-93
☐	EI-BDY*	Boeing 737-2E1A	ex ALT, G-BNYT, EI-ADY, C-GNDD, CN-RML, C-GNDD, EI-BDY, C-GEPB, N70720, C-GEPB, N4039W, C-GEPB. *St Brigid*. Stored. CoA expired 26-3-91.	09-93
☐	EI-BEM*	Short 360-100	ex ALT, East Midlands, G-BLGC, G-14-3642. *St Senan*. Crashed 31-1-86. Cabin trainer.	09-93
☐	EI-BIA	Cessna FA.152	crashed 28-9-80. Wreck.	05-92
☐	EI-BSF*	HS.748-1 105	ex Ryanair, EC-DTP, G-BEKD, LV-HHF, LV-PUM. *Spirit of Tipperary*. CoA expired 21-5-87. Cabin Trainer. See notes above.	09-92

| ☐ G-BHIA | Cessna F.152-II | Crashed 16-2-85. Stored, poor shape. | 05-92 |
| ☐ 5N-ANO | Boeing 707-3F9C | ex Nigeria Airways. Open store. | 08-93 |

FOYNES (Limerick)

■ **GPA Flying-Boat Museum** : Among other items at this nascent museum located at the former trans-Atlantic flying-boat base are the engines and other remains from BOAC Sunderland III G-AGES, which came to grief off Kerry on July 28, 1943.

✉ GPA Flying-Boat Museum, Foynes, Limerick. ☎ 069 65416.

GORMANSTON AIRFIELD (County Meath)

■ **IAAC** : Chipmunk T.20 168 remains airworthy as the only component of the IAAC's unofficial 'historic flight'. Fellow T.20 172 had departed by January 1993, possibly to a museum at Loch Erne — more details appreciated.

| ☐ 168 | Chipmunk T.20 ▲ | airworthy. See notes above. | 01-93 |
| ☐ 199 | Chipmunk T.20 | spares use. | 01-93 |

GOWRAN GRANGE (Dublin)

Two gliders (at least) are stored at the gliding site, the Kite being *very* long term.

| ☐ EI-102 | Kite 2 | stored. See above. | 06-93 |
| ☐ WZ762 | Grasshopper TX.1 | with wings of WZ756. Stored. | 06-93 |

INISHMORE (Arran Islands)

Islander EI-BBR was found to be but a small pile of metal pieces here by May 1993.

KILMOON (County Meath)

The pair of Cubs are thought still to be found here.

| ☐ EI-AKM | J-3C-65 Cub | ex Weston, N88194, NC88194. CoA expired 30-6-60. Stored. | |
| ☐ EI-BCO | J-3C-65 Cub | ex Dublin, F-BBIV, composite. Stored. | |

NEWCASTLE (County Wicklow)

By September 1993 two 'long-termers' from Dublin Airport had arrived, to await restoration.

| ☐ EI-ALU* | Avro Cadet | ex Dublin, G-ACIH. F/n 9 -93. Dism. | 09-93 |
| ☐ EI-AMK* | J/1 Autocrat | ex G-AGTV. CoA exp 28-8-76. | 09-93 |

POWERSCOURT (Wicklow)

Two Austers are held in store at the airstrip.

| ☐ EI-AMY | J/1N Alpha | ex Kells, G-AJUW. CoA exp 5-11-69. Spares. | 04-92 |
| ☐ EI-AUS | J/5F Aiglet Tnr | ex G-AMRL. CoA exp 2-12-75. Stored. | 04-92 |

RATHCOOLE (County Cork)

Going back to **W&R12**, Swallow EI-AFF is now thought to be nearing the end of a restoration to flying condition under a consortium of owners, location unknown. Fellow EI-AFN is thought to have only ever been small remains and should therefore be discounted. The Cub is still stored here.

| ☐ G-AXVV | L-4H-PI | ex F-BBQB, 43-29572. CoA expired 16-6-73. Stored. | 04-92 |

SHANNON AIRPORT (Clare, south of Ennis)

Has expanded in its role as a resting place for a cosmopolitan collection of *aluminium overcast*. Of those listed in **W&R13**, Boeing 707-138B N46D was scrapped by early 1992 and 707-321C N454PC joined Gambia Airways as C5-GOC in July 1992. See under Waterford for a *possible* fate for Aztec EI-BLW and under The Curragh for a *possible* resurrection of Boeing 707 4R-ALB.

| ☐ EI-BLW | Aztec 250C | ex Shannon Executive, G-BBAV, PH-KNV, LN-NPD, SE-EPW. CoA exp 7-7-89. Stored. See notes above. | 09-91 |
| ☐ A6-EMC* | Boeing 727-2K5 | ex Emirates, D-AHLU. Stored. Arr 30-6-93. | 02-94 |

☐	CCCP-58641	An-26 *Curl*	ex Peruvian AF. *Aeroflot* markings. Stored.	02-94
☐	EL-AKD	Boeing 720-023B	ex Omega Air, OD-AFN, N7543A. Stored.	02-94
☐	ET-AHK*	Boeing 727-260	ex Ethiopian. Stored. Arrived 3-8-92.	02-94
☐	ET-AHL*	Boeing 727-260	ex Ethiopian. Stored. Arrived 27-8-93.	02-94
☐	ET-AHM*	Boeing 727-260	ex Ethiopian. Stored. Arrived 3-8-93.	02-94
☐	TF-AIA*	Boeing 727-276	ex Atlantic Island, YU-AKO, TF-FLK, VH-TBL. Arrived 4-12-92.	02-94
☐	YN-CCN	Boeing 707-123B	ex Omega Air, Aeronica, 5B-DAO, G-BGCT, N7526A. Stored. Arrived 12-6-91.	02-94
☐	5N-ABJ	Boeing 707-3F9C	ex Nigerian. Stored.	02-94
☐	9G-ACM*	DC-9-51	ex Ghana AW. Stored. First noted 9-93.	09-93

SLIGO (County Sligo)
■ **Gerry O'Hara** : Gerry's homegrown aircraft are *believed* to be still stored here.

| ☐ | | IAHC 7 | Sligo Concept | single seat low wing monoplane. Stored, unflown. |
| ☐ | | IAHC 8 | O'Hara Gyroplane | on Bensen lines. Unflown. Stored. |

WATERFORD AIRPORT (County Waterford, south east of Waterford)
■ **Airport** : Emeraude G-ARIW became EI-CFG and was flying by 1993. Displayed inside the terminal is an unmarked microlight.

| ☐ | G-ASNG | Dove 6 | ex Cork, (EI-BJW), Coventry, HB-LFF, G-ASNG, HB-LFF, G-ASNG, PH-IOM. Fire dump. | 08-93 |
| ☐ | * | Eagle | displayed in terminal. | 06-93 |

■ **South East Aviation Enthusiasts** (SEAE) : For one reason or another the museum is leaving the airport site, but the destination of the airframes is not yet known. (Perhaps New Ross.) Only those listed were on site during August 1993, leaving the following unaccounted for : — an unmarked Aztec hulk (see under Shannon for a possibility) that had appeared during June 1993 but moved on by August 1993; Chipmunk T.20 173; Dove 6 '176' (VP-YKF) present up to June 1993; and HM.14 *Flea* IAHC.1. For a variety of reasons it is now doubted that there *ever* was a Gemini cockpit at Waterford — refer to **W&R13**. As will be seen under the Dublin Airport entry, the former Ryanair HS.748 did *not* come here.

☐	G-AOIE 'EI-AWA'	Douglas DC-7C	ex Shannon, Autair, Schreiner PH-SAX, G-AOIE Caledonian, BOAC. Caledonian colours starboard, Aer Turas port .	08-93
☐	VP-BDF	Boeing 707-321	ex Dublin, N435MA, Bahamas World AL, G-14-372, G-AYAG, N759PA. Nose.	08-93
☐	184	Provost T.51	ex Casement, IAAC.	08-93
☐	187	Vampire T.55	ex Casement, IAAC. Fuselage pod only.	08-93
☐	192	Vampire T.55	ex Casement, IAAC.	08-93

WESTON AERODROME (Dublin)
With only one recent confirmation, it is assumed that the **W&R** situation at this pleasant airfield remains unchanged.

☐	EI-ALP	Avro Cadet	ex Castlebridge, G-ADIE. CoA exp 6-4-78. Stored.	08-93
☐	EI-BBG	Rallye 100ST	CoA expired 1-12-83. Stored.	08-93
☐	EI-BEA	Rallye 100ST	CoA expired 10-5-86. Stored.	08-93
☐	EI-BFP	Rallye 100ST	ex F-GARR. CoA expired 1-10-87.	08-93

Run by the Irish Aviation Historical Council, the IAHC register operates on very similar lines to the BAPC Register. It has remained at a total of nine entries for a long time. As there are so few, they are given in greater detail here.

1	Mignet HM.14 *Flea*	Current status unknown. See under <u>Waterford</u>, Co Waterford.
2	Aldritt Monoplane	See under <u>Wannock</u>, East Sussex.
3	Mignet HM.14 *Flea*	Original, *circa* 1937. See under <u>Carbury</u>, Kildare.
4	Hawker Hector	Fuselage frame. Thought under restoration in Florida, USA.
5	Morane Saulnier MS.230	Fuselage frame. Thought scrapped.
6	Ferguson Monoplane replica	See under <u>Holywood</u>, Co Down, Northern Ireland.
7	Sligo Concept	Single-seat low wing monoplane. See under <u>Sligo</u>, Co Sligo.
8	O'Hara Autogyro	Bensen-style gyroplane. See under <u>Sligo</u>, Co Sligo.
9	Ferguson Monoplane replica	See under <u>Holywood</u>, Co Down, Northern Ireland.

LOST & FOUND!

THIS SECTION seeks to get readers scratching around to solve some of the many 'unfinished' stories within the pages of **W&R**. Listed below are aircraft that have been shunted into the *LOST!* column from the pages of this edition, or that have remained 'chestnuts' from previous **W&R**s. The ultimate aim is to 'find' these, and this mostly takes the form of a confirmed scrapping, or similar. A few airframes, however, are sufficiently resilient to make a 'come back'. Note that, as with all of the book, the criterion for an aircraft entering *LOST!* or *FOUND!* is a <u>physical</u> input and not assumption or interpretation of registration changes etc. Over to YOU!

Compiled by **Tom Poole**.

Lost!

G-ACDA Tiger Moth : Was under restoration at Chilbolton, Hants, along with fellow **Tiger Moth G-AKUE**. Since the closure of the airfield, both are unaccounted for. [Edition 13, page 65 — 13/65]

G-AGYH J/1N Alpha : Departed from Potter's Bar, *circa* 1990, reportedly bound for the Barrow-in-Furness, Cumbria, area. Without any confirmation of this, it has been decided to include it here in the hope of stirring up some information. [Edition 13, page 81 — 13/81.]

G-AKUW Super Ace 2 : Was at Allesley, W Mids, until it reportedly moved to the Daventry, Northants, area, *circa* 1990. [13/113]

G-ANPP Proctor III : Under restoration at/near Stansted Airport, Essex, until its removal by road in 1990. [13/61]

G-ARLH Terrier 1 : Previously listed under the general heading of 'Southampton', Hants, the status of this aircraft is doubted. Further details welcomed. [This edition.]

G-ARSL Terrier 2 : Along with **Terrier 1 G-AVCS** were part of the Vintage Aircraft Team collection at Cranfield, Beds, until leaving for pastures new in 1991. [13/16]

G-ATIC CEA DR.1050 : As threatened in **W&R13**, with no sighting at its last reported 'home' (Shawdene, Berks) for over a decade, this Jodel is now *LOST!* until proven otherwise. (Restored to the register during December 1993 to an address in St Agnes, Cornwall.)

G-AXNY Fixter Pixie : Previously stored at Chatteris, Cambs, in poor condition. It has not been sighted for a long time. Locals report it moved on, and to a museum, but where? [This edition.]

G-AZIO SNCAN SV-4C : Was at Wycombe Air Park, Bucks, for a long time, reportedly awaiting conversion to an SV-4L Lycoming-powered conversion. Not physically noted for a very long time. Any ideas? [13/29]

G-BFBN Pawnee : Roaded out from East Winch, Norfolk, during 1989 for spares use. [13/115]

G-BGAU Rearwin 9000L : Removed from Biggin Hill, Gtr Lon, *circa* 1990, said to be going to the Isle of Wight. (Also rumoured as going to the USA.) More details? [13/102]

G-BINH Tiger Moth : Was on rebuild at Shipdham, Norfolk, until being removed in May 1991 — destination? [13/117]

EI-ASU Terrier 2 : Stored at Rathcoole, Cork, but gone by 1991. Anything new? [13/22]

WV444 Provost T.1 : 'Disappeared' from Peterborough, Sibson, Cambs, in 1991. [13/38]

XD452 Vampire T.11 : Last reported at Whixall, Shrop, briefly in 1991. [13/132]

XG592 Whirlwind HAS.7 : Gone from the Wales Aircraft Museum at Cardiff-Wales Airport, S Glam, by September 1991. Destination? Fate? [13/214]

XL879 Westland Whirlwind HAS.7 : The cockpit section was at Manadon, Devon, until it was used during a fire fighting training exercise at an open day in 1990. Is this the end, or did it live on? [13/49]

XM409 Jet Provost T.3 : Up for disposal at Halton, Bucks, by June 1989. Fate? [13/25]

XM467 Jet Provost T.3 : Removed from Halton, Bucks, by February 1991. Fate? [13/25]

XP586 Jet Provost T.4 : Was part of a cache which were disposed of from the Staravia yard at Finchampstead Ridges, Berks. The others were **XP642**, **XP669** and **XP685**. Reports at the time suggested three of them went to Egham, Surrey, and the other to the 'Midlands' for preservation. [13/21]

XR243 Auster AOP.9 : Part of the St Athan Historic Aircraft Collection, S Glam. Auctioned September 21, 1989 — 'hammered' at £6,500. [13/214]

XS869 Wessex HAS.1 : Along with an anonymous **Buccaneer S.2** nose section are unaccounted for since the closure of the Naval Air Medical School at Seafield Park, Lee-on-Solent, Hants, during September 1991. [13/70]

XT443 Wasp HAS.1 : Was part of the Westland training airframes at Sherborne, Dorset, until its closure in 1991. To Malaysia? [13/53]

XV141 Scout AH.1 : Used as an instructional airframe at Arborfield, Berks, until it departed by road on March 28, 1990. [13/21]

A-20 Auster AOP.6 : Spares ship for G-BKXP at Royston, Herts. Fate uncertain since the relocation of 'KXP to Little Gransden, Cambs. [13/81]

MM54099 T-6G Texan : Arrived at Audley End, Essex, from Rochester, Kent, by September 1990. It had moved on by January 1992, destination unknown, but becoming G-BRBC during September 1992. [13/54]

And...

G-MMUL Ward E47 Elf : With Mick Ward's diminutive P45 Gnome G-AXEI and his 600cc Citroen Ami powered HM.14 *Flea* 'F50' now at Breighton, Humbs, thoughts centre on his other aircraft, the Elf biplane of 1984. This craft donated its engine to the *Flea*, and the airframe was sold. Current whereabouts?

Found!

G-AEJR BAC Drone : Was with Phil Dunnington as a spares ship for G-ADPJ (see under Breighton, Humbs, in this edition) until being sold to a collector in Yorkshire for his BAC VII project. This is now known to be EQY (BGA.2878) and flown from Dishforth, N Yorks. [10/121]

G-APRA Tiger Moth : Was stored at Kells, Meath, until its disappearance around 1977. Restoration was complete in 1993 and it is now airworthy with the 'period' marks EI-AHI. [7/93]

G-AVZY MS.880B Rallye Club : See under Chiseldon, Wilts.

BAPC.27 HM.14 *Flea* : Exists only as the wings, fuselage side walls and other detail parts with a member of the Midland Air Museum. As such it is too small for full inclusion within **W&R**.

BAPC.38 / 'A1742' Bristol Scout replica : Well and truly found by Graham Warner and his team from the Aircraft Restoration Company, "in the proverbial barn". See under Duxford, Cambs.

AGRICULTURAL

AgCat G-BDZF, seen at East Winch, Norfolk, and since exported to the United States. *W J Taylor, July 1992*

Pawnee G-BENL awaits possible rebuild near Wainfleet, Lincs. *W J Taylor, April 1991*

Fieldmaster G-NRDC and the fuselage of a test specimen (left) dumped out at Sandown, Isle of Wight. *Ken Ellis, July 1992*

BAPC REGISTER

Salvaged from a long layover at Lympne, Kent, by the Aircraft Restoration Company, Fiat G.46 BAPC.79 at Duxford, Cambs.
Tony Marsh, November 1993

Ken Fern's superb Flying Flea 'G-ADVU' (BAPC.211 - carried on the rudder) uses a small amount of the original Burns Garage, Stoke-on-Trent, Staffs, example.
Alf Jenks, June 1993

Out of the public gaze for four decades, the Broburn Wanderlust sailplane BAPC.233 is now on show at the Museum of Berkshire Aviation, Woodley, Berks, a stone's throw from its birthplace.
Ken Ellis, March 1993

BRUNTINGTHORPE

Wessex HU.5 XT755 showing off the dreaded 'blue cross' with Phoenix Aviation.
Roy Bonser, September 1993

Canberra B.2/6 XH568 flew into Bruntingthorpe, Leics, on November 25, 1993, the same day as Victor K.2 XM715 — see the front cover. It has since been registered as G-BVIC with the aim of acquiring a Permit to Fly.
Robert Rudhall, November 1993

Mixture on the Vintage Aircraft Team site, Hunter T.7 XL578 and a stripped-down Vampire T.11 pod.
Roy Bonser, September 1993

BUCCANEERS

DRA Bedford Buccaneer S.2 XX897
served as a test-bed for Tornado radar
— hence the modified nose section. It
was delivered to Source Classic Jet at
Bournemouth Airport, Dorset, on
19 August 1993.
Cliff Knox / Source Jet, August 1993

Another Bedford Buccaneer, but in
decidedly different health. The mortal
remains of S.1 XK530 in the fire pits
at Thurleigh, Bedfordshire.
Steve Hague, August 1992

Blue crossed and stripped-out,
Buccaneer S.2 XZ432 awaits its fate
at Lossiemouth, Grampian.
T Gibbons, July 1992

CANBERRAS

B.6RC WJ775, replaced by Harrier GR.3 XZ998 with the CSDE at Swanton Morley, Norfolk, before removal to St Athan, S Glam, on 17 April 1993. *W J Taylor, April 1993*

B.6(mod) WT301at the DODS, Chattenden, Kent. Replaced in whatever role it played by Phantom FGR.2 XT907 and moved to the yard at Stock, Essex, by November 1993. *Tony Marsh, September 1993*

Displayed within Allenbrooke barracks, what was Bassingbourn Airfield, Cambs, is PR.7 WJ621 as a monument to the days of 231 OCU. *Ken Ellis, February 1993*

CESSNA SINGLES

The hulk of T.210K G-MIST at Barton, Greater Manchester.*Andy Wood, September 1992*

Nestled within the undergrowth at the former 9th Air Force base of Spanhoe Lodge, Northants, lies C.152 II G-BNJJ. *Ken Ellis, May 1993*

Two primered and stored airframes at Little Staughton, Cambs, F.150G G-AVGU and (left) PA-38 Tomahawk 112 SE-GVH. *Andy Wood, September 1993*

Para-trainer U.206A G-BRID sits atop a chest of drawers at Grindale, Humbs. *Andy Wood, Nov 1992*

CRANWELL

Bearing Gulf War nose-art and 'pink' camouflage, Jaguar GR.1 XX747/8903M *Sadman* within the Airframe Technology Flight at Cranwell, Lincs.

Harrier GR.3 XZ132/9168M, within the ATF at Cranwell. Canberra rear fuselage behind.

Shades of the immortal 111 Squadron Black Arrows. Servicing Instruction Flight Hunter T.8B XF967/9186M arrived at Cranwell during April 1993, and is on the SIF ramp on the eastern end of the base. *All W J Taylor, September 1993*

EASTERN EUROPE I

During July and September 1993 a consignment of L 29 Mayas arrived at Cumbernauld, Strathclyde, for assembly and resale by Computaplane. 'Red 09' (591378) was an early one to be assembled. Others moved to the store at Chester Airport, Clwyd, joining the massed influx through Liverpool Docks. *Paul Crellin, September 1993*

Assembly underway of Graham Hinkley's second 'MiG-15' in the Southernair hangar at Shoreham, W Sussex. '008', SBLim-2 09008 arrived on 12 October 1992. *Ken Ellis, October1992*

Two former Libyan Air Force L 39ZO Albatrosses were imported into the UK via Robs Lamplough after being 'liberated' in Tchad. N159JC can be found at North Weald, and N162JC is stored at Southend Airport, both in Essex. *I F Mowell, March 1993*

EASTERN EUROPE II

On October 27, 1993 the MV *Kreylis* docked in Liverpool and unloaded a large and varied cache of former Soviet hardware, all 'leavings' in Latvia. All have, or will, be moving to Chester Airport, Clwyd, for storage prior to sale. MiG-23 Flogger-B '71' (65982) was one of a pair imported.

Mi-2 Hoplite CCCP-20320 with An-2 behind.

Sukhoi Su-17 Fitter-H '55' with national insignia painted out.

One of a pair of Mi-24 Hind-Ds, looking decidedly uneasy in Liverpool's dockland!
All Roger Richards, November 1993

FLEET AIR ARM MUSEUM

Sea Venom FAW.22 WW138 newly-painted as '227-Z' with Suez Operation *Musketeer* markings.
R G Turner, June 1993

Barracuda II rebuild project DP972 returned to Yeovilton during September 1992.
R G Turner, September 1992

MiG-15bis G-BMZF (01420) in North Korean colours, ready for installation in the Korean War exhibit. *R G Turner, April 1993*

HARRIERS

See-through GR.3 XV778 on the dump at Valley, Gwynedd, with the wing of Vulcan B.2 XL392 in the foreground. *Peter Mears, November 1989*

Causing many a traffic surge on the A1 south of Stamford, GR.3 XV779 guards the gate at Wittering, Cambs. *Nigel Price, September 1993*

GR.3 XZ998 arriving at Swanton Morley, Norfolk, having arrived from St Athan, S Glam, 13 October 1992. *W J Taylor, October 1992*

HEMSWELL

Within the main site of what was
RAF Hemswell, Lincs, can be found
the Bomber County Aviation
Museum, amid what is now a huge
antiques centre. Largest exhibit is
Canberra T.19 WJ975.

Sycamore HR.14 XG506/7852M
missing its main gear and rotorblades.

Vampire T.11 XD445 amid the mess
buildings at Hemswell.

Mystere IVA 101 '8-MN'.
All Peter Spooner, September 1993

HERALDS

The Herald Society's Srs 100 G-APWA arrived at Woodley, Berks, from Southend, Essex, on 29 August 1992. *Ken Ellis, March 1993*

Guernsey Airport's Srs 209 G-BAZJ wears a military-looking overall grey colour scheme and is used for non-destructive fire rescue training. *Andrew Powell, May 1993*

Having retired Srs 209 G-ATDS, Channel Express passed it on to the firemen at Bournemouth Airport, Dorset, on 15 February 1993. *Roger Richards, September 1993*

HUNTERS

Proof that all is not necessarily what you think it is. For a long time, W&R has had T.8C 'WT722' in store at Shawbury, Shrop. However, WT722 serves FRADU as '878' whereas this machine is '879'. A squint under the wings reveals this to be T.8 WT799 wearing the tail of WT722 — and the fin from a TWU example! Of such things are long-lasting 'legends' made! *Alan Allen, September 1992*

Gate guardian at Henlow, Beds, is F.1 WT612.
Steve Hague, August 1992

Jet Heritage's composite T.7 at Bournemouth Airport, Dorset. JHL are working to open the collection to visitors on a regular basis.
Roger Richards, September 1993

Occupant of the dump at Cottesmore, Leics, is T.7 XL618. Artwork on the nose helpfully shows the direction of flight! *Nigel Price, May 1993*

INTERNATIONAL HELICOPTER MUSEUM

Largest helicopter on display in the
UK is SA.321F Super Frelon
F-BTRP. This huge beast arrived at
Weston-super-Mare, Avon, on 28
April 1993 as a gift from
Aerospatiale at Merignac.
Tony McCarthy, November 1993

Not all of IHM's airframes are
exhibits as such, several being held
for spares or exchanges. Two former
Danish Air Force S-55s and
Whirlwind HAR.10 XP404 'out to
grass'. *Brian Roffee, September 1993*

Westland has been a loyal supplier of
airframes to the IHM: WG.30-100
G-BGHF.
Brian Roffee, September, 1993

272

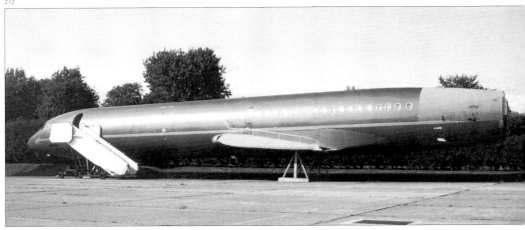

JETLINERS

Trident 3B-101 G-AWZI serves the
Surrey County Fire Brigade
Headquarters at Reigate, Surrey.
Colin Strachan, September 1992

At the Brooklands Museum, Surrey,
the test-shell VC-10 nose section has
acquired BOAC colours.
Ian F Howell, May 1993

Parked out and engineless at Filton,
Avon, since 1988 BAe 146-200
G-BMYE.
Martin Perkins, October 1993

JET PROVOSTS

T.3 8352M (XN632) used for fire crash rescue training at Chivenor, Devon. *Morley Lester, October 1993*

The equestrian cross country course at Halton, Bucks, includes T.4 XR672 proving the versatility of the design! *Nigel Price, June 1993*

Yorkshire Air Museum at Elvington, N Yorks, has acquired several JPs. 'Blue cross' T.4 XP640 arrived in October 1993.
Steve Hague, August 1993

JP T.4 during restoration work by the Jet Aviation Preservation Group at Long Marston, Warks.
Stewart Holder, October 1993

LIGHTNINGS I

Thanks to the Lightning Preservation Group, Bruntingthorpe in Leics is a Lightning haven. Founder member and regularly fast taxied is XR728 'JS'. *Nigel Bailey-Underwood, March 1993*

Next to arrive with LPG was the nose section of F.6 XS932, complete with trailer to allow it to be exhibited at airshows and other events. Note the Esk 730 stencil on the nose. *Col Pope, September 1993*

Former BAe Warton F.6 XS904 touched down at Bruntingthorpe on 21 January 1993 and joined XR728 in regular run-ups. *Nigel Bailey-Underwood, March 1993*

LIGHTNINGS II

Displayed amid the greenery at the
Bush Barn, Robertsbridge, E Sussex,
is the Robertsbridge Aviation
Society's F.3 nose section XP701.
RAS are busy converting a building
to bring the nose indoors.
Ken Ellis, August 1993

Long established gate guardian at
A&AEE Boscombe Down is T.4
XL629. *Roger Richards, July 1992*

F.6 XR753 'BP' in 11 Squadron
colours, is displayed outside one of
the hangars at Leeming, N Yorks.
Steve Hague, September 1993

LUFTWAFFE I

Part of the former Soviet treasure-trove moved to Lancing, W Sussex, Bf 110E-2 w/nr 4502.
Chris Michell, July 1992

Bf 109F-4 w/nr 8147, was at Lancing but has since moved to Colchester, Essex. *Chris Michell, April 1993*

Fw 189A-1 w/nr 2100, the most exotic of the imports.
Chris Michell, April 1992

LUFTWAFFE II

Bf 109E-1 w/nr 3579, one of two at
Colchester, Essex, for the Museum of
Flying at Santa Monica.
Chris Michell December 1992

Pilatus P.2 mock-up, made for an
Indiana Jones epic, at the entrance to
the Blue Max Museum at Wycombe
Air Park, Bucks.
Andrew Powell, May 1993

Former Spanish Bf 109E C4E-88 on
show at Tangmere, W Sussex. It
moved to Hungerford, Berks, in early
1994. *Ken Ellis, October 1992*

MANSTON

Hunter FGA.9 XJ615 (with the tail section of XF519) plus crude blue cross at the Central Training Establishment, Manston, Kent.

Jet Provost T.3 XN602 in suitable 'crashed' pose and blue cross on the nose. Behind is Devon C.2/2 VP971.

Battered and burnt Wessex HU.5 XT475.

Sooper-Super VC-10 ZD239, with ZD233 bringing up the rear.
All Alan Allen, August 1993

NEWARK

Newark Air Museum's impressive aircraft display hall has allowed the workshop to become just that instead of a store. Accordingly, the Museum can boast a series of aircraft being restored and rolled into public view. Venom NF.3 WX905 and Anson C.19/2 VL348.
NAM, September 1993

Prentice T.1 VR249 in Cranwell colours as 'FA-EL'. *Ken Ellis, 1993*

Heron Srs 1 G-ANXB newly-completed in BEA Scottish markings as *Sir James Young Simpson*. *NAM, September 1993*

NORTH EAST

'The first wide-bodied airliner on display in the UK,' a tongue-in-cheek claim by the North East Aircraft Museum, Sunderland, Tyne & Wear. Former Gill Aviation SD.330-100 G-OGIL arrived by road during April 1993.

Striplin Lone Ranger microlight G-MBDL,

Much travelled C-10A nose mock-up, acquired from the Booker Aircraft Museum.

Luton Minor BAPC.97, up against Avro XIX-2 G-AWRS.
All Ken Ellis, May 1993

NORTH WEALD I

Swiss Vampire T.55 U-1234.

Aces High's fleet at North Weald, Essex, has seen some changes. Lincoln 2 G-29-1 has been offered for sale.

Former Empire of the Sun mock Zero, T-6G 11470.

Restoration of CASA 2-111 G-AWHB is making visible progress. *All Ian F Howell, May 1993*

NORTH WEALD II

Three from the 39 Restoration Group. Provost T.1 WV499 'G' — note 39 Squadron 'winged bomb' on fin.

Meteor TT.20 WM224, founder-member of the Group.

Meteor TT.20 WD646, arrived from Birmingham, W Mids, during August 1993. *All Paddy Porter, October 1993*

PHANTOMS

MiG-killing F-4C-21-MC 37699 at
the Midland Air Museum, Coventry
Airport, Warks. It arrived by road on
7 October 1993 from Upper Heyford,
Oxon. *MAM, October 1993*

The Adams yard at Glasgow, Strath,
took on a large batch of Phantoms
from Leuchars, Fife; all faced the
'fragmentiser'.
Charles MacKay, August 1993

Nostalgic red-white-blue roundels on
FGR.2 XT853 at Scampton, Lincs.
Jon Wickenden, June 1993

'PLASTIC' GUARDIANS

First of the exhibits-for-guardians'
replicas to move base was Spitfire
BAPC.229 which was on show at
Church Fenton, N Yorks as 'L1096',
but moved to Digby, Lincs, becoming
'MJ832'. *T Wixcey, July 1993*

Impressively posed over the race
track at Donington Circuit, Spitfire
replica 'K-W'.
Nigel Price, August 1993

Hurricane 'L1710' (BAPC.219) at
the Memorial Chapel, Biggin Hill,
Gtr London. *Ken Ellis, May 1992*

PROJECTS

Meteor T.7 WA662, at Chalgrove.
Oxon, as a 'kit of parts' while being
offered for disposal. It moved to
Willington, Derby, in late 1992.
Alan Allen, July 1992

One of four Harvard IVs under offer
at Shoreham, W Sussex (G-BSBB,
'D, 'F & 'F). Two readers have
supplied the 'phone number given on
the fin as an identity!
Paul Crellin, March 1993

Dick Melton's fabulous Walrus I
W2718 (G-RNLI) underway in his
Winchester, Hants, workshop.
Ken Ellis, February 1993

RADIAL RELICS

Pembroke C.1 XL929 (G-BNPU) at the Northbrook College, Shoreham.
Ian F Howell, May 1993

Long forlorn and forgotten, TB-25N-NC '151632' (NL9494Z) awaiting a disposal decision at Coventry Airport, Warwickshire.
Ken Ellis, September 1993

Another forgotten warrior, Beech D.18S N96240 at Rochester, Kent.
Brian Roffee, September 1993

RAF MIXTURE I

Last of its breed — intact. Nimrod AEW.2 XV263/8967M serves the Air Engineer Squadron as a ground instructional airframe, at Finningley, S Yorks. *Nigel Price, June 1993*

Interesting collection of the dead and dying at Kinloss, Grampian. Left to right: Nimrod AEW.2 XZ282, Buccaneer S.2 XW549 and Comet 4C 8882M (G-BDIU). *Mike Smith, June 1992*

Comrod (or is it Nimet?) XW626 at DRA Bedford, Beds. It carries legend 'For Sale — Buyer Collects' on its ample nose. *Steve Hague, August 1992*

RAF MIXTURE II

Victor K.2 escape trainer, B.1 XA917 at Marham, Norfolk. This aircraft exceeded Mach 1 in a shallow dive during tests and deserves a better fate than the axe. *Ken Ellis, January 1993*

Andover C.1 XS642 on the very public fire-dump at Benson, Oxon. *Ken Ellis, March 1993*

Tornado F.2 ZD932 awaiting spares recovery and melt-down at St Athan, S Glam. *Alan Allen, June 1993*

RAF MUSEUM, CARDINGTON

Impossible to photograph in its entirety, because of the impressive 'dry dock' that it lies in, Southampton I N9899 is nearing the end of its painstaking restoration. Parts of the fuselage will be left uncovered, to show internal detail and the outstanding quality of work.

A few parts of Hampden I P1344 are on show as a 'taster' to visitors to the RAF Museum at Hendon, but the bulk of the project is to be found at the Restoration & Storage Centre at Cardington, Beds. This major project will follow the Southampton in the workshops.

MiG-15bis 01120 with P-47D-40-RA 13064 beyond. *All Ken Ellis, November 1993*

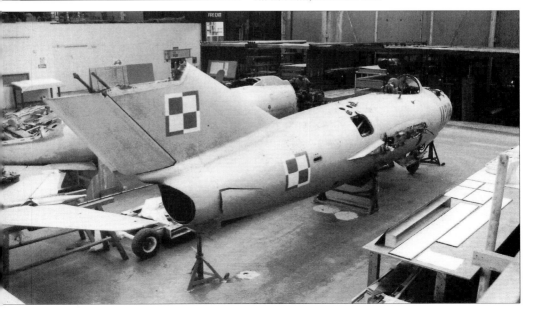

RAF MUSEUM, HENDON

Kittyhawk IV 'FX760' a composite from the USA in the colours of 112 Squadron.

'Flying' in the lobby of the RAF Museum, Hendon, Greater London, is Grasshopper TX.1 WZ791.

Hanriot HD.1 HD-75.

All Ken Ellis, July 1992

RALLYES

Kamikaze Ken's Minerva 220 G-BCAC now tries to sell kitchens at Trafford Park, Greater Manchester. *Barry Swann, May 1992*

MS.880B G-BGZO in decidedly rural surroundings, near Shoreham, W Sussex. *Bob Kent, December 1992*

Rallye 110ST G-BLDA and others, Biggin Hill, Greater London. *Bob Kent, December 1992*

ROTORCRAFT I

Three Bond Bolkow Bo 105Ds at Bourn, Cambs — G-BTBD, G-AZTI and another.
Andrew Powell, May 1993

Brooklands Gyroplane G-AWIF at Husbands Bosworth, Leics. It moved to St Merryn, Corn, by May 1993.
Jon Wickenden, December 1992

Bo 105D G-PASA resting after investigations at Bourn, Cams.
P Middleton, August 1993

ROTORCRAFT II

Sea Cadets Wessex HAS.1 XS886 at
HMS *Explorer*, Evesham, H&W.
Peter Spooner, June 1993

Former Westland 606 mock-up, Lynx
XW836 at the DRA site, Lasham,
Hants.
Gawayne Hodgkiss, September 1993

Two Wessex HU.5s (XS481 and
XT471) plus Whirlwind HAR.10
XJ727 at Dishforth, N Yorks.
Paul Crellin, April 1993

ROTORCRAFT III

Skeeter AOP.12 XM564 hovers over the tanks at Bovington, Dorset.
Nigel Price, May 1993

Whirlwind HAR.10 XJ723 at Montrose, Tayside, with the OPI Training Board. It moved to the nearby airfield museum in late 1993.
Paul Crellin, November 1992

Lynx 1-02 XW835 (G-BEAD) shell, at Dishforth, N Yorks.
Paul Crellin, April 1993

SCRAP MERCHANTS I

Hanningfield Metals at Stock, Essex, remains the most prolific of UK scrapyards. DRA Viscounts XT575 and XT661 arrived during August 1993. *P Middleton, August 1993*

Viscount 806 G-LOND plus Phantom FGR.2 XV486, the former arriving by March 1993.
Alan Allen, March 1993

Camouflaged Queen Air A80 G-ASRX from Chelmsford Fire Brigade, Essex, started some imaginative, but non factual 'reports' about a U-8 at the yard.
P Middleton, August 1993

SCRAP MERCHANTS II

Elgin, Grampian, a mountain of scrap — including Buccaneers XT281 and XW533. *John G Chree, April 1993*

Whirlwind HAS.7 XG597 still survives at Siddal, W Yorks. *Mike Smith, May 1992*

SH-3D Sea King XV372 and unidentified coach at Trowbridge, Wilts. *Alan Allen, August 1993*

STRATHALLAN

Lysander III 'V9441' (G-AZWT)
was prepared for a potential flying
season during 1993 at its home base
of Strathallan, Tayside.

Another Soviet invader, 811506, a
Yak-52.

Sea Hawk FGA.6 XE340 moved to
Montrose, Tayside, by November
1993. *All Gavin Troon, March 1993*

SWINDERBY

This attractive base closed during 1993. Vampire T.11 XD506 was still on the gate as late as October 1993. *W J Taylor, July 1993*

Gnat T.1 XM706 was removed by a Nottingham scrap merchant during November 1993. *Nigel Bailey-Underwood, May 1993*

Chipmunk T.10 escape trainer WG362. *Ken Ellis, May 1993*

WELLESBOURNE MOUNTFORD

Three airframes lovingly looked after by the Wellesbourne Aviation Group. Provost T.1 fuselage 7615M (WV679) undergoing restoration.

Sea Vixen FAW.2 nose XJ575 on its brick podium.

Vampire T.11 XK590.
All Andrew Powell, June 1993

YORKSHIRE AIR MUSEUM

Refugee from the pull-back from Europe, Canadian CT-133 21417 arrived during October 1993. *Steve Hague, October 1993*

Lightning F.6 XS903 within the display hall. *Ken Ellis, August 1992*

Facing the Lightning is Buccaneer S.2 XN974, built 'up the road' at Brough. *Ken Ellis, August 1992*

☞ Readers should now be well familiar with this section — just in time to see it shrink away to nothing within a couple of editions if current trends continue! This is a listing of all British military aircraft to be found in the **W&R** categories on Crown territory or property. It is not the intention to list any foreign aircraft that may be found in such locations. Only exception to this is on the Falklands where former Argentine machines are planned to form part of a museum. It need also be said that sightings are all the rarer for these locations and that particularly in what was West Germany, the pace of withdrawal/consolidation is making most information quickly obsolete. Please note also that this section does *not* appear in the Locations Index or Type Index at the rear.

Cyprus

AKROTIRI
■ **RAF Akrotiri** : Other than the delivery of a Phantom for crash rescue duties, no other changes.

☐	XD184	8787M	Whirlwind HAR10	ex 84 'A' Flt, 1563F, 228, 155. Displayed. 10-90
☐	XJ437	8788M	Whirlwind HAR10	ex 84 'A' Flight, 22, 202, 22, SAR Flt, HAR.4, 228, 225, 155. BDR. Poor state. 10-90
☐	XS929		Lightning F.6	ex Binbrook, 11, LTF, 11, 56, 11. Gate. 10-90
☐	XV470*	9156M	Phantom FGR.2	ex 56, 228 OCU, 19, 228 OCU, 92, 56, 92, 56, 17, 14, 2. 'D'. Arrived 7-92. Crash rescue. 07-92

NICOSIA
■ **16 Flight** : Took delivery of two Scouts for battle damage training during December 1992.

☐	XR602*	Scout AH.1	ex Netheravon, Wroughton, 659, 652, 653. BDR. Arrived 12-92. 04-93
☐	XT648*	Scout AH.1	ex Netheravon, Wroughton, 659, 669. BDR. Arrived 12-92. 04-93

Falkland Islands

MOUNT PLEASANT AIRPORT
■ **RAF Mount Pleasant** : Sooner than bring the Phantoms of 1435 Flight back to face the axe, they were scrapped here during August 1992. For posterity they were : XV442 'H', XV466 'D' and XV472 'B'. XV409 was given a stay of execution and is displayed within the base.

☐	XV409* 9160M	Phantom FGR.2	ex 1435 Flt, 29, 228 OCU, 56, 111, 56, 111. 'H'. *Hope*. Displayed. First noted 8-92. 07-93
☐	A-529	FMA Pucara	ex Stanley, Pebble Island, FAA. Composite, using A-509 and A-514. Stored. 02-92
☐	AE-410	Bell UH-1H	ex Stanley, Stanley Racecourse. Stored. 02-92

SALVADOR SETTLEMENT
Robin Pitaluga still keeps the hulk of a Whirlwind HAR.9 at his home here.

☐	XM666	Whirlwind HAR.9	ex *Endurance* Flt, A&AEE, *Endurance* Flt, *Protector* Flt, 846, 737, 700H. Ditched 17-12-69. Stripped and rotorless.

Germany

General Notes : On April 1, 1993 RAF Germany was dissolved and became a part of Strike Command's 2 Group. Major changes are still underway, both with RAF units in Germany and AAC units operating within BAOR. Laarbruch and Bruggen are now the only RAF airfields within Germany, but both of these are really on borrowed time.

BRUGGEN AIRFIELD

■ **RAF Bruggen** : There are bound to be changes to the overly-long list below, but reliable data is hard to come by.

☐ XE608	8717M	Hunter F.6A	ex 1 TWU, TWU, 229 OCU, CFCS, AFDS, CFE. BDR.
☐ XL566	8891M	Hunter T.7	ex Shawbury, Kemble, Laarbruch SF, 4 FTS, 208, 1417F, 43, A&AEE. BDR
☐ XM970	8529M	Lightning T.4	ex 19, 92, 60 MU *hack*, 226 OCU, 92, LCS.
☐ XM973	8528M	Lightning T.4	ex 19, 226 OCU, 23, 111, 226 OCU, 74, AFDS.
☐ XN783	8526M	Lightning F.2A	ex 92, 19, 92.
☐ XN789	8527M	Lightning F.2A	ex 19, Handling Squadron, 92.
☐ XN792	8525M	Lightning F.2A	ex 92. BDR.
☐ XP403	8690M	W'wind HAR.10	ex 22, SAR Wing, 202, 228. 431 MU for BDR.
☐ XS901	8965M	Lightning F.6	ex Binbrook, 11, 5, 11, 5, 11, 56, 5. BDR. 05-88
☐ XT467	8922M	Wessex HU.5	ex Gutersloh 'XR504', Wroughton, 771, 707. 06-93
☐ XV425	9094M	Phantom FGR.2	ex 228 OCU, 56, 23, 29, 17. BDR. 04-91
☐ XV475*	9105M	Phantom FGR.2	ex 19, 92, 19, 56, 2, 17. 'H'. BDR. Arrived 11-7-91. 07-91
☐ XV481	9135M	Phantom FGR.2	ex 56, 23, 19, 29. 'H'. Flew in 16-2-92. 02-92
☐ XV485	9106M	Phantom FGR.2	ex 19, 29, 228 OCU, 23, 228 OCU, 29. 'M'. Flew in 11-7-91. 07-91
☐ XV569	9063M	Phantom FG.1	ex Wildenrath, 111, 43, 111. Fire dump. 01-92
☐ XV782	8982M	Harrier GR.3	ex Swanton Morley, St Athan, 4, 1453F, 4. BDR.
☐ XV789	8966M	Harrier GR.3	ex 1, 233 OCU, 1, 1453F, 1, 4. wfu 20-8-87. BDR.
☐ XV793	8980M	Harrier GR.3	ex Swanton Morley, St Athan, 4, 1, 3, 20, 233 OCU. BDR.
☐ XW922	8885M	Harrier GR.3	ex Foulness, Enfield, 233 OCU, 1, 233 OCU, 1. BDR 06-93
☐ 'XX822'	8563M	Jaguar GR.1	complex composite based upon nose and forward fuselage of S.07 XW563. Displayed. 12-92
☐ XZ630	8976M	Tornado GR.1	ex BAe Warton, A&AEE. WLT. 08-88
☐ ZE357	9081M	F-4J(UK)	ex 74, USN 153892. 'N'. BDR. 12-92

DETMOLD

■ **4 Regiment, Army Air Corps** : The Regiment and 71 Aircraft Workshops are due to move to Wattisham, Suffolk, during March 1995, joining the already 'retreated' 3 Regiment. As with almost all of the references within Germany, there must be changes to the list below.

☐ XL739		Skeeter AOP.12	ex 15/19 Hussars, 1 Wing, 651, A&AEE, BATUS, A&AEE, C(A). 'Gate'.
☐ XP900		Scout AH.1	ex Wroughton, ATS, ARWF. BDR. 06-87
☐ XP903		Scout AH.1	ex Wroughton, 657, 663, 664, 663. Less boom. BDR. 09-91
☐ XR637		Scout AH.1	ex Wroughton, 657, 658, 8 Flt, 653, D&TS, 653, D&TS. Less boom. BDR. 09-91
☐ XS571		Wasp HAS.1	ex Wroughton, 703, 706. Boom of XT436. BDR. 05-89
☐ XT474		Wessex HU.5	ex Wroughton, 820, 771, ETPS, A&AEE, 846. 10-91
☐ XT550		Sioux AH.1	ex Middle Wallop, Wroughton, 651. 'Gate'. 04-89
☐ XT764		Wessex HU.5	ex Wroughton, 845, 847, 707. 10-91
☐ XV627		Wasp HAS.1	ex Wroughton, *Hermione, Antelope*. BDR. 05-89
☐ XW615		Scout AH.1	ex Wroughton, Netheravon, 3 CBAS, 657, 663, 665. Pod. BDR.

GATOW AIRFIELD

■ **RAF Gatow - Berlin** : The RAF are due to pull out of here during 1994 amid rumours that the airfield will be used for a huge aviation museum. Hopefully the Dakota and Hastings will find a place in this.

☐ TG503	8555M	Hastings T.5	ex SCBS, A&AEE, BCBS, MoA, BCBS, C.1 RRE, RRF, A&AEE, AFEE, A&AEE.	06-93
☐ WF382	8872M	Varsity T.1	ex 6 FTS, 1 ANS, 2 ANS, 5 FTS, 1 ANS, 2 ANS, 1 ANS, 3 ANS, CNCS. Fire dump.	
☐ A65-69	ZD215	Dakota III	ex RAAF A65-69, USAAF 43-49866.	06-93

GUTERSLOH AIRFIELD

■ **RAF Gutersloh** : Hunter F.6 XG152/'XF949' to the *Luftwaffen* Museum near Hamburg, during mid-1993. Canberra B(I).8 XM244/8202M is thought to have perished by March 1993. Clearing up **W&R13**, Wessex HU.5 XT467 moved on to <u>Bruggen</u>. Harrier GR.3 XW917/8975M left by road on March 5, 1993, destination unknown. 1 Regiment, Army Air Corps moved in from Hildesheim during May/June 1993 bringing with them at least a Sioux in terms of **W&R** airframes.

☐ XM244	8202M	Canberra B(I).8	ex 16, 3, 16, 3, 16. Fire dump.	
☐ XP358		W'wind HAR.10	ex Farnborough, RAE, Wroughton, 28, 103, 110, 103, 225. BDR.	
☐ XT548*		Sioux AH.1	ex Hildesheim, Middle Wallop, Arborfield, Middle Wallop, Arborfield, 658. Arrived by 7-93. Displayed.	07-93
☐ XZ989	8849M	Harrier GR.3	ex 1, 233 OCU. Cr Falklands 9-6-82. BDR, fuselage minus cockpit plus wings.	
☐		Harrier GR.3	BDR.	01-89

HILDESHEIM

■ **1 Regiment, Army Air Corps** : No 1 Regiment moved to Gutersloh during May/June 1993. Preserved Sioux AH.1 XT548 moved to <u>Gutersloh</u>, Germany, by July. At least one of the two instructional airframes listed in **W&R13** was still present in May 1993, so in the absence of information to the contrary, they are listed again :—

☐ XP852		Scout AH.1 notes.	ex Wroughton, ARWF, 651. Pod. BDR. See 05-93	
☐ XT438	A2704	Wasp HAS.1	ex Detmold, Wroughton, BRNC, *Juno, Tartar, Andromeda*. Pod. BDR. See notes.	

LAARBRUCH AIRFIELD

■ **RAF Laarbruch** : Apart from the Hunter displayed within the base, the current status of other airframes could do with updating.

☐ 'XJ673'	XE606	Hunter F.6A	8841M, ex 1 TWU, TWU, 229 OCU, 92, 74, 65, 54, CFE. 8737M ntu. 20 Sqn c/s.	12-92
☐ XN732	8519M	Lightning F.2A	ex 92. Mocked-up to resemble a MiG-21.	02-90
☐ XN788	8543M	Lightning F.2A	ex Bruggen, 92, 111, 92. BDR.	02-90
☐ XN956	8059M	Buccaneer S.1	ex Lossiemouth. BDR.	02-90
☐ XR758	8964M	Lightning F.6	ex Binbrook, 11, LTF, Binbrook Wing, 23, 74, 11, 23, Leuchars TFF, 5. BDR.	02-90
☐ XV412	9104M	Phantom FGR.2	ex 29, 92, 19, 92, 228 OCU, 41. BDR.	06-93
☐ ZE350	9080M	F-4J(UK)	ex 74, USN 153768. 'T'. BDR.	06-93
☐ ZE352	9086M	F-4J(UK)	ex 74, USN 153783. 'G'. BDR.	06-93
☐ ZE363	9082M	F-4J(UK)	ex 74, USN 155868. 'W'. BDR.	06-93

MINDEN

■ **Army Air Corps** : The base has closed and fates are awaited for Scout AH.1 XP898 and Gazelle AH.1 XX376.

SENNELAGER

■ **Tank Regiment Centre** : A Wessex and a Scout are used for 'debusing' drills here. The Wessex, a former Navy example has been here since about 1989, while the Scout arrived in 1990.

☐	*	Scout AH.1	see notes above.	12-93
☐	*	Wessex	see notes above.	12-93

SOEST

■ **3 Regiment, Army Air Corps** : The Regiment relocated to Wattisham, Suffolk, during July 1993. Sioux AH.1 XT190 had moved to <u>Wattisham</u> by June 26, 1993. Wasp HAS.1 XT436 moved to Detmold by June 1987, but is thought long since perished. Scout AH.1 XP897 is unaccounted for.

WILDENRATH AIRFIELD

■ **RAF Wildenrath** : The base closed as an RAF facility on March 31, 1992, and was officially transferred to German control on November 1, 1992. The four **W&R** airframes are listed here, therefore very tentatively — details appreciated.

☐ WV701	8936M	Pembroke C.1	ex 60, 21, WCS, SCS, Seletar B&TTF, 267, FECS, A&AEE. Inst.	03-91
☐ XM995	8542M	Lightning T.4	ex 92.	03-91
☐ XN778	8537M	Lightning F.2A	ex 92, 19.	03-91
☐ XR727	8963M	Lightning F.6	ex Binbrook, 11, 5, LTF, 23. BDR.	03-91

Hong Kong

SEK KONG AIRFIELD

Scout AH.1 XP906 and Wessex HC.2 XR500, mentioned in **W&R13**, are thought demised. 660 Squadron was declared non-operational during September 1993 and disbanded, ahead of schedule, on December 12, 1993.

☐ XP894*	Scout AH.1	ex 660, 11 Flt, 660, 656. Spares. F/n 2-89. 'G'.	11-93
☐ XP901*	Scout AH.1	ex 660, 11 Flt, CBAS. BDR. F/n 2-93. 'E'.	11-93
☐ XT614*	Scout AH.1	ex 660, 11 Flt, 652, 655, 651, 656. BDR. First noted 11-93. 'C'.	11-93
☐ XT618*	Scout AH.1	ex 660, 656, 664. Spares. F/n 3-90. 'H'.	11-93
☐ XT627*	Scout AH.1	ex 660, 11 Flt, 656. Spares. F/n 2-89.	11-93
☐ XT628*	Scout AH.1	ex 660, 11 Flt, 652, 656. BDR. First noted 11-93. 'E'.	11-93

Italy

DECIMOMANNU (Sardinia)

■ **NATO Weapons Camp** :

☐ XV758	9089M	Harrier GR.3	ex 4, 3, 233 OCU, 1, 3, 233 OCU. Gate.	04-91

FOUNDED in 1967, the British Aviation Preservation Council (BAPC) links national, local authority, independent and service museums with private collections, voluntary groups and other organisations in the advancement of the preservation of aviation heritage. Quarterly meetings are held allowing groups large and small to meet and exchange views. A quarterly newsletter, *Update*, covers a wide range of topics. Comments relating to the recent activities of the BAPC are made in the Preface — see page 7. Below can be found the composition of the Executive Committee, an index to member organisations mentioned in the main text, and details of those who are not (all as of March 1994).

Honorary President
Sir Peter Masefield, MA, CEng, FRAeS

Honorary Vice-President
David Ogilvy AMRAes

BAPC Executive Committee
Chairman — David Lee; **Vice Chairmen** — John Berkeley, Mike Hodgson, Commander Dennis White. **Secretary** — Don Storer. **Membership Secretary** — Peter Kirk. **Treasurer** — Denise Southern. **Press Officer** — Paul Brown. **Committee Members** — John Bagley; Trevor Matthews; Steve Thompson.

Associated Officers
Editor *Update* — Trevor Green. **Project Co-Ordinator** — Tony Southern. **Registrar, BAPC Register** — Ken Ellis.

Honorary Members
Canadian Aeronautical Preservation Association. ● *Federation Francais des Aeronefs.* ● Irish Aviation Historical Council.

Member Organisations
There follows an index of current BAPC member organisations mentioned in the main text, so that reference can be made directly. Any changes of name are signified within the index. Beyond the index, can be found brief mention of member organisations not listed in the main text.

Flambards Village Theme Park - 52
Fleet Air Arm Museum - 172
Fresson Trust (The) - 223
Friends of Cardington Airship Station - 17
Friends of the DC-3 - 24
Gloucestershire Aviation Collection - 78
Hemswell Aviation Society - 125
Herald Society (The) - 27
Imperial War Museum - 35, 139
International Helicopter Museum - 14
Jet Aviation Preservation Group - 201
Jet Heritage Ltd - 61
Lashenden Air Warfare Museum - 107
Leicestershire Museum of Technology - 116, 118
Lightning Association - 120
Lightning Preservation Group - 114
Lincolnshire Aviation Society - 125
Lincolnshire Aviation Preservation Society - 125
Macclesfield Historical Aviation Society - 46
Manchester Museum of Science and Industry - 141
Medway Aircraft Preservation Society Ltd - 109
Dick Melton Aviation - 93
Meteor Flight (Yatesbury) - 208
Midland Air Museum - 198
Midland Warplane Museum - 200
Miles Aircraft Collection (The) - 27
Military Aircraft Preservation Group - 46
Montrose Aerodrome Museum Society - 230
Mosquito Aircraft Museum - 99
Museum of Army Flying - 87
Museum of Army Transport - 102
Museum of Berkshire Aviation - 27
National Museums of Scotland - 225
Newark Air Museum - 156
Night Fighter Preservation Team - 210
Norfolk and Suffolk Aviation Museum - 178

North East Aircraft Museum - 195
Project XW550 - 77
Real Aeroplane Company - 102
Restorations Unlimited - 188
Robertsbridge Aviation Society - 189
Rolls-Royce Heritage Trust (Bristol Branch) - 14
Rolls-Royce Heritage Trust (Coventry Branch) - 145
Rolls-Royce Heritage Trust (Derby Branch) - 57
Ross Aviation Services - 94
Royal Air Force Museum - 17, 133
Royal Berkshire Aviation Society - 27
Russavia Collection - 96
Science Museum (The) - 133, 138, 207
Second World War Aircraft Preservation Society - 84
Shuttleworth Collection (The) - 22
Solway Aviation Society - 55
Southampton Hall of Aviation - 91
South Yorkshire Aviation Society - 213
Tangmere Military Aviation Museum - 194
Thorpe Camp Preservation Group - 130
Thirty Nine Preservation Group - 59
Torbay Aircraft Museum - 59
Ulster Aviation Society - 248
Ulster Folk and Transport Museum - 248
Vampire Preservation Group — renamed Jet Aviation
  Preservation Group
Vintage & Rotary Wing Collection - 177
Wales Aircraft Museum — renamed Aviation Museum
  (Wales) Ltd
Wellesbourne Aviation Group - 202
Wiltshire Historic Aviation Group - 205
Winbolt Collection (The) - 13
Yorkshire Air Museum - 209
39 Restoration Group - 72
390th BG Memorial Air Museum - 181

● **Computair Consultants**, Jeremy Parkin, 6 Wakefield Close, Byfleet, Surrey, KT14 7NA. *Helicopter consultants.* ● *Flying Flea* **Archive**, Ken Ellis, address on page 3. *Charting and recording UK Flying Fleas, past and present.* ● **Grantham Aviation Society**, G Cole, Secretary, 43 Denton Avenue, Grantham, Lincs, NG31 7JD. ● **Hovercraft Museum**, Warwick Jacobs, 15 St Marks Road, Gosport, Hants, PO12 2DA. *Establishing a museum at Calshot, Hants.* ● **MM Aviation**, Michael Coghlan, 9 Park Hill, Charlton Marshall, Blandford, Dorset, DT11 9NW. ● **Nene Valley Aviation Society**, K Rooksby, 8 Newtown Road, Raunds, Northants NN9 6LX. *Enthusiast and historic research society.* ● **R & S Wings**, S Oversby, 44 The Rogers, Green Lane, Shanklin, Isle of Wight, PO37 7HH. *Maintenance and restoration organisation.* ● **Shoreham Aviation Heritage Trust**, Alan Jones, 38 Cranworth Road, Worthing, Sussex, BN11 2JF. *See notes on page 193.* ● **South Wales Swallow Group**, A T williams, 4 Hilview Crescent, Pont Faen, Newport, Gwent, NP9 0NS. *Operating BA Swallow 2 G-AFGD.* ● **Viscount Preservation Trust,** Paul St John Turner, *Cades Peak*, Old St John Road, St Helier, Jersey. *Supporting the preservation of G-ALWF at Duxford.*

Associate Members
Such members wish to support the work of the Council, but feel that they do not fill the criteria to be Full Members. As some of the Associate Members of the Council are preservation groups themselves, or support the work of other preservation bodies, and therefore may be of interest to readers, greater details are given here. Other Associate Members are given a brief mention at the end.

● **Airfield Research Group**, John Nicholls, 220 Woodland Avenue, Hutton, Brentwood, Essex, CM13 1DA. *Uniting all interested in airfields — past and present — publish a superb magazine.* ● **Chiltern Aviation Society**, Keith Hayward, 52 Pinn Way, Ruislip, Middx HA4 7QF. ● **Historical Radar Archive**, S/L Mike Dean, Little Garth, High Street, Scampton, LN1 2SD. *Archive, research and advise on radar and its history.* ● **International Friends of the DH.89**,

Graham Simons, 67 Pyhill, Bretton, Peterborough PE3 8QQ. *Uniting operators and researchers of the Dragon Rapide etc.* ● **Lincolnshire Aircraft Recovery Group** — see page 124. ● **Lincolnshire's Lancaster Association** — see page 122. D C ● **Manchester Airport Archive**, Dr Vivienne Caruana, Airport Archivist, Manchester Airport, Manchester M22 5PA. *Archive and research organisation.* ● **Shuttleworth Veteran Aeroplane Society** — see page 22.

Also : ● Air-Britain (Historians) Ltd — see *Further Reading.* ● *Aircraft Illustrated.* ● *Aviation News.* ● *FlyPast.* ● LAASI International. ● Macclesfield College of Further Education. ● Southern Aviation Research Associates. **And overseas** : ● Australian War Memorial. ● *Gruppo Amici Velivoli Storici*, Italy; ● Museum of Transport and Technology, New Zealand. ● Naval Aviation Museum, Australia. ● Royal New Zealand Air Force Museum. ● United States Air Force Museum. ● Vintage Air Spares, Canada. ● Western Canada Aviation Museum. ● *World War One Aeroplanes.* **Observers** : — Gerhard Everwyn, Peter Green, Bob Ogden, Brian R Robinson, Olive & Peter Swettenham, Brian Waters, John Webb.

BAPC REGISTER OF AIRCRAFT

FEW READERS should need introduction to the BAPC Register of Aircraft. Essentially it serves to provide a 'tag' for aircraft that have not (or could not) aspire to any other form of registration system. **W&R13** provided a Type Index to the BAPC Register (Nos 1 to 231) but with so few new additions to the register, it has been decided not to include such an index in this issue.

Registration Index

Entries are indexed by page number. Symbols and abbreviations : **HG** - hang-glider; **ML** - micro-light; **MPA** - man powered aircraft, ie fixed-wing; **MPG** - man powered gyroplane, ie rotary wing; **MPO** - man powered ornithopter, ie flapping wing thing; ¶ replica, largely/totally faithful in construction technique, flying or non-flying; § static external replica, ie looks like the aircraft intended, but constructional methods are not close to the original, eg mock-up, moulding etc : Δ current status unknown — details appreciated.

118 Albatros D.V ℐ
Scrapped - see page 177
119 Bensen B-7 Gyroglider - 197
120 Mignet HM.14 - 126
121 Mignet HM.14 - 101
122 Avro 504K ℐ Δ
123 Vickers Gunbus ℐ
Reduced to components by 1987
124 Lilienthal Type XI ℐ - 138
125 Clay Cherub
Scrapped, no longer extant
126 D.31 Turbulent - 200
127 Halton MPA - 190
128 Watkinson Cyclogyroplane IV MPG - 16
129 Blackburn 1911 Mono ℐ Δ
see page 52
130 Blackburn 1912 Mono ℐ - 177
131 Pilcher Hawk ℐ Δ
132 Bleriot Type XI Δ
133 Fokker Dr.I ℐ
See page 156
134 Pitts S-2A - 152
135 Bristol M.1C Monoplane Δ
136 Deperdussin 1913 ℐ
On display at the Air Racing Museum, Reno, Nevada, USA
137 Sopwith Baby ℐ Δ
138 Hansa Brandenburg ℐ Δ
139 Fokker Dr.I ℐ Δ
140 Curtiss R3C-2 ℐ
On display at the Air Racing Museum, Reno, Nevada, USA
141 Macchi M.39 ℐ
On display at the Air Racing Museum, Reno, Nevada, USA
142 RAF SE.5A ℐ
See page 52.
143 Paxton MPA Δ
144 Weybridge MPA Δ
145 Oliver MPA Δ
146 Pedal Aeronauts MPA - 100
147 Bensen B-7 Gyroglider - 179
148 Hawker Fury II ℐ - 163
149 Short S.27 ℐ - 174
15 SEPECAT Jaguar GR.1 § - 239
151 SEPECAT Jaguar GR.1 § - 240

152 BAe Hawk T.1 § - 239
153 Westland WG-33 § - 16
154 D.31 Turbulent - 125
155 Panavia Tornado GR.1 § - 240
156 Supermarine S.6B ℐ
On display at the Air Racing Museum, Reno, Nevada, USA
157 WACO CG-4A Hadrian - 111
158 Fieseler Fi 103 (V-1) - 106
159 MXY-7 Ohka II - 106
160 Chargus 18/50 HG - 226
161 Stewart MPO Δ
162 Goodhart MPA - 208
163 AFEE 10/42 Rotachute ℐ - 88
164 Wight Quadruplane ℐ - 91
165 Bristol F.2b Fighter - 134
166 Bristol F.2b Fighter - 190
167 RAF SE.5A ℐ
See page 156
168 DH.60 Moth ℐ - 191
169 SEPECAT Jaguar GR.1 § - 31
170 Pilcher Hawk ℐ - 231
171 BAe Hawk T.1 § - 239
172 Chargus Midas Super E HG - 208
173 Birdman Grasshopper ML - 208
174 Bensen B-7 Gyroglider - 208
175 Volmer VJ-23 Swingwing ML - 141
176 RAF SE.5A ℐ - 213
177 Avro 504K ℐ - 184
178 Avro 504K ℐ Δ
179 Sopwith Pup ℐ - 179
180 McCurdy Silver Dart ℐ - 18
181 RAF BE.2b ℐ - 134
182 Wood MPO - 141
183 Zurowski ZP.1 - 158
184 Supermarine Spitfire IX § - 72
185 WACO CG-4A Hadrian - 89
186 DH Queen Bee - 99
187 Roe Type I Biplane ℐ - 184
188 McBroom Cobra 88 HG - 208
189 Bleriot Type XI Δ
190 Supermarine Spitfire § - 47
191 BAe/McDD Harrier GR.5 § - 240
192 Weedhopper JC-24 ML - 49
193 Hovey Whing Ding ML - 49

194 Santos Dumont Demoiselle ℐ - 184
195 Moonraker 77 HG - 226
196 Sigma 2m HG - 226
197 Cirrus III HG - 226
198 Fieseler Fi 103 (V-1) - 139
199 Fieseler Fi 103 (V-1) - 138
200 Bensen B-7 Gyroglider - 215
201 Mignet HM.14 - 243
202 Supermarine Spitfire § - 243
203 Chrislea Airguard ℐ - 143
204 McBroom HG - 49
205 Hawker Hurricane § - 135
206 Supermarine Spitfire § - 135
207 Austin Whippet ℐ - 196
208 RAF SE.5A ℐ - 81
209 Supermarine Spitfire § - 193
210 Avro 504J ℐ - 91
211 Mignet HM.14 - 177
212 Bensen B-6 Gyroglider - 16
213 Cranfield Vertigo MPG - 16
214 Supermarine Spitfire § - 92
215 Airwave HG - 92
216 DH.88 Comet § - 98
217 Supermarine Spitfire § - 130
218 Hawker Hurricane § - 130
219 Hawker Hurricane § - 131
220 Supermarine Spitfire § - 131
221 Supermarine Spitfire § - 137
222 Supermarine Spitfire § - 139
223 Hawker Hurricane § - 146
224 Supermarine Spitfire § - 149
225 Supermarine Spitfire § - 150
226 Supermarine Spitfire § - 159
227 Supermarine Spitfire § - 226
228 Olympus HG - 197
229 Supermarine Spitfire § - 124
230 Supermarine Spitfire § - 212
231 Mignet HM.14 - 56
232 Airspeed Horsa I/II - 100
233 Broburn Wanderlust - 28
234 Vickers FB.5 Gunbus - 47
235 Fieseler Fi 103 (V-1) ℐ - 212
236 Hawker Hurricane ℐ - 212
237 Fieseler Fi 103 (V-1) - 18
238 Waxflatter Ornithopter - 33
239 Fokker D.VIII ℐ - 179

FURTHER READING

MANY REFERENCES are made while assembling **W&R**, and this section serves to act as both a bibliography and to point readers at other sources that may be of help to them. In the case of the enthusiast magazines, a stamped addressed envelope to the addresses given below will bring details of subscriptions, membership etc.

Enthusiast Magazines

Air-Britain News, Aeromilitaria, and *Archive,* monthly and quarterly magazines from Air-Britain (Historians) Ltd. ⊠ David Crook, 36 Nursery Road, Taplow, Maidenhead, Berks, SL6 0JZ.

Air North, monthly journal of the society of the same name. ⊠ Tony Jarvis, 61 Oakfields, Busnopfield, Newcastle-upon-Tyne, Tyne & Wear, NE16 6PQ.

Air-Strip monthly journal of the Midlands Branch of Air-Britain. ⊠ John Withers, 7 Nailers Drive, Burntwood, Staffs WS7 0ES.

Airfield Review, quarterly journal of the Airfield Research Group. ⊠ John Nicholls, 220 Woodland Avenue, Hufton, Brentwood, Essex, CM13 1DA.

British Aviation Review and *Roundel* monthly and bi-monthly journals of the British Aviation Research Group. ⊠ Paul Hewins, *Aorangi*, Beech Road, Tokers Green, Reading, Berks, RG4 9EH.

Hawkeye, monthly journal of the Gatwick Aviation Society. ⊠ Mike Green, 144 The Crescent, Horley, Surrey RH6 7PA.

Humberside Air Review monthly journal of the Humberside Aviation Society. ⊠ Pete Wild, 4 Bleach Yard, New Walk, Beverley, Humberside HU17 7HG.

Irish Air Letter monthly journal published by Paul Cunniffe, Karl Hayes and Eamon Power. ⊠ 20 Road Five, Kempton, Navan Road, Dublin 7, Ireland.

Osprey monthly journal of the Solent Aviation Society. ⊠ Doreen Eaves, 84 Carnation Road, Bassett, Southampton SO2 3JL.

Scottish Air News, monthly journal of the Central Scotland Aviation Group. ⊠ Archie McGeoch, 11 West Riverside Drive, Dundee, Tayside, Scotland.

Stansted Aviation Society News, monthly journal of the Stansted Aviation Society. ⊠ Peter Wright, 271 Birchanger Lane, Birchanger, Bishop's Stortford, Herts CM23 5QP

Strobe, monthly journal published by Strobe Aviation Research. ⊠ Alan Warnes, 56 Landsdowne Walk, Orton Longueville, Peterborough, Cambs, PE2 7GE.

SWAG-Mag, monthly magazine of the South West Aviation Group. ⊠ Morley Lester, 32 Water Park Road, Bideford, Devon, EX39 3RB.

Winged Words monthly journal of The Aviation Society. ⊠ Evan Higson, 14 Brooklawn Drive, Prestwich, Manchester M25 5GS.

Magazines and Periodicals

Aeroplane Monthly, monthly magazine published by Reed Business Publishing Ltd.
Air Forces Monthly, monthly magazine published by Key Publishing Ltd.
Aviation Letter, monthly magazine published by Lundkvist Aviation Research.
Aviation News, fortnightly magazine published by Hall Park Publications Ltd.
FlyPast, monthly magazine published by Key Publishing Ltd.
Pilot, monthly magazine published by Pilot Publishing Ltd.
Popular Flying, bi-monthly magazine published by the Popular Flying Association.
Propliner, quarterly magazine published by Tony Eastwood.
Update, quarterly bulletin published by the British Aviation Preservation Council.
Warbirds Worldwide, quarterly published by Warbirds Worldwide Ltd.

Books

Airfields of Lincolnshire since 1912, Ron Blake, Mike Hodgson and Bill Taylor, Midland Counties Publications, 1984.
Anson File, Ray Sturtivant, Air-Britain, 1988.
Aviation in Northamptonshire, An Illustrated History, Michael L Gibson, Northamptonshire Libraries, 1982.
Avro's Maritime Heavyweight : The Shackleton, Chris Ashworth, Aston Publications, 1990.

Avro Vulcan, Robert Jackson, Patrick Stephens, 1984.
Blackburn Beverley, Bill Overton, Midland Counties Publications, 1990.
Bottlang Airfield Manual, Flight Guide UK/Ireland, Jeppesen & Co, 1993.
British Aerospace HS.748, F G Barnes & R J Church, Air-Britain, 1986.
British Civil Aircraft Registers 1919-1978, John Appleton & Ian Cave, Midland Counties Publications, 1978.
British Experimental Jet Aircraft, 1941-1986, Barrie Hygate, Argus, 1990.
British Gliders, Phil Butler, Merseyside Aviation Society, 1980.
British Homebuilt Aircraft since 1920, Ken Ellis, Merseyside Aviation Society, 1979.
British Military Aircraft Serials 1878-1987, Bruce Robertson, Midland Counties Publications, 1987.
British Military Aircraft Serials & Markings, Mike Draper, Martin Pettit, Doug Rough, Trevor Stone, British Aviation Research Group, 1980.
Broken Wings of the Samurai, Robert C Mikesh, Airlife, 1993.
Cadet Corps Airframes, Midland Counties Aviation Society, 1975.
Civmilair, John Ryder, LAAS International, 1984.
Coastal, Support & Special Squadrons of the RAF, J D R Rawlings, Jane's, 1982.
DH Dove & Heron, C Barber, D Shaw & T Sykes, Air-Britain, 1973.
Douglas DC-3 and its Predecessors, Mike Gradidge, Air-Britain, 1984.
English Electric/BAC Lightning, Bryan Philpott, Patrick Stephens, 1984.
English Electric Canberra, Ken Delve, Peter Green & John Clemons, Midland Counties Publications, 1992.
European Wrecks & Relics, Mike Bursell, Midland Counties Publications, 1989.
Falklands — The Air War, Mike Draper, Martin Pettit, Doug Rough, Trevor Stone, Dave Wilton, British Aviation Research Group, 1986.
Handley Page Halifax, K A Merrick, Aston Publications, 1990.
Handley Page Victor, Andrew Brookes, Ian Allan, 1988.
Harrier, Francis Mason, Patrick Stephens, 1983.
Harvard File, John Hamlin, Air-Britain, 1988.
Hawker Hunter : Biography of a Thoroughbred, Francis Mason, Patrick Stephens, 1981.
Hawker Siddeley Gnat F.1 & T.1, Paul Jackson, Alan W Hall Publications, 1982.
High Ground Wrecks, Dave Smith, Midland Counties Publications, 1989.
History of Black County Aviation, Alec Brew, Alan Sutton Publishing, 1993.
Jet Airliner Production List, Tony Eastwood & John Roach, The Aviation Hobby Shop, 1989.
Meteor : Britain's First Jet Fighter, Steve Bond, Midland Counties Publications, 1985.
Mosquito Survivors, Stuart Howe, Aston Publications, 1986.
Museums and Art Galleries in Great Britain & Ireland, S Alcock (Ed), British Leisure Publications, 1991.
Mustang Survivors, Paul Coggan, Aston Publications, 1987.
Piston Airliner Production List, Tony Eastwood & John Roach, The Aviation Hobby Shop, 1991.
RAF Squadrons, W/C C G Jefford, Airlife, 1988.
Royal Air Force Aircraft WA100 to WZ999, Jim Halley, Air-Britain, 1983 — and others in the series.
Royal Navy Instructional Airframes, Naval Research Group, British Aviation Research Group, 1978.
Short Sunderland, Chaz Bowyer, Aston Publications, 1989.
Shuttleworth Collection, David Ogilvy, Airlife, 1982.
Source Book of the RAF, Ken Delve, Airlife, 1994.
Spitfire : The History, Eric Morgan & Edwin Shacklady, Key Publishing, 1987.
Spitfire Survivors Around the World, Gordon Riley & Graham Trant, Aston Publications, 1986.
Squadrons of the Fleet Air Arm, Ray Sturtivant, Air-Britain, 1984.
Squadrons of the Royal Air Force 1918-1988, Jim Halley, Air-Britain, 1988.
Turbo-Prop Airliner Production List, Tony Eastwood & John Roach, The Aviation Hobby Shop, 1990.
Ulster Aviation Handbook, Ulster Aviation Society, 1993.
United Kingdom & Eire Civil Registers, Malcolm Fillmore, Air-Britain, 1993
United States Military Aircraft Designations & Serials since 1909, John Andrade, Midland Counties Publications, 1979.
Viking, Valetta & Varsity, Bernard Martin, Air-Britain, 1975.
Warbirds Worldwide Directory, John Chapman & Geoff Goodall, Warbirds Worldwide, 1992.
Wings over Gloucestershire, John Rennison, Piccadilly Publishing, 1988.
World War One Survivors, Ray Rimell, Aston Publications, 1990.

AUCTIONS

Enquiries relating to aircraft auctions can be made to :
Robert Brooks — 81, Westside, London, SW4 9AY. (071 228 8000)
Christie's — 85, Old Brompton Road, London, SW7 3LD. (071 581 7611)
Onslow's — Metrostore, Townmead Road, London SW6 2RZ. (071 793 0240)
Phillips — *Blenstock House*, 7, Blenheim Street, London, W1Y 0AS. (071 629 6602)
Sotheby's — 34-35, New Bond Street, London W1 2AA. (071 493 8080)

September 13, 1992 — Onslow's : Rendcomb Aerial Derby

Held prior to the atmospheric display at Vic Norman's lovely airfield a wide variety of aeronautica was hammered, but none of the aircraft sold.

Boeing PT-13D Stearman	G-ERIX	£30,000	
DH Tiger Moth	G-APAO	£17,500	
Piper J-3 Cub	N2MD	£11,200	
Fokker Dr I replica	G-ATJM	£20,000	ex Robs Lamplough, North Weald, Essex.
Yak (SPP) C.18A	G-BMJY	£29,000	Robs Lamplough, North Weald, page 72.

September 19, 1992 — Sotheby's : Billingshurst

Held at the auctioneer's attractive 'Summer Place' a variety of aircraft were offered for sale *in absentia*, along with a wide array of aeronautica. Only the Hunter Wing Jet Provost (part of a sizeable package from Hunter Wing/Jet Heritage) sold. The Hunter and Meteor from Tangmere were entered to see what the market was like, particularly well timed as they took delivery of the former Cosford record breaking Hunter and Meteor that very day! As well as the Jim Pearce Focke-Wulf the rear end of Ju 87R-4 w/nr 6234 was also offered with a catalogue estimate of £28,000 to £32,000. It was withdrawn when bidding failed to move beyond £8,000!

Soko Kraguj	G-BSXD	£15,000	
Focke-Wulf Fw 189A-1	2100	£30,000	
Percival Provost T.1	G-AWVF	£15,000	Hunter Wing, Bournemouth, page 61.
Hawker Sea Hawk FGA.4	WV795	£2,000	Jet Heritage, Bournemouth, page 61.
BAC Jet Provost T.52A	G-JETP	£69,000	Hunter Wing, Bournemouth, page 61.
Hawker Hunter T.53	G-BOOM	£70,000	Hunter Wing, Bournemouth, page 61.
Folland Gnat T.1	G-NAAT	£10,000	Hunter Wing, Bournemouth, page 61.
Gloster Meteor F.8	WA984	£2,000	See under Tangmere, page 194.
Hawker Hunter F.51	E-412	£1,900	See under Tangmere, page 194.

January 13, 1993 — Helicopter Museum of Great Britain, Blackpool Airport

See under Blackpool Airport, Lancs, page 111.

April 20, 1993 — Exeter

A sale of a series of 'poorly' airframes was staged here on the above date. Only scant details are to hand, the sale involving the following :— Partenavia P.68B G-BCNT (CoA expired 17-10-88) dismantled; Navajo Chieftain 350 G-GTAX (CoA expired 25-5-89), dismantled; Navajo Chieftain 350 G-HTAX (ex N54305, no UK certification) dismantled; the fuselage and starboard wing of a Seneca II; wings from a Navajo Chieftain and misc Pembroke/Sea Prince components.

May 1, 1993 — Sotheby's : Falmouth

See under Helston, Cornwall, page 52.

June 19, 1993 — Brooks' : Goodwood

Staged during Goodwood House's Festival of Speed, the auction was a staggering mix of sports and racing cars, plus a selection of classic aircraft. Tiger Moth G-ARAZ and Moth G-AAVJ sold, the Lysander was withdrawn and the rest went unsold.

DH Tiger Moth	G-ARAZ	£35,000	Sold, private buyer
Moth Corp DH.60GM Moth	G-AAVJ	£47,500	To Wessex Aviation & Transport (WA&T), Dorchester, page 64.
Boeing PT-13D Kaydet	N4712V	£34,000	WA&T, page 64.

DH Hornet Moth	G-ADLY	£37,000	
SNCAN SV-4L	G-BMNV	£50,000	WA&T, page 64.
Westland Lysander IIIA	G-BCWL	withdrawn	WA&T, page 64.
MS.500 Criquet	G-AZMH	£58,000	WA&T, page 64.

July 8, 1993 — Phillips' : London

Another Ministry of Defence auction, managed this time by Phillips. There were 19 aircraft lots (Lot 1 was a hovercraft) and there was some lively bidding. Details as follows, aircraft in lot number order. Location codes (refer to the main text) are as follows :— DRA — DRA Bedford, Beds, LOO — Linton-on-Ouse, North Yorkshire, SHY — Shawbury, Shropshire, STA — St Athan, South Glamorgan.

DH Vampire T.11	XD506	£2,900	See under Swinderby, page 127. Unsold.
Percival Provost T.1	XF545	£12,500	LOO. Moved to Thatcham, page 26. Thought bound for USA.
Hunting Jet Provost T.3A	XN461	£15,000	Last flown at LOO 29-1-93.
Hunting Jet Provost T.3A	XM479	£17,000	Last flown at LOO 29-1-93. Became G-BVEZ, Binbrook, page 121.
EE Canberra TT.18	WK126	£9,000	Last flown 26-10-90. STA, page 240.
EE Canberra TT.18	WK142	£7,800	Last flown 15-4-92. STA. Became N76764, see page 240.
EE Canberra TT.18	WJ614	£7,800	Last flown 16-11-92. STA. Became N76765, see page 240.
Folland Gnat T.1	XR538	£48,000	See under Halton, page 28. Became G-RORI, Cranfield, Beds.
DHC Chipmunk T.10	WK511	£20,000	Last flown 23-9-92. SHY. Became G-BVBT, Cranfield, page 19.
HS Andover C.1	XS637	£80,000	Last flown 2-4-92. SHY. See Southend, page 73.
HS Andover C.1	XS597	£86,000	Last flown 25-3-92. SHY. See Southend, page 73.
BAC Jet Provost T.5A	XW326	£8,000	Last flown 10-88. SHY.
BAC Jet Provost T.5A	XW310	£9,200	Last flown 9-88. SHY.
BAC Jet Provost T.5A	XW355	£8,000	Last flown 10-88. SHY.
EE Canberra T.4	WJ992	withdrawn	Last flown 18-2-93 at DRA.
EE Canberra B.6(mod)	XH568	£9,800	Last flown 10-11-92 at DRA. Became G-BVIC, see Bruntingthorpe, page 114.
Vickers Viscount 838	XT661	£140,000	Last flown 2-89. DRA. See Stock, page 75.
Vickers Viscount 837	XT575	£140,000	Last flown 1991. DRA. See Stock, page 75.
HS Buccaneer S.2B	XX897	£16,500	Last flown 7-10-92 at DRA. See Bournemouth Airport, page 61.

November 27, 1993 — Sotheby's : Billingshurst

Another large sale, including another array of aircraft being bidded for *in absentia*. Reflecting the economy, not that many sold, but it must have been pleasing to see G-BOOM find a buyer, part of another contingent from Jet Heritage/Hunter Wing at Bournemouth Airport, Dorset.

Folland Gnat T.1	G-NAAT	£4,200	Hunter Wing, Bournemouth, page 61.
DHC Chipmunk 22	G-AORW	£23,000	Sold, to be based at North Weald.
EE Lightning T.5	XS420	£1,000	See under Narborough, page 148.
EE Lightning T.5	XS459	£1,200	See under Narborough, page 148.
Piper J3F-65 Cub	NC1776	£15,000	*Flitfire* — on sale in Maryland, USA.
Hunting Provost T.1	G-AWVF	£24,000	Hunter Wing, based at Goodwood, W Sussex.
Hawker Hunter F.4	G-HHUN	£55,000	Hunter Wing, Bournemouth, page 61.
Cessna C-34 Airmaster	NC16403	£20,000	Based at Thatcham, Berks.
NA Harvard IIB	G-CTKL	£42,000	Based at North Weald, Essex.

Hawker Hunter T.53	G-BOOM	£130,000	Hunter Wing, Bournemouth, page 61. Sold, will be based at North Weald.
Hawker Tempest II	G-BSHW	£80,000	See under Audley End, page 66.
EE Lightning T.5	XV328	£3,200	See under Cranfield, page 18.
EE Lightning T.5	XS452	£5,800	See under Cranfield, page 18.
EE Lightning T.5	XV458	£6,000	See under Cranfield, page 18.
EE Lightning F.6	XS898	£2,500	See under Cranfield, page 18.
EE Lightning F.6	XS899	£2,200	See under Cranfield, page 18.
EE Lightning F.6	XS923	£2,200	See under Cranfield, page 18.

ABBREVIATIONS

WITHOUT THE USE of abbreviations for the 'potted' histories of the aircraft listed in **W&R**, the book would be perhaps twice the size. Readers will face few problems, especially if they have previous editions to refer to. There follows a decode of abbreviations to help readers to wend their way through the individual histories. Footnotes have been added to go into greater depth with some entries. To save repetition, abbreviations that are clearly combinations of others are not listed in full, eg MEAFCS, breaks into MEAF and CS, ie Middle East Air Force Communications Squadron.

A&AEE	Aeroplane and Armament Experimental Establishment as was, and now... Aircraft and Armament Evaluation Establishment
AAC	Army Air Corps
AACU	Anti-Aircraft Co-operation Unit
AAFCE	Allied Air Forces Central Europe
AAIU	Air Accident Investigation Unit
ACC	Allied Control Commission
ACSEA	Allied Command, South East Asia — see **Note 1**.
ACU	Andover Conversion Unit
ADS	Air Director School
AE&AEOS	Air Engineers and Air Electronic Operators School
AEF	Air Experience Flight
AES	Air Engineers School
AES	Air Engineering School (FAA)
AETW	Air Engineering Training Wing
AFDS	Air Fighting Development Squadron,
AFDU	Air Fighting Development Unit
AFEE	Airborne Forces Experimental Establishment
AFN	Air Forces North
AFNE	Air Forces North East
AFS	Advanced Flying School
AFTS	Advanced Flying Training School
AFU	Advanced Flying Unit
AFWF	Advanced Fixed Wing Flight
AIU	Accident Investigation Unit
ALAT	*Aviation Legere de l'Armee de Terre* - French army aviation
AMARC	Aerospace Maintenance and Regeneration Center
AMS	Air Movements School
ANG	Air National Guard
ANS	Air Navigation School
AONS	Air Observer and Navigator School
AOTS	Aircrew Officers Training School
APS	Aircraft Preservation Society
APS	Armament Practice Station
arr	arrived, denotes airframe arrived at location by surface transport.
ARWF	Advanced Rotary Wing Flight,

AS	Aggressor Squadron
AS&RU	Aircraft Salvage and Repair Unit
ASF	Aircraft Servicing Flight
ASS	Air Signals School
AST	Air Service Training
ASWDU	Air-Sea Warfare Development Unit
ATA	Air Transport Auxiliary
ATF	Airframe Technology Flight
ATAIU	Allied Technical Air Intelligence
— SEA	Unit - South East Asia
ATC	Air Training Corps
ATDU	Air Torpedo Development Unit
AuxAF	Auxiliary Air Force
aw/cn	AWaiting CollectioN — see **Note 2**
AWFCS	All Weather Fighter Combat School
AWOCU	All Weather Operational Conversion Unit
AWRE	Atomic Weapons Research Establishment,
BA	British Airways
BAAT	British Airways Airtours
BAC	Bristol Aero Collection
BAC	British Aircraft Corporation
BAe	British Aerospace
BAF	British Air Ferries
BAFO	British Air Forces of Occupation
BAH	British Airways Helicopters
BAM	Booker Aircraft Museum
BANS	Basic Air Navigation School
BAOR	British Army of the Rhine
BAPC	British Aviation Preservation Council
BATUS	British Army Training Unit, Suffield. (Canada)
BBMF	Battle of Britain Memorial Flight
BBML	British Balloon Museum and Library
BC	Bomber Command.
BCAL	British Caledonian Airlines
BCBS	Bomber Command Bombing School,
BDR	Battle Damage Repair
BDRF	Battle Damage Repair Flight
BDTF	Bomber Defence Training Flight
BDU	Bomber Development Unit

BEA	British European Airways
BEAH	British European Helicopters
BEAS	British Executive Air Services
BFTS	Basic Flying Training School
BFWF	Basic Fixed Wing Flight
B&GS	Bombing & Gunnery School (RCAF)
BG	Bomb Group
BIH	British Independent Helicopters
BLEU	Blind Landing Experimental Unit
BMA	British Midland Airways
BOAC	British Overseas Airways Corporation
BPPU	Bristol Plane Preservation Unit
BRNC	Britannia Royal Naval College
BSE	Bristol Siddeley Engines
B&TTF	Bombing & Target Towing Flight
BTF	Beaver Training Flight
BTU	Bombing Trials Unit
BUA	British United Airlines
BW	Bomb Wing
C(A)	Controller (Aircraft) - see also CS(A) and **Note 3**
CAA	Civil Aviation Authority
CAACU	Civilian Anti-Aircraft Co-operation Unit
CAF	Canadian Armed Forces.
CAFU	Civil Aviation Flying Unit
Cam Flt	Camouflage Flight,
CATCS	Central Air Traffic Control School
CAW	College of Air Warfare
CBE	Central Bombing Establishment,
CC	Coastal Command.
CCAS	Civilian Craft Apprentices School,
CCF	Combined Cadet Force
CF	Communications Flight — as suffix with other unit, or for an airfield.
CFCCU	Civilian Fighter Control and Co-operation Unit
CFE	Central Fighter Establishment - see CFE-EAF.
CFE-EAF	Central Fighter Establishment - Enemy Aircraft Flight
CFS	Central Flying School
C&TTS	Communications and Target Towing Squadron
CGS	Central Gliding School
CGS	Central Gunnery School
CIFAS	*Centre d'Instruction des Forces Aeriennes Strategiques*, French Air Force
CIT	Cranfield Institure of Technology
CNCS	Central Navigation and Control School,
CoA	Certificate (or Permit) of Airworthiness, generally quoted with expiry date.
Cott	Cottesmore, in relation to

	V-Bomber wings.
CPF	Coastal Patrol Flight
cr	crashed, or other form of accident.
CR	Crash Rescue, training airframe.
CRD	Controller, Research and Development
C&RS	Control and Reporting School
CS	Communications Squadron, as a suffix with other units, or for an airfield.
CS(A)	Controller, Services (Air), see also CA and **Note 3**
CSDE	Central Servicing Development Establishment,
CSE	Central Signals Establishment
CSE	major flying school and fixed-base operator at Oxford Airport.
CSF	Canberra Servicing Flight
CTE	Central Training Establishment
CTTS	Civilian Technical Training School,
C&TTS	Communications & Target Towing Squadron
CU	Communications Unit, as suffix
CU	Conversion Unit, as suffix
dbr	damaged beyond repair, to distinguish an aircraft that was written off but did not crash
deH	de Havilland
del	delivered, denotes an airframe that arrived by air.
Det	Detachment, flight or other unit detached from main base.
DFLS	Day Fighter Leader School
DRA	Defence Research Agency
DU	Development Unit, as suffix
EAAS	East Anglian Aviation Society
EASAMS	European avionics consortium
ECTT	*Escadre de Chasse Tous Temps*, French Air Force
EE	English Electric
EFTS	Elementary Flying Training School
EP&TU	Exhibition, Production and Transportation Unit
ERFTS	Elementary & Reserve Flying Training School
ERS	Empire Radio School
Esc	*Escadre*, French squadron.
ETPS	Empire Test Pilots School
ETS	Engineering Training School
ETU	Experimental Trials Unit
EWE&TU	Electronic Warfare Experimental and Training Unit
F	Flight, suffix to four-figure number.
FAA	Fleet Air Arm.
FAA	*Fuerza Aerea Argentina*, Argentine Air Force

FAAHAF	Fleet Air Arm Historic Aircraft Flight	HSA	Hawker Siddeley Aviation
FAAM	Fleet Air Arm Museum	HTF	Helicopter Training Flight
FAF	French Air Force	IAAC	Irish Army Air Corps
FAH	*Fuerza Aerea Hondurena*, Honduras Air Force	IAF	Indian Air Force
		IAM	Institute of Aviation Medicine
FC	Fighter Command	IGN	*Institut Geographique National*, French national cartography service
FC&RS	Fighter Control and Reporting School		
FCS	Fighter Control School	IHM	International Helicopter Museum
FEAF	Far East Air Forces — see **Note 1**	ITF or 'S	Instrument Training Flight / Squadron
FECS	Far East Communications Flight	IWM	Imperial War Museum
FF	Ferry Flight	JASS	Joint Anti-Submarine School
FF&SS	Fire Fighting and Safety School	JATE	Joint Air Transport Establishment
FGF	Flying Grading Flight	JCU	Javelin Conversion Unit
FLS	Fighter Leader School	JEHU	Joint Experimental Helicopter Unit
FOAC	Flag Officer, Aircraft Carriers	JMU	Joint Maritime Unit
FOCAS	Friends of Cardington Airship Station	JOCU	Jaguar Operational Conversion Unit
FOFT	Flag Officer, Flying Training	JWE	Joint Warfare Establishment
FONA	Flag Officer, Naval Aviation	LAS	Light Aircraft School
FONAC	Flag Officer, Naval Air Command	LCS & 'U	Lightning Conversion Squadron / Unit
FP	Ferry Pool		
FPP	Ferry Pilots Pool	LTF	Lightning Training Flight
FRADU	Fleet Requirements and Direction Unit	LWRE	Long Range Weapons Research Establishment
FRL	Flight Refuelling Ltd	MAM	Midland Air Museum
FRS	Flying Refresher School	MBA	Museum of Berkshire Aviation
FRU	Fleet Requirements Unit	MC	Maintenance Command
FSS	Ferry Support Squadron	MCS	Metropolitan Communications Squadron
FSS	Flying Selection Squadron		
FTC	Flying Training Command	MEAF	Middle East Air Force — see **Note 1**
FTS	Flying Training School		
FTU	Ferry Training Unit	MECS	Middle East Communications Squadron
FU	Ferry Unit		
FWS	Fighter Weapons School	MGSP	Mobile Glider Servicing Party
GAM	*Groupe Aérien Mixte*, French Air Force	MinTech	Ministry of Technology, see also MoA, MoS and **Note 3**
GCF	Group Communications Flight	MoA	Ministry of Aviation, see MinTech, MoS and **Note 3**
GE	*Groupement Ecole*, French Air Force		
		MoD	Ministry of Defence
grp	Glass-fibre reinforced plastic	MoS	Ministry of Supply, see MinTech, MoA and **Note 3**
GS	Glider School		
GSU	Group Support Unit	MoTaT	Museum of Transport & Technology, New Zealand
GTS	Glider Training School		
GU	Glider Unit	MOTU	Maritime Operational Training Unit
GWDS	Guided Weapons Development Squadron	MPA	Man powered aircraft
		MU	Maintenance Unit see **Note 4**
HAB	Hot air balloon	NACDS	Naval Air Command Driving School
HAM	Historic Aircraft Museum, Southend		
		NASA	National Aeronautical and Space Administration
HC	Home Command		
HCEU	Home Command Examining Unit	NASU	Naval Aircraft Servicing Unit
HCF	Hornet Conversion Flight	NBC	Nuclear, Bacteriological and Chemical
HDU	Helicopter Development Unit		
HGSU	Heavy Glider Servicing Unit	NCS	Northern Communications Squadron
HQ	Headquarters		
HS	Handling Squadron	nea	Non effective airframe — see **Note 2**

NECS	North Eastern Communications Squadron	RPRE	Rocket Propulsion Research Establishment
NIBF	Northern Ireland Beaver Flight	RRE	Royal Radar Establishment
NSF	Northern Sector Flight	RRF	Radar Reconnaissance Flight
ntu	Not taken up, registration applied for, but not worn, or paperwork not concluded	RRHT	Rolls-Royce Heritage Trust
		RS	Radio School
		RSRE	Radar and Signals Research Establishment
(O)AFU	(Observers) Advanced Flying Unit	RSS & 'U	Repair & Servicing Section / Unit
OCTU	Officer Cadet Training Unit	RTR	Royal Tank Regiment
OCU	Operational Conversion Unit	RWE	Radio Warfare Establishment
OTU	Operational Training Unit	SAAF	South African Air Force
(P)AFU	(Pilot) Advanced Flying Unit	SAC	School of Army Co-operation
PAX	Passenger, as used in Chipmunk PAX trainer	SAF	School of Aerial Fighting
		SAH	School of Aircraft Handling
PCSS	Protectorate Communications and Support Squadron	SAR	Search and Rescue
		SAREW	Search and Rescue Engineering Wing
PEE	Proof & Experimental Establishment	SARTS	Search and Rescue Training Squadron
PFA	Popular Flying Association	SC	Signals Command
PFS	Primary Flying School	Scamp	Scampton, to distinguish a V-Bomber wing.
PFTS	Primary Flying Training School		
PP	Pilots' Pool	SCBS	Strike Command Bombing School
PPS	Personal Plane Services	SCS	Southern Communications Squadron
PRDU	Photo Reconnaissance Development Unit		
		SER	Static External Replica, outwardly a replica of the aircraft in question, but using non-original construction techniques
PRU	Photographic Reconnaissance Unit		
PTF	Phantom Training Flight		
PTS	Primary Training School		
QF	Queen's Flight	SF	Station Flight, usually prefixed by an airfield name
RAAF	Royal Australian Air Force		
RAE	Royal Aircraft / Aerospace Establishment	SFTS	Service Flying Training School
		ShF	Ship's Flight
RAeS	Royal Aeronautical Society	SLAW	School of Land/Air Warfare
RAF	Royal Air Force	SMR	School of Maritime Reconnaissance
RAFA	Royal Air Force Association		
RAFC	Royal Air Force College	soc	Struck off charge — see **Note 2**
RAFEF	Royal Air Force Exhibition Flight	SoRF	School of Refresher Training
RAFG	Royal Air Force Germany	SoTT	School of Technical Training — see **Note 5**
RAFGSA	Royal Air Force Gliding and Soaring Association		
		SRCU	Short Range Conversion Unit
RAFHSF	Royal Air Force High Speed Flight	SRW	Strategic Reconnaissance Wing
RAFM	Royal Air Force Museum	SS	Signals Squadron
RAN	Royal Australian Navy	SS	Support Squadron
RC	Reserve Command	SU	Support Unit
RCAF	Royal Canadian Air Force	SVAS	Shuttleworth Veteran Aeroplane Society
RCN	Royal Canadian Navy		
RCS	Rotary Conversion Squadron	TAC	The Aeroplane Collection
Regt	Regiment	TAF	Tactical Air Force
RFS	Reserve Flying School	TAW	Tactical Airlift Wing
RHK	Royal Hong Kong	TC	Transport Command
RMAF	Royal Malaysian Air Force	TEE	Trials and Experimental Establishment
RNAY	Royal Navy Aircraft Yard		
RNEC	Royal Naval Engineering College	TEU	Tactical Exercise Unit
RNGSA	Royal Navy Gliding and Soaring Association	TF	Training Flight
		TFF	Target Facilities Flight
RNHF	Royal Navy Historic Flight	TFS	Tactical Fighter Squadron
RNZAF	Royal New Zealand Air Force		
ROC	Royal Observer Corps		

TFTAS	Tactical Fighter Training Aggressor Squadron
TFW	Tactical Fighter Wing
Thum Flt	Temperature and Humidity Flight
TMTS	Trade Management Training School
toc	Taken on charge - see **Note 2**
TRE	Telecommunications Research Establishment
TS	Training Squadron
TTC	Technical Training Command
TTU	Torpedo Training Unit
TWU	Tactical Weapons Unit
UAS	University Air Squadron — see **Note 6**
UNFICYP	United Nations Forces In Cyprus
USAAC	United States Army Air Corps
USAAF	United States Army Air Force
USAF	United States Air Force
USMC	United States Marine Corps
USN	United States Navy
VAFA	Vintage Aircraft Flying Association
VAT	Vintage Aircraft Team
VGS	Volunteer Gliding School
Wadd	Waddington, denoting a V-Bomber wing
WAP	Wycombe Air Park
WCS	Western Communications Squadron
wfu	Withdrawn from use
Witt	Wittering, denoting a V-bomber wing.
WLT	Weapons Loading Trainer
WSF	Western Sector Flight

NOTES

1
RAF 'Holding Units' : For administrative purposes, the history cards of some RAF aircraft become fairly vague when transferred to either Middle East or Far East theatres of operations. Accordingly, the following abbreviations denote the 'operator' for the segment of an aircraft's life in that theatre, even though it may have been used by several front-line units : **ACSEA, FEAF, MEAF**.

2
History Card 'milestones' : There are several RAF aircraft history card 'milestones' referred to in the main text. Essentially an aircraft starts off as <u>A</u>w<u>a</u>iting <u>C</u>ollecti<u>on</u> (**Aw/cn**) — a signal from the manufacturer that the aircraft is ready for issue to service; it is then taken on charge (**toc**) and becomes a part of the RAF; after service life, it may eventually to be declared a non-effective airframe (**nea**) and down-graded to instructional or fire-training use; the final act is for it to be struck off charge (**soc**), either being written-off in an accident, scrapped, sold to another user etc etc.

3
Government 'owning' bodies : Technical 'owner' of UK military machines is the **C(A)** or **CS(A)** and at times these are noted within the aircraft history cards instead of a unit, although it may well be a pointer to the aircraft being operated at that time of its life by a test or trials unit. In similar manner, **MinTech**, **MoA** or **MoS** can appear, frequently meaning operation by the RAE, or DRA.

4
Maintenance Unit (MU) : The following are mentioned in the main text : **4** Stanmore Park (detachment); **5** Kemble; **6** Brize Norton, **7** Quedgeley; **8** Little Rissington; **9** Cosford; **10** Hullavington; **12** Kirkbride; **14** Carlisle; **15** Wroughton; **16** Stafford; **19** St Athan (also 32); **20** Aston Down; **22** Silloth; **23** Aldergrove; **27** Shawbury; **29** High Ercall; **32** St Athan (also 19); **39** Colerne; **44** Edzell; **46** Lossiemouth; **47** Sealand; **48** Hawarden; **54** Cambridge; **57** Wig Bay; **60** Leconfield; **71** Bicester; **431** Bruggen.

5
School of Technical Training (SoTT) : The following are mentioned in the main text : **1** Halton; **2** Cosford; **4** St Athan; **8** Weeton; **9** Newton; **10** Kirkham; **12** Melksham.

6
University Air Squadron (UAS) : Prefixed with a university name,with the following abbreviations : **Abn** — Aberdeen, Dundee & St Andrews; **Bir** — Birmingham; **Bri** — Bristol; **Cam** — Cambridge; **Dur** — Durham; **Edn** - Edinburgh; **Elo** — East Lowlands; **Ems** — East Midlands; **G&S** — Glasgow & Strathclyde; **Lee** — Leeds; **Liv** — Liverpool; **Lon** - London; **Man** — Manchester & Salford; **Nor** — Northumbrian; **Not** — Nottingham; **Oxf** — Oxford; **QUB** — Queens University Belfast; **Stn** — Southampton; **Wal** — Wales; **Yor** — Yorkshire.

LOCATIONS INDEX

🍏 Blessed are the cheesemakers....

New titles from Midland Publishing

The rural county of Lincolnshire can perhaps lay claim to being England's premier aviation county. It is the home of the Royal Air Force College at Cranwell, and was host to thousands of Allied aircrew during the Second World War. The county's illustrious aviation heritage is now an attraction for many aviation enthusiasts and general tourists.

This new pictorial chronicles Lincolnshire's strong ties with the worlds of both civil and military aviation from before the First World War. The five sections begin with ballooning in the nineteenth century and continue through the First World War, the inter-war period, the Second World War and post-war to the present day Tornado and Sentry.

In addition to the aircraft, the personalities such as B C Hucks, Sir Alan Cobham and Alex Henshaw are

included. The photographs come from local archives and private collections.

For the enthusiast, this is a fascinating gap-filler, and for the less committed, it is a useful introduction to Lincolnshire's diverse aviation history.

WINGS OVER LINCOLNSHIRE

Peter Green, and Mike Hodgson

Softback
200 x 210 mm, 48 pages
135 photos
1 85780 024 9
£7.95

This the official history you've been waiting for! Written with the total co-operation of Lockheed's Advanced Development Company, this is the closest thing yet to a definitive history of this most enigmatic aircraft design and production facility.

In a major 'pulling back' of the veil of secrecy, the official histories of such noteworthy products as the U-2, A-12, D-21, SR-71, and F-117 are finally brought to light, authentically described by the company and the men who designed and built them.

Contents include: P-80; RB-69; Saturn; Constitution; T-33; F-94; XF-90; X-7; R7V-2; T2V; F-104; XFV-1; C-130; the hydrogen-fuelled CL-400; U-2; JetStar; A-12; D-21; F-12; SR-71; Have Blue; F-117; F-22. Lists all production quantities, serial numbers, Lockheed build numbers, and other related facts and figures. Appendices cover significant personalities; origins of the Skunk Works name; Post-Skunk Works production, and technical data.

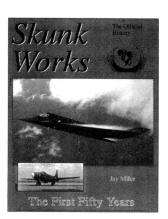

LOCKHEED'S SKUNK WORKS
The First Fifty Years

Jay Miller

Softback
305 x 229 mm, 216 pages
479 b/w and 28 colour photos
1 85780 016 8
£19.95

New titles from Midland Publishing

WAR PRIZES

Phil Butler

Foreword: Capt E.M.'Winkle' Brown, RN

Hardback
282 x 213 mm, 320 pages
with 450 photos.
0 904597 86 5
£29.95

Meticulously researched study of the many German, Italian, and Japanese aircraft taken to Allied countries or flown by the Allies during and after the Second World War. With extensive new information, some long held myths debunked and an unrivalled selection of photographs, many previously unpublished. The coverage includes civilian aircraft and sailplanes as well as military types; post-war production of German designs and details of surviving aircraft in museums.

UK chapters include such units as RAE Farnborough, 1426 (Enemy Aircraft) Flight, and many other squadrons, organisations and manufacturers. The US chapters deal with aircraft flown by the USAAF at Wright Field, Freeman Field, and in Europe by 'Watson's Whizzers', the US Navy-led TAIC at Anacostia, TAIUs in Australia, the Philippines, and many other units in all theaters of war.

FOREIGN INVADERS
The Douglas Invader in Foreign Military and US Clandestine Service

Dan Hagedorn and Leif Hellström

Hardback
282 x 213 mm, 200 pages
265 b/w photos + 8pp colour
1 85780 013 3
£22.95

The Douglas A-26 Invader is without doubt one of the most unsung of combat aircraft, with a long and chequered history. It served worldwide with many air forces even until the 1970s, and was also quite popular with the CIA for clandestine operations, including the notorious 'Bay of Pigs' invasion of Cuba.

This book focuses on the non-US military use of the Invader, covering service in twenty countries. Also covered in fascinating depth is use by a host of paramilitary forces and clandestine users, in over a dozen wars, conflicts and coups.

Here two immensely qualified and thorough authors present a deeply researched insight into all these operations, including a wealth of rarely published information and refuting some long perpetuated 'facts'. This is supported by a fine collection of photographs, most previously unpublished.